UNDER THE EDITORSHIP OF

LEONARD CARMICHAEL *President, Tufts College,
and Director Tufts Research Laboratory of
Sensory Psychology and Physiology*

Norman Cameron, M.D., Ph.D.
UNIVERSITY OF WISCONSIN

THE PSYCHOLOGY OF

BEHAVIOR DISORDERS

A Biosocial Interpretation

HOUGHTON MIFFLIN COMP
BOSTON · NEW YORK · CHICAGO · DALLAS · ATLANTA · SAN
The Riverside Pre

To E. S. C.

Contents

Editor's Introduction

NO ONE DOUBTS that psychology and psychiatry are closely associated fields of study. Sometimes in the past, however, it has been difficult to explain in detail the relationship between these fields. It is clear to every student that anatomy is basic to surgery and biochemistry to physiology, but modern experimental psychology has not in a similar way been seen as basic to psychiatry. Probably because of the way in which psychology and psychiatry have each developed in the present century, it has come about that the relationship between the two fields has received much less emphasis than might have been expected. In the recent past even some of the world's outstanding psychiatrists have been uninterested in the solid advances of modern scientific psychology. Similarly, some psychologists who have written in the field of abnormal psychology or who have discussed behavior disorders have done so without the advantage of general medical training and adequate clinical experience.

The present book effectively bridges the gap between these two great fields which deal with normal and abnormal human behavior. In a sense the book is unique. Its author is a man of originality and insight, and he has also had the advantage of full professional training in both modern objective scientific psychology and in modern scientific clinical psychiatry.

Dr. Cameron holds the degree of Doctor of Philosophy in psychology from the University of Michigan and the degree of Doctor of Medicine from the Johns Hopkins University. He has done important research in both psychology and psychiatry. He has taught university and medical students both psychology and psychiatry. After taking his medical degree he was for a number of years successively house officer, assistant resident, and senior resident in psychiatry at the Johns Hopkins Hospital. He is now Professor of Psychology and Chairman of the Department of Psychology in the University of Wisconsin as well as Professor of Psychiatry in the Medical School of the University of Wisconsin.

The present book is no mere static or pedestrian synthesis of psychology and psychiatry by one who happens to have been well trained in both of these disciplines. It is, rather, an important and novel positive contribution to both fields. Its author deals with the problems of various behavior disorders in the manner of a modern objectively trained scientist. In the pages of this book the reader will find no trace of hypotheses which banish thinking, imagination, dreams, and motives from the naturalistic and scientific world in order to locate them in a vague cloudland of a so-called conscious or unconscious *psyche*. The author believes that this old-fashioned dualistic approach to behavior problems is as outmoded today as is the similar ancient notion that the arteries were filled with spirits concocted in the stomach and warmed in the heart.

In the present volume the student, as he undertakes the study of behavior disorders, will not be called upon to forget anything that he has learned in physics, chemistry, biology, or general psychology.

This book will certainly have a far-reaching and important effect upon the thought of alert modern professional workers who are called upon to understand and deal with behavior disorders. Students of medicine, psychology, sociology, education, and related fields will profit by the study of the clearly written and thought-provoking pages of this book.

LEONARD CARMICHAEL

TUFTS COLLEGE

Preface

AS THE TITLE IMPLIES, this is a presentation of the neuroses and psychoses from a consistently biosocial point of view. It follows a prediction made five years ago that psychopathology — or *behavior pathology* as I propose to call it — will shift progressively in emphasis, from speculations about a psyche in a somatic container, to the study of the operations of human organisms in a social field. The inadequacies of the prevailing psychic theories, as I pointed out then, cannot be blamed upon any one contemporary group or school of thought.

"We are all in this difficulty together because we still look upon our material in an antiquated fashion. It is only because of this that we have on our hands an oversystematized psychopathology which treats language behavior and emotional conduct as though they belonged in another world. We have already wasted years of effort in trying to work out the internal structure of a fictitious psyche and its esoteric love life, when we might better have been working out the dynamics of the organization, disorganization and reorganization of human behavior — of action and reaction, of thinking, wishing, loving, hating, learning, fearing, forgetting, avoiding, desiring and hiding — but all these studied as the activities of a social organism, not the dreams of a ghost. . . . When we turn to psychiatry, we do not enter a new and different world. The psychiatrist is still the physician, an organism, working with a patient, another organism. They share and operate within a common social environment; they communicate by means of socially determined signs and sounds. These are the materials of medical practice as well as of psychology and psychopathology." [1]

[1] N. Cameron, "Psychological research in psychiatry," in F. Sladen (editor), *Psychiatry and the War* (Springfield, Ill.: Thomas, 1943), pp. 114-115.

This is essentially the *biosocial* point of view. It differs radically from the contemporary *psychosomatic* approach to the behavior disorders by breaking completely with the tradition of mind-body dualism. There is no need to begin by accepting the ancient and gratuitous assumption that an invisible and intangible psyche lurks within the soma, or is coextensive with it. We begin instead with what we find, a biological organism operating in and by means of a social environment. We thus create no artificial need to solve such meaningless conundrums as, *How does the soma affect the psyche? How does the psyche influence the soma? And how is non-psychic reality ever contacted and tested by an insubstantial psyche?* These questions are not inherent in the problems which our patients present. They are the offspring of psychosomatic dualism and we can discard them with their parent.

The point of view which I have developed in this work differs from classical *behaviorism* in rejecting reflexes, instincts and emotions as building blocks out of which human behavior was supposed to be constructed. It is holistic and analytical rather than atomistic and synthetic. In dealing with biosocial behavior, normal and abnormal, the emphasis is less upon the physiological machinery of the individual than upon communication, learning, role-taking and socially derived self-reactions. The biosocial interpretation departs from traditional *psychobiology* by dispensing entirely with the concept of consciousness and the distinction between mental and non-mental. This concept and this distinction are both residues from the once flourishing systems of psychosomatic dualism. We can neglect them in behavior pathology without missing them.

In developing a systematic biosocial orientation toward my material I have been deeply influenced by the philosophers William James, George Mead, John Dewey and Max Otto, as anyone conversant with their writings can see. I share with the rest of my profession the great debt that behavior pathology owes to Sigmund Freud. But my own greatest obligation is to my teacher, Dr. Adolf Meyer, with whom over a period of seven years I was in almost daily contact. During my four years of training in the psychiatric residency at the Johns Hopkins Hospital his presence was always a challenge. He showed an unusual willingness to delegate responsibility to those who could assume it. One did not have to view the

patient through his eyes; he was tireless in his insistence that everyone must begin with the patient and not with fixed principles and
preconceptions.

I have attempted to indicate the degree of my indebtedness to
my wife and colleague, Dr. Eugenia S. Cameron, by dedicating the
book to her. Without her encouragement it might never have been
begun. During the twenty months of its final preparation, the
manuscript has been scrutinized in detail by my fellow staff member, Dr. Ann Magaret. Her criticisms and suggestions have constituted an invaluable contribution to its structure and its clarity.
I wish to thank Mrs. D. A. Grant and Mrs. L. W. Coleman for their
assistance in making the manuscript legible, Mr. Raymond C. Bice
for helping in the preparation of the illustrations, and Miss Mary
Hargrove for guarding me from unnecessary interruptions while I
worked.

N. C.

SHOREWOOD HILLS,
MADISON, WISCONSIN

1   *Introduction*

THE NEUROSES AND PSYCHOSES, which together
we call behavior disorders, are a natural part of our everyday environment. As adults all of us have dealings with neurotic and
psychotic persons, and our children are being brought up among
them just as we once were. It may be the grocer or cobbler who is
a bit eccentric, or one's aunt with perpetually frayed nerves, or an
uncle who belches after meals, takes bicarbonate of soda and says
all doctors are imbeciles. Perhaps the child next door is being unintentionally trained by his overanxious mother to worry as much
over his health as she does. The teacher at school may be one who
grows restless, tense or unreasonably cranky if anything in the
classroom is the least bit disarranged or the slightest change made
in her timetable.

Even the policeman on the beat is sometimes neurotic. I remember one in New York, years ago, who had anxiety attacks whenever he heard footsteps behind him on a lonely street, even in broad
daylight, and another who, when they put him on night duty, had
to resign from the force because he had always been terrified by the
dark. A child's own father may be a man who sleeps poorly, has
temper tantrums and shouts when he is displeased; or his mother
may be unable to resist going downstairs several times every single
night to see that doors are really locked, lights out and the gas
turned off. Perhaps there is a girl in school who, otherwise healthy,
loses her voice in emotional crises and goes limp; or one's younger
brother has spells of being afraid that he will stop breathing in his
sleep, and never wake up again. Any such incidents as these are
likely to be a part of maladjustive behavior that is serious enough
to deserve being called neurotic; and they are all exceedingly common.

1

Psychoses are unquestionably much less common than neuroses; but they can be so impressively abnormal that their influence upon our general conception of the behavior disorders is actually greater. Every child sees psychotic people or hears others talk about them. He reads about them in story books and the comic strips. He occasionally runs into a queer person in the street who glances furtively about or seems confused and talks to himself. There is usually someone in the neighborhood who threatens child trespassers outrageously, or peers at them from behind curtained windows, or will do no more than open the front door a crack and give short answers heavy with suspicion. Children also hear their elders gossip about this person's maniacal outburst and that one's suicide in depression. Not a few children are reared with a mixed-up, forgetful grandmother right in the home who tends to wander about the house at night and once in a while starts breakfast at two in the morning, resisting all attempts to get her back to bed. The average child can have only the haziest notion of the real meaning of such disturbances, since his elders are none too clear about psychoses themselves, but he cannot escape some contact with them, directly or through vivid hearsay.

We adults likewise come in almost daily contact with neurotic or psychotic individuals, in the home or out of it, and whether we know enough to recognize them as such or not. Who among us, for example, does not know at least one hypochondriacal person who has made the care of some healthy part of his body the center of his life? Most of us know also a business executive who flies into a rage and says unreasonable things the moment his judgment is questioned or someone else makes a mistake. And then there is the housewife whose home is scrupulously clean and rigidly in order, day in and day out. Woe to the hand that moves a chair or cushion one inch from its appointed place, and to the foot that leaves a grain of dirt to sully her spotless rugs. The scene she then creates springs from personal needs that go much deeper than the conventional reasons she sincerely offers for her anxiety. Not uncommon, too, is the man or woman who is perpetually fatigued and unwell in spite of almost constant resting, who finds that the penalties of ordinary effort far outweigh personal gains and social pleasures, and yet seems to have no systemic disease, lives long and grows little worse with age.

Among our business and social acquaintances, or in our circle of intimates, we can always find individuals who seem chronically uneasy about the intentions, attitudes and inferences of other persons. One of these may feel himself the unjust target of suspicion. Insecure, anxious, guilty, for reasons that are unclear to himself and may never be understood by others, he expends his best efforts fruitlessly in attempts at self-justification or self-vindication. Another such person may show continual preoccupation with the impression he makes on others. He is easily made to feel misunderstood, and plants protective hedges of qualifying phrase and clause around almost every statement. Or it is a defensive, lonely individual who tends to challenge innocent remarks quite unexpectedly with, "Just how do you *mean* that?" and is always in danger of intercepting verbal darts in conversation that were actually aimed at someone else.

Most of us run across the occasional vague, dreamy, perplexed man or woman who seems not to be quite living our life, who is still preoccupied with adolescent riddles concerning the meaning of life, and reports semimystical experiences that no one else can share. All of us know the inadequate person who lives on praise but is not nourished by it. He feels himself unfairly treated, undervalued and passed over for less worthy persons who seem to him to earn little and get all. And who has not seen both men and women being mercilessly driven, onward and upward, by an insatiable craving for that complete security which nobody can ever find? Each time they score a gain it is as though they said, "To be thus is nothing, but to be *safely* thus!" And on they press again in the pursuit of certainty. All these we shall meet again in later chapters. We shall go on meeting them in our daily lives and, perhaps, in time come to understand them better than we do now.

Behavior disorders as a national problem

Never before in their history have the American people had as great a desire to understand neuroses and psychoses as they are showing today. There is good reason for this awakening. The information given out in recent years by selective service and the military [1] has shocked us all into a sudden awareness that these

[1] See for example, "Symposium on military psychiatry," *Amer. Jour. Psychiat.*, 1943, vol. 100, pp. 11-143; *Causes of Rejection and Incidence of Defects*, Med. Stat. Bull. No. 2, Washington, D.C.: National Headquarters Selective Service System, 1943; T. Rennie and L. Woodward, "Rehabilitation of the psychiatric casualty," *Ment. Hyg.*, 1945, vol. 29, pp. 32-45.

behavior disorders are, indeed, a grave national problem. The fact is not new but our facing it is. Benjamin Franklin called public attention to it even before we were a nation. Through four decades in the middle of the nineteenth century Dorothea Lynde Dix, called by some the greatest woman in our history, whipped the public conscience and goaded the legislators into action on behalf of the wickedly neglected psychotic. Clifford Beers and the National Committee for Mental Hygiene have revived the issue of prevention, treatment and care of neuroses and psychoses, and kept it alive down to our own day.[2] Now at last we are able to see that the problem of behavior disorders belongs, not alone to those who have them and those who directly treat or care for them, but to all of us.

The full magnitude of our national problem is very hard to estimate. We know that in the United States today there are about 600,000 patients in civilian psychiatric hospitals, nearly all of them psychotic and over half of them schizophrenic. This number is actually greater than the total of civilian patients in our hospitals for all the other medical and surgical illnesses put together. The annual public expenditure for psychiatric care and treatment in the United States amounts to $210,000,000. But if we add to this figure the estimated loss of income suffered by persons hospitalized for psychoses, the total annual cost to the nation rises to $777,000,000.[3] Nor does this amount tell the whole story.

Those who have studied the national situation estimate that, were reasonably adequate facilities available in all our states, instead of in the very few, more than a million psychotic men and women would now be in hospitals. In most American communities, even in some of the richest, the facilities provided by their citizens for early psychiatric diagnosis and treatment are far below the minimal standards that are observed in the same localities for other medical and surgical specialties.[4] This situation alone bars or discourages many thousands, who definitely need it, from seeking out-patient

[2] For an account of the struggle, from colonial times to the present, see A. Deutsch, *The Mentally Ill in America*. Garden City, N.Y.: Doubleday, Doran, 1937.

[3] H. Pollock, *Mental Disease and Social Welfare*. Utica, N.Y.: State Hospitals Press, 1941.

[4] V. Vogel, "Our inadequate treatment of the mentally ill as compared with treatment of other sick people," *Public Health Reports*, 1941, vol. 56, pp. 1941-1947.

help and hospital treatment. Hence, the reported incidence of psychoses falls well below their actual incidence, and particularly so in the psychiatrically more backward and irresponsible communities.

Another influence that holds down artificially the national admission rate for psychoses, and deprives those who should have it of early treatment, is our ancient cultural tradition of guilt and shame over insanity. This tradition we have received from frightened, superstitious ancestors who could not see the kinship between psychoses and other illnesses. To them psychosis seemed a visitation from the spirit world, the mark of perversity or sin, some strange inhuman taint in the blood that would inevitably crop out again and again in the family tree. So lively are such legends still that families, who know it is urgently needed, decline to seek or to accept psychiatric help for a relative lest, in doing so, the shadow of public disgrace should fall upon their own and future generations. This deadly fear of what others will think is by no means unjustified. The public, as anyone can see by the plots of popular stories and movies, is still dominated by the belief that behavior disorders are weird, inevitable and dangerous in ways that other illnesses are not. Until we can be brought to understand that any behavior disorder is as legitimate and natural in a family history as are other forms of sickness, crippling or defect — until we *believe* this ourselves as well as say it — thousands of otherwise curable patients must yearly drift into incurability through our fear and neglect.

The public is largely unaware of the fact that there are also large numbers of mildly and moderately depressed, manic, paranoid and schizophrenic patients who are being successfully treated, or at least kept going, by clinicians in office practice. These never get into our national statistics. Another uncounted army is made up of those border-line persons who among their relatives and friends pass for sad dogs and chronic mourners, gay irresponsibles, eccentrics, reformers and faddists, cantankerous and litigious neighbors, or who are looked upon as ineffectual dreamers and thought to be "a little psychic." Librarians, lawyers, ministers, politicians, actors and others in public life make the acquaintance of a great many of these individuals. Finally we must add the thousands of old people being cared for at home who suffer from serious memory defects, personality decline and periods of confusion, and countless others of all ages who develop a transient delirium through infection, high fever or intoxication. No satisfactory method has yet been devised for estimating all these auxiliary battalions of the psychotic and near-psychotic. While it may be quite true that a great many who are not under active treatment do not need it or would not benefit by it, they all belong within the field of the psychology of behavior disorders which we are entering.

It is still more difficult to estimate the incidence of neuroses in America. Few neurotic persons require hospitalization, and none but the well-to-do can really afford it for very long. Hospital statistics, therefore, tell us very little about neuroses. Judging from the large numbers of neurotic persons we chance upon in casual contact, or discover in the course of some unrelated investigation, it is clear that the great majority in this category do not understand the nature of their difficulty and never seek treatment for it. Also — and about this we shall have a good deal more to say later on — it is easy and natural in our culture to mistake neurotic symptoms, which are ignorantly despised and ridiculed, for signs of organ or tissue pathology or constitutional frailty, which are respected and earn from others special attention and open sympathy. These are not reckoned with the neuroses by either patient or therapist.

It has been loosely calculated that perhaps one person in five now of grade-school age will at some time during his life stand in genuine need of expert help because of a neurosis. It has been estimated, also on admittedly incomplete data, that approximately one person in twenty will some time in his life be hospitalized for a psychosis, while another person in twenty will be similarly incapacitated, but for one reason or another will not be hospitalized.[5] A prewar study of the clientele of a metropolitan general hospital revealed that, regardless of initial complaint, about 30 per cent of all patients coming to its doors were suffering mainly or solely from neuroses or psychoses. This study tells us relatively little about the general population, since its sample is a highly selected one, but it shows unmistakably how important a role the behavior disorders must actually play in enlightened general medicine.

Are neuroses and psychoses on the increase? Some competent observers believe that neuroses definitely are and psychoses probably are not, excepting for the group tied up with increasing longevity.

[5] C. Landis and J. Page, *Modern Society and Mental Disease.* (New York: Farrar and Rinehart, 1938), pp. 23-25.

However, in our natural eagerness for concise, finalistic answers, we must not forget the many sources of unreliability in these estimates. In such comparisons the past, with which our current uncertain figures must be matched, has its own special uncertainties. Our present widespread recognition of neurotic and mildly psychotic signs and symptoms in general medicine, social work and nursing is still a very recent achievement. We have all become noticeably much more alert to them even within the past twenty-five years — a very short period for demonstrating trends with such complex origins. Many matters now stressed in clinical observation and history-taking — such as the patient's anxieties and fears, his personal conflicts, the nature of his childhood, his sexual life and its degrees and kinds of gratification, etc. — were not so long ago slighted or dismissed as trivial and unworthy imaginings. The medical, nursing and social records of today are incomparably superior in these directions to those kept early in the present century. Since, in plain truth, no one can ever really know how prevalent behavior disorders were in times past, while even today we have at best only a fragmentary picture of the situation, we must accept the fact that all such comparisons are but skillful guesses and no more.

Normal and abnormal personality

Neuroses and psychoses are often referred to as disorders of personality because in them the disturbance in one's interpersonal relationships is so fundamental. The distinction between normal and abnormal personality, from our point of view, must rest upon the relative adequacy of a given individual's performance, in comparison with his previous level and with the cultural norms that are current in his society for persons of his status. One further distinction must be made. Normal personalities are not the same as ideal or perfect personalities. The latter do not exist; the former are on every hand. Everyone behaves in an irregular or unpredictable way now and then, but this does not automatically place him outside the broad range of normality.

We would speak of personality [6] as abnormal, for example, if at any age an individual who was otherwise in good health grew seriously or progressively ineffectual as a social person. We would

[6] A more extended discussion of personality development in relation to the behavior disorders appears in Chapters 2, 3 and 4.

call it abnormal if, in order to carry on ordinary activities, he were obliged to expend disproportionate effort, in comparison with his previous level and with others of his age, physique, intelligence and training. We would speak of abnormal personality if an individual proved incapable of organizing and maintaining socially adequate relationships with other persons, if he proved unable to derive personal satisfactions from these, or if his behavior became socially inappropriate in terms of the prevailing cultural norms.

This rough criterion of normal and abnormal personality — the relative adequacy of performance, now and in the foreseeable future — is not peculiar to the field of behavior pathology. We use the same yardstick when we judge whether or not one of our internal organs is normal. We use it, moreover, to judge the normality of a machine, a factory or a whole industry, of a community, a nation or a family of nations. For example, we call that kidney normal which excretes competently and shows no serious signs of oncoming incompetence. But the normal kidney is never an ideal or perfect kidney. Like the normal person, it too may now and then do irregular and unexpected things. When it does, we look for an explanation in its intricate relationships with other organs, with food intake, water balance, body temperature, blood-stream or urinary tract infection, and the like. Sometimes the explanation eludes us and we chalk it up to renal complexity and our own ignorance. From the same standpoint, a normal industry or a normal community is never ideal or perfect. We say it is normal if it carries on its own affairs with reasonable competence, maintains an economical balance with other related organizations, and shows no serious signs of heading progressively into trouble or of deteriorating.

As every close observer of human action knows, it is sometimes quite impossible to account for a person's odd conduct or unexpected attitude. Neither he nor anybody else can understand it. From this some draw the immediate conclusion that therefore we must introduce an unnatural, unknowable factor or some otherworldly influence to fill the gap. That is giving in to the challenge of ignorance without a struggle. In our present state of knowledge we should expect to find human behavior often unintelligible. We should expect chance factors to play a larger role than in simpler dynamic systems. Consider for a moment how enormously complex our relationships with our fellows are, how meaning-laden are the countless cultural objects and symbols that saturate our daily life. Consider how many half-digested, unassimilated, contradictory attitudes we all carry along in our personality organizations.

In behavior pathology we must expect very often to face too many unanalyzed and uncontrolled variables for our present stage of development in scientific knowledge and technique. The cure for this deficiency, however, lies not in retreating to something less clear and certain, but in advancing to meet the challenge with better formulations of our problems, with better recognition of what we could but do not know, with new and better techniques, with more objective studies of behavior pathology and its precursors.

Neuroses and psychoses

Behavior disorders, or personality disorders, *are relatively fixed, crystallized patterns of maladaptive attitudes and responses.* Traditionally they have been divided into two main classes, the *neuroses* or "minor psychoses," and the *psychoses* or "major psychoses." This division, while still convenient, depends less upon medical or psychological science than it does upon legal and practical necessity. Certain of the behavior disorders are apt to demand prompt and often prolonged hospitalization if a catastrophe is to be averted. Others are not. Unfortunately, it is in the former that patients are least able to accept advice, supervision, treatment or detention in a hospital. In countries where the rights of individuals are jealously guarded, the forcible abduction and detention of any person on grounds of "mental incompetence" is no light matter.[7] Here is a loophole through which abuses might creep in to threaten the political safety of everyone. It was out of this medico-legal conflict that formal distinctions were finally worked out between the behavior disorders rendering a person legally committable to an institution, and those leaving him free. The former correspond roughly to what we call *psychoses,* while the non-committable behavior disorders include what we call today the *neuroses* or *psychoneuroses.*

The further subdivision of neuroses and psychoses has not been so simple. A confusing variety of classifications has been proposed

[7] S. Warson, "A review of the concept of insanity," *Amer. Jour. Psychiat.,* 1941, vol. 97, pp. 1288-1300; G. Stevenson, "Ideals and principles for proper management of the mentally ill," *Ment. Hyg.,* 1942, vol. 26, pp. 227-234.

from time to time for the neuroses, none of them entirely satisfactory. Beard has bequeathed to us the term *neurasthenia,* which originally meant weak nerves, and Janet has left us *psychasthenia,* or weak psyche, both of which terms survive today but with altered meanings. Freud made a distinction between those neuroses which he believed to be purely and simply physical processes, the direct result of an oversupply of hypothetical sexual toxins, and those neuroses which he considered to be of mental origin. The first group he named the *actual neuroses,* the second group the *psychoneuroses.* This differentiation is no longer considered valid, but the latter term has persisted, and is used today interchangeably with *neuroses.*

Freud made further theoretical distinctions which have left a residue of synonyms. The ancient Greek term *hysteria* he renamed *conversion hysteria* because he believed its symptoms to represent the conversion of psychic energy into somatic disorder, a view that may have been influenced by nineteenth-century interpretations of electromagnetic phenomena. Freud also favored the unfortunately confusing term *anxiety hysteria.* He felt that there were two distinctly different kinds of anxiety disorder, one of them purely physiological and therefore an "actual neurosis," the other partly mental, and therefore a "psycho-neurosis." The latter he called anxiety hysteria. This distinction is no longer considered valid, since all anxiety disorders have been found in practice to include important personal factors.[8] Nevertheless, Freud's positive contributions have been so many, and he and his disciples so productive, that such terms as these have gained a permanent place as alternatives in the current literature.

The evolution of our current classifications of the psychoses is too long and involved a story to tell here.[9] It was Kraepelin who managed to reduce the confusion of many seemingly independent clinical syndromes to a few large groupings. His progressive syntheses extended over a period of several decades, beginning in the latter part of the nineteenth century. One modification of Kraepelin's classification was officially adopted in Great Britain in 1933,[10]

[8] D. Henderson and R. Gillespie, *A Textbook of Psychiatry for Students and Practitioners,* 6th edition (London: Oxford University Press, 1944), pp. 159-167.

[9] See N. Cameron, "The functional psychoses," in J. Hunt (editor), *Personality and the Behavior Disorders* (New York: Ronald Press, 1944), pp. 861-921.

[10] G. Fleming, "The revision of the classification of mental disorders," *Jour. Ment. Science,* 1933, vol. 79, pp. 753-757.

and a somewhat different modification by the American Psychiatric Association in 1934.[11] There is quite general agreement in both countries today that our present clinical groupings are seriously in need of revision. An important step forward has recently been taken by psychiatrists in the United States Army who have provided a tentative revision which not only modernizes the Kraepelinian classification but also leaves the way open for further modification.[12]

A biosocial classification of behavior disorders

In our account of the behavior disorders we shall use a modification of the United States Army classification which agrees also in most essential respects with the official American Psychiatric Association system, but is less cumbersome and involved. However, we shall not make a clear-cut distinction between neuroses and psychoses. It is true that the committable behavior disorders as a group are much more likely than the non-committable ones to exhibit severe distortions of social behavior. But it is also true, as Freud was the first to recognize, that behavior disorders in both groups arise from and are perpetuated by the unskilled or inappropriate use of the same basic adjustive techniques. These similarities in behavior pathology are far more significant than the differences in medico-legal status. We only multiply our problems needlessly when we segregate psychotic from neurotic patients in our thinking as we tend to segregate them in our anachronistic institutions.

We shall recognize eight main clinical syndromes, or clusters of related signs and symptoms, among the behavior disorders. These are (1) *hypochondriacal disorders*, (2) *fatigue syndromes*, (3) *anxiety disorders*, (4) *compulsive disorders*, (5) *hysterical inactivation* and *hysterical autonomy*, (6) *paranoid disorders*, (7) *schizophrenic disorders*, (8) *manic and depressive disorders*. We follow the United States Army classification in regarding reactions of *cerebral incompetence* as essentially "non-psychiatric" unless the

[11] C. Cheney, *Outlines for Psychiatric Examinations*. Utica, N.Y.: State Hospitals Press, 1934. Also reprinted in full in A. Rosanoff, *Manual of Psychiatry and Mental Hygiene*, 7th edition (New York: Wiley, 1938), pp. 967-985.
[12] *United States Army Technical Medical Bulletin No. 203*. Washington, D.C.: United States Government Printing Office, October 19, 1945, Section 18. Also reprinted in *Jour. Ment. Science*, 1946, vol. 92, pp. 425-441, and in *Ment. Hyg.*, 1946, vol. 30, pp. 456-476.

cerebrally incompetent patient develops a behavior disorder, in which case his psychiatric diagnosis places him in one of the above eight syndromes. Each of the behavior disorders will be characterized briefly here and treated in greater detail in its own chapter.

(1) *Hypochondriacal disorders* are characterized by habitual preoccupation with a supposed disease or defect in an organ or a body part which is actually functioning within normal limits. We also include as hypochondriacal an habitually exaggerated concern over organs or body parts which are defective or diseased.

(2) By *fatigue syndrome* we mean the habitual preoccupation with complaints of fatigue or easy fatigability by a person who is not suffering from systemic disorder or defect, or whose systemic disorder or defect does not justify his complaints. The typical fatigue syndrome responds neither to rest nor to overfeeding unless therapeutic suggestion is deliberately or unintentionally included.

(3) *Anxiety disorders* may be chronic or acute. In the *chronic anxiety reaction* the patient suffers from persistently heightened skeletal and visceral tensions. These tend to disturb his habitual rhythms of living and predispose him to give exaggerated and inappropriate responses on relatively slight provocation. The *anxiety attack* is an acute episode of emotional decompensation. It usually appears in the setting of chronic anxiety, and exhibits to a pronounced degree the characteristics of normal fright. Maximal anxiety attacks are usually called *panic reactions.* We shall group the *phobias,* or pathological fears, with anxiety disorders, instead of following Janet who for theoretical reasons placed them with compulsions under his "psychasthenia." Phobias are anxiety disorders in which the immediate anxiety excitants are specific and can be identified by the patient, although he usually regards them as inexplicable.

(4) In *compulsive disorders* there are irrepressible tendencies to do, say or think something in a particular way, which persist in spite of strong contrary tendencies. In this situation anxiety reactions develop and their periodically rising intensity leads to indulgence, followed by temporary relief.

(5) *Hysterical disorders* (Freud's "conversion hysteria") are characterized by the development of persistent inactivation or persistent autonomy. This resembles superficially the inactivation or autonomy produced by neurological damage or disease; but it lacks an adequate basis in organ or tissue pathology. Common varieties

of hysterical disorder are sudden disturbances of speaking, hearing or seeing, the sudden appearance of paralyses, tremors or seizures, and topical amnesia, with or without flight from a conflict situation or temporary loss of personal identity.

(6) In *paranoid disorders* the patient's behavior is dominated by more or less systematized delusional reactions. There is little or no tendency toward disorganization or deterioration.

(7) In *schizophrenic disorders*, on the other hand, the distinctive change is a disorganization and desocialization of the acquired behavior systems that constitute personality. These systems are in part replaced by behavior that is dominated or determined by private fantasy. Schizophrenia usually includes the development of weird, bizarre delusions and hallucinations, extraordinary verbal confusions, and symbolic motility disorders which seldom follow any of the familiar patterns of neurological disease.

(8) The chief characteristics of *manic excitement* are marked elation, or aggressive self-assertion, which often reaches delusional proportions, and energetic overactivity without serious disorganization. In the *agitated depression* there is restless overactivity, also without serious behavior disorganization, but despair and apprehensive or self-condemnatory delusions dominate the clinical picture. In the *retarded depression* the patient's behavior is slowed down, and his activities are restricted in their range but not disorganized. Sadness, dejection and self-depreciatory delusions prevail. Approximately 25 per cent of the patients in this group have both manic and depressive attacks, usually separated by years of good health, but in exceptional cases alternating in cycles.

The emphasis we must place upon personal, social and cultural factors in the behavior disorders may at first seem strange to the biologist who is most at home with physiology and tissue pathology. For to understand disease in an organ or a physiological system we need not, as a rule, go beyond the *milieu interne* and the immediate impersonal outside environment for our data. If other persons and cultural objects enter the clinical picture at all, they do so only indirectly or incidentally, — with the obvious exception of cases in which there has been deliberate assault, deprivation or poisoning by another individual. But the patient's personality and its biosocial development, the outcome of years and years of interaction between a human organism and its natural social habitat, are always prime considerations in behavior pathology.

Physiologically and medically trained men may well regret the necessity for including these less predictable and often poorly formulated social interrelationships in their conception of behavior disorders. They may impatiently turn to those whose limited grasp of human conduct allows them to prophesy that some day everything will be solved by the invention of a better microscope or a more delicate stain. Similarly, persons who lack physiological or medical training may wish that they could somehow delegate the responsibility for biological factors in behavior pathology to someone else. But it is in this very field of biosocial interaction that our most significant behavior problems originate. If we are to make further headway with them, that is where we shall have to study them.

2 Personality Development and Behavior Disorders

EACH OF US is born into this complex social world of ours with neither instincts nor any other biological blueprints to guide us. We cannot speak the language of our own native land. We do not understand the simplest signals or share the feeblest thoughts of those around us. In the beginning we are pure organism, somewhat human in form but altogether animal in conduct. Throughout the long years of infancy, childhood and adolescence we slowly acquire skill in the social techniques by which this intricate life with others must be managed. We learn to live as human beings, and in doing so we develop human personality.

Personality is something that each of us must necessarily build up during the period of his biological growth. It is not an inheritance, not a gift. At birth our physiological equipment at once develops needs; and our main task in early life is to learn to satisfy them through our own individual efforts. The human society that receives us understands our primary biological needs and is prepared to help us meet them. Its own social organization is built upon the same needs. Even our modern industrialized life is so tightly organized around animal want that, were hunger and thirst, sex and its consequences, and the need for warmth, shelter and protection all miraculously eliminated — though this brought heaven — society and culture would collapse. For not only our whole economy, but also our most treasured customs and values, are rooted or find their chief expression in eating and drinking, in mating and parenthood, in the covering, guarding and housing of our biological bodies.

Consider the dinner table for a moment. In home life it is rarely a mere feeding surface or a trough. It is the principal and most

15

intimate occasion of daily family gathering where attitudes and information are traded face to face. There children get important basic training in the difficult practical arts of sharing, cooperation and self-control — training that generalizes to other needs in other human situations. Outside the family circle we use hunger and thirst in feasting and toasting. We eat and drink together to honor courage, beauty and achievement, to negotiate and seal bargains, to promote mutual understanding, heal personal wounds or signify membership, and even to symbolize the deepest religious beliefs. We shall not wonder, then, at finding ideals and animal needs so often confused in the behavior disorders. It will not mystify us to learn that serious disturbances of eating, drinking and alimentation arise, not only through gastrointestinal disease, but also because of conflicts and perplexities over the important social relationships they represent in human life. The complaint is still biological, but its source is in the social personality.

The term *personality* in our language is used with many different meanings.[1] If we are to discuss it at all intelligently, we must begin by fixing upon a single arbitrary definition to fit our present purpose, which is that of understanding the behavior disorders. For us *personality* will mean *the dynamic organization of interlocking behavior systems that each of us develops through learning processes, as he grows from a biological newborn to a biosocial adult in an environment of other individuals and cultural products.* In studying the behavior disorders we shall unavoidably emphasize the social aspects of human life. But this must not lead us to forget for a moment that even the most socially mature adult is still every bit as biological as a newborn baby. Indeed, in many ways he is actually more competent biologically than he ever was in infancy. We therefore speak of him as *biosocial* to indicate that his biology has been made to operate socially, in terms of others' needs and others' interests as well as his own.

It is almost meaningless to speak of personality in the newborn. Individual differences between babies there are at birth, just as with other mammals, and some of these biological differences may be alone important enough to determine a part of one's basic life pattern. Sex is one of these. The color of one's skin, hair or eyes may be another. Often one's size, rate of growth, contour or ana-

---

[1] G. Allport, *Personality, a Psychological Interpretation* (New York: Holt, 1937), pp. 27-50.

tomical symmetry will open some doors of opportunity, later on, and close others. So also may differences in sensory acuity, in strength or energy level, in general coordination or intelligence.[2]

A large, handsome, intelligent and well-coordinated boy, for instance, is likely to receive quite different treatment throughout his formative years from that experienced by an undersized, homely, dull and clumsy boy, and to enter into many satisfying activities that are virtually barred to the latter. Girls with beauty, symmetry, grace and pleasing natural colors likewise meet preference and approval, from early childhood on, that are unknown to their biologically less fortunate sisters. Myopia may make a scholar or a snob, and one short leg a recluse or a stoic. The retarded child brought up among superior siblings, and the superior child reared in a mediocre or inferior family, may both develop attitudes toward others in the home that influence the whole pattern of their later personality growth.

But even in such cases it is never the biological factor by itself that makes personality differences. What counts is always the reaction of other people to it. Their behavior gives the child his preferred or rejected status and builds up in him the corresponding attitudes and expectations. The same retarded child would develop quite different attitudes toward himself and others were he to be adopted early into a dull family and raised among dull companions. As a result, his personality might be fundamentally different, even though his biological limitations remained the same. On the other hand, our handsome, intelligent boy and pretty girl might grow into less stable and happy adults if their good looks met with resentment or ridicule in the home, or if they were regularly exploited for their elders' advantage. Well-favored as well as ill-favored persons are therefore to be found in the ranks of the neurotic and psychotic. It is always this interplay of biology and society. In the end, the two influences become so intricately interwoven that the old controversy over normal and abnormal personalities — whether they be inherited or acquired — loses all its meaning.

The distinction between biological maturity and social maturity is more significant. They are, of course, to some extent interdependent; but they are certainly not identical and they are often out of step. Although either one may get ahead of the other, it is social immaturity that raises by far the most problems. The so-

[2] J. Macfarlane, "The guidance study," *Sociometry*, 1939, vol. 2, pp. 1-23.

called *age of resistance* is a simple and, in our culture, quite normal example. Somewhere between the age of two and four years many children go through a phase of stubborn, self-assertive rebellion. They have newly acquired a degree of strength, skill and initiative that is simply not supported by a comparable mastery of the social pattern of permissions and taboos. Clashes with the human environment in this period show a sharp rise.[3]

Again in early and middle adolescence the rapid biological changes may similarly outstrip social learning and lead to still more serious outbursts, both in the home and in the wider community. Social standards to which the adolescent is held also show marked fluctuations and many real as well as apparent contradictions. They are for the most part much less consistent than biological growth, and in many respects are more closely related to tradition and adult opinion than to the physiology of adolescence. Individual differences in habitual overt aggression and initiative in the child or adolescent, individual differences in the flexibility, anxiety level and self-assertion of adults in charge, and the relative tolerance of the social atmosphere, seem to determine whether adolescence and the age of resistance shall be periods of fair weather or foul.

In every culture and subculture there are rough standards of maturity current for each biological age-group in the two sexes. By these standards an individual's behavior is judged by his elders and his peers to be mature or immature, and he is treated on this basis in accordance with the expectations and the prejudices his critics entertain. Unfortunately, one's elders and one's contemporaries do not see eye-to-eye in many respects when it comes to standards of maturity. Whence it is that children, and especially adolescents, are apt to find themselves obliged to live according to a double standard, their parents' generation's and their own.

We begin life as biological individuals in our mother's oviduct and uterus. We enter life as biosocial persons when we are born into an already organized environment of other human beings. For most of two decades we spend our time learning, through our own behavior, the business of living among others built like ourselves and with the same fundamental needs that must be met. Each of us individually must learn in active service the cultural patterns of satisfaction, delay, denial, reward and punishment that he finds in

[3] G. Murphy, L. Murphy and T. Newcomb, *Experimental Social Psychology*, 2d edition (New York: Harper, 1937), pp. 389-397.

operation from infancy on. We learn to develop modified and sub-stitute gratifications and develop special techniques for dealing with the inevitable conflict and frustration which family and other group living bring to everyone. Now we shall escort our human being swiftly through these first two decades to see what influences he comes under, and what reactions he himself develops toward them, that may throw light upon our main objective, the behavior disorders.

Life in the uterus

The human individual comes into being when an errant sperm unites with an ovum to begin a dramatic series of interactions that result in the embryo and fetus. Whatever biological inheritance the infant is to receive from its parents is determined at the instant of fertilization. From that moment on, up to its birth, the new organism's progress will depend upon such factors as the biological quality of the original fertilized ovum, its successful implantation in the uterine wall, the formation of placenta and auxiliary structures that protect the growing organism and bring its circulation into functional relation with the mother's, the adequacy of interactions within the embryo and fetus itself, and the goodness of physiolog-ical cooperation between mother and child-to-be. Their relation-ship during pregnancy is entirely in terms of these biological processes. There is no intermingling of embryonic or fetal blood with the mother's blood. There are no neural connections through which the mother may directly affect her unborn child.

The life and times of the unborn child have for centuries been the subject of romantic prose that has frequently mistaken itself for fact. Not so many years ago, for example, the claim was vigorously put forward that repressed memories of intrauterine bliss play a significant role in adult neuroses and psychoses. Frustrated men and women were said to be dominated by a manifest or latent urge to reverse the birth process, to creep back into the mother's womb or some worthy substitute therefor, and remain there forever at rest. In the deepest places of their psyche, it was said, these un-happy ones treasured up an unconscious, prenatal remembrance of the good old days when they lived securely in peace and plenty, floating undisturbed in a warm, dark, quiet world of unparalleled intimacy with the beloved mother. This is a tranquil picture and a pleasant tale, but its materials seem now to have come only from folklore and the induced fantasies of imaginative persons.

The facts of prenatal life are not so romantic. It has been reported that simple conditioned responses may perhaps be experimentally established and extinguished in the human fetus during its last two gestation months.[4] But we have no objective evidence whatever to support the hypothesis that a fetus can react in terms of complex interpersonal relationships, or that retention and recall of the circumstances of intrauterine life are biologically possible. The many studies made of infant behavior during early postnatal life yield no sign of these abilities. The burden of proof, therefore, rests heavily upon those who claim that a relatively undeveloped fetus, confined in the amniotic bag of waters, can react to its surroundings in ways that are far beyond its postnatal abilities weeks or months later, and under environmental conditions that are infinitely more favorable.

All the available evidence indicates, then, that before birth the human organism's adjustments are carried out at non-social levels. Normal uterine arrangements ensure protection of the embryo and fetus against cold, drying, pressure, strain, blows and other sudden changes. The unborn child does indeed dwell in a warm, dark chamber, half-suspended in a fluid and provided with continuous room service. It need not breathe, it need not suck or swallow, it need not digest or evacuate in order to live. So long as the maternal blood supplies what the fetus requires for growth and maintenance, so long as waste products are removed fast enough, most of the primary physiological needs of postnatal life, with their stimulating tensions, can hardly arise. However, if for any reason these services are interrupted, the fetus has no way of surviving. Clearly, prenatal life has few responsibilities; the dependence of the unborn child upon its mother is one-sided and complete. But this dependence is, at least for the fetus, a very unromantic biological one, involving only housing, automatic protection and free interchange of solids, fluids and gases via the placenta. The rest is fiction.

Birth and the newborn

The birth process has inspired countless theorists, from ancient times right down to the present. Most noted among the moderns is Otto Rank, who based an elaborate system of speculation about personality on the supposed after-effects of the child's forcible ex-

---

[4] D. Spelt, "Conditioned responses in the human fetus in utero," *Psychol. Bull.*, 1938, vol. 35, pp. 712-713.

pulsion from his uterine paradise. He maintained, for example, that specific phobias could be traced to repressed memories of the psychic birth trauma, especially fear of small, closed places and the dark, and of small animals that go in and out of little burrows.[5] Freud criticized these specific conclusions of Rank on logical grounds. He himself taught that anxiety states at any period of life might be replicas of the birth anxiety, rearoused by later threats of separation from some loved object.[6] He credited the birth experience with being "the primal anxiety" and suggested that traumatic war neuroses may be derived from it. These interpretations of birth still exert a considerable influence upon current theories regarding personality and the behavior disorders.[7]

Rank's hypothesis and the others derived from it miss fire because they run counter to the evidence. After all, our decision to adopt or reject them hinges upon something more than their internal logical consistency. The main question is whether or not the process of being born can actually be a basis for later recall. All the objective studies on infant remembering reported so far indicate that it cannot.[8] The claim is often made, however, that the birth trauma is forgotten because the memory of it has been repressed. This claim not only takes the possibility of such recall for granted, but it also assumes that forgetting necessarily implies repression, which is far from true. It is not possible to accept the statements, sometimes made by patients, that they can recall their own birth, without further corroborative support. Well-authenticated instances of even the most fragmentary recall by adults rarely date back before the first birthday, regardless of their character. None of them goes further back than the sixth postnatal month.[9]

The relevant established facts about birth are briefly these. In being born the human organism goes through a physiological revo-

5 O. Rank, *The Trauma of Birth* (New York: Harcourt Brace, 1929), pp. 12-17.

6 S. Freud, *The Problem of Anxiety* (New York: Norton, 1936), pp. 90-132.

7 See for example M. Ribble, "Infantile experience," in J. Hunt (editor), *Personality and the Behavior Disorders* (New York: Ronald Press, 1944), pp. 621-651; E. Simmel, "War neuroses," in S. Rado (editor), *Psychoanalysis Today* (New York: International University Press, 1944), pp. 227-248; O. English and G. Pearson, *Emotional Problems of Living* (New York: Norton, 1945), pp. 19-21.

8 R. Sears, *Survey of Objective Studies of Psychoanalytic Concepts* (New York: Social Science Research Council, Bulletin No. 51, 1943), pp. 106-110.

9 C. Dudycha and M. Dudycha, "Childhood memories: a review of the literature," *Psychol. Bull.*, 1941, vol. 38, pp. 668-682.

lution unparalleled during the rest of its days. It leaves an aquatic habitat in the amniotic sac for a life on dry land where, for the first time, it must use muscular effort in entirely new ways to get oxygen and food, rid itself of waste products by intermittent excretory and eliminative acts, and perfect mechanisms that regulate its own body temperature and skin moisture. It lies now on surfaces that introduce new pressures and postures. It is subjected to new stimulation from light, sound and manipulation by others.

The birth process itself is certainly hard on the baby as well as on the mother. During birth the fetus is subjected to very strong pressures, because of the powerful uterine contractions behind it and the resistance of maternal tissues in front of it. The uterine thrusts finally succeed in propelling it slowly through the narrow birth canal, from which it emerges into its new world. The normal molding of the newborn's head testifies to the severity of the birth ordeal; in exceptional cases there may even be severe anoxia or intracranial injury. Nevertheless, it is a waste of good effort to build hypotheses that attribute "conscious memories" or "unconscious impressions" to this event, since there is no valid evidence that recall in any form goes back to so remote a period of life, and none to indicate that children or adults model their behavior disorders upon it, in war or in peace.

From the standpoint of the behavior disorders the most important new event in birth is neither head-molding nor anoxia. It is neither possible intracranial injury nor hypothetical psychic anxiety. It is the introduction of a new dependence for the organism, a dependence upon another individual's convenience and good will. No longer are the newborn's needs satisfied as they arise, automatically, by his own and his mother's machinery. His mother has become a separate person who can grant, neglect or deliberately withhold the means of infant satisfaction. Delay has now entered the pattern of his life, delay between need and supply, bringing with it tension, want, unrest and pain.

Early training

Unintended delays and unplanned interruptions are inevitably the lot of every human infant. Even the most devoted mother can hardly forsake all her other duties to care continuously for her child. She cannot ignore completely the many little household emergencies of everyday life — the doorbell and the telephone, something burning on the stove, a day or two of malaise, another child's sudden need or an unexpected visitor. Sooner or later every infant must also be introduced to intentional delays and denials, and eventually these are formalized for him into some kind of a daily schedule. His early training is under way.

Schedules, no matter how flexible and tolerant they may be made, can never conform exactly to a baby's own individual needs. They must always be in certain respects arbitrary. At best they represent a compromise between the timing of the infant's biological wants and the life pattern of the family unit in which he belongs. Schedules are apt to fluctuate with changes in prevailing customs. There is a world of difference, for example, between the cold, "scientific" feeding techniques that Watson [10] advocated in 1928 and the Aldrichs' insistence in 1939 upon the importance of warm mothering during feeding.[11] But whatever the prevailing custom, schedules always reflect the mother's own dominant personality trends. They may also be in part determined by the father's habits, to the extent that these affect household routines. Thus, from its very inception, an infant's training is under the influence of interpersonal factors.

As a child grows in strength and general skill, more and more of his behavior is brought under the regulations that govern the pattern by which his elders live. He is inducted into new rhythms of function, of need and satisfaction, of quiescence and activity. Crying and restlessness at the wrong time, for example, are deliberately ignored, whereas at first they brought him company, milk, soothing or a change. During the weaning process, a bottle, and then semi-solids in a hard spoon, gradually replace the warm, soft breast. Eventually, the child must also learn to eliminate and evacuate at predetermined times and in arbitrarily chosen places, if he is to keep the security of parental approval and win release from the toilet chair.

It is especially important for us to realize that a child's first moral lessons are learned in relation to feeding, cleansing and toilet-training, and not in relation to abstract principles. That which his mother requires of him, in these specific situations, he learns is

10 J. Watson, *Psychological Care of Infant and Child*, New York: Norton, 1928.
11 C. Aldrich and M. Aldrich, *Babies Are Human Beings*, New York: Macmillan, 1939.

good. For this she gives her approval and her love, or at the very least she releases him from urging and confinement. Refusal to eat, dirtiness, genital manipulation and failure to "do his duty" on the toilet are all *bad.* They earn him nothing but nagging and restraint, rough handling, isolation, maternal rejection, or some other form of retribution for his evil. It is obvious that the young child has little grasp of the wider ethical implications of this training. In five-year-old children, for example, it has been found that excessive modesty is more closely associated with elimination than with masturbation.[12] The child at this age is unable to make a distinction which seems self-evident to us adults, but which can have little or no meaning in terms of his own mode of life.

The effects of these early lessons in *visceral ethics,* however, are never quite lost. They become especially obvious in the behavior disorders. In both neuroses and psychoses one finds endless confusion of cleanliness with godliness, of genital function and problems of evacuation with social wickedness, of eating with pregnancy and sexual sin. One encounters disguised visceral ethics in the worried or self-righteous preoccupation over diet, digestion, elimination and reproductive rhythms that so many hypochondriacs show. They are more afraid of malfunction, and more proud of good function, than the circumstances of their adult life can possibly justify. The same criticism can be made of many ritualistic performances seen in the compulsive disorders. In terms of adult verbal logic they seem aimless and bizarre. The neurotic or psychotic person who is caught in this type of ethical confusion does not suspect and cannot recognize its infantile and early childhood origins. But to the student of behavior pathology its genesis is clearly in the child's misunderstanding of cultural demands made upon him very early, and quite emotionally, in the name of right and wrong.

His parents are the chief interpreters to the child of the culture in which he is destined to live. They lay out the pattern as they see it, and he fits into it as best he can. In the beginning his biological needs spur him on to act, while his social environment determines how his action shall be timed and how molded. He learns to give specific reactions in particular situations at first, but these later generalize to other aspects of similar and equivalent situations. His environment is not only a social one but it is also intensely personal and intimate. Rewards and punishment come with

[12] J. Macfarlane, "The guidance study," *Sociometry,* 1939, vol. 2, pp. 1-23.

simple directness from persons, never from abstract symbols. On this basis he learns to react differentially to the permitted and the forbidden. He also learns anticipatory attitudes from the direct time sequence of *permitted act-approval* and *forbidden act-disapproval*, thus laying the groundwork for social conscience in his own behavior.

Adults have at their disposal every means they need for enforcing their demands. They control nearly all the sources of a small child's satisfactions — food and drink, warmth, cleansing and comfort, play and protection, emotional acceptance and mothering, relief from loneliness, from restraint and pain. Adults can therefore reward conformity to their wishes by granting satisfactions, and punish nonconformity by withholding them. They can provide compelling motives for the resisting or disobedient child by introducing pain, confinement or immediate ostracism, accompanied by appropriate gestures, words and general manner. Later on, the gesture, word or manner alone becomes an adequate stimulus to control and coerce the child, by arousing in him the anticipatory tensions that we call anxiety.

We must not miss the point that the parents' own personal needs and wishes are very important in determining what they shall demand of a child. By compelling him to satisfy his needs in ways that they prescribe, and in schooling him in their own needs, they assimilate his behavior to the family pattern. This has significant results for us. If, for example, both parents encourage a son to acquire his father's attitudes and needs, he will develop similarities in personality organization that are often mistakenly attributed to simple biological inheritance. By the same process of social learning his parents can develop in him the family taste for cultural objects, customs and opinions, which the public usually ascribes also to heredity. The child's whole pattern of faith, suspicion, disbelief, solace and anxiety may thus be brought into line with that of one or both parents. Their way of life becomes his; they have successfully inducted him into their culture.

Of course this need not have been at all the parents' plan. Their goals may have been selfish and immediate — to minimize the child's nuisance value, to train him to unquestioning compliance with their personal wishes, and to gain satisfaction for themselves by making him in their own image. But the average parent owes most of his own derived needs and wishes to the culture or subculture in which he himself was reared. He demands of his child essentially what his parents demanded of him, and for much the same reasons. What he considers good and desirable, or wrong and intolerable, most of the other adults around him also do. And so, for the average child, to learn to fit into his parents' pattern of permission and taboo is also to learn the adult permissive pattern of his culture, and so he is partially prepared for his future in the wider community.

Such direct, intimate activities as feeding, body care and toilet training are important, not alone to a child's moral development, but also to his most fundamental social relationships. They are all based upon physiological need, but their role in personality development cannot possibly be understood at the level of physiological exposition. Today we have reason to believe, for instance, that in infant feeding, the oral stimulation, sucking exercise and stomach filling may each contribute something essential to the complete satisfaction of an infant's hunger need.[13] However, were we to stop our consideration of feeding here, at the asocial level of oral titillation, sucking satiation and gastric repletion, we would be repeating the reflex behaviorist error of studying the human being as an isolated machine. Nor would we fare better by neglecting the facts of interpersonal behavior for untestable hypotheses about the imaginations of babes at the breast — that they are preoccupied there, for example, with fantasies of scooping out their mother's entrails and devouring them.[14]

We can begin instead with the simple fact that infant feeding involves the cooperation of two persons. Nursing is the child's first occasion of active social participation, his first date with his most important social contact, the mother. What this and future dates shall develop into depends upon the kind and degree of satisfaction they afford the child. For the responses an infant learns to give in the beginning to feeding and its approach tend to generalize later on to the feeder when she is not at the moment part of a feeding

[13] H. Halverson, "Infant sucking and tensional behavior," *Jour. Genetic Psychol.*, 1938, vol. 53, pp. 265-430; D. Levy, "Experiments on the sucking reflex and social behavior in dogs," *Amer. Jour. Orthopsychiatry*, 1934, vol. 4, pp. 203-224.

[14] M. Klein, "Early development of conscience," in S. Rado (editor), *Psychoanalysis Today* (New York: International University Press, 1944), pp. 64-74; M. Klein, "Mourning and its relation to manic-depressive states," *Int. Jour. Psychoan.*, 1940, vol. 21, pp. 125-153.

situation. Thus, if a mother's behavior toward her suckling is skillful, relaxed and accepting, his feeding can proceed smoothly, without discomfort or distraction, to its completion. His satisfaction eventually goes beyond mere hunger satiation to include the whole situation and the accepting mother.

If, however, a mother feeds her infant in the same spirit that she makes the beds and washes the dishes — routinely, as an impersonal duty, or unwillingly and resentfully — she is almost sure to handle him mechanically, or tensely and hurriedly. If he is a so-called "scientific" bottle-feeder he will not be handled at all. In the former his mother functions like a quick-lunch counter, and in the latter he eats, in effect, alone. Neither situation is socially adequate. Both leave it entirely up to the feeder to get what fun he can out of his job. Both pass up valuable opportunities for establishing interpersonal relationships that mother and child will need later on as the basis for the latter's further socialization. Of course what holds for feeding holds also for other mother-child interactions. The rejecting, indifferent or "scientific" mother generally maintains the same fundamental attitudes through the rest of infant care and companionship, using similar techniques and producing similar effects.

It is not only the indifferent, "scientific" or rejecting mother who develops tense, unsatisfied behavior in a child. Anxious, inflexible, overconscientious and domineering mothers may do the same even though they accept their infant completely. Many of these make of feeding, body care and toilet training the occasion of coercion, scolding, punishment, restraint and moral intimidation. To such treatment the child may react, quite automatically and unavoidably, with increased tensions that make it difficult or impossible for him to cooperate. If his non-cooperation in turn renders the mother herself more tense, and hence more insistent, their interactions may spiral up into a series of daily brawls. What might have been a situation fostering valuable social relationships instead tends to promote mutual anxiety, resentment and distrust.

Attitudes such as these, learned originally in a specific social setting, are known to generalize to other situations and to interactions with other persons. Although the data from child behavior studies are still too fragmentary to be completely unequivocal, there are indications that they may lead a child to develop habitual rage reactions to any frustration, restriction and criticism, and to be generally hostile toward authority. If, on the other hand, the resentful, rebellious child is early overcome by force and kept in submission through punishment and loss of affection, he may instead develop habitual anxiety over the consequences of what he does or fails to do. He may learn to give up easily in the face of frustration and to lean heavily upon the approval of others. Both overaggressive and oversubmissive trends are found in adults with such a childhood background, and both are well-known antecedents and components of behavior disorders.

We have most illuminating examples of the home origin and the generalization of aggressive and submissive tendencies, in David Levy's study of maternal overprotection. He distinguishes two main varieties, the indulgent and the dominating. The former produces a relatively undisciplined child who has simply been allowed to continue utilizing infantile forms of aggression indefinitely. The dominated child, in contrast, has been overtrained in dependent, submissive reactions until he is no longer able to rebel openly. The influence of their early training is obvious when they come into free social contact with their contemporaries in the neighborhood. The indulged child at once tries bullying, fighting, temper tantrums and obstructionist tactics. The dominated child remains timid, submissive and withdrawn. Neither is successful. After he has been teased, rebuffed or beaten by other children, he handles the situation by avoiding thenceforth groups of his own age, either because of fear or because his irresistible needs to dominate are persistently frustrated.[15]

Two results emerge from Levy's study of especial significance for us. One is the unmistakable evidence that particular reactions, learned in relation to the mother in specific situations at home, generalize as social techniques in equivalent situations with strangers outside the home. The other is that, in spite of their being socially unsuccessful and personally disastrous, these techniques were not replaced by better ones. Both varieties of the overprotected carried their home training outside, into the wider community. The indulged children tried domineering, and the dominated children played the dependent little one. Neither group was able to meet its peers on an equal footing. Therefore neither was given the status of equals or accepted, after the usual try-out

[15] D. Levy, *Maternal Overprotection* (New York: Columbia University Press, 1943), pp. 101-111 and 161-184.

as one of the crowd. Their social techniques were grossly inappropriate for any but infantile situations. Some of them knew how to be little kings, and the others little slaves, but none of them could play the role of self-sufficient commoner. Hence they failed, and in failing cut themselves off from future companionship with children of their own age. None of them was accepted into the normal play groups of childhood where, as we shall see, social role-taking gets unintentional practice that helps equip a child to live on equal terms with others in adulthood.

The other result in Levy's study is no less significant. Even though they met uniform failure, these children did not shift to different tactics that might have gained them acceptance by their peers. For one thing, they had been overtrained in but one kind of strategy and had no other method ready to which they could shift. That was the established way. And, what is fully as important, they had been schooled by an overprotective mother, with her own unusually strong personal needs, to develop reciprocal needs that were equally imperious and could, unfortunately, be satisfied only by such a mother or a replica of her. No like-aged average child could possibly take her place.

It is quite clear that, in order to readjust their behavior to the demands of their new peer culture, such children would have to change not only their whole strategy, but also their imperious needs. They did neither. Instead, they accepted ostracism and the company of younger and smaller children. Here is a fact that we shall need to remember in understanding behavior pathology. Techniques that have been overlearned, especially if they have been related to strong biosocial need, will often persist indefinitely even though they are no longer appropriate, and bring a person failure, humiliation or suffering. Accordingly we must learn to look everywhere for the origins of abnormal behavior, in the present situation and its immediate antecedents, in the patient's historical past, and in his interpersonal relationships all the way back into his childhood and infancy.

No one any longer questions the potentialities of early behavior trends for later personality organization. There is, however, growing dissatisfaction with the still popular but static hypothesis that pictures infantile experience as being preserved forever in a rigid, immutable personality nucleus at the very core of one's being. On the contrary, longitudinal studies of personality growth show that patterns of reactions to frustration, privation and punishment can often be rather easily altered by appropriate changes in environment and skillful handling later in childhood. This is a cardinal principle in treatment by child-placement in foster homes. As a matter of fact, definite and persistent changes in relative ascendancy have been experimentally induced in preschool children, and these changes have also been found to generalize to other social situations.[16]

There are good reasons why the effects of infantile and early childhood experience should seem immutable when actually they are not. In the first place, unless behavior trends in one phase of personality development are modified, deliberately or by chance, they are very likely to help determine the direction of development in a succeeding phase. Another factor making for continuity and consistency is that the family atmosphere in which a child is reared remains, as a rule, substantially the same. Through infancy, childhood and adolescence he keeps the same parents, and unless something radically alters their attitudes toward him or each other they give him essentially the same kind of treatment throughout. And finally, the habitual modes of reaction, which the growing child acquires in one phase, sensitize him to certain aspects of his experience and dull him to others. When he enters new surroundings and meets new people, he is more ready to respond in one direction than another, and this readiness itself acts selectively to bring him more of similar kinds of experience. Thus he develops his basic personality organization by a continuing process, certain behavior trends initiated early in life being reinforced and perpetuated through his similar reactions in related situations later on.

Behavior trends can, in fact, be altered to some extent at any life period, in childhood and adolescence, in full adulthood and even in old age. This is the solid foundation upon which our modern systems of therapy in the behavior disorders are being built. Its cornerstone is our recognition that, although continuity and consistency are characteristic of an ongoing personality development, plasticity and resilience are in no sense infant monopolies.

[16] L. Jack, "An experimental study of ascendant behavior in preschool children," *Univ. Iowa Stud. Child Welfare*, 1934, vol. 9, No. 3; M. Page, "Modification of ascendant behavior in preschool children," *Univ. Iowa Stud. Child Welfare*, 1936, vol. 12, No. 3.

The family

Parents determine their offspring's biological inheritance simply and finally, when their individual contributions merge at conception to form the single cell whose product, the child, exhibits characteristics traceable to each. Parents are also instrumental in determining their child's cultural inheritance. Its conditions, however, are never simple and its effects may never be final. The conditions and the effects of cultural inheritance are complex and mutable because a child's two parents usually differ from each other in personality, and because they and he are always more or less affected by the cultural impact of the wider community. Moreover, these two parents are not just two human organisms that happen to be domiciled together for procreative ends. They are themselves a dynamic interacting unit, two biosocially different individuals who are functioning toward each other in a complementary relationship. Therefore, what the infant and child shall experience at their hands will be a resultant of interparental relationships, as well as the direct product of each parent's personal needs and wishes.

Human parenthood is always expectant for a long time before it finally becomes actual. This means that babies, whether they are welcomed or not, are born into a psychologically prepared situation. The materials for this prepared situation include the diverse personalities of the two parents, each of whom brings his or her unique cultural contribution to the biosocial partnership. There is first the sex distinction. It is not always recognized that, even within a single family living together under the same roof, the customs, traditions, attitudes and experiences of the male subculture usually differ markedly from those of the female subculture. This is a most important source of sex differences in perspective. In addition, husband and wife generally come from different family cultures as well, with their different social techniques, values, standards and goals, and their different preconceptions in relation to children, how they should be reared and what exact function each parent should perform in the process. Their patterns of expectation with regard to each other, as husband and wife, may be widely different, depending upon the interparental patterns in their respective homes, and how each has reacted to them.

These and a great many other differences like them enter into the phase of marital readjustment that normally precedes a first child's advent. Many of them are commonly settled by compromise, many more by willing or unwilling sacrifice and revision. Some are simply driven into concealment or disguise, but not eliminated as potential influences in the rearing of children. Some differences remain unconcealed and unsettled, as present or future sources of marital discord. Many of them cannot or need not be resolved. They persist openly as accepted distinctions between the paternal and the maternal personality in a given household, and may have a reciprocal or a balancing effect in parent-child relationships.

The degree of acceptance that a child enjoys and his general treatment during infancy and childhood will be affected, not alone by the quality and character of interparental adjustment, but also by the specific personal needs, hopes and expectations of each parent individually. Each may entertain in advance a definite preference as to the child's sex, and hopes regarding its ultimate appearance and special abilities. Each may cherish expectations and harbor secret fears concerning the child's general temperament in relation to what they consider their spouse's or their own to be, or in relation to someone else on one side of the family or the other. Because marital partners very often do differ fundamentally in their interpersonal techniques, and because popular thinking ascribes an almost superstitious finality to biological heredity in the determination of personality trends, this preoccupation is much deeper and more widespread than the facts warrant. None the less, the expectations or fears of a parent, to the extent that they enter into his overt interactions with the child and the other parent, may play a decisive part in shaping the child's social behavior patterns.

All parents daydream and talk about their child's future, even before he is born. Some go so far as to choose his career much as they choose his name, that is, more in accordance with what appeals to them personally at the time than with an eye to its possible harmony with wishes the child may later himself develop. Their choice is often shaped by the career they had once promised themselves or envied in someone else, by their own disappointment or distaste, or by the fate which their experiences or personal anxieties make them fear for their child. Anyone who counsels adolescents knows how widespread and how insistent this form of parental pressure is, and what severe conflicts it can arouse in the young adult when he realizes that to satisfy his own need he must destroy his parent's lifelong dream. The behavior pathologist finds many echoes of these unhappy dilemmas in neurotic and psychotic solutions of the filial conflict.

It seems to be the mother in American society who is the more influential parent in determining her child's early personality development. She it is, apparently, who gives him his basic ideals and standards of conduct, and through her daily behavior toward him builds up his early patterns of expectancy in relation to his reception and treatment by persons outside the family. We have already seen how seriously an inadequate pattern of expectancy can distort a child's social development in the examples of maternal overprotection. Lois Murphy asserts that normally mother-identification, among boys as well as girls, is the rule in our culture up to the age of four or five years.[17] When boys give up mother-identification, they appear to do so more because they are thrown with older boys, who deride feminine patterns, than because of any direct paternal influence.

Although it is unquestionably the mother who carries most of the burden of parenthood in our society, it is also she who holds most of its prestige. In urban communities, at least, the average American father's role in the home is culturally ill-defined, and in practice his direct parental influence and authority during the early years are very limited. He appears as a rule only intermittently at the periphery of his infant's activities and interests, where he may play the part of bored spectator, assistant nursemaid or buffoon. If on some special occasion he is entrusted with his child's whole care, he is rarely so skilled and thorough that anyone regrets the mother's return. In some households, were it not that the father is the principal wage-earner, he could be said to have practically no other function than procreation, like the male ant.

If the child brings satisfactions to the needs of one or both parents and gives them hopes and expectations, he also introduces problems for them which may, in turn, affect their attitudes toward him. Parenthood increases a person's responsibilities, necessitates changes in living arrangements, with perhaps a reduction in standards, and adds to whatever inconvenience and restrictions of liberty marriage may already have imposed. It modifies certain of the privileges and opportunities each parent has enjoyed inside the house as well as outside of it. It always means a division of atten-

[17] L. Murphy, "Childhood experience," in J. Hunt (editor), *Personality and the Behavior Disorders* (New York: Ronald Press, 1944), pp. 652-690.

tion, particularly on the mother's part, and a restructuring of the affectional balance. Not infrequently the baby seems at first a rival for the other parent's affection, an instrument of emotional exclusion. This reaction is commoner among men than women, as might be expected from the former's lesser significance at the time of childbirth and in the direct care of the infant afterward. It is exceedingly difficult to correct if the jealous parent has already managed to become established in a relation of childlike dependence upon the other one before a child is anticipated.

Most couples adjust to such problems successfully, regarding them as an integral part of parenthood, but there are important exceptions. Serious difficulties often arise, for example, among adults who have never fully understood or accepted the social implications of their sex role, as man-husband-father or woman-wife-mother. Many of these, for a variety of reasons, have not adequately rehearsed in play, talk, fantasy or practice the part they are expected to take when the curtain suddenly rises on the nativity. In consequence they may, as far as they are able, reject the proffered role and the child too. Exaggerations of parental rejection are frequently seen in the amnesias, disowning tendencies and withdrawal into fantasy of both hysteria and schizophrenia. They also appear occasionally in an agitated depression. Initial rejection is often a recognized origin of maternal overprotection, the mother reacting with compensatory excessive affection to her own guilt.

The children who are unwanted and rejected, whatever the parental defect responsible for it, may suffer serious personality distortion. There is general agreement that rejected children tend to be seclusive, detached and have few friends.[18] Some of them seem apathetic and unable to respond to the affection of others, or restless, fearful and insecure. Some are hyperactive, aggressive, rebellious or resentful of authority. Rejected children are reported to show a relatively very high susceptibility to behavior disorder and delinquency.[19] Some of them develop characteristics with constructive value, at the high cost of being rejected, evidently as de-

[18] See summaries and bibliographies in L. Wolberg, "The character structure of the rejected child," *Nervous Child*, 1944, vol. 3, pp. 74-88; F. Clothier, "The treatment of the rejected child," *Nervous Child*, 1944, vol. 3, pp. 89-110.

[19] A. Simon, "Rejection in the etiology and treatment of the institutionalized delinquent," *Nervous Child*, 1944, vol. 3, pp. 119-126; M. Field, "Maternal attitudes found in twenty-five cases of children with behavior primary disorders," *Amer. Jour. Orthopsychiatry*, 1940, vol. 10, pp. 293-311.

fense or compensation.[20] Many seem able to survive rejection without serious personality damage.

The relationship between rejection and childhood personality can hardly be a simple one. Many unplanned and unwanted children are welcomed when they actually come, while some of those deliberately planned for are rejected. Children who are unwanted and rejected at birth may later be accepted because interparental attitudes or extraneous factors have changed meanwhile, because parenthood brings unlooked-for satisfactions, or because the child becomes more of a companion and less of a burden as he grows out of helpless infancy. Conversely, children accepted at birth may for various reasons be rejected later.[21] What further complicates the picture is that most rejecting parents seem to be highly ambivalent in their behavior, mingling or alternating guilt, anxiety and compassion with their basic hostility or neglect. Finally, there is always the other parent to consider. In spite of marital discord which very often accompanies rejection, or even because of it, to irritate a marital partner and gain sympathy, one parent may counteract to some extent the effects of another.

Among the most fertile of all soils for childhood personality maladjustment are chronic marital discord and broken homes.[22] We know that interparental tension is very often associated with child behavior problems. Therapeutically, elimination of interparental strife may alone be sufficient to make a child's behavior disorder disappear. Even in homes without marital discord it has been found that preschool children show increased tension in nursery school behavior when interparental tension has increased at home.[23]

If the first child comes after marital discord has already been

[20] M. Borgum, "Constructive values associated with rejection," *Amer. Jour. Orthopsychiatry*, 1940, vol. 10, pp. 312-326.

[21] L. Thompson, "Attitudes of primiparae as observed in a prenatal clinic," *Ment. Hyg.*, 1942, vol. 26, pp. 243-256; H. Campbell, "Emotional maladjustments from unplanned parenthood," *Virginia Medical Monthly*, 1941, vol. 68, pp. 682-687.

[22] J. Macfarlane, "The relationship of environmental pressure to the development of a child's personality and habit patterns," *Jour. Pediatrics*, 1939, vol. 15, pp. 142-154; L. Kanner, *Child Psychiatry* (Springfield, Ill.: Thomas, 1935), pp. 87-105.

[23] D. Baruch and J. Wilcox, "A study of sex differences in preschool children's adjustment coexistent with interparental tensions," *Jour. Genetic Psychol.*, 1944, vol. 64, pp. 781-803; D. Baruch, "A study of reported tension in interparental relationships as coexistent with behavior adjustment in young children," *Jour. Exper. Education*, 1937, vol. 6, pp. 187-204.

established, it may widen the rift instead of closing it. The dissatisfied expectant parent knows that in his neighbors' and his relatives' eyes a baby puts the final seal on marriage, and not everyone can accept this unwelcome finality without an increase in resentment. If married life has seemed burdensome before, the personal duties and economic responsibilities of parenthood will not lighten it. In a very common pattern of compromise the load is divided by tacit consent, each parent playing the social role he cannot evade, and making that role his all. For the mother this means taking over the whole personal side of parenthood, and rearing the child herself, while her already unsatisfying social relationships with her husband are allowed to deteriorate further. The father drifts into the status of a semi-detached breadwinner. The dissimilar activities of the two parents set them on divergent paths. He, by not sharing in domestic affairs, is able to regain some of his premarital independence, while she plunges deeper into motherhood.

Unfortunately, women who are driven to seek most of their marital satisfaction from their children do not always make the best of mothers. It is significant that 75 per cent of Levy's abnormally overprotective mothers had little social life in common with their husbands while in an additional 10 per cent, whose general social relationship with the husband was rated as satisfactory, there was definite sexual incompatibility. Mothers whose social life was virtually restricted to their overprotected child showed striking tendencies to keep him infantile and actively to prevent his making any friendships whatever,[24] apparently seeing in them a threat to the security of their main source of personal gratification. The resulting limitations this places upon the child's personality development in relation to the play group have already been pointed out. The literature of behavior pathology cites well-authenticated cases of small boys who have been trained, or encouraged, to develop overt reactions toward their mothers that are typical of adult courting behavior. Correspondingly extreme liaisons are less frequently reported for small girls and their fathers, presumably in part because fathers are not home most of the day. It is, of course, by no means a foregone conclusion that every child reared in an atmosphere of domestic tension and strife, and every child overfond of a parent, will necessarily develop a behavior disorder. There is al-

[24] D. Levy, *Maternal Overprotection* (New York: Columbia University Press, 1943), pp. 156-158.

ways the healing influence of the wider community to consider, the resources and the independence the child may develop in response to adversity [25] and, finally, the likelihood that he will some day acquire a sibling or two.

The birth of a sibling into the family constellation means another redistribution of attention and affection all around. This is usually hardest on the erstwhile only child because it is his first experience with the change. He has been the sole recipient of maternal love and care in the family, and now the focus of his mother's interest shifts abruptly to an interloper called, "Your Baby Brother" or "Your Baby Sister." It is difficult if not impossible for a willing mother to conceal the fact that she has a new attachment. But it is not difficult for her to prepare her older child for his approaching change of status well in advance, or to see to it that the change has rewarding aspects for him and that he is genuinely included as a functional part of the new family set-up. The mother who neglects her first child for the pleasures of her second, or rebuffs him for interfering with them, is treating him to an experience of emotional rejection that may be no easier for him than rejection rooted in maternal indifference or hostility.

The intensity of a first child's jealousy for his younger sibling cannot possibly be anticipated by an adult, unless he realizes how intimate and complete the small child's dependence is upon his mother in the early years. Even if his father has been his rival, the child has had the field to himself on working days, and their competition has always gone along at different levels of appeal. The new baby is quite another kind of rival. He can be obtrusively present by day and by night. He competes at a lower level than the father did. As an infant he can win hands down, and without even trying, in any contest based on helplessness. Under these circumstances, the older child is likely to resort to whatever aggressive or regressive tactics he can hit upon to regain his lost sense of belonging and significance, or to avenge his displacement.[26] Failing these, he may do what is less troublesome to his parents but no less serious to his own personality development, drift apathetically to the fringe of domestic life and take refuge there in fantasy and lonely play.

[25] M. Borgum, "Constructive values associated with rejection," *Amer. Jour. Orthopsychiatry*, 1940, vol. 10, pp. 312-326.

[26] D. Levy, "Studies in sibling rivalry," *Res. Monog. Amer. Orthopsychiatric Assn.*, 1937, No. 2, pp. 1-96; D. Levy, "Hostility patterns in sibling rivalry experiments," *Amer. Jour. Orthopsychiatry*, 1936, vol. 6, pp. 193-257.

Siblings from the very start are potential rivals for the same love and consideration, the same life-space and the same goods. It is hardly surprising that the larger and stronger one should frequently fall back on simple aggression to prevail over his competitor. Sometimes this takes the form of direct action. The baby is covered up, restrained, poked, slapped, deprived of something it has or allowed to fall. Instances are not rare in which an older sibling's assault has imperiled an infant's life. Fries, for example, reports threats made by a boy that he might hit his sibling over the head with a hammer.[27] In a case known to the writer attempts to do so were actually made. An openly jealous girl of four years, according to Levy, tried twice to throw her baby sister out of the window.[28] Usually, however, on the basis of social learning and repression the aggressions quickly become covert, indirect and subtle. Often they are limited entirely to belittling comments and amused, unfavorable comparisons flavored with contempt. Sometimes covert hostility toward a sibling is the source of anxiety or tense irritability in a child, the significance of which may be completely missed by the mother and by the jealous child himself.

The other reaction of especial interest to the student of adult behavior disorders is the appearance of regressive behavior, either alone or with aggressions, following the birth of a sibling. The older child may suddenly lose some of his gains in biosocial maturity and revert to more infantile levels. New skills and newly acquired control, which he has not yet thoroughly consolidated, are most likely to be involved. Such a disruption of learned behavior is usually incidental to the child's general emotional disturbance over the situation, and not unlike other regressive reactions that he will have shown before, when lonely or in conflict. But regression may also appear in the form of direct and open competition with the new baby for the kind of care it is getting. The older child begins to whine again, talks babyishly, wets and soils himself, lies on the floor, crawls like an infant or declines to eat in ways that he has learned.

Both aggressive and regressive tactics tend to disappear when the child is again fully accepted by his parents, and in such a way that he can feel genuinely wanted, loved, significant and secure. Just what the connection is between sibling jealousy and adult

27 M. Fries, "Mental hygiene in pregnancy, delivery and the puerperium," *Ment. Hyg.*, 1941, vol. 25, pp. 221-236.

28 D. Levy, *Maternal Overprotection* (New York: Columbia University Press, 1943), pp. 25-26.

emotional problems we do not as yet know. There is, however, convincing evidence that patterns of interpersonal relationships acquired in the home become the bases of social interaction in the wider community. Macfarlane reports both clinical and statistical indications that jealousy is important as a factor in other severe childhood maladjustments, and a tendency for more children with siblings than without to fall into the jealous group. Her clinical impression is that the older of a pair of boys is not as likely to show confidence and ease in intimate social relationships, while the younger is not as likely to show confidence in his own abilities.[29] Behavior pathologists have long been struck by the similarity between the aggressive-regressive patterns of infants or young children, and some of the most prominent characteristics seen in the behavior disorders.[30] There are a great many indications that the two phenomena are genetically related, but we still lack complete longitudinal studies to establish the connection.

Sibling rivalry in childhood probably never disappears. It merely undergoes socialization along with the rest of behavior. Many of its fruits have positive, constructive social value. The very distribution of parental affection and attention may be beneficial, in protecting each child from getting more than is good for his personality development. Siblings can be comrades and fellow-conspirators as well as rivals. Punishment by an adult, for example, has been found to unite siblings against him, even though previously they may have been competing for his attention.[31] The presence of siblings in the home gives each child practice in multilateral interaction and prepares him for the later direct cultural impact of neighborhood, gang and school. If both sexes are represented among them, siblings can also make the highly important discovery of sex difference at home,[32] instead of in the neighborhood where interfamilial crises are more likely to result.

[29] J. MacFarlane, "Study of personality development," in R. Barker, J. Kounin and H. Wright (editors), Child Behavior and Development (New York: McGraw-Hill, 1943), pp. 307-328.

[30] For a critical review of the literature, see R. Sears, "Experimental analysis of psychoanalytic phenomena," in J. Hunt (editor), Personality and the Behavior Disorders (New York: Ronald Press, 1944), pp. 306-332.

[31] R. Gottemoller, "The sibling relationships of a group of young children," Nervous Child, 1943, vol. 2, pp. 268-277.

[32] M. Montagu, "The acquisition of sexual knowledge in children," Amer. Jour. Orthopsychiat., 1945, vol. 15, pp. 290-300; J. Conn, "Children's reactions to the discovery of genital differences," Amer. Jour. Orthopsychiat., 1940, vol. 10, pp. 747-754.

Brothers and sisters learn in one another's company the techniques of sharing, not only parental love and parental annoyance, but also objects and activities. They learn how to cooperate, compete and compromise, how to defend, evade, attack and escape. Because they are like-aged and do the same kinds of thing in the same general ways, they unwittingly train one another in methods and skills that parents alone cannot easily manage. An older sibling learns to enjoy the experience of having and protecting a younger one. Younger siblings benefit by the diversions and extra stimulation provided by an older child who is less busy and dignified than their mother. When one has brothers and sisters there is a greater tendency for we-ness to develop, the sense of belonging to a clan. All this is capable of giving the small child a head start when his time arrives for cruising around the neighborhood.

The wider community

As soon as possible after he has gained a little skill in locomotion, the average child emerges from the home on his own power. He now enters the expanding social universe as an individual, no longer accompanied and monitored by an older person. The neighborhood, spontaneous play groups and gangs begin to take over his further socialization. Later on the more formal secondary groups add their influence — clubs, church organizations and the school. Into this wider community the child carries whatever behavior equipment he has succeeded in developing, as a part of his growing personality, in the more intimate and protected home environment. There, for example, he will have acquired a variety of manual skills and freedom in handling objects and materials, both of which are necessary if he is to play on equal terms with the neighborhood children. He will have learned at home some of the essential social techniques used in associating with other persons in group situations, and in behaving himself as one member of a group.

During his early years in the home, it has been necessary for the parents to shelter their child, give him special privileges and intimate emotional acceptance in order to satisfy his simple direct needs and aid him in building security out of helplessness. Once this period of obligatory family incubation is over, however, it is just as esssential to see to it that he escapes from too warm dependence into the cooler and less intimate neighborhood atmosphere. One of the greatest contributions the neighborhood can offer a child is that of providing him with conditions for personal interaction which approximate more closely the adult pattern than anything he could ever find at home.

The moment he steps out of his home unaccompanied, the child loses his status as a privileged and protected individual, and becomes merely one more individual in the neighborhood. The patterns of friendliness, aggression and defense he now encounters are different, and less predictable for him than the ones in which he was reared. Other children are apt to be casual and unconcerned about him, or surprisingly hostile and critical. Differences that arise are usually settled directly between the contestants without adult intervention or, if adults do mix into a squabble, it is often only to aid their own child. Friendly adults treat a neighborhood child more objectively than his parents do, more like a person, less approvingly but less critically, and with quite different emphases.

If home has sufficiently prepared a child for the realities of life with others, and if there are no serious interferences by parents and other adults, his further socialization in the wider community will usually progress rapidly. Outside the home he experiences new freedom from supervision and a great expansion of living space. Opportunities for learning new manual skills and play techniques open in many directions. His social horizons are widened by his coming in daily contact with children whose family backgrounds and social attitudes are different from his own. He learns new social role-taking as one member of a large, loose, heterogeneous community of children, instead of being limited to the few roles possible within a tight little family society dominated directly by adults. As language develops further, the child gains the use of an instrument that enables him to participate in the everlasting verbal comment and exchange of opinion around him. Through this he acquires a still broader base for his own social interactions.

If a child is to get the most out of his social operations in the wider community, he must above all have a secure and dependable home base, one that he can leave without anxiety, one he can return to confidently for supplies, repairs and reassurance. The protection of home is necessarily limited in scope. No parent can possibly spread it out over the whole neighborhood, neither can an older sibling be expected to be forever watching over a younger brother or sister. Therefore, every child is bound to suffer rebuffs, belittling, discrimination, mishandling and downright defeat from time to time at the hands of his associates. If, however, he can be sure of his home, if life there provides emotional security and support when he needs them, a child can learn to absorb neighborhood reverses just as he learned to weather frustration and correction at home, and by using the same general techniques that he acquired there.

Chronically punishing, denying and hypercritical parents cannot very well provide a safe harbor for a growing child. Neither can homes in which the atmosphere is tense with interparental enmity. If children from such family backgrounds carry out into the neighborhood the expectations and reactions they have learned from their parents, they may unwittingly arouse hostility or dislike in the other children, and so find the outside world as unfriendly as their home. If for any reason they gain the acceptance among others which they have not enjoyed at home, they may instead welcome social contacts. Many children with uneasy homes succeed in identifying themselves with their playmates' parents in place of their own. Not a few cherish the childhood belief that they are actually the kidnapped or bartered offspring of highborn parents — a theme that is often encountered also among schizophrenics and may have similar origins.

His parents' own insecurities and unsatisfied personal needs also enter as a factor in a child's personality development in the wider community. Many children emerge into the neighborhood already oversensitized to danger by exaggerated maternal warnings that stem from unusual maternal fears. In consequence they tend to overreact selectively to the hostile and threatening aspects of their surroundings. Others, accustomed at home to protective domination by a possessive mother, find the normal challenging conduct of some would-be playmates cruel or alarming, and the indifference of most associates cold, mean and heartless. The child whose mother has greatly indulged him, and trained him by her submissive behavior to expect submission from others, is rudely shocked and repelled by the reception his habitual aggressive demanding gets from his neighborhood peers, whose ways are very different from his mother's.

The children of insecure, domineering, possessive and overindulgent parents are usually incubated too long in the home before being released to the neighborhood. Hence they are, as a rule, definitely inferior in social techniques and skills to others of their own age who have been able to get an earlier start.[33] Childhood illness, weakness or handicap may similarly retard social maturing if it seriously delays an individual's induction into neighborhood play groups, isolates him from them for a prolonged period after he has already been inducted, or restricts his participation in their group activities.

The isolation of children is occasionally a result of deliberate parental policy. Adults who for some reason feel themselves to be socially superior or morally in hazard may forbid their offspring to mingle freely with neighborhood children. This limitation is perhaps less serious in large families with large grounds, ample means and freedom to seek companions in other localities. However, the haughty and the morally uneasy are often in poor or moderate economic circumstances. Their self-imposed aloofness amounts to virtual imprisonment for the children in a small yard or an apartment. All such social isolates, rich or poor, become the target of neighborhood resentment, hostility and ridicule. One or both parents may also be chronically suspicious of outsiders, and harbor delusional attitudes beyond that of their superior quality or purity. The effect of this situation is sometimes to develop corresponding suspicions and delusions in the child.

In socially isolated families the only boy with many sisters, and the only girl with many brothers, grow up under an additional handicap unless the like-sexed parent takes pains to offset it. They are either too special and their siblings indulge them, or they are overwhelmed by the attitudes and techniques of the other sex and fail to develop adequately those of their own. Clinically one runs across combinations of these isolating, incomplete and lopsided family backgrounds in lonely, eccentric and paranoid adults.

It is always possible, of course, that a bad start can be completely overcome. A frightened, socially retarded, isolated or over-aggressive child can be greatly helped if he is above average strength, has some special ability that impresses other children and can form an alliance with a generally accepted child.[34] Occasionally a child, who has been held in check or looked down upon by

[33] D. Levy, *Maternal Overprotection* (New York: Columbia University Press, 1943), pp. 71-100.

[34] H. Jones and others, *Development in Adolescence; Approaches to the Study of the Individual.* New York: Appleton-Century, 1943.

others, adopts and carries through an enterprising social role out of sheer rebellion against his domineering, critical parents or his patronizing companions. Their reaction to his success, and his own reaction to their changed attitudes, may permanently raise his social status.

Nothing a child can do in the wider community is more important for his personality development than play. There, as at home, play gives him unlimited practice in manual, locomotor and verbal coordination. It is for many years his chief source of social experience. In it he learns that the responses and the attitudes of other persons, be they protagonists or opponents, have to be allowed for all the time. At first, in solitary and parallel play this may amount to no more than learning to avoid or hold off encroachment in relation to others present in the same general play space. Later on, however, children learn in associative and cooperative play to share objects and activities with others, to participate in joint projects and eventually to gain experience in division of labor and the subordination of individual to group needs and aims.[35]

Some of the earliest participative games involve simple forms of social role-taking. The little child must act the baby or the pupil, as directed, so that an older or ascendant child may play mother or teacher. He must later on learn the techniques of taking sides in group games, of showing unflinching loyalty to his own side and steadfast opposition to the other, even though the line-up of individuals varies from day to day. By playing a variety of roles and performing different play functions, children get experience in what they can expect of others under varying conditions, and what others are going to expect of them. They master these difficult social techniques in play for the simple reason that, unless they learn to fit into the established patterns, they are excluded from participation in this most engrossing of childhood activities.

Out of play activities, and other group enterprises, emerge the highly significant companionship and friendship patterns of social behavior. As he grows older, the child tends to move from relatively loose and casual contacts to more stable and lasting interpersonal relationships with his peers. He and his companions form a peer subculture in which all may gain experience in social interac-

[35] M. Parten and S. Newhall, "Social behavior of preschool children," in R. Barker, J. Kounin and H. Wright (editors), Child Behavior and Development (New York: McGraw-Hill, 1943), pp. 509-525.

tion on a level of equality that is rarely if ever possible between a child and his elders. His peers, in giving him opportunities for growing into succeeding phases of social organization among contemporaries who can understand him, perform a function very similar to that performed earlier in the home by his siblings.

Out of this childhood companionship and friendship behavior develop, not only the patterns of adolescent and adult friendships, but also those of courting and mating. Such an evolution is foreshadowed by a striking increase in the closeness of prepubescent and early adolescent friendship between children of the same sex. In these so-called "crushes," an observer may often witness the possessiveness, the jealous exclusion of potential rivals, and the appearance of sudden, tense quarrels that are typical of later heterosexual attachments. There is little doubt that some cases of adult homosexuality crystallize during this phase of personality development although, as far as the actual dynamics are concerned, we are still far richer in theory than in data.

A child's formal schooling waits upon his acquisition of adequate conventional language behavior, since language and its derivatives are the chief instruments for molding him into conformity with his culture. In the typical American classroom situation, a child begins many years of a kind of training that has this unique quality: that it is more or less divorced from any immediate usefulness, indeed from any immediate possibility of application. He learns things out of their context, about people who are dead, about functions he rarely thinks of performing himself, and places he never expects to see. He is initiated into the cabalistic mysteries of the symbolic arts — reading, writing, grammatical structure, ciphering and drawing. Under the social pressures of classroom and home, he builds up a background, mostly verbal and pictorial, for his adult life in the community. Through the childhood and adolescent years he slowly acquires vast, conglomerate systems of substitutive behavior in these terms. If, as an adult, he develops a behavior disorder these symbolic systems are sure to enter into and complicate its symptomatology, and sometimes to influence its course and outcome.

Adolescence and adulthood

The chasm in our society between childhood and adulthood is very wide. Adolescence is the long biosocial bridge that spans it.

The duration and complexity of the adolescent phase of personality development are more or less peculiar to modern industrial society. In other societies the transition from childhood to adulthood seems to be achieved more quickly and simply. Children are able to share progressively in the serious functions of the community life, beginning at a relatively early age. They are not held rigidly, as our children are, to a dependent status that differentiates them sharply from adults. The induction of the children of other societies may therefore be a graded process that allows each growing individual to learn adult techniques in adult situations well in advance of the time when he is held responsible for putting them into practice. Less delay is interposed also between biological fitness and social privilege than in our culture.

Among subhuman species, adolescence as we understand it is unknown. The growing wild mammal does whatever his own individual phase of development permits, whenever his need and his opportunity appear together. There is no consensus of his elders or peers to worry over. He and others of his kind have neither the biological response equipment nor the social organization with which to set up uniform standards of time-bound expectation in relation to one another's behavior. They are able neither to make nor to communicate critical analyses and appraisals of their own or of others' conduct.

Not so the human adolescent in our society. He must mature in an atmosphere thick with expectation and appraisal. His actions, needs, wishes and plans are all subject to the critical scrutiny of his peers, his elders and himself. During mid-adolescence the influence of the peer subculture is very strong.[36] The predominant trend then is toward conformity to the group patterns of one's own contemporaries, to group needs and group aspirations, even though the behavior that results is combatted and condemned by adults. However, although it is true that conspicuous elements of the adolescent peer culture need not correspond to coexistent adult norms, we must not forget that adolescent subcultures represent attempts to anticipate and interpret the adult status. They are derived from contemporary adult roles quite as much as they are from momentary social interactions at the adolescent level. The resistance that he develops to adult disapproval and restraint becomes an impor-

[36] C. Tryon, "The adolescent peer culture," *Yearb. Nat. Soc. Stud. Educ.*, 1944, vol. 43, pp. 217-239.

tant component of the adolescent's struggle to secure and maintain ultimate independent status as an adult himself.

When an adolescent is exposed simultaneously to pressures from the family and pressures from his peer culture he must learn a double orientation and serve two masters. His parents' expectations are sure to be colored by conditions prevailing twenty or thirty years earlier when they were adolescent. His contemporaries, on the other hand, look upon the ways of past generations with amusement and scorn. Their accents are different. Things that one age considers vital seem trivial or absurd to the other. The adolescent in this situation must direct one part of his behavior toward satisfying the standards of his parents, who seem to him unaware that they are hopelessly behind the times. The other part is keyed to what he considers the modern pitch, to life as seen by his peers with whom he must be in harmony if he is to be happy and accepted in his friendships, at a time when friendships are close and understanding. For the conscientious and for the dependent adolescent his double orientation may be very disturbing. It is uncomfortably ambivalent, it makes him feel at once guilty and resentful, it breeds conflict and promotes anxiety.

Many parents, and especially those who had planned on sharing in and guiding the life of their offspring into adulthood, find his growing secretiveness, his rebellious conduct and his often transparent duplicities painfully disillusioning. Their adolescent child inexplicably turns his face away from them to invest a group of immature young strangers with the confidence and affection that they feel belong to themselves. Their security and their significance in the parental role seem seriously threatened. When the adolescent also shows signs of increasing sex interest, any misgivings his parents may have been entertaining over social change and sin are apt to be reinforced by anxieties revived from the conflicts of their own adolescence. In other words, this *second age of resistance*, like the first one in early childhood, is complicated by personality problems of his parents as well as by the adolescent's own biosocial growth.

Early in adolescence growth changes appear that may pose their own biosocial problems. Radical alterations in the endocrine balance develop, and the body contour begins to approximate adult sex differences. During adolescence there are cycles of acceleration and deceleration of growth, which are very often asynchronous for different parts of the body. Because of uneven, unfamiliar or disproportionate development both sexes pass through periods of clumsy awkwardness that for some individuals prove quite humiliating. The adolescent may be acutely dissatisfied with his or her size, weight, facial appearance and general body proportions, if they seem to compare unfavorably with those of associates or with family standards and expectations. In a careful study of ninety-three adolescent boys, for example, it was found that somatic variations had definitely disturbed twenty-nine, while for five they had constituted a major problem in adjustment.[37]

For one thing growth peculiarities expose the adolescent to disparagement and ridicule at a time when he is exaggeratedly responsive to the opinions of others. He is dependent upon them for acceptance and social status, and upon social status for his own self-esteem. This situation also accounts for the unusual concern over skin blemishes, body odor and general cleanliness that characterizes the adolescence of a great many boys and girls. A typical adolescent need is the need to conform, to be like his peers, to avoid being considered in any respect out of step or peculiar. It must not be forgotten that, although wide individual variations in all phases of development are the rule in this phase, our society maintains a scale of expectations in appearance and behavior that really makes little allowance for inequalities. However, inability to conform to the expectations of elders and peers is not as a rule sufficient to precipitate adjustment problems by itself. There must also be general insecurity in social relationships, habitual anxiety over the impression one makes upon others or a lack of genuine satisfactions in other aspects of one's life.

Sexual developments during adolescence help materially to introduce important changes in social behavior. The definite shift in attitudes and interests that follows establishment of the menstrual cycle is a case in point. It has been found that almost regardless of age, size, previous interests or family background, girls react to this first impressive sign of adult sexuality by significant increases in attention to appearance and adornment, in heterosexual interests and activities, in the avoidance of vigorous exercise and in daydreaming.[38] Nothing could illustrate better the dynamic interplay

[37] H. Stolz and L. Stolz, "Adolescent problems related to somatic variations," Yearb. Nat. Soc. Stud. Educ., 1944, vol. 43, pp. 80-99.
[38] C. Stone and R. Barker, "Attitudes and interests of premenarcheal and postmenarcheal girls," Jour. Genetic Psychol., 1939, vol. 57, pp. 393-414.

of biological and social factors in personality growth. The girl experiences a new physiological incident and reacts to it by adopting seriously those characteristics of the adult feminine role which the change implies for her, a role which she has already learned in childhood play, reading, talk, fantasy and the movies.

It is often taken for granted that all children and young adolescents welcome impatiently the signs of oncoming maturity. On the contrary, many greet them with regret, anxiety, resentment or perplexity. If, for example, a girl's previous training and experience have made her overvalue childhood dependence or shun as sordid and sinful the sexual and maternal aspects of adult life, the indications of approaching womanhood may well upset her. She may seek in every way possible to conceal, minimize or deny them. There are boys also who find their maturation upsetting, grow anxious and guilty over tumescence and nocturnal emissions, delay lowering the pitch of their voice and lament the appearance of fuzz on lip and cheek. These reactions are likely to be accentuated if an insecure, hypersensitive adolescent happens to mature more rapidly than others of his age and so to be the subject of taunting comments.

Whether adolescence is in itself necessarily a period of emotional upheaval or whether, as students of other societies hold, it is our particular culture that makes it so, is still an open question.[39] There can be little doubt, however, that most serious adolescent problems are traceable to childhood difficulties. The child grows into and through adolescence to adulthood by a continuing biosocial process. Typically there is no break in that continuity. The techniques and attitudes of late childhood are modified through social learning to become the techniques and attitudes of early adolescence, and these in turn are similarly modified in the successive phases of adolescence and adulthood.

Adolescence is anything but a socially static period of development. Shifts in status and in the demands made upon a given individual, such as we find during childhood, occur here also. In schoolgirls, for example, it has been found that the patterns of social behavior carrying group prestige in early adolescence change

---

[39] See the discussion in G. Bateson, "Cultural determinants of personality," in J. Hunt (editor), *Personality and the Behavior Disorders* (New York: Ronald Press, 1944), pp. 714-735; R. Linton, *Cultural Background of Personality* (New York: Appleton-Century, 1945), pp. 67-68 and 125-153.

place in mid-adolescence with behavior previously condemned.[40] It is obvious that to meet such shifts, it is more useful for a girl to have learned to be adaptable and personally secure than to have learned to behave in one set fashion or to lean constantly upon the approval of others for support.

In short, the biosocially competent child stands a good chance of becoming a competent adolescent, while the child who reaches pubescence a diffident, asocial, romantic daydreamer, or an anxious, overconscientious worrier, stands at least as good a chance of daydreaming or worrying on into adolescence, and developing characteristic maladjustments there. The social attitudes and techniques with which adolescents meet their more grown-up world are essentially the ones they learned at home, in the neighborhood and on the school playground. If an individual cannot adapt progressively to the shifting conditions of adolescent and early adult life, it is far more likely that the fault lies in his own learned organization of social behavior than that it is our "modern times," his new companions, or adolescence-in-the-abstract that is to blame.

As an adolescent grows more and more into adult ways, and choices that once seemed fictional now loom directly ahead, the range and depth of his insecurity may sharply increase. He discovers that, in practice, freedom from parental discipline has all sorts of qualifying riders attached to it. When he gets a real job he finds himself bound to work for strangers, all day and every day. If this is his first experience in a genuine work situation, he is likely to be unpleasantly surprised by the contrast between his employers' attitudes toward him and the expectations he had built up on the basis of authority patterns at home and in school. To him it may also seem as though his fellow-workers seek advancement by any means at hand, even deliberately at his expense. This whole situation duplicates on a more organized adult level what he found, if he was given the opportunity, when he first emerged from his protecting home to play and compete among unfeeling contemporaries in the neighborhood. But now the game is for keeps and the stakes are social status and a living.

The close and increasingly mature relationships with outsiders which the average person develops in late adolescence and young

[40] C. Tryon, "Evaluation of adolescent personality by adolescents," *Monog. Soc. Res. Child Devel.*, 1939, vol. 4, pp.1-88.

adulthood, and his normal secretiveness over his own affairs, very often bring him into conflict at home. As his tastes and interests approach adult patterns, his activities tend to encroach more and more upon those of his parents, and to disregard the needs of his younger siblings. He and his friends move in on the parents of an evening, for example, and unless resisted may dispossess them from their own living space. Because of his need to maintain prestige among his peers, the late adolescent can no longer brook dictation or open criticism of himself or his friends, whether or not it is justified. Either his parents must make all the concessions or he must live elsewhere.

If his decision is to move out, the adolescent or young adult will find that, while he gains considerable freedom in choosing his associates, he must now do almost everything in public or semi-public places, except wash and sleep. He is usually obliged to take a step downward in living standards, to a drab and lonely room, where he is likely to discover that interested strangers persist in keeping a vigilant eye on his coming and going. He will miss the kind of relaxation and off-duty companionship he once had at home. If his standards of sex conduct have been rather strict, his normally increased sex tensions may raise new conflicts or aggravate old ones. Eventually, if he is not to become a chronic dependent, a social isolate or a vagrant, he must find a place for himself in the socio-economic framework of his community, loosen or break the emotional home ties, and choose a wife with whom to establish a home and produce his own family. When he has done this he will have fulfilled the objective conditions for biosocial adulthood.

Young women, for their part, must choose a man who can give them the emotional and economic security they need to organize a home and raise a family. Their own eventual socio-economic status, and that of their children, will to a very large degree be determined by the success and satisfaction of their husband. Hence it is that, although they must often find work at first too, girls and young women are far more preoccupied with questions of marriage than are boys and men, whose status depends mainly on their own career.

In certain respects a maturing woman is not required to achieve the same independence and initiative that a man is. She expects to remain somewhat protected by her husband, to lean upon him emotionally as well as economically. Nevertheless she also must loosen her parental ties and assume sexual and domestic responsibilities. She must learn to make and carry through her own work schedules and subordinate many of her girlhood wishes to necessity. Others expect her to welcome pregnancy and to accept gladly the duties of motherhood, as prescribed by social convention and her child's biological needs. The responsibility for providing maximum comfort and health for the family, within the limits of her husband's income, also rests upon her shoulders. So does the general standing of her household in the neighborhood community.

Many of the personality problems that lead over into behavior disorders during adolescence and adulthood seem to begin with defective emancipation from the parental home, and to arise out of strongly ambivalent attitudes toward adult responsibilities and adult sexuality. An individual who crosses the adolescent bridge holding onto the parental hand, and carrying with him his childhood attitudes, will arrive at adulthood still playing the role of filial dependent. He will be inexperienced in walking alone. He will be emotionally tied to an older generation instead of free to form attachments with his own. He will see the world from the perspective of his position at his parents' side. Because of inexperience with adult roles and adult perspectives, he may be afraid and insecure when the time comes to strike out toward full adult status. If the opportunity for an adult sex partnership with emotional equality comes to him, he may find himself anxious, guilty, indecisive and perhaps unable to abandon the security of his dependent filial role.

For those persons whose attitudes and social role-taking remain at immature, dependent levels, many adult situations that seem quite ordinary to the average individual may constitute formidable obstacles or raise insoluble conflicts. The relative social incompetence that such men and women show, the result of inadequate or distorted personality development, must indeed be reckoned among the most important sources of individual susceptibility to the behavior disorders. For just as normal personality development depends upon one's organizing interlocking systems of attitude and response into appropriate and effective roles, so the development of behavior disorders depends upon the crystallization of personal reactions and social role-taking into inappropriate and maladaptive patterns.

3

Behavior Organization
and Behavior Pathology

IN THE NEUROSES AND PSYCHOSES it is often quite obvious, even to a relatively unskilled observer, that something is decidedly wrong with the organization of a person's behavior. The patient's attitudes appear remarkably rigid and unalterable, or they seem disconcertingly unstable and confused. His responses may be glaringly contradictory, ineffectual, exaggerated, apathetic, inappropriate or grotesque. The unpracticed observer, no matter how hard he tries, is apt to find himself unable to enter into and grasp the patient's point of view as to what is going on in their common surroundings. The patient, for his part, is also quite incapable of looking at his own experiences from the more detached standpoint of the observer. In short, neither observer nor patient is able to take the role of the other person effectively, to share his attitudes and see things from his perspective.

Here we have come upon a fact of fundamental importance in our field — that behavior pathology is to a considerable degree based upon serious defects in the techniques of sharing the perspectives common to one's own society. The difficulty in a specific case may stem from a failure to acquire adequate social skill in role-taking during early personality development, or it may represent the loss or distortion of role-taking in a person who had once acquired sufficient skill. Indeed, we shall find that sharing attitudes and taking roles are matters of the utmost significance for therapy also. For one of the most difficult tasks in the treatment of behavior disorders is that of learning to see a patient's problems from his highly individualistic, personal perspective, while leading the patient to share some of the therapist's impersonal detached attitudes toward symptoms and their origins. This is the basis of rapport and one of the factors in transference.

53

All of the attitudes and responses found in behavior pathology are in some way related to and derived from normal biosocial behavior. A great many of them turn out to be little more than ineffectual attempts to meet adult frustration, deprivation and conflict with reactions that occur normally in infancy, childhood or adolescence. The behavior is socially immature, or as we often say, *regressive*. But even the most bizarre distortions of behavior, as we shall see in the compulsive disorders and schizophrenia, can be traced to origins in anticipation, disorganization, ambivalence, special sensitivity or symbolic confusions, such as any normal person may experience temporarily or to a minor degree. Hence, if we are to orient ourselves and feel at home in the presence of behavior disorders, it is essential that we begin by running through some of the directly pertinent facts of behavior organization.

Attitudes and responses

Attitudes, whether normal or abnormal, are important chiefly because they determine the range of specific responses that a person gives in any stimulating situation.[1] For example, a man's attitude in entering a room will be one thing when he expects to find a welcome friend waiting there for him, and quite another when he expects to find a bill-collector or a bore. The attitude may begin before he enters, continue as he greets his visitor and converses with him, and persist even after the visitor leaves. The man's wife, if she knows his attitude, can predict quite accurately the range of his specific responses, the character of the greeting, the course of the conversation and even some of the phrases, her husband's parting salutation, and his after-reaction if he joins her when the visitor has left. In other words, attitudes may be determinative to a degree that enables the person who is familiar with them to predict the character and drift of another's specific behavior. If a person can foresee his own attitude in an anticipated situation, he may likewise be able to predict a good many of his own responses to it.

In the field of behavior pathology we shall find it necessary to distinguish between the attitude and the responses, as constituents of a unitary reaction. *The attitude is the relatively widespread,*

---

[1] A critical review of the concept of *attitude* in contemporary psychology may be found in the articles by M. Sherif and H. Cantril, "The psychology of 'attitudes,'" *Psychol. Rev.*, 1945, vol. 52, pp. 295-319, and 1946, vol. 53, pp. 1-24.

diffuse aspect of a reaction which functions as a behavioral back-ground, preparing for, supporting and prolonging certain responses and not others. In contrast to this, *a response is the more specific, localized aspect of a reaction which emerges from, and is supported by, the more sustained attitude.* Putting the distinction in configurational terms, an attitude is the behavioral *ground* while the responses are its *figures.*

As a further illustration of this distinction let us take the meeting of two friends. When they sight and accost each other in the street, the adient kinetic and tensional patterns that bring and keep them close together we can include as part of the behavioral background — the *friendly attitude.* The smiles and gestures, the words of greeting and the handshake or kiss are *friendly responses* which are facilitated and supported by the attitude. If the supposed friend proves at close quarters to be a total stranger or if, in our earlier example, the man enters the room jauntily because he expects a friend and finds the bill-collector, there is at least a momentary disorganization of response. Until a shift can be made to a new attitude appropriate to the situation, the reacting person is very likely to show confusion and incoordination. He lacks the attitude he needs to support the appropriate responses. We shall find abundant opportunity for the application of this principle when we come to consider the often weirdly inappropriate behavior of the delirious and the schizophrenic.

From what we have been saying, it must be obvious that attitudes are dynamic, ongoing behavior just as are the responses they facilitate and support. In studying behavior pathology we must never lose sight of the fact that, no matter how complex and confused they may become, human attitudes are always the biosocial activity of human organisms. At no point in their development or their operation need we assume that attitudes have suddenly disappeared into a mind or *psyche* — like a bat disappearing into an attic.

Anticipation and behavior pathology

We have said that an attitude may not only determine the range of a person's responses, in any given situation, but also prepare the ground in advance for his responses to appear. This function we ordinarily call *anticipation,* and the phase of any act preliminary to a given response sequence we call the *anticipant attitude.* As might be expected, anticipant attitudes play a very prominent part in behavior pathology. We see them repeatedly in the protracted tensions of anxiety, apprehension, worry and remorse as these appear in the neuroses and psychoses. Anticipant attitudes figure also in the quite different, but no less abnormal, patterns of elation and ecstasy in paranoid disorders, schizophrenia and mania.

Let us turn once again to infant feeding for a normal illustration of the development of anticipation. The hungry infant, brought into oral contact with a nipple, reacts with specific grasping and sucking responses, and these are supported and facilitated by a simultaneous attitude pattern of movement and tension. With practice, both the grasping-sucking responses and the suckling attitude improve in organization. The attitude begins to appear more readily and grows progressively more effective in facilitating the nursing responses, while it simultaneously inhibits those responses which compete and interfere with nursing.

It is clear from this illustration that anticipation arises as a temporal extension of the attitude. The widespread, diffuse movement and tension patterns of nursing after a while begin to appear while the nipple is approaching, but definitely before oral or digital contact is possible. Eventually these attitudinal patterns develop in relation to the first sounds and movements that a mother habitually makes in preparing to feed her baby. *It is this temporal extension of the attitude, which prepares a behavioral background in advance of the appropriate responses,* that we have called the *anticipant attitude.*

Anticipation often leads also to an individual's giving reactions in the early phases of a sequence which belonged originally to the consummatory phase or climax, or belonged even to the after-phase that follows consummation. Thus, our hungry infant comes in time to smile, coo, gurgle and reach when his mother merely appears upon the scene or only speaks to him, in spite of the fact that his need-tensions may be increased and not alleviated by her advent. His mother now feels justified in saying proudly, "Yes! He *knows* he is going to be fed!" We, in the more restrained tradition, are permitted to say merely that he is now showing anticipant behavior, and to mean by this only that he is reacting to early phases of a developing situation in ways originally given by him to a climactic or an after-phase.

The temporal extension of attitudes, into more or less protracted anticipant phases, also prolongs the period during which an act may be influenced by other simultaneously occurring processes. Moreover, the sustained tension of anticipation, if it is of moderate intensity, may facilitate learning. In brief, the development of anticipation multiplies opportunities for the extension and elaboration of behavior patterns — and that frequently on the basis of mere proximity in space-time. An act acquires new excitants and becomes secondarily related to and integrated with other attitudes. Through these and other processes, occurring in the thousands and tens of thousand learned reactions of everyday living, we all acquire attitudes or behavior backgrounds that overlap and interlock, because they have occurred in space-time proximity, have similar or identical components, or acquire equivalent excitants.

This brings us to a conclusion of prime significance for behavior pathology. *Human reactions may acquire new excitants and undergo important modifications which are wholly inexplicable on grounds of verbal logic, whether we call it conscious or unconscious logic.* Because symbolic confusion is so prominent and so fascinating a characteristic of some behavior pathology, the mistake has been made of insisting that therefore *all* symptom-formation must be explained in terms of verbal distortion, inversion, punning and shrewd concealment or disguise. In contemporary psychopathology we are still devoting incredible effort to the task of converting the facts of social learning into the fiction of unconscious verbal logic. The truth is that a great deal of symptom-formation develops in accordance with the *logic of non-verbal operations*,[2] through extensions and modifications such as we have already mentioned. We must continue to keep on the alert for symbolic mutations and distortions, since human beings all live by the word, but we cannot dismiss all other possible origins of behavior pathology, just because symbols appear more learned and profound than other operations.

While it is true that in some behavior disorders the peculiar pattern of anticipation or its great intensity is the most arresting feature, in others the chief abnormality is in neither the design nor the intensity of anticipation, but in its being socially invalid. Thus, a patient may prepare for an expected disaster or ecstasy in the shared field of social operations, when all of the incidents that might justify such expectant behavior lie wholly within his unshared, private fantasy. For example, a patient of ours prepared

[2] For a definition and further discussion of this, see Chapter 6.

for a marriage, engaged a minister and invited guests, although everything leading up to this social, overt conduct had been carried on in his own thinking. There was indeed a prospective bride, a person known to the minister and the invited guests, but she had neither given her consent nor been notified of the wedding arrangements. The patient's confusion when she failed to appear for the occasion showed the extent to which his asocial fantasy activities had spilled over into the field of social operations, where public fact contradicted private assumptions not grounded in it.

Exclusion and inclusion in behavior organization

Competence and adequacy in behavior organization, like success in baking a cake, depend as much on what is left out as what is included. The normal acquisition of skill illustrates this. As a child learns to write, for instance, the writhing, shifting, tongue-twisting and grimacing, which are initially present, gradually disappear. Likewise, competence and adequacy in baseball playing, sewing and auto-driving are just as much products of exclusion as functions of accuracy and poise. When precision suffers under ordinary emotional disorganization, it is the reappearance of previously excluded responses that helps to make one's performance ineffectual, and gives to the observer an impression of awkward floundering.

Maximal effectiveness is reached in precise, more or less automatized operations when contradictory, competing and irrelevant reactions have been excluded from participation. On the other hand, for maximal effectiveness in relatively unpredictable developing situations, it is essential that the organization of behavior remain such as to permit the inclusion of any one of a number of possible variant reactions. The behavior organization at one extreme we should call *stable and exclusive*, and that at the other extreme *unstable and inclusive*. Normal complex behavior shows considerable variation between these extremes.

Some fascinating exaggerations of these normal behavior variants can be found in the behavior disorders. In hysterical inactivation, for example, one sees remarkable extremes of *overexclusion*. Not only may the particular reactions of a hand be eliminated, if they contradict an hysterical disability that is necessary to the patient, but the exclusion quite often carries with it nearly all activity of the member, and we have hysterical paralysis. If and when the behavior systems responsible for this inactivation have been reorganized by appropriate therapy, the hysterical paralysis may simply disappear without special attention to it. Through treatment of thwarting and conflict, the *need* for eliminating reactions of the hand is removed or satisfied and the hysterical reaction, which was originally developed in relation to this need, goes with it.

In the opposite direction, certain compulsive and schizophrenic patients show an exaggerated instability of behavior organization with a relative inability to exclude contradictory, competing and irrelevant reactions (*overinclusion*). In compulsive doubting, which gives rise to some very interesting ritualistic practices, the patient is often unable to exclude even the most remote and insignificant considerations from influencing a developing act. These are typically marshaled on opposite sides of a decision, and peeled off in opposing pairs to offset each other, like partners in a folk dance. A common result of this vacillation is that the patient's behavior cannot develop direction and enter upon a consummatory phase. The untreated patient either learns to avoid situations that arouse compulsive vacillation, or he develops rituals which in one way or another bring him a closure effect that serves him as consummation and, at least temporarily, reduces the tensions of conflict and suspense.

Extravagant *overinclusion* is characteristic of schizophrenic disorganization. A patient's unstable behavior organization does not limit the number and kind of simultaneously effective excitants to a relatively few coherent ones. In consequence, his reactions are not sufficiently restricted in range for him to deal with even the ordinary situations of daily living. Schizophrenic patients often complain of the way everything seems jumbled up and crowding in on them, but it is actually their own behavior disorganization that makes the situation seem impossibly unrestricted and confused. In extreme cases, as in the clinical example about to be given, a patient may grow so bewildered by the infinite ramifications of his own reactions that he is helpless to cope with ordinary everyday demands. Living arrangements have to be artificially simplified and routinized for him, as they are in well-run psychiatric hospitals, if he is ever to reorganize his behavior and regain his health.

The following verbatim statements, taken down in shorthand by the writer during an experiment with schizophrenic subjects,[3] will

---

[3] N. Cameron, "Schizophrenic thinking in a problem-solving situation," *Jour. Mental Science,* 1939, vol. 85, pp. 1012-1035.

illustrate the confusion that such disorganization can bring to a patient. The experimental task was that of sorting colored blocks of several shapes into a specified number of groups. This could be achieved only in accordance with one principle of grouping which was left to the subject to discover and formulate. The sorting was carried out on the office desk. No culturally defined useful objects — such as boxes, papers, blotters, food or watches — were included in the test, but only the meaningless blocks. Throughout the trials our patient was cooperative and earnest. He exhibited, however, an irresistible tendency to include objects on the desk and on the experimenter's person, parts of the room, things he pulled from his pockets, a racial problem of color discrimination, the clothing of a man we could see outside the window on a porch, and even the experimenter himself whom the patient recommended be remade of wood and cut into blocks. Here are some of his comments that bring out the instability and lack of exclusion which helped make the problem for him completely insoluble.

> "I've got to pick it out of the whole room. I can't confine myself to this game." . . . "Three blues [test blocks] — now how about that green blotter? Put it in there too. [Green] peas you eat [4] — you can't eat them unless you write on it [pointing to the green blotter]. Like that wrist-watch [on experimenter's wrist, a foot from test board] — I don't see any three meals coming off that watch." . . . "White and blue [blocks] is Duke's Mixture. This [pulling out cigarette paper] is white. All this wood and Japan [producing match box]. There's a man out there [on porch] with a white tie — that's got something to do with white suits." . . . "To do this trick you'd have to be made of wood. You've got a white shirt on — and the white blocks. You have to have them cut out of *you!* You've got a white shirt on — this [white hexagonal block] will hold you and never let you go. I've got a blue shirt on, but it can't be a blue shirt and still go together. And the room's got to be the same. . . ." Considering the feasibility of grouping certain white and yellow blocks together, the patient asked, "Are there any Chinese working here?" (*No.*) "Only white ones — then you can't put *them* together."

Ambivalence and ambitendencies

To be able to think about and choose what one is doing, or about

---

[4] The patient had come straight from the dining room where peas had been served as part of the meal.

to do, is a great and indispensable human privilege, but to be unable to do anything without pondering and choosing can be a deadly curse. Well-routinized activities — such as walking, dressing, opening the morning mail, starting one's daily machine operation or one's housework — almost take care of themselves. Indeed, the less ruminating and choosing one includes in going through habitual movement sequences, the more likely they are to tick off smoothly and easily.

These seemingly banal and self-evident statements become unexpectedly pointed the moment one begins to study compulsive disorders. When, for instance, it turns out that almost every step in a formerly routine behavior sequence now calls for a specific decision by the patient before it can be completed, the observer suddenly recognizes the blessings of economy and freedom that the organized routine normally bestows. After he has watched a compulsive take two hours of vacillation to complete what should have been a fifteen-minute dressing routine, and emerge from it perspiring and exasperated, he is struck afresh by the simple truth that behavior routinization is one road to personal liberty for the situations deserving choice and cogitation.

But no matter how much routine enters into one's daily living, there are always left a great many situations that present us with alternatives and the necessity or the privilege of choosing. Naturally, if the preponderance of deciding factors heaps up on one side of the balance, our hesitation will be slight and momentary. If, on the other hand, the situation calls out behavior trends which are opposed and approximately equal, our choosing may become a prolonged and difficult labor. Our consummatory response will then be held in suspense until some less immediate factors come into the situation to throw the decision one way or the other. If, for example, a restaurant menu allows us roast pork or baked salmon, and we dislike fish, the decision comes quickly. But if we like them both very much the waiter waits. Secondary considerations must have time to enter the lists — what will our companion order, and how important will fishy breath or fat digestion be later on in the evening? Perhaps a religious proscription tips the balance; pork is forbidden or fish mandatory. Eventually the strains of indecision are relieved by the consummatory response, and then one is free for conversation, fantasy or the evening paper.

We call reactions, in which simultaneously opposing trends play a significant part, ambivalent reactions, and we speak of *the tendencies to react in opposite directions as ambitendencies.* Obviously ambitendencies are common occurrences in behavior and ambivalence is a characteristic of everyday normal, as well as of pathological, reactions. Ambivalence often develops for the simple reason that an excitant appears in a context demanding an opposite reaction, as when a boy's mother shows up on the playground where mothers are held in low esteem, or an adult's loathed enemy unexpectedly sits down next to him in church. Ambivalence also occurs when a person is distracted, or preoccupied, even in relatively unemotional situations, simply because some component response in a behavior sequence happens to belong at the same time to another behavior sequence where it operates differently. A man starts to dress for dinner and suddenly finds himself vacillating between donning pajamas and reaching for a suit.

Nowhere in normal behavior is ambivalence more prevalent, and nowhere in behavior pathology are its implications more serious, than in a person's affectional relationships and in those ethical and religious attitudes whose early development ties them in with his affectional behavior.[5] After all, parents must play the dual roles of giver-denier and comforter-punisher, and inevitably rear children whose filial attitudes are ambivalent. Ambivalence grows also out of the interpretations a child places upon interparental behavior, particularly if parental rivalry divides his loyalties.

One danger of pronounced filial ambivalence is that, like other learned reactions, as it becomes established it is likely to generalize to other sources of affection and authority, sacred and secular, as well as to one's adolescent and adult friendship and love relationships. We know that emotional acceptance and emotional attachments play a leading role throughout personality development, and to a considerable degree determine one's effectiveness as an adult biosocial person. Smooth care, comfort and mothering spell security for the infant. In childhood, acceptance and reassuring affection from two parents at peace with one another provide the secure base from which a boy or girl may explore and test the wider community. Practice in well-defined affectional relationships at home, which generalize and mature biosocially among one's childhood friends, prepares the way for emotional effectiveness in one's adolescent peer culture. Many social skills not particularly emotional in character

---

[5] Compare the discussion of this under *"Early Training,"* in Chapter 2.

can be built effectively only upon a foundation of emotional ease and rapport with one's companions, that is, upon the acquired ability to share attitudes and social perspectives. Strong ambitendencies in these fundamental, direct relationships with others leave one tense and awkward in social interbehavior. The unusually tense and maladroit adolescent or adult, whose ambitendencies have kept him from entering into the social life of others, is more susceptible to behavior disorder than the average. He lacks the social skills upon which emotional acceptance and support from others depend, and since it is from these that most adolescents and adults derive their security, he also lacks security.

Enough has already been said about sibling rivalry, and about friendship patterns in child and adolescent peer cultures, to prepare us for the ambivalent attitudes of competition-cooperation and hostility-affection which normally appear in these relationships and spread to other and later equivalent situations. We see the same phenomena in adult life, complicated by the intricate and often contradictory relationships in mature sexuality, marriage and parenthood. Ambivalent attitudes toward pregnancy and motherhood may lead a woman, who cannot accept the role now given to her to play, toward a disorganizing division of behavior. She may actually deny her marital and pregnant state and, after delivery, be unable to recall her pregnancy or accept the baby as her own. It is this overt exaggeration of behavior trends — in normal conduct at most obscurely hinted at, implied or vaguely felt — that makes behavior pathology an attractive and potentially fruitful field for the student of human personality. In the following case, for example, we plainly witness an abrupt shift from filial love to filial hate, representing an open alternation of responses which have an abnormally unstable background of ambivalent attitudes.

The widowed mother of a twenty-two-year-old unmarried woman failed for several years to recognize that her daughter's progressive ineffectuality and withdrawn asocial conduct were more serious than simple laziness, flightiness and inherited eccentricity. When finally the mother gave in to expert opinion, she and a nurse accompanied the patient to the hospital in a railroad train drawing room. Early in the trip mother and daughter were obviously on friendly, affectionate terms which both nurse and worried mother took as a happy omen. However, with no warning or sign of a coming change other than a brief period of quiet, the patient suddenly struck her mother in the face and was only prevented from further assault by the nurse's intervention. After several minutes of struggle, during which she reviled her mother obscenely, the patient became suddenly tearful and penitent over what she had just done and said. She was unable herself to account for the outburst which seems to have been almost as unexpected to her as to her companions.

Such abrupt shifts from affection to aversion are common incidents in schizophrenic behavior. They merit more intensive study than they have so far been given.

We are all familiar with the ambivalences that characterize ethical and religious conflict. Some persons seem to carry over into adult problems of right and wrong the unresolved ambitendencies of their childhood filial attitudes, or they may generalize from mortal father to God the Father. Others, perhaps on similar grounds, react to any strong social taboo as to a personal challenge. It is the rebellion that is sacred rather than the cause. To many individuals the secret excitement and danger incidental to wrongdoing constitute the great temptation; and they may even be equated to sexual excitement, as we shall see in compulsive shoplifting. To every human being, who is still in some respect imperfect, there remain some fascinations not approved in his society, some reaction tendencies that are held in check by their opposing trends, but never quite extinguished. From these residual fascinations may come, in optimistic mood, some indulgence in a forbidden enterprise or, in pessimistic mood, remorse and shame at the mere remembrance that one had ever been so much as tempted to indulge.

Mood can be mightier than conscience. No one who has observed others impartially can help being impressed by the influence of a person's prevailing mood upon his choice of one horn or the other in an ethical dilemma. As a rule optimism favors sinning if sinning means indulgence, and pessimism virtue if virtue means denial. One sees such a contrast sharply drawn when the same person arcs through a hypomanic swing into a mild depression, especially when neither change incapacitates him, and he remains a free agent in his usual environment. For deeds, words and unsaid attitudes that seem to the patient natural and commendable during mild elation, may give way within the space of a few hours to contrition and humiliating self-condemnation, when the mood dips. This shift in ethical standards with the mood, important as it so

often is for normal persons, becomes literally a life-and-death matter for the frankly depressed or manic patient, the one often seeking punishment in suicide and the other jeopardizing his own and
others' safety through a reckless initiative.

Frank ambivalence in ethical and religious matters becomes most
manifest in the compulsive disorders, and most grotesque in schizophrenia. The common outcome in compulsions is an alternation
between irresistible sinning, direct or substitutive, and equally irresistible penance and self-purification. In schizophrenia one sometimes encounters bizarre confusions of self-beatification and self-
revilement. These may culminate in mystical symbolic sacrifice and
occasionally, but for the observer unforgettably, lead to gruesome
self-mutilation or immolation. In practice it is often difficult to distinguish between the vague preoccupations with abstract moral and
cosmic questions that plague adolescents, and the beginnings of
abnormal compulsive thinking or of schizophrenic disorganization.
Here, as elsewhere, normal and pathological overlap. But although
one may merge imperceptibly into the other, it is still only the very
exceptional case that passes from adolescent pondering into pathological behavior.

Reaction-sensitivity

It is not difficult to show that one's special sensitivities may be
derived from what one does, what one thinks, fears, hates and
loves. Not so long ago the belief was almost universal that sensitivities were usually a matter of delicate sense-organs and nerves.
Thus, composers and performers of music were supposed to keep
their hair long to protect their hypersensitive ears. The clear superiority in visual perception that an experienced sailor shows at sea
was likewise held to mean superior optic sensitivity, and few
doubted that slender, hypersensitive fingers were basic equipment
for skillful surgery.

Today even children know that Beethoven was deaf during most
of his career, and no serious music-lover would be disturbed if news
leaked out that Shostakovitch would soon be as bald as Sibelius.
Under the uniform conditions of an eye clinic or a psychological
laboratory, any number of landlubbers can be found who test
higher in visual acuity than the average seaman, even though they
are unquestionably inferior to him in detecting a landfall or ships
on the horizon. As for surgery, some of the world's most proficient

and eminent operators have short stubby fingers and yet, though wearing rubber gloves, they can still feel things that the most slender-fingered layman could not detect with his bare hands.

No one, of course, questions the basic fact that skilled, experienced persons actually do perceive things clearly, within the range of their professional work, which remain imperceptible to others. But if their sense-organs are not necessarily hyperacute, and if in some cases of unusual excellence the sense-organs involved are actually inferior, to what are we going to ascribe their selective sensitivity? The answer seems to be that a person, whose receptors give no evidence of being in any way unusual, can still be rendered highly sensitive by his own reactions, by the organized special attitudes and responses he acquires. He is, in other words, not receptor-sensitive but *reaction-sensitive*. In behavioral terms, the acquisition of special reactions, in relation to certain situations, gives the excitants of those reactions prepotence when such situations arise. The special organized attitudes and responses, in short, leave an individual selectively sensitized to whatever stimulation habitually arouses them.

We may now define *reaction-sensitivity* as *a selective readiness-to-react to certain components of a stimulating situation and not to others, which is the result of one's having acquired a system of related attitudes and responses.* Thus, two men with different habits may enter an objectively identical situation and react oppositely. Or one man may give a prompt reaction because he has acquired special behavior in previous similar situations, and another give no specific appropriate reaction because he has no reaction ready which the situation can elicit. It is obvious from this definition that reaction-sensitization depends upon developing anticipant attitudes that operate selectively. It will be equally clear, from the illustrations we are about to give, that reaction-sensitivity is as important in normal living as it is in the behavior disorders.

Let a lifelong city dweller go suburban and take to gardening. Within a few weeks his newly acquired reactions to grass and bushes, to vegetables, flowers and trees, will have sensitized him to a world that before had not existed for him. Gardens, lawns and landscapes, seen from the train window on his way to town, will progressively undergo a transformation into intelligible, meaningful designs. Species made familiar by new activities may seem suddenly to stand out from the background he passes, as if a spotlight had been focused on them. The new convert to gardening begins to overhear remarks from all sides about planting time and the quality of produce, about fertilizers and insect pests. The magazines, the radio and the newspapers seem now filled with gardening information and advertisements that before had never caught his eye or ear. His new activities have organized new attitudes which facilitate and support their congruent responses and render these prepotent in appropriate situations. The man has become reaction-sensitive to a group of related things which before had meant nothing to him.

The procedure by which our suburbanite becomes selectively sensitized to new meanings and references, through his own new activities, is basically the same procedure as that by which he might have developed a system of delusions. Under other circumstances, the brooding, jealous, insecure person begins in like manner to notice things about his surroundings which before had passed unheeded. He overhears remarks that seem related to his worry or his guilt. He finds corroboration for his incipient suspicions in papers, radio and magazines. One reason that public gardening and unshared anxious fantasy bear different fruit is that they spring from different needs. Another reason is that the materials and methods of one occur in the shared field of social operations, where public verification and social modification are always possible, while the other goes on in private, unshared fantasy and unchecked solitary watching, neither of which leads in the direction of social validation.

Different habitual activities may sensitize two persons differentially, even though both are immersed in the same stimulating atmosphere, as the following normal illustration shows. The mother of a small baby is entertaining evening guests in her living room. In the midst of a relatively noisy general conversation the baby, in a room above, begins to cry. The mother promptly excuses herself and disappears upstairs, whereupon it turns out that no one else had even heard the baby. For her to be able to react selectively in this way, it is not at all necessary that her hearing be superior to that of her husband or her guests. Neither need her attention have been divided before the crying started, for she can react just as effectively right out of a sound sleep, even though her husband neither stirs at the time nor recalls a disturbance in the morning.

The husband, although he misses this range of infant sounds to which his wife has been sensitized, hears noises in the furnace room that she does not. When they sit together in the front seat of their automobile, it is again he who detects significant noises under the hood, or in the gear box, which she may dismiss as his imagination. Each has been selectively sensitized through acquiring special attitudes that facilitate and support the appropriate responses. We shall have occasion to recall this quite normal organization of special sensitivity, on the basis of special need and interest, when we come to study hypochondriacal patients and those with chronic complaints of fatigue. These persons learn to react sensitively and differentially to internal events that do not exist for the reactions of normal men and women. Normal and neurotic persons start with the same general internal environment; but the individuals who develop hypochondriacal complaints and fatigue syndromes are ones who have learned to be reaction-sensitive in ways which the average person fortunately has not.

Among the behavior disorders we shall find some impressive differences in reaction-sensitization. Many paranoid and paranoic persons, for example, are painfully sensitive to slights and alert to every possible insinuation, but remain unmoved by threats even of capital punishment. On the other hand, agitated depressed persons are as a rule acutely sensitive to anticipated dangers, but often care little or nothing for slights. Compulsives may be alike indifferent to danger and insult while, at the same time, detecting the faintest whiff of sin in the atmosphere. A remarkable feature of many anxiety states is that the patient often discounts, or handles creditably, an immediate actual threat to life, but cringes helplessly before an anticipated possibility which seems remote or trivial to an observer. For instance one of our patients, capable of strong reactions to her own imagined perils, accepted stoically and without serious after-disturbance the news that her own child had just been burned to death. The most extreme of all the general *reaction-insensitivities* are to be found among hysterical and schizophrenic patients who may grow more incapable of participating in the everyday life around them than if they were deaf and blind.

Progressive reaction-sensitization

We saw that in normal personality development a child's acquired reactions play an important part in determining the direction of his subsequent experience and activities. What a child does successfully today he is likely to repeat if similar circumstances arise tomorrow. What he learns to do easily and well in a certain situation will lead him to prefer and seek out corresponding situations that stimulate him to do it. If gratification, praise or other reward follows the performance, the activity becomes a means whereby the newly acquired need can be satisfied. Thus, for example, a child who has opportunities for, and experiences success in, playing with simple mechanical devices becomes sensitized by his learned reactions to each new mechanical device, tends to seek out situations where more may be found, and may progress toward developing special mechanical aptitude. Another child, who has not had the opportunity or has met with pain and failure in handling simple mechanical devices, is more likely to develop his abilities and preferences progressively in some other direction. Thus, as the two children mature, their preferred activities, and hence also their experiences and even their friendships, will tend to diverge in nature more and more.

What is true of mechanical aptitude may be equally true of other behavior patterns. The child whose freedom of overt action is restricted early in life may develop compensatory skills in fantasy and passive observation, which in turn lead him to prefer and seek out situations where these can be practiced. He may even choose an occupation, finally, in which imagination and observation are highly valued. Here we have a selective factor in a person's own acquired reactions that is capable of inducing a progressive deviation in the direction of his personality growth. The child becomes reaction-sensitive in some specific direction and his sensitivity then leads him to further sensitization along the same line. A single new learned activity may lead into a whole sequence of successive sensitizing reactions, in this way, and make a child progressively more and more different from other children the older he gets. Many such special abilities or disabilities, which are usually misidentified as merely the unfolding of an inherited talent or a constitutional weakness, are in reality examples of what we call *progressive reaction-sensitization.*

By *progressive reaction-sensitization* we mean *the process in which a person, once he has become reaction-sensitive in some specific direction, continues to develop further readiness-to-react in the same direction on the basis of successive acquired reactions.* Here in the acquisition of learned behavior sequences we have a selective factor of great potential significance for personality deviations and behavior pathology, one that may determine an individual's relative immunity or susceptibility to behavior disorder. We have said that progressive reaction-sensitization can result in a child's acquiring special aptitudes of value to him. But the same process may also lead to his developing special incapacities that seriously impair his effectiveness as a child and sometimes induce later personality distortion. The initial acquired reaction-sensitivity often seems trivial to adults because they do not understand cumulative behavior modification. A selective readiness-to-react not only spreads to new excitants but also restricts the range of a person's reactions. Early in life such restriction may interfere with a child's having balancing experiences, which he needs for adequate socialization, by making him too unlike other children to gain acceptance into their play groups. We encountered an impressive example of this in Levy's overprotected children. The patterns of expectancy they learned from their domineering or indulgent mothers barred them effectually from normal play and companionship sequences, and therefore made them prefer and seek a deviant developmental path.

There is a great deal of evidence in the clinical histories of neurotic and psychotic patients to indicate that progressive reaction-sensitization often plays an important role in determining what direction behavior pathology shall take. One child, for example, sensitized progressively by early training to think in terms of sin and guilt, reaches adolescence with such exaggerated self-reactions that when biosocial pressures grow acute he succumbs to compulsive ritual or depressive self-castigation. Another child, trained by his anxious mother instead to progressive reaction-sensitivity in relation to weakness and fatigue, shows neither compulsive guilt nor agitated remorse when trouble comes. He has learned to react to life in terms of conserving strength, and not of sinning. Where the one seeks refuge from conflict in ritual and repentance, the other finds it in seclusion, rest and self-solicitude. Similar progressive deviations underlie the many different hysterical, schizophrenic and paranoid developments of adolescent and adult life.

For behavior deviations to persist or increase it is not, of course, necessary that the conditions responsible for inducing them persist and multiply. Depressions, for example, even when clearly provoked by known environmental pressures and personal difficulties, usually show no improvement for a long time after the pressures have ceased and the original personal difficulties have disappeared. Indeed, it is common clinical experience that behavior disorders often grow steadily worse in spite of improved circumstances. However strange this may at first seem theoretically, it becomes quite intelligible when one studies actual cases clinically. Then one finds that a person, once he has developed a behavior disorder, grows reaction-sensitive to influences which normally would not touch him. If he gets depressed, for instance, he may almost at once show acute reaction-sensitivity to innumerable possibilities of guilt in his own behavior, both in his present activity and in what he recalls of the past. If this reaction-sensitivity becomes progressive, an increased severity of the depression results, but in relation to the newly recalled or newly experienced guilt and not necessarily to what started the depressive disturbance at all.

The persistence and ingravescence of behavior disorders, in spite of improved circumstances and the disappearance of the original personal difficulties, have led some theorists to deny the possibility that depression, mania, schizophrenia and paranoia can have environmental or personal origins. To them it seems impossible that such clinical pictures can be anything but simple brain disease, even though the existing evidence fails to support this conclusion. They maintain that if some specific press or specific conflict is responsible for precipitating a behavior disorder, its removal should bring prompt recovery, much as the removal of pressure from a submerged cork allows it to pop to the surface.

But even at the level of physiopathology one seldom finds such a simple therapeutic result as this. Cardiac decompensation, obviously precipitated by overexertion in a susceptible person, does not disappear the moment one rests, and it may well progress to a fatal outcome regardless of what anyone does. Cardiac decompensation, once initiated, may lead also to other physiological inadequacies, such as respiratory embarrassment or renal insufficiency, that tend to perpetuate the heart's incompetence and prevent the establishment of compensation. Pathological deviations in behavior, once begun, often proceed similarly to develop their own succession of reactions which makes them persistent or cumulative. And these secondary reactions are likely also to be related rather to the patient's pathological behavior, as this progresses in the illness, than to the original precipitating agent.

EMOTIONAL REACTIONS

For the sake of simplicity, we have up to now virtually ignored two constituents of behavior that actually deserve first place in any discussion of neuroses and psychoses. These are the emotional and the symbolic components of human reactions. The *emotional component*, although implicating the whole of the reacting organism, operates in such a way as to direct our special attention to visceral activities. For it is the concerted contribution of our internal organs, with their neural coordinators and vascular network which forms the kinetic behavior matrix in all emotional behavior. The *symbolic component* may also implicate the whole organism, but its focus of interest lies in our language organization and in those derivatives of language from which the social patterns of our thinking are acquired. In the operations of the emotional and the symbolic components, both of them directly or derivatively related to socially shared behavior, we shall find some of our most challenging problems and illuminating solutions.

For us, one of the most serious recurrent fallacies is that of attempting to explain away behavior pathology by reifying emotion as an unbridled psychic force, and then opposing it to a supposedly rational and equally reified intellect. Starting with the observed fact that human behavior more often violates than follows the rules of verbal logic, scholars of the past illogically concluded that man must therefore be divided into two persons, one emotional and one intellectual, or one unconscious and one conscious. The latter is the current *Siamese-twin hypothesis,* according to which everyone of us is condemned to a life of petty, hateful unconscious wrangling between two fictitious selves which are joined together unwillingly in the flesh. Each self desires to go his own way, but instead must lead an existence of perpetual frustration, intrigue, spite and joyless compromise.

It is really most unfortunate that such an implausible hypothesis should have been salvaged from the nineteenth-century philosophical middens and used in the foundation of contemporary psychopathology. The fact is that, far from being opposed and at war, emotional and symbolic components are as a usual thing so interdependent and intricately related in human behavior, that only our inability to grasp their respective contributions by any other means justifies our separating them artificially now. Let us then reemphasize this, that in discussing emotion we merely stress one recognizable aspect of behavior, and in discussing language and thought we merely stress another. Both aspects may, in some re-actions, be dominant together, or the first may hold the center of the stage at one time and the second at another. With this as our general orientation, we shall take up first the emotional component of behavior and after that proceed to discuss the symbolic com-ponent, that is, language and thinking, in the next chapter.

Visceral contributions to emotional reactions

Since it is the visceral contributions that are chiefly responsible for such salient characteristics of emotion as diffusion and persis-tence, we shall begin with a consideration of internal organ activ-ity. No study of human behavior can afford to lose sight of the fact that our viscera are physiologically capable of participating in any or all of our reactions. Sometimes they do so powerfully and ob-trusively, sometimes mildly or negligibly. But whether a person be awake or asleep, whether he be running, walking, standing, sitting still or lying down, whether talking, listening, reading or thinking, he has always with him this shifting, kinetic visceral pattern as an incidental or a prominent background for his conduct.

Under ordinary conditions, the shifting visceral background plays a minor, although not necessarily an unimportant, role in one's gen-eral behavior. But every now and then visceral activity may dom-inate behavior, or determine its course and its outcome, and color it recognizably in a variety of ways. Thus, kissing a sister whom one does not in the least dislike, and kissing one's beloved sweet-heart, may both include visceral participation, but in one the con-tribution is minimal and in the other it is maximal. The same con-trast can be made between boxing for exercise and street-fighting for keeps, or between routinely jogging along a road in training for a cross-country race, and the same activity when a hostile, eager dog suddenly joins in. Under some conditions an observer may not be able to detect signs of the shift from slight to great visceral participation, but to the emotionally aroused individual within whom it occurs, the difference is unmistakable, even if at the time he is too busy to stop and write a report on it.

In what follows, we shall mean by an *emotional reaction one whose visceral contribution dominates or determines it, or colors it distinctively, but one that is not directly responsive to or regulated* by the immediate local visceral conditions. Thus vomiting in response to irritative gastric contents we do not consider an emotional reaction, but vomiting induced by bad news we do. Tachycardia and tachypnea that result directly from an oxygen-debt following exercise are not considered part of an emotional reaction, but tachycardia and tachypnea that come when one's lover steps off the train most certainly are. Our definition recognizes emotion as a variable characteristic of behavior, not something apart from or added to behavior. It localizes emotion neither in the visceral structures, nor in the autonomic nervous system with its central nuclei, but in one's *reactions.*

The prominent part played by our viscera in emotional reactions, and certain well-known peculiarities of coordinated visceral responses, together go a long way toward accounting for the remarkably protracted and pervasive influence that emotional components have within general behavior. Visceral tensions and glandular activity, once aroused, are very likely to persist and to spread without further stimulation. This is because smooth muscle is normally slow to contract, slower still to relax, and capable of maintaining a state of tension with little fatigue. It is because the distribution of smooth muscle, as for example in the vast blood-vessel network, is practically coextensive with the body itself. Finally it is because glandular secretions circulate until broken down or excreted, and because they may act both upon the autonomic nervous system, and directly back upon the glands, to continue their own secretory activities. The upshot of all this is that visceral activity, by virtue of its physiological basis, is able to contribute a sustained and far-flung kinetic background to the rest of behavior. Through their direct neural connections and their humoral ramifications, the viscera may thus act persistently, diffusely and cumulatively upon the skeletal musculature, energizing it or inhibiting it, improving its coordination or disorganizing it.

Displaced and cumulative emotional reactions

A common result of this visceral prolongation in one's emotional attitudes is that subsequent behavior comes under emotional influences having no logical relation to it. This is true of normal as well as of pathological reactions, as in the familiar *emotional displacement* that so often follows personal humiliation, fear, joy, thwarting or triumph. Much or all of one's conduct may be determined by emotional attitudes for some time after the situation initiating a strong emotional reaction has passed.

The *origin* of the strong emotional reaction, and therefore also of the persistent emotional attitude, may be wholly unrelated to the new reactions, and indeed quite forgotten by the person now reacting. Nevertheless, the emotional attitude still illogically dominates the scene. One treats the wife generously because of earlier success and praise on the golf links, to which she contributed nothing but her absence. One scolds a child unjustly in the evening because of trouble at the office in the afternoon. A narrow escape from a taxicab at a street-crossing leaves one tense, shaky and irritable for a while, and helps determine one's preferences and judgments illogically during the after-period, and in matters entirely unrelated to taxicabs and street-crossings. The connection between a displaced emotional reaction and its original excitant is particularly difficult to retrace when the original excitant is an errant thought which is promptly repressed. Some of our most important therapeutic techniques have been developed to meet the last-mentioned situation, and some of our most elaborate psychic theories have been constructed to make it sound logical.

The mere fact that the visceral contribution to emotional reactions, once initiated, is slow to die down also favors *cumulative sequences*. If, for example, a resentful attitude has been aroused, and some ordinarily annoying outside stimulation keeps reappearing, we may find that at each new presentation of the stimulus the individual is more reactive to it than at the preceding one. Summation occurs. The widespread visceral and skeletal tensions of the emotional attitude keep mounting stepwise until they may culminate in a frantic outburst. The stimulation in everyday life may be actual repetition, as when a sound is repeated almost identically and fear grows, but more often we find that the stimuli are equivalent rather than repetitive. The annoyance of an unimportant marital squabble at breakfast can lead to unwonted irritability and surliness toward one's fellow-passengers en route to work, and this to mounting anger over ordinary incidents at the factory, store or office, until there is a climactic outburst of fury that may cost someone his job.

Such cumulative emotional behavior depends, of course, upon relatively rapid progressive reaction-sensitization. The early stimulation sets up a readiness-to-react, and this readiness increases with each subsequent stimulation. The readiness-to-react is selective in that the organism becomes more and more reactive to annoying, fearsome, erotogenic or disgusting stimuli in its surroundings. What would ordinarily pass unnoticed becomes part of an additive stimulation sequence. When such a cumulative process, whether of short or long duration, ends in an uncontrollable emotional outburst, we call the climactic behavior *emotional decompensation*.

Cumulative emotional sequences do not require external stimulation at the time to be raised step by step toward a climax. A man may lie in bed or sit quietly in a chair and yet work himself up to the point where he quivers with fury, passion or fright. Thinking can be a most effective booster in making one's emotional tensions spiral upward. Indeed, we often find clinically that paranoid suspicions incubate best in undisturbed seclusion. They may halt or recede when an acceptable schedule of active participation with other persons can be arranged. In most cases, normal as well as abnormal, external stimulation and the organism's private symbolic activities both contribute to a mounting emotional tension and its climax. On such a basis anxiety [6] may advance to greater and greater severity, until emotional decompensation comes in the form of a panic state, with frank delusions and hallucinations, which sometimes leads to chronic schizophrenic disorganization. The following case illustrates this succession.

> A twenty-eight-year-old married clerk in a New York insurance office was present during some idle talk about sex perversions. Someone suddenly noticed that he was blushing and accused him of "being one of those people." His reaction was so exaggerated that he became the target of continual badgering and obscene epithet over a period of about three weeks. The first change his wife noticed in him was that he seemed preoccupied and uncommunicative. Gradually, however, he grew sleepless, lost his appetite, and began harping tensely upon the very real persecution he was undergoing at the office. He ended up finally with emotional decompensation in a violent outburst of shouting and threatening that brought the police and an enforced hospitalization.
>
> In the hospital he was actively hallucinating; he believed that his reputation was ruined and his life in danger, and he accused attendants of planning assaults upon him. In one access of fear he pulled his bed to pieces, barricaded himself in a corner of the

[6] For a discussion of normal anxiety in relation to emotional behavior, see Chapter 6.

room and, when the physician arrived, threatened to brain him with an iron bed-rail if he approached another step. In time the whole panic reaction died down, but the patient never completely recovered. The office force in launching its campaign of teasing had come close to the truth. The delusional misinterpretations and hallucinatory experiences of this man's excited, disorganized panic-phase unfortunately led to further and more permanent behavior disorganization.

We have here an example from behavior pathology of rapidly mounting tension which culminated in emotional decompensation when the individual's anxiety-tolerance was exceeded. The case also gives us the process by which a behavior disorder, once precipitated, may lead to the development of new complications — in this case delusions and hallucinations — which in turn delay or prevent recovery.

Emotional interference with local visceral function

Emotional behavior and routine visceral function are not the same, even though both implicate the same organs. Either may influence the other determinatively, perhaps reinforcing, perhaps inhibiting it. For example, the presence of an enemy at the table retards digestion while that of a friendly companion aids it. Conversely, human beings have for millennia recognized that gastric dysfunction is capable of terminating any enterprise that depends on optimism or joy. In emotional reactions, we have said, the visceral contribution is not directly responsive to and regulated by the immediate local visceral conditions, but is related to something extra-visceral — to stimulation from an external source, for example, or to stimulation from one's own talking and thinking.

Emotional behavior is not only distinguishable from routine visceral activities; it is very apt to work in direct opposition to them. In severe fright or extreme joy, for example, the pattern of gastro-intestinal activity may be entirely inappropriate for the stage of digestion which the gastrointestinal contents have reached. The gastric contents, because of emotional hypermotility, may be hurried on faster than they would otherwise have been; or they may be held where they are for longer periods than necessary because gastric motility has been slowed in a sad or deeply pessimistic emotional reaction. If the visceral contribution in a severe emotional reaction climaxes its activity with visceral violence, such as we commonly see in the vomiting and diarrhea of acute anxiety, we have a response that is doubly inappropriate. It neither aids nutrition nor increases one's effectiveness toward meeting the demands of the situation.

This, then, is the crux of the *visceral performance in emotion,* that *it is responsive to and regulated by occurrences lying outside the strictly visceral functions, occurrences in the field of shared behavior or in one's personal, unshared thinking.* Analogically, we may speak of digestion, excretion, respiration and ordinary cardiac action as *domestic functions* of our viscera, while their participation in emotional behavior we may call their *community functions.*

This dual and often contradictory relationship of visceral function to general behavior has direct implications for behavior pathology. For example, the intense concern of a hypochondriac over his digestive process is, ironically enough, the very thing to lead him into digestive disorder. Worry and anxiety involve the gastrointestinal tract in emotional activity at the very time when it should be left free to carry on its routine, autonomous domestic function. It is like the situation in which a busy housewife has her pressing domestic duties disrupted by the presence of a critical, uninvited neighbor who lowers her effectiveness by watching and evaluating her performance while it is in process. The hypochondriac can lower the competence of his own digestion, similarly, by merely watching and evaluating it.

One other example, from among a score of possible others, is the common occurrence of bizarre visceral delusions in depression. We know that the patient's gastrointestinal motility may be greatly slowed down during a depression, bariumized residue being detectable in the intestines by x-ray as long as two weeks after its ingestion.[7] This is very likely the basis of assertions frequently made by depressed individuals that their bowels are dead, have turned to stone, dried up, or ceased to exist. Such delusions have a practical as well as a theoretical bearing on the subject, since they may conspire with the depressed person's physiological inappetence to make him refuse food altogether and endanger his life.

Social modification of emotional behavior

What has already been said about the conditions and conse-

[7] G. Henry, "Gastrointestinal motor functions in manic-depressive psychoses," *Amer. Jour. Psychiatry,* 1931, vol. 88, pp. 19-28.

quences of learning, in this and the preceding chapter, applies of course to behavior that is strongly emotional as well as to that which is not. There is, however, one characteristic of emotional learning that deserves special emphasis because of its wide implications for behavior pathology. Emotional behavior in the very young consists of complete overt-covert reactions, given frankly and directly to obvious stimulation. In our society, as we have already indicated, a child finds as he matures that his overt behavior is more and more restricted, particularly with respect to reactions having strong emotional components. On the other hand, the visceral contribution and the isometric skeletal responses in emotion are such that they can still operate covertly with intensity and persistence. The result is that, as also in his symbolic behavior, the child learns early in life to give *overtly* the permitted or expected conventional patterns, and to retain some of the forbidden reactions *covertly*.

In short, the overt components of an emotional reaction are visible and invite social modification and control, while the covert components are hidden and can to a much greater degree escape society's coercion. This introduces the conditions for a split between the covert segment of an emotional reaction and its overt, public segment which may have quite a different pattern. Thus, a skillful adult can be angry inside but appear pleased or complacent to others. He can be eager and delighted inside but keep a poker face or look annoyed. As in language and thinking, so in emotional reactions, covert behavior may say one thing while overt says nothing or flatly contradicts what covert says.

Complications multiply when such a division of emotional behavior appears within an individual's own private behavior. To a set of conditions a person may give a conventionalized reaction which he can accept as his own. But he may also have an unsocialized emotional reaction to the same set of conditions, one that he cannot accept as his own, and does not admit in his self-reactions. We shall discuss some of these contradictory reactions, one conventional and accepted, the other asocial or antisocial and disowned, when we come to conflict and repression. They are important sources of the apparent split in behavior that one often finds in compulsions, hysteria, depression and schizophrenia.

Although emotional behavior shares this split into socialized overt and potentially asocial covert reactions with language and thought, there is one important difference that must be mentioned.

Whereas covert thinking in adolescents and adults has at some time been largely organized by social communication, covert emotional reactions as a rule have not. Adult thinking is at least derived from talking to a considerable degree. Emotional reactions, on the contrary, are at best imperfectly communicable and often they are incommunicable. The non-symbolic origins of emotional behavior, and the preponderance of invisible, unlocalized and unshared reactions in it are perhaps basic to its relatively incommunicable status in our society. But to this start must certainly be also added the relatively excessive control that we are all obliged to acquire over our socially expressed emotional reactions.

For these and related reasons, emotional reactions play a leading part in behavior disorders and pose exceedingly difficult problems for patient, diagnostician and therapist. An unformulated anxiety [8] or an indescribable secret joy, like a diffuse vascular or obscure abdominal disorder, cannot easily be located and conceptualized by the patient or shared in language with another person. True, techniques have been evolved, largely through Freud's influence, which permit the articulate patient to work through some of his emotional difficulties — and in this sense share them — with a trained, impartial therapist who understands what part he must and must not play in the therapeutic situation. But even these techniques have limited application and limited success. Emotional behavior is still the least readily formulable and one of the least accessible of human reactions, to therapist and patient alike.

Of course we all realize that emotional components, even though difficult to formulate and share publicly, may still exert an important influence upon the outcome of one's behavior. It is no more necessary that emotional components be recognized as such, for them to be determinative, than it is for cardiac or gastric changes to be identified before they can determine the character of one's reaction. Indeed, even those emotional attitudes which *remain* inaccessible to others, incommunicable in form and unacknowledged to oneself, may play a role of the highest importance in directing the course of shared public behavior and, indirectly, the outcome of social communication. Thus the character and course of a man's private thinking, and its consequences for his social operations, are often both dominated and determined by the kinetic pattern of his visceral contribution.

[8] Anxiety is defined, and its relation to the social modification of behavior is discussed, in Chapter 6.

4   Language, Thought and Role-Taking in Behavior Disorders

MAN IS NOT, of course, the only animal to have dominant and determinative emotional reactions, nor the only one faced with the problem of learning to inhibit or modify emotional behavior in accordance with human demands. Domestic animals, particularly dogs and cats, must learn similar lessons under similar conditions. But man is unique in having developed the infinitely complex systems of communication which we call language, and in having culturally transmitted such systems from generation to generation over a period of many thousand years. The development and elaboration of language in man's cultural history, and its acquisition as systematic behavior in each individual's childhood and youth, have consequences in behavior pathology that make them no less significant for us than emotion. For it is the virtual absence of elaborate language behavior in other animal forms which principally accounts for the fact that nothing approaching complex human behavior disorders can be demonstrated below the human level.

If language behavior did no more than provide a convenient instrument of communication between individuals, it might still occupy a central position in behavior pathology. But the effects in an individual's life of acquiring and using language do not stop with interindividual signalling and symbolizing; they go right on to influence his thinking also. It is talk in childhood that does the lion's share of organizing thought into an intraindividual instrument whose use can have the most vital and socially valid consequences in shared activities, or lead on to more and more thinking. Although for convenience we shall have to make a distinction between language behavior and thinking, in practice it is often exceedingly difficult to say when one begins and the other leaves off, since in older children and adults one is largely organized in terms of the other. Language and thought, which together we shall call symbolic behavior, must never be looked upon as something apart from the rest of human living. Language behavior is learned by each of us in action, and social thinking is derived directly from it. Indeed, so intimately are language and thought tied in with the rest of human reactions that we shall sometimes find ourselves hard put, in the chapters that follow, to distinguish between what is symbolic behavior and what is not.

We shall define *language behavior and socially derived thinking* as *interlocking systems of biosocial activity which make use of conventionalized gestures, signs, sounds and neuromuscular tensions as substitutes for and modification of more direct or immediate action.* If this activity is in the form of visible or audible language behavior, it can serve as a source of overt stimulation for other persons sharing the same system. It can also serve as stimulation for the individual who is actively communicating, since he can hear and often see his own language responses, as well as react to his own neuromuscular tension patterns. If the symbolic activity is invisible and inaudible, as in covert speech and thinking, it can still serve as a most effective form of private, unshared stimulation for the person engaged in it.

For the behavior disorders the most significant thing in this discussion of language and thought is that together they provide everyone who acquires them with a flow of almost continuous behavior sequences. These symbolic behavior sequences, even though infinitely more flexible, are self-stimulating and self-perpetuating in the same way that walking, hand-sewing and machine-operating are self-stimulating and self-perpetuating. In all these activities, each successive reaction pattern in a sequence is also the organized stimulus pattern for the next reaction. Talking and thinking, like other sequential acts, are to a large degree predictable if one has sufficient data regarding antecedent and existing conditions, and the usual behavior of the individual in question.

The same thing can be said of symbolic behavior that we have already said of the visceral component, namely, that all or nearly all of human behavior may influence or be influenced by it. Sometimes symbolic activity is dominant or determinative; often it runs along simultaneously with some other unrelated behavior, as when one talks and thinks about other matters while working or playing; sometimes it plays a negligible role. But even in routinized, mechanical learning we find it virtually impossible to exclude the participation of at least some verbalizing. Talk and thinking develop originally with each of us in relation to overt activity, and normally they never completely lose this relationship.

Early communication

The beginnings of rudimentary conversation and the active sharing of mutual situations appear in a little child's behavior long before he has acquired systematic conventional speech habits. These rudimentary conversations develop while the child and an older person are engaged in some conjoint activity, the sounds uttered by both being at first simply a part of their mutual performance. The child's contribution to conversation consists mainly of gestures, many of which are the beginnings of previously performed actions, and of a speech-form that has been named *expressive jargon* — i.e., babbling with exclamatory, inquiring and assertive inflections.[1] The older person also contributes gestures and speech forms to the shared situation. But his sign and sound behavior has, of course, long since undergone the gradual process of symbol conventionalization which the child is only now beginning. The adult's gesturing and talk, because they are already organized into a stable, efficient pattern, will be repeated almost identically when the appropriate situation recurs. The child's gestures, and especially his sounds, because they have not been so organized and reinforced by repetition, will be relatively unstable.

Under these circumstances, the stable organized language system of older persons will always in the end prevail, and replace a child's individualistic jargon and gesture. For the little child, in trying at first to share in activities with older individuals by means of his unstandardized symbols, is like a person who tries to trade by offering odd bits of metal to people accustomed to dealing in standard coins. Conventional words and phrases are the standard coins of communication. As media of verbal exchange they have

[1] N. Bayley, "Mental growth during the first three years," *Genet. Psychol. Monog.*, 1933, vol. 14, pp. 1-92; A. Gesell and H. Thompson, *Infant Behavior, Its Genesis and Growth* (New York: McGraw-Hill, 1934), pp. 243-257 and 286-291; D. McCarthy, "Language development in children," in L. Carmichael (editor), *Manual of Child Psychology* (New York: Wiley, 1946), pp. 483-487.

relatively stable and predictable values, and by their use one can better control the outcome of social behavior transactions than by trusting to expressive jargon. In aphasia that results from brain damage, and in schizophrenic asocial speech, one witnesses the devastating effects of the deterioration of standardized language forms upon the patient's social behavior.

The earliest stabilization of a conventional speech form in the child's behavior is a relatively simple matter. When something resembling a word or phrase appears in a child's verbal play, or in his expressive jargon, it wins the attention and praise of persons around him. The sound he has made, which of course he also hears himself, is likely to receive additional reinforcement from its repetition by the adults in the form of animated exclamations. These consequences of his making a sound help to single it out and stabilize it, rather than others, as a rudimentary speech habit — particularly if each time he makes it he is rewarded by the reactions of older persons. Once the child acquires a specific conventional sound, he may learn to make use of it as reaction-getting behavior, which reduces his dependence upon others' whims to the extent that it controls their reactions to him. This process is comparable to the much earlier control of adults that many infants acquire through their crying and breathholding behavior.

The speed with which a child's vocalizations become conventionalized, under such influences as these, is indicated in McCarthy's study [2] which reports a reduction in utterances unintelligible to non-relatives, from 74 per cent at eighteen months of age, to practically zero at fifty-four months. That pressure from the human environment is an important factor in speeding the development has been demonstrated by comparative studies of the linguistic progress of normal twins, non-twins and only children. The twins, who habitually played together on the same developmental level of sharing, were least under the necessity of acquiring conventional words as the price of companionship and cooperation. Hence, they were the slowest group in acquiring a conventional vocabulary. Only children whose early companions were necessarily adults accustomed to continual reliance upon words, were found to acquire their elders' speech the most rapidly. The non-twins having siblings, who therefore had companions at both child and adult levels, took

[2] D. McCarthy, "The language development of the preschool child," *Univ. Minn. Institute Child Welfare Monog. Ser.*, 1930, No. 4.

on conventional speech habits at a rate intermediate between that of the twins and that of the only children.[3]

Although at first a child learns conventional speech as part of shared activity in a specific concrete situation, it is not long before he is found saying a word or a phrase as its object disappears, or even when it is missing. Ultimately he learns to verbalize appropriately in the complete absence of the object or the situation of which the words originally were an integral part, and of course generalization and differentiation play an important part in the further elaboration of what he specifically learns. The child talks *about* situations and occurrences, as well as *in* them, and not only to other persons but also to himself — the latter procedure being essential to the development of organized thought and self-control, however amusing it may sound to adults hearing it.

In learning to use verbalizations appropriately, out of their specific context and in the absence of acts and objects to which they once belonged, the child has taken a long step forward. He has laid his own behavioral foundation, in words that substitute for deeds, things and events, for the organization and exchange of complex social reactions which he could not have mastered without word symbols. As his vocabulary and his facility grow, he frees himself from many of the limitations imposed by the logic of non-verbal operations, the only logic that subhuman animals have. He learns to carry out public and private manipulations with verbal counters, and to get results by verbal methods that no one could possibly achieve in dealing directly with objects in their full context. The fact that verbal operations may differ from the non-verbal manipulations they are supposed to represent, and may give different results, is of the highest significance for the behavior disorders. Schizophrenics, in particular, fall into verbal traps of their own making. They sometimes divorce the word and thought so completely from the deed that what they say about what they are doing may only add to their confusion instead of helping to clarify.

Social conformity in language and thinking

Human beings pay for the gift of words by losses in the individu-

---

[3] E. Davis, "The development of linguistic skill in twins, singletons with siblings, and only children from age five to ten years," *Univ. Minn. Institute Child Welfare Monog. Ser.*, 1937, No. 14; E. Day, "The development of language in twins," *Child Development*, 1932, vol. 3, pp. 179-199 and 298-316.

ality of their attitudes and in privacy. Language begins by conventionalizing one's social behavior and then goes on to intrude upon one's private thought. To be able to communicate, of course, a person must speak as others speak, say the things they say, and arrive at conventional conclusions by conventional routes. The child, in acquiring linguistic habits, is at the same time, willy-nilly, acquiring innumerable ready-made social attitudes which are already crystallized in the words, phrases and sentences that he takes over intact from others in his culture. To this extent he gives up his individuality of method and conclusion by adopting the prevailing techniques of social intercommunication as his techniques. In conforming to the conventions of language behavior he conforms also to what these conventions imply in his culture.

What the child acquires in linguistic skill, in company with others, he naturally goes on using when he is quite alone. The structure of verbal communication, which is decidedly a social product, acquired by every new individual at first in overt social form, comes in time to modify also the structure of private, covert thinking concerned with one's immediate personal needs. Each of us thus brings the techniques and the attitudes derived from public intercommunication, which we all take over from our society, into his most intimate thought, and in so doing organizes private thinking along social lines. This is one source of the many concurrences we find between the unspoken thoughts of different individuals which are romantically attributed to thought-transference by some, and to a racial Unconscious by others. It is also one explanation for the remarkable similarity of delusional systems cropping up in different patients who have not communicated with one another. They fear or cherish intensely and fixedly what normal men fear or cherish mildly or for a moment.

Sharing one's responses and attitudes overtly with other persons is the most effective way of bringing them into line with those of the prevailing cultural patterns. Reactions which for any reason are left uncommunicated and unshared with others are likely to play a leading part in behavior pathology because they lack this controlling influence. Socially taboo subjects, and matters traditionally couched in vague, ambiguous, prescientific formulations, seem to present special hazards to many adolescents and socially immature adults. This may account for the fact that we find sexual, ethical, cosmological and religious preoccupations holding such a very prominent place in the symptomatology of neuroses and psychoses, and apparently also in their origins. The child or adolescent, if he has learned to seek his chief satisfactions in the asocial techniques of passive observation and covert fantasy, is certainly in graver danger of misusing these techniques later on than the one whose predominantly overt, shared satisfactions follow the design of his culture, and include the reciprocal behavior of his fellow human beings. In popular terminology, we say that the former's attitudes do not correspond to "reality," by which we mean that they are not oriented adequately to the field of shared social operations.

No one can ever succeed in formulating all his attitudes completely in words. Human attitudes are a multidimensional spectrum with infinite variation, while words are discrete fragments that we string along a time-line. Sometimes overt attitudes speak more clearly than words do, even when social communication is far from a person's intent. We see this all through the behavior disorders. Nothing, for example, could be more eloquent than an attitude of abysmal depression, nothing more dramatically communicative than an hysterical seizure or more arresting than the grotesque posturing of a schizophrenic. But this medium has very restricted uses. No one but Panurge could carry through a prolonged debate in attitudes. Their inclusive character limits their flexibility. For all that words themselves are rigid little fragments, capable of combining in only one dimension, they can operate in many contexts which they may organize to order as they go along. By crystallizing out phases and single aspects from the flow of behavior, words become our chief tools in the analysis, identification, manipulation and recall of events, whether these occur in the shared field of social operations as talk, or in the covert patterns of response and attitude that we call thought.

The biosocial nature of thinking

To launch at this juncture upon a systematic account of the nature of thought would carry us too far afield. However, because preoccupation with fantasy and symbolic confusions enter into so much of behavior pathology, it is necessary that we make certain fundamental points clear before leaving our introduction to the subject. The average layman conceives of thinking as a wholly nonmaterial process which frees us from the determinism of reality because it is not a part of this world. Such a romantic view is not, of course, the contemporary layman's invention. It is his cultural heritage from a very old philosophical tradition which maintained that thought was not in the body or *soma*, but in the mind, or *psyche*. However, in this same prescientific tradition, it was also held that arteries were filled with spirits, concocted in the stomach and warmed in the heart, and that these spirits traveled by convection through the blood-vessels to the brain, where they somehow influenced what the *psyche* thought. Physiologists have discarded this kitchen-inspired theory of gastric and arterial function, but the mystical attitudes toward thinking still persist, while new physiological rationalizations are adopted to give them a solid look.

These traditional hypotheses which banish thinking, imagination and dreams from the naturalistic world, and locate them in a conscious or unconscious *psyche*, are entirely out of step with present-day interpretations of the rest of human conduct. The behavior pathologist or therapist who clings to such anachronistic speculation brings himself face to face with this ancient and insoluble psychosomatic riddle, *How can a psyche in a psychic world determine the activities of a soma in a physical world, or vice versa?* If this had been the riddle that the Theban Sphinx asked Oedipus, he would never have lived to wed his mother. The psychosomatic riddle has no answer and, for us, no meaning either.

We know today that thinking is affected by fever, fright, toxins, starvation, anxiety, fatigue and malnutrition, in the same general ways that other biological coordinations are. Thinking can be sped up and slowed down, controlled, predicted and changed within the same general limits and under the same general circumstances as those altering and governing other biosocial behavior. It shows typical practice effects, it can be impaired by disuse and disease, and it always reflects an individual's culture and the organization of his particular society. There is neither advantage in nor necessity for excluding thought from the category of human behavior.

What we speak of collectively as *thinking* includes a number of great systems of symbolic or substitute reactions, most but not all of them covert. Thought is not simply mute or amputated language; neither is language merely the expression of pre-existing thought. But a great deal of thinking in adults shows an unmistakably intimate relationship with linguistic forms. Active, structured thinking, that deals with events customarily formulated in words, will tend to follow language organization. Dreams, daydreams and passive imagining, which deal with infrequently and incompletely communicated matters, tend toward more non-verbal organization, including isometric muscle tensions and those residua of perceptual reactions which we loosely term imagery.

Language habits are social habits, social in origin and social in structure. Therefore, the more thinking is organized in accordance with language structures, the more likely it is to be socially valid, and to lead toward adequate social behavior that corresponds to the patterns of group living. The reverse may also be true. For example, in the behavior disorders wherever social communication in language suffers disorganization or deterioration, thought may show a corresponding change. This we shall see most clearly in schizophrenia when prolonged nonparticipation in shared activities results in a disabling, though not always incurable, disorganization of language and thinking, to the point where both are practically useless as social instruments.

From what we have already said, it must be obvious that thinking has a great deal in common with emotional reactions. Both are displayed quite publicly in early childhood, both come under the organizing and inhibiting influence of social learning, and both grow increasingly private as an individual matures. Neither, however, loses completely all of its asocial characteristics. Emotional components enter into a great deal of thinking; and thinking is involved in a great many emotional reactions. Perhaps only the most casual thinking is without some touch of emotional attitude in its background. Certainly the two are closely related in origin and mode of operation. Both being predominantly covert and internalized, they may organize the field of private, unshared reactions between them. Their activities, far from being fundamentally opposed as the mediaevals taught, are complementary and compenetrate. This intimate relationship is of especial importance in the organization of interlocking attitude systems into social roles, where emotional thinking and socially modified emotion play leading parts in normal behavior and its pathological distortions.

ROLE–TAKING AND BEHAVIOR DISORDERS

In our discussion of personality development we saw that social roles are organized and differentiated quite early in life. These roles are acquired through the child's interbehavior with his parents, his siblings and the other persons making up his human environment, and they are defined in terms of this interbehavior. Since the attitudes and responses of a child's seniors to him are largely prefabricated by the culture into which he and they are born, and in which he and they are reared, his own role-taking must inevitably show the same cultural influences as theirs. For us, a person's role-taking habits are of very great significance because defects, distortions and exaggerations in their operation can give rise to all kinds of damaging behavior pathology, especially in adolescent and adult life. This is most obvious in compulsions and hysteria, as well as in delusional and in hallucinatory developments, where we shall discuss role-taking in some detail. But before we go on to consider frustration, conflict and the so-called "psychological mechanisms" or adjustive techniques, we shall need to understand just what the basic implications of role-taking are for personality organization and the behavior disorders.

Let us begin by defining our terms. We mean by *the role, a comprehensive and coherent organization in behavior of functionally related, interlocking attitudes and responses.* The role is a product of social learning, which has been culturally defined by the behavior of others, and is based either upon direct personal interaction, or upon the symbolic substitutes for personal interaction in conventional language and thought. By *role-taking*, we shall mean *the living out of such a social behavior organization, whether as play, as social imitation, or as one's real-life situation.* In real-life situations, role-taking means earnestly behaving as, and therefore actually being, a particular social person in relation to other persons. It also includes overtly or covertly acting as, *without being*, a particular social person and, by so doing, getting hold of the social attitudes and the perspectives of that other social person. Role-taking of the latter kind is carried out regularly in verbal and pantomime soliloquy and in fantasy, substituting for full-dress rehearsals, or functioning as preparation for anticipated trouble, or as anticipation of hoped-for pleasures. Role-taking always includes the highly important social and asocial play-activities that human beings carry on in all walks of life, and at all ages.

Early role-taking

The first role that every human being acquires is the one he must first learn to live — *the baby of the family*. What this shall include and how it shall be played are determined, biologically by the way the child is constructed, and culturally by the reactions of other persons toward his appearance and behavior. Their reactions and the cultural design of his environment together shape his role and train him in taking it. Before long, new sub-roles are differentiated in a growing child's behavior and these organize, expand and differentiate farther with his increasing biosocial maturation. He learns different reactions to his two parents, for example, becoming *mother's boy* primarily to one and *father's boy* primarily to the other. In some families these relationships are quite differently organized and, although each role is restricted to the appropriate parent, its organization may have important effects upon the operation of the other role — a fact that competing parents are not slow to recognize. Within each of these two roles are differentiated the sub-roles of *good boy* and *bad boy*, which we discussed in Chapter 2, and these may also be differently structured in relation to what each parent demands, rewards and punishes.

We must realize, of course, that such basic social roles are neither deliberately planned nor deliberately chosen by a child. They are, as we have pointed out, culturally defined by the behavior of others and in part imposed upon a child's behavior patterns by the limitations and demands of his human environment. Acquiring role-taking functions is, for the child, simply a result of his learning in particular situations with their contexts what he can, may or must do, and gaining skill in doing it through practice. What has already been said about the organization, spread and differentiation of attitudes and responses applies with equal force to these most inclusive behavior units, the social roles. A very young child lacks the ability to recognize, identify and analyze what he is living out as a social role. Until he has acquired considerable facility with language behavior and socially organized thinking, he cannot foresee, anticipate or predict very much beyond the stimulating here and now.

Play and role-taking

The social significance of play in personality development has already been touched upon. In his earliest solitary and parallel play a child gains practice in manipulation, locomotion and talk, and to a very limited degree interprets simple adult roles in terms of what he sees and hears. But it is in his associative and cooperative play with other children that he best acquires skill in sharing activities, privileges, responsibilities and consequences. As the price he must pay for being admitted to the game and the group, a child must learn the techniques of subordination and superordination, as well as those of cooperation, competition and direct antagonism. Thus, by playing participative games with his peers, he is unwittingly advanced far beyond the limits of his real-life roles, as *the child in society*, and inducted into roles patterned after those expected of older persons. Long before he really needs to understand them, for example, the growing child learns to play at being schoolboy, worker, policeman, soldier and parent, as interpreted of course by his playmates and himself. In other words he is getting practice, without recognizing it or caring about it, which may repay him and society later on.

Childhood play, even though carried on at the time for its immediate rewards, is unintentionally fruitful in other directions. For by taking this role or that in fun, children learn incidentally to see things from something approaching the diverse standpoints of all the social persons whom they pretend to be. Each child finds out, in each role he plays, what he can look for in the behavior of children playing dominant, dependent or other reciprocal roles, and what he must do to meet, accept, resist or evade others' demands in those roles. In each role he gains experience in doing and saying things, in having things said and done to him, and in maintaining consistent and appropriate organized attitudes, none of which belongs to his real-life role of *the child of such-and-such a family.*

Role-taking and shifting perspectives

It is true that a person lives out as an adult very few of the roles he plays as a child. Play's most significant contribution is not so much rehearsal in the role as practice in role-taking, in acting in concert with others and sharing or opposing their aims, in acquiring skill in reciprocal functions. Perhaps most important of all, is the skill play allows one to acquire in the techniques of making a shift from one role to another, when the need arises for gaining an impartial view of one's own behavior, or understanding the point of view of someone else. A child learns in group play to adopt as realistically as he is able, for example, the attitudes and points of view of father and mother as well as of their baby, of doctor and nurse as well as of patient, of teacher as well as pupil, of storekeeper and customer at the same time, of cop and robber, of defending friend and attacking enemy, of princess, cowboy, admiral and Indian, the pursuer and the pursued. He gains skill in abandoning one role at a moment's notice and adopting an opposite or reciprocal role, and in doing so he unwittingly discovers the advantage he then has in being able to anticipate what the other child, who takes over his discarded role, will do next.

To the extent that an individual, in the course of personality development, learns to take social roles skillfully and realistically, acquires an adequate repertory of them, and becomes adroit in shifting from one role to another when he is in difficulty, he should grow into a flexible, adaptive social adult with minimal susceptibility to behavior disorders. The more effectively he is able to allow the attitudes and responses of others, which he predicts in symbolic role-taking, to influence his own reactions, the more competent he ought to be in social situations. He need not do exactly what others do, or even what they wish, but whatever he does should bear some functional relation to the ways they may be expected to react.

If, for example, a man is able to predict the reactions of others, by putting himself in their place and gaining momentarily their points of view, he thereby immediately wins a strategic position from which he can predict and prepare for their behavior from its very inception. To anticipate the reactions of many different persons, a man must have a repertory of many perspectives, and skill in going through its roles. To surmount or evade personal difficulties that seem at first to be insurmountable or unavoidable, a person often needs to be able to abandon his particular point of view, no matter how cogent it may seem and, in a different role, to gain a more workable perspective from some different standpoint.

Individual differences in the ease and adequacy of shifting from one social role to another, in fantasy and discussion, seem to underlie differences in individual susceptibility to some kinds of behavior disorder.[4] Muncie has called attention, for example, to what he terms the "rigid personality" of many individuals developing persistent psychoses.[5] It is our suggestion that these susceptibles are

[4] Compare the study of individual differences in the rigidity of behavior in young children in E. Lerner and L. Murphy, "Methods for the study of personality in young children," *Monog. Soc. Research Child Development,* 1941, vol. 6, No. 4.

[5] W. Muncie, "The rigid personality as a factor in psychoses," *Arch. Neurol. Psychiat.,* 1931, vol. 26, pp. 359-370.

persons who, for one reason or another, have failed to develop the social skills involved in running through a repertory of different perspectives, particularly if strong emotional reactions are prominent. When insurmountable personal difficulties arise, they cannot abandon the non-adaptive perspective by shifting through others to one that might offer a different solution. This fixity of perspective, which is so characteristic of nearly all delusions, is what psychiatrists mean when they say that a patient lacks insight. He sees things only from a single standpoint for which he seems unable to substitute any other, even for the purposes of the moment.

Discrepant and contradictory social roles

Role-taking behavior normally appears in situations that resemble or are in some way equivalent to the situations in which the particular role was originally organized. When, for example, we step from a certain kind of situation into a different kind, into one that provides us with different companions, responsibilities and rewards, we ordinarily change our role to one that is appropriate to the new situation. The behavior discrepancies that may appear between two major roles are common sources of maladjustment. Some persons regret them or worry over them, some rationalize or defend them, while some grow virtually amnesic in one role for all that goes on in the other. Even the most glaring contradictions in role-taking behavior do not in themselves alone constitute behavior pathology, nor are they necessarily even a sign of hypocrisy and deceit. They are usually no more than indications that a person has very different functions in two or more different capacities and that his behavior has, at some time previous, been organized separately and practiced separately in accordance with each role.

We can illustrate the normal contradictions in role-taking, which have far-reaching implications for behavior pathology, by two common examples. The man who acts the kindly husband and father at home, sincerely and with all his heart, may act the hard-bitten, relentless manager at work, and with equal wholehearted sincerity. No one can justly accuse him of posing or pretense in either role, and yet in each he may be all but unrecognizable to those who know him only in the other. Look at such a man in still other situations. He is one person at church and quite another in a tavern, yet earnest and acceptable in both places. He is one person coping with a haughty and valuable client and something else in the role of jolly-boy the same afternoon, as he buys tickets to a ball game with his cronies.

Consider also the married woman who can, in a single day, play genuinely and with complete earnestness the roles of loyal wife to her husband, devoted daughter to her parents, protective mother to her children and aggressive president to her fellow club members. In every role she is a different person, known for different functions and valued for discrepant reasons, and yet in each role she can be honestly herself. But for some individuals the contradictions in role-taking may under certain circumstances lead into behavior pathology. We shall see roles at war in the compulsions, bitterly and sometimes dangerously attacking one another in depressions, mingling confusedly in schizophrenic disorganization and formed into imaginary persecutors in paranoid disorders. We shall see them also reaching a solution, in impasse, in hysterical disabilities and amnesia.

Language and thought in role-taking

Language habits creep so gradually into all reactions that no one can really say of a child's behavior, "Here at this instant role-taking in terms of *language* had its start." In play, language at first functions merely as a component or an accompaniment, but later and secondarily it acquires status as a semi-independent, equivalent form of behavior that allows its possessor to take roles first in words without deeds, and then in fantasy as well. We have pointed out that language habits mold us into conformity with our culture, because language is a cultural product and highly conventionalized, and we have said that through language our covert symbolic behavior is also organized along social lines. On the other side of the ledger is the fact that language and organized thought are together a means of enriching our potentialities for social role-taking enormously.

Talking becomes in itself not only the most effective instrument of interpersonal communication, eventually superseding all others, but also the medium through which one builds up a repertory of social roles. By learning to say what others say in context, a child learns first to express their attitudes and then, by expressing these conventional attitudes appropriately, he tends actually to acquire them as his own. When he corrects someone else or himself, he speaks his mother's words, with her inflections and something of her look and stance. This sort of thing enables the child to speak and act as others in his culture do, to take their attitudes and play their roles when he wishes. In so doing he is also able to hold their perspectives and have their social reactions toward people, things and events, and even toward himself as an object. These attitudes, roles and perspectives he can also carry away with him and use in his private talk and fantasy, and to them he can add still other make-believe parts from the stories he hears and reads.

The uses to which symbolic role-taking can be put are infinite. Every half-grown child who has erred and strayed in some specific way more than once knows the value of being able to predict what will happen on his return. Role-taking exercises in words, pantomime and fantasy may, for example, completely preoccupy a boy as he moves homeward late again for supper. He sees his mother in imagination greet him. What ought he say and how will she react?

To play through such a drama in advance, a boy must be already practiced in the art of shifting roles, of alternating between being himself and saying things to his imagined mother, and then taking his mother's role to receive what he says, and react to it from her perspective, not his own. Now he makes his excuse in his own role and quickly parries it in hers. He runs through another and another formulation in the same fashion, rehearsing his own phraseology as well as her imagined acceptance of this or that verbal peace offering, or her annoyed rejection of it. Clearly, the more skilled and faithful he is in taking her attitudes, and the greater his agility in slipping in and out of roles, the more successful he is likely to be in readying his craft for the approaching domestic storm. Parents, who find themselves bested by such predigested tactics, should comfort themselves with the realization that their child is learning strategies of inestimable value for his career, and for his home life as an adult.

Once a person has acquired the language habits of his culture, and through them developed organized social thinking, he can play roles through entirely in words and fantasy if he so desires, and without bringing them to bear upon any public activities whatever. Roles played in words and fantasy can be made more varied, less conventional and self-consistent than those acted out overtly in the company of others. Moreover, they need not correspond at all to what the talking or thinking role-taker could possibly do or be himself. He can, for instance, fantasy or act out alone in symbols that he is rich, powerful and handsome, or poor and persecuted, even though he be none of these. He can play in symbol substitutes a role that no human being can take in direct overt action. In fantasy a man may cut the world in two, or snuff the sun out like a candle, walk on clouds, live ten thousand years or change into a potato.

Unquestionably role-taking that is confined to fantasy and talk brings rewarding experiences to normal persons. It passes time, relieves the boredom of waiting, brings us little unearned dividends of pleasure, allows us to do and be things, to see, hear and say things which stubborn public facts forbid. We use such role-taking in fiction, poetry, drama, religion, painting and sculpture. We employ fantasied roles in private to relive or change the remembered past, to predict and shape a future we expect, or one we know will never come.

Unfortunately, role-taking confined to words and fantasy introduces its user to serious risks. One can become addicted to its pleasures, and even to its threats, more hopelessly than to morphine. Every state hospital houses men and women who have learned to live so completely their fantasied roles that they have become socially useless, sometimes incapable even of feeding and dressing themselves without constant help. Their fantasies have overwhelmed and enslaved them. Ungovernable fantasy is also found in many a chronically anxious mother who goes through an imagined drama in which, for example, her child is killed horribly whenever he is merely late in coming home from school. The lonely, puzzled brooding of paranoid individuals may also bear ill fruit. Quite suddenly — in one of our cases after two and a half years of solitary puzzling — everything may seem clear to the uncommunicative thinker (*sudden clarification*), and lead to his taking irretrievable action on the basis of imagined events.

Self-reactions and role-taking

By a *self-reaction* we mean *the behavior of an individual in direct relation to himself as a social object.* A person's *self-responses are, therefore, the specific patterns which he has acquired in relation to his own appearance, his competence, his conduct and his status.* His *self-attitudes are the behavioral backgrounds that facilitate and support specific self-responses.* In configural terms, a *self-re-*

sponse is the *figure* and its *self-attitude* the *ground*. A self-attitude, like any other attitude, may be aroused without leading at the time to a specific response, but it may none the less influence the course and outcome of a developing situation, and determine the character of responses to other persons and things.

This process of reacting to oneself as to a social object is only a special case of acquired role-taking, in itself neither mysterious nor profound. In our childhood, we learn from others to look at and speak about our own bodies in the same way that we learn to look at and speak about other objects within the range of our responses. We learn in childhood to comment on what we are doing or have done, in the same manner and by the same behavioral techniques as those we use in commenting on our mother's competence and conduct, or the postman's or the dog's. We learn from others to say who and what we are, and to give our social status a name, under the same conditions as those by which we learn to state other inter-personal relationships, who and what our father is and what his status is in society. In the self-reaction the only aspect that is special is the *focus* of our behavior. The behavior techniques and the way they are acquired are common to all ordinary products of social learning.

Reacting to oneself as a physical object

One product of the growing infant's own behavior is that it helps him differentiate in action between what is his own body and what is not. He may play with his toes as he plays with other objects, but the stimulating effects upon him are not confined to his hands and, moreover, the toes are always around and bear a peculiar relationship to his behavior. He may be able neither to identify nor to analyze these special characteristics, but they influence what he does to his toes and how often. He can likewise pound his finger with a block, in just the same way that he pounds the floor. But pounding a finger produces reactions in him that terminate the activity, and substitute avoidance and protective modifications of his play, just as less direct but equally painful situations later on develop defensive avoidance and protection, by their effects upon him. A child's hands also learn to localize the accessible body areas, through his reflex scratching and incidental manipulation, and where his hands go his eyes may follow.

By these and countless other such maneuvers, multiplied and

compounded, a child learns to treat his own body parts differently from other targets of his behavior. But what is of still greater significance to us than this, he has meanwhile also been learning in terms of his own action the limits and characteristics of his body as a *physical object*. He has learned to treat his body as a physical object through the use of techniques which, even though more cautious and considerate, are of the same kind as the ones he uses in dealing with other objects. He treats his body as a thing, a *special* object, but still an object. We shall need to recall this process and this fact when, in the behavior disorders, we find someone talking about, hurting and even mutilating himself as punishment for sin, acting for all the world as though his body were something he could disown and detach from himself.

Reacting to oneself as a social object

Reacting to oneself as a *social object* is the same thing as reacting to oneself as a *physical object* with this one addition, that it implies social evaluation in terms of status. Children learn to react to what they look like, how they are dressed, what they themselves do and say, and who or what they are in relation to others — all in the words and gestures they take over from the older children and adults around them. In this way a child, through his own acquired behavior, becomes a social object to himself as well as to others. His behavior makes him into an object that he can defend, approve, criticize and discuss evaluatively, almost as though it were another person.

From the day of his birth, a human infant is the subject of endless evaluative discussion — about how he looks and acts, how cute, funny, bright or dull he seems to be. His face is talked about and each part of it, his hands and feet, his arms and legs, how fat or thin his body, what his weight is, what his color, rate of growth and general health, what his prevailing disposition is and where he gets it. Daily he is compared with friends' and neighbors' babies. The infancy of his siblings is recited over him, and that of his parents, his cousins, uncles, aunts and other relatives. He lives immersed in an atmosphere of proud, dubious or critical comment, his crib a show-case, his carriage a decorated float on street parade. This is the social matrix from which his self-reactions one day bud.

Language and thought in self-reactions

Children's self-reactions antedate the appearance of useful

speech, but speech enormously increases their effectiveness, crystal-lizes and conventionalizes them. The child quickly learns to say the same words that others use in commenting on his appearance, competence, conduct and status. He hears and he says, "Good boy" when he cleans his plate, "Naughty" when he makes a mess or dis-obeys, "No-no" as he reaches for something forbidden. The little girl learns to call her best dress *pretty*, and herself pretty when she is in it. At first these evaluative words come straight out of some-thing someone else has just said. The child's earliest versions of self-response are apt to sound mechanical and unconvincing, be-cause they lack appropriately developed self-attitudes to give them an adequate background. They are something like the comments of a trained parrot. But soon the child learns also the inflections, the gestures, and even the personal mannerisms of those around him. Eventually he is able, in simple and familiar situations, to pass judgments upon his performance, status and appearance that agree closely with those of his domestic associates.

What a child learns to say he can also learn to think. What he learns to think he can keep to himself and use for his own private purposes. The self-reactions that a child or a grown-up does not share with someone else are not debatable by others. They can-not be amended or contradicted directly by another person, and they do not expose an individual to criticism, ridicule or loss of prestige. Even though the child originally adopts his self-reactions from the behavior of other persons toward him, and toward others around him, he may keep them private — hidden and inaccessible to other persons and sometimes, through repression, inaccessible even to self-analysis.

A child, an adolescent or an adult can learn to use his self-reac-tions also in fantasy, as we shall see abundantly illustrated in the behavior disorders. Although reacted to by those around him as weak, dull and unworthy, he may in fantasy take completely or in part the role of some other social person who is strong, clever and valued. A young adolescent girl who finds her real-life social role to be that of a homely, unintelligent, unrespected person, can with-·out fear of contradiction fantasy herself as a lovely, wise, desirable princess. In her daydreams she reacts to herself as a social object from this fantasied perspective, even though her daily life belies the dream. Thus a seventeen year old dishwasher built up such a strongly organized role in her fantasied self-reactions that it finally prevailed. She considered herself a beautiful duchess, walked on her tiptoes, her mien proud and sweet, her gestures graceful and commanding. Other therapeutic efforts failing, contact was finally re-established through insulin shock therapy and the patient recovered well enough to return home.

Self-approval and self-reproach

When a child has learned to give his elders' responses in evaluating his own conduct and appearance, he has also acquired something of their supporting attitude, the one that goes with a particular judgment. His parents have rewarded good behavior, let us say, with smiles, kind words and emotional warmth. Bad behavior they have punished with frowns, rebukes and coldness. The child learns to react to his own behavior similarly. He can call his conduct good, praise himself *sotto voce* or aloud, and even be gratified by his own praise, smile and feel a glow of warmth when he is by himself. This is the reward that his parents have in the past given him, and he has learned how to give it to himself with similar results. We call it self-approval. It is a self-reaction to a person's own behavior whose pattern each adopts originally from his elders, and whose effects upon himself in adulthood are rewarding in the same way that his elders' approval rewarded him when he was a child.

Suppose, instead, that what a person does seems very wrong to him when he gives these self-reactions which he has derived from others. Now he frowns and takes attitudes of self-reproach; sometimes he overtly rebukes and even rejects himself as the doer of a wrong deed. These, again, are the words and attitudes of others which he has taken as his own. They punish him because they rearouse guilt and anxiety, precipitate the dismal state of the rejected, unloved child which he once learned in action at his parents' hands. In adulthood this little play sometimes grows into a tragic melodrama, where the depressed self-accused lashes himself so mercilessly in talk and fantasy that death seems the one promise left of penance and relief.

The potentialities for frustration and conflict are very great in self-reactions, as we shall see in the next chapter, but the possibility of self-deception is also great. It is hard enough to be honest with another person when honesty hurts, but at least you can get away from the one who hurts you or is hurt by you. It can be very much harder to be honest in one's self-reactions if it hurts, since flight from oneself is impossible and even distraction or forgetting difficult. When it comes to self-approval there are many temptations. It is not easy to forego the rewards of self-approval when they are so easy to bestow upon oneself. We all have little ways of modifying our recall so that painful and discreditable things may be seen in a different light, repressed, reversed or ascribed to someone else. We develop protective, defensive, nullifying techniques that help us to retain self-approval and avoid self-castigation. In thinking over an act or an omission, we subtract or add something, change a sign here and a referent there, with the result that we escape self-reproach and sometimes precipitate self-praise instead. We like to think that these somewhat shady maneuvers belong to a special class of individuals whom we call psychopaths, but the fact is — and most of us know it — that the use of such maneuvers is universal in our culture.

Because people become so easily superstitious over the word *self,* let us repeat here in closing that self-reactions, whether verbal or non-verbal, overt or covert, are no more and no less than acquired patterns of behavior. They are reactions of a biosocial man, woman or child to his own appearance, behavior and status as a social object, originally learned and practiced overtly in the company of others, and secondarily carried over into silent speech and socially organized thinking. Self-reactions always remain human behavior, never becoming transmuted into static substance, never reified or transformed by diagrams into a compartmentized *psyche.* There is no single, united self at the core of our being.[6] We are, as we have seen and shall see again more clearly, many persons in a house divided. The basis of much frustration and many conflicts is in this universal circumstance, that no man ever fuses all his self-reactions together into a single, unambiguous, coherent whole.

[6] For a contemporary discussion of the self in psychology, see G. Allport, "The ego in contemporary psychology," *Psychol. Rev.,* 1943, vol. 50, pp. 451-478; I. Chein, "The awareness of self and the structure of the ego," *Psychol. Rev.,* 1944, vol. 51, pp. 304-314; P. Bertocci, "The psychological self, the ego and personality," *Psychol. Rev.,* 1945, vol. 52, pp. 91-99.

5

Need, Frustration

and Conflict

IN ALL SOCIAL STRATA and in all phases of personality development each one of us must learn to cope repeatedly with frustrated need, with delay, thwarting and conflict. We have already sketched some of the difficulties human beings encounter in passing from the asocial behavior of the biological baby, through the complexities of childhood, domestic, neighborhood and school life, into adolescence and the biosocial maturity of full adulthood. But of course one's difficulties in conforming to the conditions of biosocial group living do not disappear when maturity is reached. Indeed they never disappear. Life's complexities seem always to exceed our immediate competence. Need and desire keep ever ahead of our behavioral resources as well as our economic ones. Throughout the successive phases of our life-span, new and different demands are continually arising that require us to develop or adapt new and different techniques with which to satisfy or circumvent them. And finally, when we have reached life's zenith, there lies right ahead of us the downward slope with its peculiar hardships, and death at the bottom.

We human beings have developed such a close-knit, interdependent social organization that we cannot escape for any long period of time the conditions out of which conflict and frustrated need arise. Each of us is impelled by the everyday conditions of his childhood to acquire special techniques enabling him to overcome, counterbalance or nullify, to evade or disown the countless difficulties that will not yield to simple head-on attack. We differ from one another in the effectiveness with which we use such techniques and in the degree of thwarting, delay and conflict we can tolerate before our techniques begin to trip us up. In behavior pathology we shall see how the chronic or progressive unskilled use of these special behavior techniques, under conditions of stress, may lead one only into new difficulties which turn out to be worse and more enduring than the original ones.

NEED AND SATISFACTION

At birth our structure is such that we at once develop needs which only the environment can satisfy. For a time these are purely biological in character, such as oxygen-need, the need for fluids and nutrition, needs to excrete and eliminate, needs for protection against drying, overheating and overcooling. Theoretically, such biological needs could be satisfied by automatic machinery which took care of each lack as it arose, thus in effect prolonging the characteristic features of life in the uterus. In practice, however, the satisfaction or removal of infant need always requires the help of older persons, and it is through the reactions of these other human beings to him that an infant becomes socialized. Before a child is many months old, nearly all of his need-satisfaction sequences show some important modification that can be related to his continued interaction with mother, father and siblings. Nor is this all. For as biosocial maturity progresses, every individual develops new needs and new satisfactions on the basis of new activities and new relationships. Throughout his life, as long as learning is possible, new need-satisfaction sequences will appear from time to time in every person's repertory of behavior.

The needs of a newborn baby determine its dependence upon the immediate environment for the maintenance or recovery of the biological equilibrium which constitutes living. The needs of an adult, on the other hand, express a dependence which has been conventionalized and elaborated through social influences, until the direct biological contributions have dwindled in importance and sometimes almost disappeared. The satisfaction of simple need gradually becomes a part of more extensive and more intricate biosocial modes of living, while other needs and other satisfactions arise which are sometimes more imperious than hunger and thirst. Men and women may choose to starve rather than abandon the satisfaction of certain acquired needs which their social training or individual idiosyncrasy has made prepotent in their behavior.

It is misleading to dismiss these socially determined needs as expressions of human instinct, as we used to do in psychopathology.

Cross-cultural studies show that needs develop differently in differently organized societies, and the techniques for satisfying them which are prescribed by one subculture may be proscribed by a neighboring one. Moreover in the behavior disorders there often arise highly individualistic need-satisfaction sequences which, notwithstanding their unique and socially invalid character, still motivate a patient to incredible effort and endurance. By this time it has become clear that, before proceeding further, we must define need and satisfaction in such a way as to include the biosocial behavior of children and adults, as well as the biological behavior of the newborn, and the reactions of abnormal persons as well as of normal ones.

With such ends in view, let us define *need* as *a condition of unstable or disturbed equilibrium in an organism's behavior, appearing typically as increased or protracted activity and tension.* Need may arise directly from a change in the organism's relationship with its environment, as when the surrounding temperature rises or drops considerably, or as a direct result of the organism's metabolic processes, as in hunger and thirst. It is also a common outcome of symbolic behavior — of talking, reading and thinking. Need is characteristic of all ongoing activity sequences, covert as well as overt.

In children and adults the increased or protracted activities and tensions of need may result directly in behavior which restores the organism to a condition of equilibrium, as for example in eating. We call the termination of need, when it is the outcome of such action, *direct satisfaction.* Need also terminates commonly through a shift in activity, through distraction by some new stimulation, or as the result of some learned substitution. The termination of need by such means we call *indirect* or *substitute satisfaction.* In the endless compromises demanded of every individual by the conditions and traditions of group living, indirect or substitute satisfaction plays a prominent role, whether the behavior involved be normal or abnormal.

Human adults, in particular, are prone to react in relation to certain need-satisfaction sequences with pleased, accepting or expansive behavior, immediately after or some time after the need has been satisfied. *This pleased, accepting or expansive after-reaction to a need-satisfaction sequence is what we mean by gratification.* Thus hunger is *need;* filling the stomach may terminate the need or *satisfy* it directly; while patting the abdomen, smiling, or commenting on the food, on the act of eating and on one's state of repletion, is the *gratification*. This after-reaction of gratification may, of course, appear when one has just eaten, and it may appear next day in recall, or next year or a score of years later.

We stop to make this distinction between *satisfaction*, as the termination of need, and *gratification* as an after-reaction, because gratification in human life is frequently more important than the need-satisfaction to which it is responsive. Talking, reading and thinking about appetite and eating, about thirst and drinking, about sex need and satisfaction, become ends in themselves to most individuals. This is one of the bases of the addiction to verbal recall we see in chronic raconteurs, and of the addiction to private fantasy we see in schizophrenia. Moreover, the after-reaction to a completed need-satisfaction sequence often undergoes a change in sign. One's after-reaction to need-satisfaction involving pain and hardship, for example, particularly if a long period of time has intervened, sometimes changes from one of disgust to one of wistful pleasure. Conversely, one may after-react to sexual need-satisfaction at the time with deep gratification, but weeks or years later the after-reaction to recall of the want may change to one of sorrow, chagrin or revulsion. The latter change is typical of anxious depressives and reformed sinners.

According to our definitions, even stumbling and itching precipitate simple but imperious needs. Their satisfaction would result in the one case from righting movements and in the other from scratching that stops the itch. In either situation gratification, as we have defined it, might or might not arise as a positive after-reaction to removal of the need. But we must remember that gratification may also appear as an after-reaction to the activity which originally achieved satisfaction or termination of the need. This is of especial importance in behavior pathology. Some compulsive patients, for example, become so seriously addicted to scratching as a source of satisfaction that their excoriations produce large areas of chronic, and sometimes severe, inflammatory skin reactions. Protection of the area from scratching usually results in rapid improvement, but unless the patient's needs are worked on, as well as his skin, the whole need-satisfaction cycle will start up again as soon as supervision flags.

Less dramatic than stumbling and itching, but of the same order of simple need, are the pressures, pulls and cramping involved in one's standing, sitting or lying in a fixed position. Obviously, direct satisfaction can be achieved through movement, or shift in tensions, which changes the pattern of stimulation and of vascular flow. Gratification may follow overtly in the form of grunts, grimaces or comments. Other simple needs arise when the skin temperature falls outside the optimal range, in either direction, when humidity and still air interfere with adequate percutaneous vaporization, and when the oxygen-carbon-dioxide balance is progressively disturbed. The organism under such conditions grows restless; the restlessness subsides when environmental circumstances change or the organism's relationship to them is readjusted.

Needs such as the foregoing often occur quite incidentally, in the course of some other activity or during sleep. Unless they are persistent or intense, their satisfaction usually does not interrupt or seriously modify a person's dominant ongoing behavior. The occurrence of organismic disequilibrium and the restoration of equilibrium, when these take place at a relatively automatic and incidental level, are popularly referred to as "unconscious" processes. This term denotes the same reactions that we have just been discussing. Unfortunately, however, it also carries ambiguous implications which have for centuries led students of behavior into metaphysical quicksands. We choose to discard the ambiguous label, "unconscious," because it confuses our problem, without in the least adding to our knowledge or increasing the adequacy of our explanatory principles. But while in the interest of scientific clarity we avoid this anachronism, we shall by no means neglect the many different genuine phenomena which in the past have been relegated to a supposed unconscious world of unreality.

Hunger and thirst

Hunger and thirst as simple needs, demanding for their direct satisfaction nothing more than the ingestion of food and drink, are seldom of direct importance in behavior pathology. In contrast, the complex biosocial needs which develop out of activities more or less indirectly related to hunger and thirst contribute significantly to the symptoms of behavior disorder. As we have seen, eating and drinking enter into a great many interpersonal relationships not directly dependent upon an empty stomach and a dry throat. In consequence, the mere ingestion of food and drink often will not satisfy an individual completely unless the associated social situation is also satisfying. If during a meal, for instance, something goes wrong with interpersonal relationships at the table, the common thing is for symptoms to appear which may easily be mistaken by everyone present as signs of digestive disorder, instead of signs of emotional disturbance. The source of this confusion lies, of course, in the dual domestic and community functions of the viscera. We need not any longer attempt to explain it away by falling back upon electrical metaphor, e.g., by postulating the "conversion" of an imaginary psychic force, energy or current into psychic dysfunction. Hunger and thirst are always behavioral events in a unitary biosocial field.

We have already seen how hunger, thirst and their satisfaction are complicated very early in life by the necessarily close mother-child contacts. The human nursling gets its first taste of social life with its first feeding. Through the intimacies of normal mothering there are gradually laid down the behavioral foundations of such derived but imperative needs as those for the company of others, for human approval and acceptance, for love and the esteem of others. A mother's nursing and body-care routines develop certain patterns of expectancy in her child, and these in part determine also the patterns of his later more general security and insecurity.

Weaning eventually terminates the intimate mother-child contacts of food-getting, but feeding still continues throughout childhood and adolescence to be one of the chief instruments of socialization. Nowhere else is the hierarchical status of a child in relation to other members of the family more clearly defined than at the meal table. At no other time of the day is the whole family simultaneously engaged in the same personal need-satisfaction activity, with everyone's moves open to the observation and comment of everyone else. The meal table in most homes is the chief place for interchanges of attitude and opinion on every conceivable subject. Mealtime is the occasion for making communal plans and decisions, and for dispensing permissions and denials of importance to the young.

The variety of personal interactions at mealtime has this important effect on childhood, that the satisfaction of hunger and thirst gets inevitably tied up with family loyalties and family strife, with reactions of gratitude, resentment, submission and aversion not logically related to eating and drinking, and even with abstract notions of good and evil, of right and wrong. None of these socially important reactions is originally a necessary part of simple hunger and thirst or of their direct biological satisfaction. But the temporal and spatial juxtaposition is quite sufficient to establish an effective acquired relationship. For example, a child may be banished from the table and excluded from participation in the family life as punishment for misbehavior in any field. Eating may thus come to symbolize acceptance and approval; only the worthy may partake. This symbolic connotation is gradually expanded to include other individuals. Asking an outsider to eat with the family is, for example, a far greater mark of acceptance and approval than merely asking him into one's house. Similar value often attaches to the giving and receiving of food as a present. Food and drink, eating and drinking, in these ways develop derived meanings and raise or satisfy derived needs that sometimes become even more fundamental to the biosocial welfare of the individual than adequate diet and fluid intake.

Hunger and eating also enter into a great deal of religious thinking, writing and practice. There are feast days and fast days, days for meat and days for fish, sacred animals and unclean animals which even the starving must not eat. The preparation of food, who prepares it and who serves it, the order in which it can be eaten, and even how it is taken into the mouth, are the subjects of stringent religious regulations.

Our modern languages are rich in metaphors concerning hunger and thirst which relate these needs and their satisfactions directly to the most sacred rituals and beliefs. Folklore, mythology and children's fairy tales are saturated with magical and superstitious incidents that link eating with sudden growth or shrinkage, with the loss or acquisition of strength, beauty and miraculous powers, with impregnation, changes in fertility or in sex, and with a multitude of other metamorphoses. Considering all this personal and cultural background, it should surprise no one to learn that eating, drinking and their actual or imagined consequences form the nucleus for so much of the common symptomatology of the behavior disorders.

To all the foregoing sources of possible behavior confusion must be added this fact, that the mouth is used in activities unrelated to actual eating. The mouth in all mammals is an important instrument of examination, manipulation and attack. These uses appear in the behavior of little children as well as animals in the form of mouthing, licking and biting inedible objects and in advances to or assaults upon others. In the behavior of older children and adults these uses appear chiefly in the symbolic forms of grimacing, kissing and speech.

Some of the gestures and grimaces that regularly go with words of contempt, aversion and revulsion, for example, leave no doubt as to the relationship between the symbolic rejection of persons or opinions and the direct rejection of food. In kissing, the mouth plays an essential role with us in denoting social acceptance, affection or sexual attraction. Our language is full of ambiguous allusions to social acceptance and rejection, to verbal and dental assault, to the gastric need for food and the spiritual need for sustenance. Thus, we eat our words and swallow our wrath, the Lord spews us forth, we sink our teeth into a problem, drink in a message, find an explanation indigestible and reject it with biting comments. When a human being, with all these verbal ambiguities in his behavior becomes confused, he often acts out as social operations what were intended to be only verbal metaphors.[1]

Such examples of the cultural and individual elaboration of complex need-habits from simple hunger and thirst illustrate a fact of basic, general significance for behavior pathology. Human beings regularly utilize the techniques they develop in satisfying biological need directly, for biosocial ends that are only remotely or symbolically related to the need. We have in this fact a key to the origins and meanings of a great many otherwise obscure and unintelligible symptoms. Although pathological symbolization tends to be more individualistic than normal, and is occasionally unique for a given patient, it more frequently follows some well-known aberrant path. These symbols are not fixed in a "racial unconscious," as the older writers insisted, but tend to develop along certain lines because human beings are anatomically and physiologically similar, and because all persons in a given culture must share the same societal organization and encounter their difficulties under similar circumstances.

Thus, loss of appetite in hysteria and depression often represents the moral rejection of something other than food, or functions as self-punishment and self-rejection because of sin. In schizophrenia

[1] W. Muncie, "The psychopathology of metaphor," *Arch. Neurol. Psychiat.*, 1937, vol. 37, pp. 796-804.

eating is sometimes confused with delusions of body change or impregnation, with sex conflicts, and with sanctification or messianic
status. Schizophrenics are not rare who must be continually drinking water to quench internal fires and purify themselves. To understand such syndromes we must be able to see that our cultural traditions, the structure of our contemporary society, and the conventional uses of language all conspire to equate our need-satisfaction sequences to one another. They all tend to bring together logically unrelated matters, by inference, allusion, metaphor and alle-
gory, and in such intricate ways that even the normal person can
easily become confused.

Sex need and satisfaction

One of the greatest achievements of twentieth-century psychiatry
has been its frank recognition that sex need and frustration play a
pre-eminent role in neuroses and psychoses. Thanks largely to the
psychoanalytic revolt, around the turn of the century, the task confronting us today is no longer one of demonstrating this fact. It is
now rather one of so broadening the base of behavior pathology
that we do justice to the multiplicity of factors leading to and perpetuating behavior disorders. There are, however, certain peculiarities of sex need and sex satisfaction which, under the conditions
imposed by group living in our society, help to explain the role of
sex in behavior pathology.

In the first place, direct sex satisfaction, unlike the satisfaction of
hunger and thirst, can be delayed for months and years or even
permanently denied without leading necessarily to death of the
organism. The physiology of sex thus permits arbitrary thwarting
and modifications of sex behavior in ways and to degrees biologically impossible in the case of hunger and thirst. A further unique
characteristic of sex activity is that, whereas direct and indirect
erotic stimulation can occur from early infancy onward, adequate
heterosexual reactions are for several years genitally impossible and
for several more years socially prohibited. These conditions of
delay, thwarting and conflict, appearing intermittently over a period
of years, are the very ones to induce substitutive tension-reduction
by the usual learning processes. This situation helps to explain the
variety of objects, situations and acts which may function in different individuals as substitutes or symbols in relation to sex need,
satisfaction and gratification.

Infants, children, adolescents and adults under conditions of privation learn to gain reduction in sex tension through non-sexual activities with varying degrees of success in different individuals and at different ages. They learn also to give sex reactions to originally non-sexual objects, to derive sex satisfaction in relation to these and develop after-reactions of sex gratification both to originally non-sexual objects and to non-sexual activities. Many substitute objects and activities are culturally determined and socially recognized as legitimate sex surrogates or symbols, either openly or by tacit consent. Many others which may be the outcome of incidental learning are socially prohibited or scorned. Even in the latter instance, however, there is considerable uniformity among the taboo sex activities (*perversions*) and the socially inacceptable sex excitants (*fetishes*). This is undoubtedly attributable to the relative uniformity of human structure and of social organization.

We need not, of course, conclude that sex behavior is socially controlled or prohibited only because control and prohibition are biologically feasible. Neither need we ascribe sex regulation, as some unhappy writers do, to the malignant envy of aged lawgivers. There are other and more cogent reasons. One is the important fact that normal sex satisfaction involves the reciprocal sex behavior of two persons, and the weaker of the two is also the one who alone must take the biological consequences of sex satisfaction, in pregnancy and childbirth. Sex need and satisfaction have this other unique distinction, that they may lead to the production of new individuals. The community, which has the job of assigning responsibility for the care of offspring to their presumptive parents, assumes the right to control the situations and activities most likely to end in procreative behavior and parenthood.

Another common outcome of human sex behavior is frequently overlooked. Out of the processes of mating and procreation, unexpectedly powerful reactions of possessiveness and jealousy may emerge which have potentialities for both good and evil in human society. Difficulties arise when the participants in sex relations do not anticipate such an outcome. Sometimes, when they encounter it in themselves, they tend to regard the whole liaison with superstitious awe. In one of our cases a fantastic delusional explanation was evolved by the patient in an attempt to account verbally for just such an unpredicted attachment.

> The patient was an unmarried graduate student, at a men's university, who had been trained by a scholarly father to take great

pride in developing reason and strength of character. He suddenly found himself falling irresistibly in love with a domestic employee of little education or personal charm. This situation, in the light of his own background and his well-laid plans for a career, was completely inexplicable to him. For it not only contradicted his most unshakable principles, but violated his conception of himself as strong-willed and superior. He confided his discovery to no one, but pondered over it constantly when he was alone.

After several weeks of solitary struggle and perplexity during which, however, he continued the clandestine affair he had begun, the patient decided that the girl must be using some special technique to break down his strength of mind so that she could prevail over him. His first hypothesis was that she might be practicing hypnotism or telepathy, and he read up on these topics in the college library. But even with the closest observation of her behavior when they were together he could find nothing to support this view. The patient next suspected that the girl was drugging him — with aphrodisiacs to arouse him and with opiates to weaken his will and make him, as an habitué, dependent upon her. Since she certainly had easy access to the kitchen from which he was served, he stopped eating at his club and took his meals at a restaurant.

When the patient found that the girl seemed rather to gain than to lose in power over him under these circumstances, he finally concluded that he was being overwhelmed by a supernatural influence. With the help of some readings he had once done in mythology, he constructed the hypothesis in his fantasy that she was in reality a goddess in disguise, the daughter of the moon, who was irresistible by virtue of her origin. To her he now considered himself dedicated and mystically married; she was henceforth, he told her, to go by his name and he by hers. This solution enabled the patient to preserve the fiction of his own strength of character and superior reason, since he had been vanquished only by a superhuman power. Unfortunately it also precipitated him into an acute excitement that lasted three months, and included auditory and visual hallucinatory behavior, bizarre delusions of extra-mundane influence, and semireligious rituals which had to do with death and rebirth. Under competently planned psychiatric therapy he made a good recovery without, however, gaining any apparent recognition of the personal significance of his illness.

Infancy and childhood. Among lower mammals, long before their sexual maturity, sex play and sex self-stimulation appear as incidents in general play and general self-stimulation. Toward maturity full heterosexual activity is established and this eventually leads to procreation. The development of human sex behavior, at least in our society, is never allowed to be as casual as this. Adults take pains to avoid sex stimulation of the young. Infants and children are permitted to play with practically all other parts of their own or another's body except the perineal structures. Against touching, examining or talking about the genitals our society imposes the strictest of taboos, and these are usually enforced with greater insistence and a stronger show of adult emotion than in the case of other taboos.

Eliminative activities and their products fall under a ban early in life which is often no less strict, although as a rule less emotionally enforced. This fact, together with the close anatomical relationships of genitals, urethra and anus, help to set the stage for the confusions that both children and adults exhibit in their attitudes toward sexual and eliminative functions. We know that even in infancy stimulation of perineal areas may arouse generalized adient responses not unlike the non-specific sexual responses which adults give to similar arousal. Let us not overlook the fact, either, that from earliest infancy onward the genitalia normally participate in many tension states which are not primarily sexual. Halverson, for example, in a series of well-controlled studies that were not designed to support or prove any theory, has demonstrated for the male that tension during nursing quite commonly includes unmistakable genital responses.[2] Erections are also normal results of bladder distention in male infants. Clinicians have long been familiar with similar reactions in non-sexual excitement and anxiety of children, adolescents and adults.

In addition to the factor of anatomical proximity, the social conditions under which the average child in our culture must develop his own sex orientation can hardly fail to confuse him. He is trained almost from the start not to give social reactions that call attention to sexual and eliminative structures or functions, and not to appear interested in them himself. He must begin to learn inhibition, substitution and repression in sexual as in other behavior long before he has acquired language habits adequate to formulate what it is that he is inhibiting, substituting or repressing, and even before he can grasp what his elders are requiring of him and why.

Infants and little children cannot possibly understand the com-

2 H. Halverson, "Genital and sphincter behavior of the male infant," *Jour. Genetic Psychol.*, 1940, vol. 56, pp. 95-136.

plex implications of sex functions in adulthood, nor in any logical way relate their own forbidden and punished experiments to adult sexuality, which of course their parents cannot help doing. In other words, adult and child do not really have a common basis for mutual understanding in this field, unless the adult can learn to take the child's role in his imagination and see things from a child's perspective, since the reverse is impossible early in life.

Those who have studied child behavior without prejudice find that interest in and curiosity about sex differences and their meaning have the same general sources and significance that interest and curiosity have in relation to other childhood observations or discoveries. Difficulties in childhood seem to arise chiefly because of adult sex attitudes, because, for example, free discussion of sex topics is often absolutely taboo, the average parent tolerating only euphemisms and circumlocutory allusions to sexual matters in the child. Of course taboo and secrecy rarely, if ever, abolish interest and curiosity in sex or in anything else. The likelihood is greater that the emphasis his elders place upon the forbidden, and their peculiarly furtive behavior in relation to it, will actually single out sex for the child's very special attention.

In the ordinary course of events a child's interest and curiosity concerning sex phenomena will naturally encourage investigation, a child's investigations will sooner or later lead to adult discovery, and adult discovery not infrequently precipitates adult panic. The following case illustrates the way in which a prudish adult can blow up a morning's incident into a neighborhood scandal.

> A five-year-old girl, who had become reasonably adroit in dressing and undressing dolls, exercised her skill in company with another little girl, aged four, by undressing a two-year-old boy left in their keeping. Just as the girls had discovered the little boy's genitals, which were evidently a surprise to them, the mother of the five-year-old arrived unexpectedly upon the scene.
>
> From the standpoint of the neighborhood community, the situation in which this mother found herself was unquestionably a delicate one. Unfortunately for everyone concerned she completely lost her head. As she dressed the little boy, her hands shook so that she could scarcely button him up, and she managed to infect all three children with her own anxiety. Back home she whipped her own child severely and angrily, then locked her alone in a room and fled to a neighbor's house. Here she related the incident so that it sounded like life in a brothel, she wept uncontrollably and declared

over and over that her daughter would grow up to be a bad woman.
The mother in this situation stood in greater need of sex reorientation than her daughter. For it was she who was reading unconscious venery and lascivious intent into a simple and common childhood event. It is evidently as difficult for many sexually sophisticated adults to grasp the limited significance of a small child's sex
adventures as it is for the child to comprehend the ramifications of
adult sexuality.

The incident just cited could have been utilized by the mothers
of both girls as a convenient occasion for giving each child, in the
privacy of her home, a chance to talk over her discovery without
fear or shame. For the neighborhood association of older with
younger children, and the mingling of boys and girls in school and
play, are certain to raise sex problems at one level or another,
whether parents find out about them or not. Naturally, the child
who shares an unfrightened, unashamed parent's confidence can
more easily weather the inevitable little crises of discovery and
surprise, and benefit from them, than the child of guilty, punitive
parents whose anger and anxiety are as likely to fascinate as they
are to frighten and alienate him.[3]
There is good reason to believe that the unplanned but effective
conspiracy in our culture, against even the most private free communication on sex topics, is an important source of sex confusion
in behavior pathology. For the child, free casual discussions with a
judicious, informed adult are almost the only means he has for acquiring a wholesome orientation toward activities from which he is
excluded. Adults sometimes try to make up for their own deficiencies by giving the child or adolescent some reading material on sex,
or by leaving something lying open for him to find and read in
secret. But the immature person's need is not primarily a need for
the information which a text and pictures can provide. He needs
much more the chance to formulate his own interpretations and
misunderstandings, to exchange perspectives regarding sex behavior
with a biosocially mature, responsible person.
In contemporary American society, the average adult is himself
still too easily embarrassed by a child's sudden sex queries to be

[3] Contrast, for example, the technique used in handling the same kind of
situation, arising among siblings in the home, as reported by M. Montagu,
"The acquisition of sexual knowledge in children," *Amer. Jour. Orthopsychiatry*, 1945, vol. 15, pp. 290-300.

able to receive them casually and answer them effectively. An adult's averse and furtive attitudes not only deprive children of opportunities to share verbally in more mature perspectives, but tend also to train them in secretive attitudes toward sex functions. Most children are left to build up their own sex orientation, as best they can, on the basis of the half-truths and skewed interpretations furnished by older companions who are less inhibited, as well as less informed, than the average parent. The upshot of most importance to the behavior pathologist is that sex attitudes, because they are commonly developed on the basis of juvenile misinformation and distortion, and because they are rarely exposed to the maturing influence of serious discussion, are as a rule more socially immature and less realistic when puberty is reached than any other biosocial attitudes of comparable importance.

The revolt of behavior pathologists in the late nineteenth and early twentieth centuries against the prevailing hypocritical sex pruderies led, not unnaturally, to an equally overdetermined insistence that everything in human life can be reduced to sex. It is quite true that, as the normal infant grows into childhood, he develops social behavior toward those who look after him and are a great deal with him which resembles some of the reactions of adults in love. Thus a young child may grow restless, agitated or disconsolate when a parent leaves him, and show great joy upon the parent's return. He may exhibit unreasonable jealousy when others try to share his mother's affection, for example, or when they divert her attention from him. A child may even turn the tables on his parents by learning to stimulate their jealousy deliberately, and to control them by withholding his affection from them when they displease him. The manifestations of affection on the part of infant and child are not greatly different from those of adult heterosexual affection and we have yet to work out satisfactorily the genetic relationships between infantile filial affection and the sexual behavior of adolescents and adults.

Unfortunately the early behavior pathologists, in their eagerness to get ahead with the task of reformulating sex development in more realistic terms, tried to proceed by simply translating the facts of early affectional relationships freely into the language of full adult sexuality, with all the old connotations still intact. Thus, for example, they attributed intent and desire, expressed in terms of adult incestuous relations, to infants and young children who, as a matter of fact, are neither mature enough biologically nor socially resourceful enough to contemplate incest as such. The average infant is indeed more completely dependent upon his parent or parent surrogate than the average adult is upon his mate. But this does not make infant love a form of incest, any more than emotional dependence upon one's mate makes adult love therefore puerile. Among biosocially mature adults one can find behavior comparable to the behavior of dependent infants and children, in many different dependent relationships, that can be called sexual only if we are to call everything sexual.

Similar defects in methodology and the same theoretical preconceptions have helped materially to fog the contemporary psychiatric picture of maternal love. It is, of course, a matter of common observation that maternal care like adult sexuality includes caressing, embracing, affectionate attitudes and words, and deep emotional preferences and prejudices. The loving mother's general behavior toward her infant is indeed similar in many ways to her general behavior toward her loved husband, and decidedly unlike her behavior toward persons outside the family. But this justifies neither one's jumping to the conclusion that these are one and the same phenomenon, nor one's going on the defensive when such confused thinking is questioned.

It is important for the behavior pathologist of today to keep two simple distinctions clearly before him. One is that, in spite of many superficial resemblances, a mother's attitudes toward her infant are not *identical* with those she has toward her husband, any more than her marital and her maternal relations are identical. The other is that her infant's reactions to her, in spite of obvious similarities, are not *identical* with the sex conduct of adults. Infantile sexuality is related to adult sexuality in about the same sense that nursing at the breast is related to an adult dinner date. Both involve certain similar needs and similar satisfactions, but the biological operations and the social implications for those participating in each are clearly not the same. These statements cannot possibly seem more self-evident and trite to the critical reader than they do to the writer. Yet even a casual inspection of the current literature will convince anyone that they still need reiteration.[4]

Adolescence and adulthood. Around puberty, and during early

[4] See the account given by O. Fenichel, *The Psychoanalytic Theory of Neurosis* (New York: Norton, 1945), pp. 54-62.

adolescence, we find many examples of strikingly jealous and possessive attachments developing between like-sexed peers, and a
great many cases of hero-worship or intense affection for like-sexed
older persons. As we have already mentioned, these close affectional companionships and "crushes" are believed to play an important role in emancipating children from too great emotional dependence upon parents. They give a child practice in developing amatory role-taking behavior in relation to persons outside the
family circle and toward persons in his own age group. They prepare the way in behavior for heterosexual peer attachments.

In some contemporary theories a great deal is made of the fact
that chums and the objects of hero-worship are usually of the
child's own sex, and of the slim but positive indications that occasional cases of adult homosexuality appear to grow out of such
comradeships and attachments. It is quite widely held, for instance, that like-sexed "crushes" are part of a universal and inevitable stage in personality growth, and the proponents of this view
have named the stage the "homosexual phase of psychosexual development." Its opponents maintain, on the other hand, that like-
sexed attachments and chumships are an incidental product of our
social organization and not an inevitable phase of sex maturation
in the human being. They assert that in situations where boys and
girls are neither ridiculed by other children nor rebuked by their
elders for doing so, they form close chum and "crush" attachments
toward individuals of the opposite sex during prepubescence,
pubescence and early adolescence. The question must be regarded
as still unanswered.

The acceleration in biosocial maturing during adolescence is in
part the result of inescapable social pressures that lead each growing individual to begin adopting some of the adult behavior prescribed for his sex in his society. With these pressures, and the concomitant biological changes, many sex problems which had been
taken care of in earlier childhood, through simple restrictive-per-
missive training, now reappear in a new social context and with
new vigor. In place of the simpler sex curiosity of infant and child,
we find our adolescent making serious attempts at interpreting
adult sex roles in terms of his own peer culture. Thus, for example,
young adolescents in mixed groups engage in banter, loud talk,
giggling and display. They deliberately accentuate sex differences
in conduct and costume. They give inexpert but unmistakable exhibitions of coyness and pursuit.

These maneuvers are the human socialized counterparts of the simple immature sex play of pubescent lower mammals. Despite the fact that the gauche sparring and fencing of the adolescent bring annoyance and anxiety to adults, they are part of an essential process in the biosocial development from normal childhood to normal adulthood. Through acting out the social role of amatory boy or girl in real-life situations, the adolescent learns gradually to take more and more mature and realistic heterosexual attitudes. He acquires skill and ease in face-to-face encounters with his opposite-sexed peers, thus unintentionally gaining techniques he will use in serious love-making later on.

Such adolescent role-taking entails serious risks and its principals often stand in need of more wise counsel and unobtrusive guidance than they want or can get. But this is true of any significant behavior at any period of life. Who can say that a little child may not suffer serious or fatal injury during his neighborhood explorations, or that an adult in learning to operate an industrial machine will not be maimed or killed? The difficulty, as the behavior pathologist sees it, is that when we keep a child forever in the house, and when we frighten an adolescent away from other adolescents or hold his clumsy maneuvers up to public ridicule, we run the serious risk of producing a half-developed, socially inadequate and usually unhappy person in adulthood.

By the time adulthood is reached, a person's sex needs and satisfactions have undergone innumerable modifications in directions prescribed by his social environment and cultural heritage. All sex behavior in our society is supposed to be oriented toward marriage and family formation. Sex physiology becomes the physiology of marriage and sex handbooks are called marriage manuals. Sex need and satisfaction must be justified in accordance with civil codes or sanctified by religious formulae. The family, which the human being organizes around the lawful satisfaction of recurrent sex need, has been made in its turn the basic unit out of which our socio-economic structure is built.

Behavior pathology naturally shows the same intricate confusions of sex problems with social, economic, ethical and religious problems that our everyday society shows. This is the general setting in which adult and adolescent sexuality must be understood and its ramifications in the behavior disorders evaluated. Legal and extra-legal sex satisfaction is a social and economic problem as well as a biological, ethical and religious one. Our marital customs, traditions and mores cannot be divorced from questions of wages, living costs, housing, industrial organization and social security. Each is interacting with the others all the time. When the depressed, hysterical, paranoid or schizophrenic patient mingles sexual, procreative and business fears or ambitions in one behavioral conglomerate, he is only doing in a more ineffectual way what all of us do normally in a somewhat more organized way, in our daily talk and thinking.

The typical domestic organization of the family unit, in our society, brings these different need-satisfaction sequences together under a single roof. Home is the place where hunger is satisfied, where the body is warmed, cleansed and clothed, where security, approval, acceptance and personal significance, as well as sex satisfaction, are sought. Thus, sex problems and pleasures are brought into effective behavioral relationship with other problems and pleasures through the establishment of a common locus of habitual satisfaction-seeking operations in the home.

Sex customs, codes, teachings and ideals have for ages participated in the evolution and practice of religious and other ethical systems. Religious confusions, exaggerations and distortions are so familiar as symptoms of behavior disorder that everyone — layman, jurist, religious worker and behavior pathologist — is impressed by the relationship. Sometimes religious preoccupations seem to precipitate an acute disturbance; more often they appear as a conspicuous but etiologically incidental part of a general emotional upheaval. They frequently constitute a compensatory reaction, for some galling sense of guilt or personal inconsequentiality, which seems to promise absolution or personal significance but at the high cost to someone of further deviant behavior. What has proved especially perplexing to all concerned is the very frequent confusion of sex with religious behavior in neuroses and psychoses. It has led some theorists to attempt the exercise of reducing all religion to sex, but this has proved no more enlightening than parallel attempts to reduce all sex to religion.

The patient's confusion of sex with religion must have many sources in normal social behavior. One of these has already been mentioned, the interpenetration of religious belief and practices with marriage, sex relationships, conception, pregnancy, childbirth, parenthood and the sex instruction of children. Another is the objective similarity between culturally endorsed attitudes in different love situations, such as the striking parallels in verbal and postural behavior between religious devotion, strong filial devotion and normal adult love. It is also quite common among some contemporary religious sects for devotees to develop habitual attitudes of possessiveness, favoritism, publicly avowed jealousy, blind faith, intolerance of all opposition or disagreement from other persons and, in some individuals, deep and reverent preoccupation with fantasies of an object of devotion. These attitudes are also found in deep normal marital, parental and filial affection.

The significant fact here for the student of behavior disorder is that *the similarity or partial identity of attitude organization,* with respect to one's beloved, one's parents and one's religious objects, lies at the bottom of the confusion between these love excitants. In other words, the similarity or partial identity of a person's love reactions to different objects relates these objects to one another in behavior. For the seriously anxious, perplexed or disoriented individual this may and does lead to their becoming not only equivalent for him but identical. For example, a biosocially immature and ineffectual adolescent, growing apprehensive and confused over parental and filial relationships, and his own uncertain heterosexual future, may easily include less specific ethical and religious conflicts in his sexual bewilderment. He may try to overcome all of his emotional confusion at once through incorporating them in penitential or propitiatory ritual, or in ecstatic contemplation for which he is ill-prepared. The anxious, guilty and overscrupulous adult may react similarly when he is exposed to stresses that call for greater personal resources than he can muster.

Pain and punishment in behavior pathology

The needs to inflict and to suffer pain or punishment occupy a place of special prominence in modern behavior pathology. Indeed, it is a common observation with all of us that many apparently normal as well as abnormal persons seem to welcome and seek suffering themselves, or derive obvious satisfaction from the pain or punishment of others. Inflicting or enduring suffering in such individuals has for one reason or another become an essential condition for the fulfillment of some imperious need. *The insistent need to inflict pain, punishment, domination and restraint upon others* we call *sadism,* and *the reciprocal need to suffer these* we call *masochism*.[5] Frequently both needs are present to a marked degree in the same person, as when satisfaction demands self-inflicted punishment, and this is termed *sadomasochism*.

The origins and significance of sadism and masochism still pose unsettled problems. Early workers in the field were struck by the unmistakably sexual character of these trends in their patients, and concluded that both were simply exaggerations of a "sexual instinct." It is true that the reciprocal infliction and acceptance of domination, restraint and pain are normal events in heterosexual relations, among subhuman as well as human species. Sex initiative and aggression being the biological prerogatives of the male mammal, and luring and submission those of the female, we should expect to find in the human species a relatively greater tendency toward sadism among normal men and a relatively greater tendency toward masochism among normal women. And so we do.[6] Nevertheless, there is still a large enough minority in each sex with opposite trends to indicate that sadism and masochism, even if we consider them as no more than modified sex behavior, rest upon greater complexity than simple exaggeration of the sex trends which man shares with other mammals.

Actually, in the sex relationships of subhuman mammals, where social regulation is minimal and cultural tradition virtually absent, we still find that courting and mating behavior does not present us with a simple, clear-cut pattern of male ascendance and female submission either. Maslow has reported, for example, that within the larger sex role the normal infra-human female primate performs limited acts of initiative and aggression while the male, for the time being, plays a reciprocal passive or submissive part.[7] We may infer from this that some of the contradictory trends in human courting and mating represent normal primate sex behavior. But beyond this, the human male-female relationship is enormously compli-

---

[5] K. Menninger, *Man Against Himself*. New York: Harcourt Brace, 1938; T. Reik, *Masochism in Modern Man*. New York: Farrar and Rinehart, 1941.

[6] G. Hamilton, *A Research in Marriage* (New York: Boni, 1929), pp. 444-474.

[7] A. Maslow, "The role of dominance in the social and sexual behavior of infra-human primates; I. Observations at Vilas Park Zoo," *Jour. Genetic Psychol.*, 1936, vol. 48, pp. 261-277; A. Maslow and S. Flanzbaum, "II. An experimental determination of the behavior syndrome of dominance," *Jour. Genetic Psychol.*, 1936, vol. 48, pp. 278-309; A. Maslow, "III. A theory of sexual behavior of infra-human primates," *Jour. Genetic Psychol.*, 1936, vol. 48, pp. 310-338.

cated by social regulations, cultural transmission and self-reactions that are foreign to infra-human species.

Among the many sources of maladjustive behavior in this area are certain special characteristics of our culture that deserve to be pointed up here. One of these is the disproportionate emphasis which our culture places upon the preliminaries in courting behavior, as contrasted with the severe taboos it imposes against mention or portrayal of the consummatory sex act. Socially approved literature and plays, social affairs, public and private discussions all reflect the same exaggerated preoccupation with the biologically incidental aspects of sex behavior. Consequently, quite early in life the relationships implied in domination, restraint and pain become familiar themes as part of romantic love and marriage. For the male a further source of confusion lies in the cultural tradition, still alive in western society, of the sacred, worshipful woman who to be won must be indulged.

For both sexes there is the childhood training in submission to a mother or a father which in many engenders strongly ambivalent emotional reactions, and in a few develops the need to enter into relationships with other persons which duplicate those suffered under the parental roof. We know that parental as well as child attitudes tend unwittingly to confuse sin, sex and punishment — goodness, love and reward — during these long years of intimate interaction. We know also that sexual excitement at least occasionally participates in the general excitement of punishment and reward, both when the child is on the giving and on the receiving end. Indeed, it is not rare for unwelcome sex excitement to occur during adolescence in non-sexual anxiety situations, such as that of writing a difficult examination.

We should be deceiving ourselves, however, if we were led by the predilections of early workers in this field to conclude that every need to punish or be punished must without exception be sexual in origin and significance. Almost any successful aggression, including sex aggression, means domination, restraint or pain for someone, while almost any submission, including sex submission, may involve its acceptance. It is a commonplace that people suffering from severe guilt, remorse, sorrow or sustained tension of any kind frequently seek and welcome punishment because it brings them at least temporary relief.

Painful punishment can perform this somewhat paradoxical function for several reasons. For one thing, reactions to pain may directly break up intolerably sustained tension patterns and substitute for them simpler tensions that are more easily terminated. For another, children and adults in our society learn over and over in the normal parent-child relationship, the sin-punishment-forgiveness sequence. They learn it under such conditions that pain-following-wrongdoing brings them peace, restitution of their lost status with others, and the consequent dissolution of guilt and anxiety tensions. Once they have paid for evil in this way they are no longer expected to maintain a high level of remorse. These sequences of need-satisfaction are found not only in established religious practice; they also form the basis of our current philosophy of crime and punishment. However absurd and inequitable the administration of this system may be in fact, it is still based theoretically upon the attempt to find formulae, in terms of sin and suffering, which will make their sum equal to zero.

We shall encounter many examples of sadism and masochism among the specific behavior disorders. Some hypochondriacal and depressive patients are remarkably successful in controlling and punishing relatives through their unplanned utilization of symptoms as retaliation. Even suicide is not infrequently a spite reaction, a grim enactment of the childhood fantasy, "They'll be sorry when I'm dead!" Suicide is sometimes self-retributive in function. In ordinary suicide, pain may be stoically endured as a necessary means but it is not courted. However, in certain cases, suicide notes and dying testimony make it clear that the suffering is as much sought after as the death.

We sometimes find that the complaints of hypochondriacal, chronically fatigued and hysterical patients are not weakened or changed in their specific reference by diagnostic procedures and treatment which include serious discomfort and restriction of activities, loss of independence and even outright pain. This situation is often interpreted as the result of masochistic trends which the patient may or may not recognize. Perhaps the most clear-cut examples of sadomasochism are those appearing in the compulsive disorders. Some patients exhibit frank gratification over self-revenge, or openly enjoy pain and submission if pain and submission mean expiation to them.

Cruel and sometimes dangerous self-mutilation, without apparent suicidal intent, occurs in hysteria, schizophrenia and remorseful depressions. The patient may incise, burn, crush or even amputate a part of his body to satisfy a frequently acknowledged need for punishment or martyrdom. Occasionally the act is carried out so deliberately, and with so little evidence of pain, that topical anesthesia is suggested. In psychiatric hospitals such events are sufficiently common to merit special investigation of the immediate behavior pathology. But as a rule the state of emergency involved tends to crowd scientific curiosity into the background until the opportunity has passed.

Primary and derived needs

It is customary in the literature to equate the term "primary need" with physiological disequilibrium, particularly in the case of hunger, thirst and sex. All other needs are then called "secondary" or "derived." The difficulty with this distinction, which at first glance seems reasonable and promising, is that for the human being it cannot in actual practice be maintained. The so-called primary needs of hunger and thirst are, as we have seen, profoundly modified in earliest childhood, and they rarely operate thereafter in uncomplicated relationships. In the dozen years of social learning that elapse between birth and puberty, sex attitudes and responses likewise become so entangled with and modified by a multitude of other need-satisfaction sequences as to render the designation "primary sex need" no more than a misleading fiction. In short, we need not and we cannot in behavior pathology distinguish a group of needs, whose determination is purely physiological, from another group whose determination is purely social. All needs of importance to behavior pathology are wholly or in large part socially derived and all are physiologically grounded.

We cannot dodge this difficulty by calling those needs "primary" which seem prepotent in behavior. For in normal as well as in abnormal reactions, we continually meet with situations in which such obviously learned needs as those for social or economic security, for approval and acceptance, for human company, for prestige and for esteem actually crowd out hunger, thirst and sex-need. Indeed, the individual variations in need prepotency from person to person, and in the same person from time to time, tend to make the question of need-satisfaction supremacy an individual and a temporal matter, rather than a fixed and universal principle.

The task of listing the names for human needs, like that of nam-

ing adult emotions and adult traits,[8] is one which should be dele-
gated to the professional lexicographer. Almost any new activity
or interest may engender a new imperious need and result in new
ways of satisfying it. The very behavior by means of which we
satisfy one need is quite capable of developing other needs that
also demand satisfaction. A man, for example, on the basis of sex
attraction chooses to sacrifice his relative freedom of action and
marry. Before long he discovers to his surprise that home life, and
the presence there of the woman he has married, have grown as
necessary to him as sex satisfaction itself.

In lesser things it is the same. We learn to work at something
new, and after a while we find that without this work we soon grow
restless and bored.[9] We learn to play golf or to bowl, and golfing
or bowling becomes essential to us. Whatever the patterns of living we acquire, they develop needs compelling our adherence to
them, or they motivate us to go on and engage in new activities
which, in turn, satisfy the new needs arising in our acquired behavior patterns. The study of everyday need-satisfaction relationships thus compenetrates the whole field of human behavior, and
the study of their unusual deviations and ineffectualities takes us
into every corner of behavior pathology.

MOTIVE AND MOTIVATION

During the past hundred years there has developed a progressive shift of emphasis, in the abnormal field, from behavior description and the cataloguing of symptoms to behavior analysis and the
formulation of motive. Today it is a fundamental tenet of behavior pathology that all organized reactions are motivated. By this
we simply mean that, if all behavior could be analyzed completely,
we would be able to identify the significant factor or factors responsible for sustaining and determining as well as instigating
every organized act. *Motive is a product of behavior analysis.* In
practice we designate, as motive, *whatever factor seems to be of
special significance in the instigation of a given need-satisfaction
sequence, in sustaining such a sequence and in determining its
course and its outcome.*

[8] Compare for example G. Allport and H. Odbert, "Trait names: a psycho-
lexical study," *Psychol. Monog.*, 1936, vol. 47, No. 211.
[9] G. Allport discusses this relationship as "functional autonomy" in *Personality, a Psychological Interpretation* (New York: Holt, 1937), pp. 191-207.

It would be a serious mistake if we were to continue deluding ourselves into thinking of motives as "forces" or "energies" somehow added to behavior, like ethyl lead added to gasoline. Motive and motivation are simply verbal designations that result from our own operations in analyzing behavior. Nor should we expect to find human motives in our field isolated, sorted out and tagged like objects after inventory. At those levels of behavior complexity which have any meaning for neuroses and psychoses, motivation is nearly always multiple. Very commonly motivation is also obscured or changed in some way through the special adjustive techniques of defense and escape which all of us develop to some degree in the face of frustration or threat.

In everyday normal life, for example, a woman may eat simply because she is hungry. But whether hungry or not she may eat as a duty, because she is pregnant or must fortify herself for some anticipated ordeal. She may eat merely to be included in a certain social group or because at the time she feels neglected and dissatisfied. It is conceivable that all of these factors might operate together in determining such an apparently simple decision as one of eating a good lunch.

Sex relations usually have multiple motivation also. Whether or not in a given instance sex tensions are dominant, sex need and its satisfaction may be influenced by need for affectional demonstration or reassurance, by a wish for progeny, by the need to meet another person's expectations, by a need to test or reassure oneself, or as a means of securing or maintaining social status among one's peers. In the neuroses and psychoses, the complexities of motivational analysis are multiplied still farther by the exaggerations of ordinary motives and the inclusion of ones that, from the standpoint of the prevailing culture, seem unusual or distorted.

In normal as well as in abnormal behavior the human being acquires a number of special adjustive techniques in relation to the demands of social living, the so-called "psychological mechanisms" which will occupy us in the next chapter. Through our use of these acquired techniques, each of us succeeds in obscuring, disguising, distorting, reversing and disowning the original motivation, in ways that baffle himself as well as the behavior analyst. The countenance we see in the mirror of our own self-reactions is covered, smoothed over and touched up by these behavior conventionalities. We tend, like the modern woman seeing her conventionalized make-up, to think of ourselves not only as *appearing* thus to others but as actually *being* thus — as indeed officially we are. So it is that, when we become socially and personally ineffectual or unhappy, we show ourselves to be as a rule poor analyzers of our own difficulties and must turn to someone else for help.

Traditionally the motives which an observer can identify or infer, but which the patient cannot, have been dubbed "unconscious motives." Those which the patient is able to identify or infer correctly have been traditionally considered as "conscious motives," whether an observer is there to recognize them or not. Contemporary psychopathologists frequently go farther than this and teach that conscious and unconscious motives are entirely different entities, the former being localized in the conscious Psyche and the latter in the psychic Unconscious. It is obvious that this distinction between conscious and unconscious is not the same as the one mentioned earlier, in which we saw that physiological disequilibrium was called "unconscious" unless it interrupted or monopolized the specific organized behavior of a person, and particularly his overt behavior. The reader who is interested in the indiscriminate confusion over the meaning of *unconscious* should consult Miller's able analysis of the situation.[10] He lists and discusses sixteen different meanings of the term in current psychological writings, and is obliged to subdivide some of the sixteen further into still other ambiguous uses.

We shall seek to avoid the multiform ambiguity of this archaic terminology by making our distinctions in terms of the adequacy with which a patient identifies, recognizes and formulates the significant factors in his behavior. Instead of the hypothetical split into a conscious and an unconscious, we shall emphasize *varying degrees in the accessibility* of a person's behavior to his own analysis, through his self-reactions, and in its *relative accessibility* to the motivational analysis of others.[11]

From this standpoint a great deal of our contemporary therapy

[10] J. Miller, *Unconsciousness.* New York: Wiley, 1942.

[11] For further discussion of this approach see N. Cameron, "William James and psychoanalysis," in M. Otto (editor), *William James the Man and the Thinker* (Madison, Wis.: University of Wisconsin Press, 1942), pp. 55-82; N. Cameron, "Psychological research in psychiatry," and "Symposium: the philosophy of psychiatry," in F. Sladen (editor), *Psychiatry and the War* (Springfield, Ill.: Thomas, 1943), pp. 105-117 and 414-417.

in the behavior disorders has developed in the direction of increasing the accessibility of behavior to motivational analysis. The therapist's task is often that of training his patient, with or without pharmacological aid, in rendering freely accessible to study those motives which have remained for one or both relatively inaccessible, of determining through one analytic procedure or another the *modus operandi* of inferred motivation, and of helping the patient to gain control over his behavior by gaining control over some of the factors motivating it.

FRUSTRATION AND CONFLICT

When we speak of *frustration*, we are referring to *a situation in which a person's ongoing motivated behavior, or his organized plan of action, is temporarily or permanently prevented from reaching consummation*. The commonest forms of frustration are those arising from delay, thwarting and conflict. *Delay* is the chief frustrating event in early infancy. Need arises and is not immediately met. It is true that the needs of infancy are relatively simple, but even so the infant's equipment and techniques for satisfying them are also quite inadequate. Satisfaction must depend upon another person's convenience, and as we have pointed out elsewhere, it is this dependence that introduces the newborn to his first delay between need and satisfaction.

From this frustrating factor of delay the human being can never completely free himself. For although as a person matures, he develops new abilities that carry him nearer to self-sufficiency in his simpler needs, his new complex activities, of course, initiate him into new needs which always keep ahead of his newly acquired skills. Simple delay can be very disturbing even in adulthood. When everybody else is ready for the picnic, and one person is late, the picnic may be ruined because of the frustrated behavior of those kept waiting. If an adult finds an essential tool mislaid when he is in the middle of making or repairing something, even though the delay involved be trivial, it can precipitate an impressive outburst of rage. Simple delay, however, is rarely if ever sufficient alone to induce or precipitate behavior pathology.

As infants grow stronger and better coordinated, their more active relations with the surroundings introduce them more and more to *thwarting*. The child's perceptual development keeps ahead of his strength and coordination. He can see and hear what he cannot reach or have. His small stature, his relative incompetence, the intervention of obstacles, and the interferences and restraint imposed by other persons become increasingly important sources of frustration. As social patterns of talk, reading and thinking develop, the child's horizons of want expand still farther. He is able to hear about, read about, see pictures of and think about things which he cannot even see directly, hear, possess or do. Thwarting is no more lost in adulthood than is delay. Increases in one's possessions or one's achievement are very apt to raise one's level of aspiration and so bring in new potentialities for frustration.[12] Moreover, thwarting may be not only immediate and direct but derived and symbolic. A barred entrance or exit, for instance, can be equally thwarting whether the obstacle be a steel grill, a policeman, a no-admittance sign, a witness or one's own ethical standards.

Conflict

The third chief source of frustration lies in conflict. So prominent is the position occupied by conflict in modern theories of behavior pathology that the subject merits special consideration at this point. For adolescents and adults, in particular, conflict is usually harder to endure and harder to overcome or escape than either thwarting or delay alone. In ethical matters, for example, a conflict may go on and on indefinitely, debated by the unhappy person covertly or aloud, much as in the soliloquies that Shakespeare wrote for Hamlet. And sometimes the conflict and the debates end similarly, in suicide or homicide. Just as thwarting usually precipitates delay, so conflict usually implies a delayed or thwarted person. If the individual in conflict carries through an act to apparent consummation in spite. of it, he may eliminate delay and direct thwarting, but he does not as a rule succeed in reaching full satisfaction, and he is not likely to have an adequate afterreaction of gratification.

When we speak of *conflict*, we mean *the mutual interference of competing reactions which prevents the adequate development, continuation or consummation of ongoing motivated behavior.* The competing reactions may be conceived of (a) as overt or covert attitudes and responses, (b) as antagonistic patterns of change in

[12] K. Lewin, T. Dembo, L. Festinger and P. Sears, "Level of aspiration," in J. Hunt (editor), *Personality and the Behavior Disorders* (New York: Ronald Press, 1944), pp. 333-378.

muscle tension and relaxation, or (c) as mere shifts in action potentials, demonstrated or inferred. For our purposes, conflicts can be conveniently grouped as *adient-avoidant, double adient* and *double-avoidant* reactions.

Adient-avoidant conflicts. The typical adient-avoidant conflict consists of two incompatible reactions, arising in the same act, one of them directed toward an object, activity or goal (*adient*), and the other directed away from it (*avoidant*). Adient-avoidant conflicts appear early in childhood when punishment or restraint prevents the adequate development, continuation or consummation of an act, but does not terminate it. If, for example, each time a child reaches toward some object, an adult slaps his hand, restrains him or scolds him, he may develop an avoidant reaction without, however, losing his original adient one. If reaching and withdrawing tendencies are approximately equal, the child's hand may remain suspended part way to the object or execute oscillatory movements toward and away from it, until fatigue, distraction or a rage response tips the balance. The reverse situation develops when an adult coaxes or compels a child to face something toward which the child's original reaction, still present, is one of avoidance.

However, as every mother knows, even the certainty of punishment does not always prevent an adient reaction from going on to consummation, nor will the most attractive reward always overcome a child's avoidant reaction. Both children and adults do and refuse to do many things in spite of their accurately anticipating painful retaliation. One reason for this, of special importance in behavior pathology, is that the sustained tensions of conflict can become in themselves so intolerable that they make one reckless of consequences. The normal small child may terminate his conflict in an outburst of rage or aggression against an interference or an offending object. In young and old alike, an outburst has the immediate, though unplanned, effect of reducing the tensions of conflict. But as a child grows older, this technique becomes less and less successful in getting rid of conflict, because of society's rising scale of taboos against temper tantrums with increasing biosocial maturity.

Among children and adults, prolonged adient-avoidant conflicts are prime sources of anxiety, and anxiety is a prominent constituent of many behavior disorders. Thus, sustained conflict often leads directly into anxiety disorders, anxiety attacks and panic reactions.

The anxiety of adient-avoidant conflict may under some circumstances lead instead to phobic, compulsive or hysterical reactions. These often protect the individual from direct anxiety at the high cost of chronic neurosis, but they do not actually resolve the conflict situations. What we call *guilt* is a special case of adient-avoidant conflict. The temptation to do something forbidden is the adient tendency while the partial inhibition of that forbidden adience, derived perhaps indirectly from previous punishment or threat, is the avoidant tendency which prevents or delays the adient consummation. The adient-avoidant conflict of guilt is clearly responsible for many delusional and hallucinatory developments, such as those we shall meet in paranoid disorders, in schizophrenia, and in mania, depressions and delirium.

Double-adient conflicts. The typical double-adient conflict consists of two incompatible reactions arising in the same act, both of which are directed toward the same object, activity or goal (*convergent adience*), or each of which is directed toward a different object, activity or goal (*divergent adience*). In *convergent adience* there is one object, activity or goal, but two competing, incompatible attitudes are aroused toward it. In *divergent adience* there are two objects, activities or goals, and one's adient attitude supports competing responses toward both at once.

Double-adient conflicts of both kinds develop in numerous common ambivalent situations. Convergent adience is seen, for example, in the simultaneous appearance of hostile aggressive attitudes and affectionate accepting attitudes toward one's parent, one's beloved or one's child.[13] Divergent adience appears in situations that offer a person parental reward, filial, community or celestial reward, in exchange for abandoning something else which he dearly wants. No matter which adient reaction he begins, he will find that he cannot escape the pull of the other adient reaction tendency.

Double-avoidant conflicts. The typical double-avoidant conflict consists of two incompatible reactions, arising in the same act, each of which is directed away from an object, activity or goal. The man in double-avoidant conflict is like a tennis ball in play; whichever way he travels he gets hurt. This is the dilemma

---

[13] *Adience* should not be confused with the so-called "pleasure principle." Adience refers to relative *direction*. A hostile aggression is adient in the same general sense that a loving approach is adient.

of the child or adult who, for example, is threatened with pain, privation or rejection if he does not go through with a disagreeable, humiliating or frightening situation. It also was Hamlet's dilemma, and the one confronting a great many suicides. Hysterical disabilities are not uncommonly the outcome of double-avoidant conflicts. Faced with the social demand that he perform some dangerous or distasteful duty, a person may be unable to escape it without incurring social retaliation and disgrace, unless there are extenuating circumstances. As we shall see, the momentary tremor, paresthesia or paralysis that develops in the anxiety of such conflict may persist indefinitely thereafter, as an hysterical symptom, which provides an extenuating circumstance acceptable to the patient and his associates.

Persistence and recurrence of conflict

Conflicts may be resolved in a great many ways. Some of them are never settled; yet they wane and disappear with time as conditions change, and seem to leave no problems behind them. In many conflict situations, some extraneous factor reinforces one reaction, or annihilates the other, in such a way that what had been only a possible choice is now elevated to the position of an automatic, dominant habit. A fully-trained soldier, for example, no longer reacts with conflict to the command, "Attention!" as he did when he was a rookie. The experienced retriever needs no reprimand and no sharp points to keep him from eating a dead or wounded bird. The conflict has disappeared through simple training.

However, a large proportion of our important biosocial conflicts are not so simply and radically settled. We very commonly evolve compromises for them which allow us to retain parts of each conflicting reaction, or at least substitutes for each. We are not permitted to attack our adversary with fists and teeth, so we argue with him, tease and belittle him, or we play against him in fun and in earnest. Some persons move deliberately out of the range of one stimulus-source by moving nearer the other. A man may, for example, settle his double-adient conflict by marrying one of two girls who attract him equally. Some individuals leave the field of conflict entirely. They leave it literally, as when a man moves to another city to escape a situation he cannot solve (seen pathologically in *hysterical fugue*), or they leave it symbolically, as when one abandons an activity, a plan or a way of thinking, because it arouses or threatens to arouse painful conflicts.

A great deal of behavior pathology can be traced to the fact that human conflicts are so often incompletely resolved and therefore so frequently recur. Of course, even fully settled conflicts sometimes recur weeks, years or decades later, when situations similar to those that once aroused them reappear. Much theoretical capital has been made of the return of an old conflict, as if something mysterious and subterranean were involved. Actually it is psychologically no more peculiar than the recall of forgotten experiences, or the unheralded reappearance of forgotten tunes and dance-steps when old acquaintances meet again in an old familiar setting.

Nevertheless, as we all have reason to know, it is the unsettled or inadequately resolved conflict that tends most easily to recur. When nothing else holds our interest, and we should be relaxing, the nagging conflict, which our previous activities had apparently laid to rest, crops up again. Sometimes we can put our finger on what has brought it back; sometimes we can almost but not quite identify the excitant; and sometimes it seems to recur without an identifiable related antecedent.[14]

The continual recurrence of conflict tensions, during periods ordinarily set aside for relaxation, is one of the most troublesome sources of insomnia and inappetence in anxious persons. It contributes definitely to the perpetuation of anxiety disorders and, indirectly, to the development of those neurotic syndromes which hold off anxiety. The beneficial effects in anxiety disorders and agitated depressions of an active, organized routine with attractive occupational therapy can in large part be ascribed to the clinically obvious relief from tension which results.

Human beings are unfortunate in this, that no other activity is more effective in rearousing, reinforcing and perpetuating conflict than talking and thinking. When a dog is arbitrarily confined to quarters, for instance, he soon settles down, works on his fleas and then goes off to sleep. He cannot discuss his predicament with other dogs or his master, and he does not stay awake long enough to damage himself by prolonged rumination. Human beings may also go to sleep sometimes when there is nothing much to do. But, because they of all animals are not limited to immediately present

---

[14] It is possible that some reappearances of unresolved conflict are special cases of the *Zeigarnik effect*, i.e., the experimentally demonstrated tendency some subjects exhibit to recall uncompleted activities more easily than completed ones.

situations, they are infinitely more vulnerable to rumination and apprehensive anticipation. Through the operation of symbolic reactions, in language and social thinking, a man can manipulate, repeat and dwell upon past, absent or imagined difficulties without let-up. He can elaborate and discuss them with other persons, or debate them silently with himself. Through talking and thinking he can arrive at untested and untestable conclusions, build up exhausting conflict tensions, and maintain them or revert to them almost indefinitely.

Accessible and inaccessible conflicts

Conflicts in older children, adolescents and adults can be divided first into the shared ones and the private ones. The private ones can then be separated into the fully accessible and the relatively inaccessible. Shared conflicts are necessarily formulated to some extent in language, the instrument of communication. Private or unshared conflicts may also be formulated to some extent in language and debated aloud when one is alone, or mulled over quietly in socially organized thought. Popularly, conflicts that are shared with others, and unshared conflicts which one can formulate in some way that is adequate for intra-individual communication, are both called "conscious conflicts." Both, in other words, are accessible to the individual's own self-reactions. He can identify or infer them correctly, and either share their formulation with another person or keep them, like any other secret, to himself. Accessible or "conscious" conflicts, shared and unshared, often play a leading role in human maladjustment — a fact which the public is apt to overlook. A man's troubles do not dissolve just because he can identify their origin or infer it accurately.

Today everyone who has worked actively in the field agrees, however, that it is the relatively or wholly inaccessible conflict — the one a patient cannot adequately identify, infer, recognize or evaluate, and may not even suspect — which raises the most difficult diagnostic and therapeutic problems. This is the conflict popularly termed "unconscious." It is the one that older behavior pathologists located in a hypothetical psychic realm, the *Unconscious,* to which they ascribed racially primitive and archaic forms of thought.[15] For reasons already indicated in connection with

[15] A recent representation of this approach may be found in O. Fenichel, *The Psychoanalytic Theory of Neurosis* (New York: Norton, 1945), pp. 33-53.

motive and motivation, we shall avoid the unnecessary ambiguities
and the archaic thinking which divide our naturalistic world between conscious and unconscious realms in a hypothetical psyche.
We shall use instead the more realistic distinctions between conflicts that are shared and those kept private, and between unshared
conflicts accessible to a patient's own self-reactions, and those relatively or completely inaccessible to them.

The possible reasons for the complete or relative inaccessibility
of conflicts are very numerous. The more specific and the more
complex we shall take up later in direct relation to specific and complex behavior pathology. A few of the simpler and more general
factors will be mentioned here by way of introduction.

(a) *An effective conflict may remain inaccessible to one's self-
reactions because of prior punishment or threat.* The punishment
or threat in early childhood must come from other persons. Later
it may come directly from others or appear in one's own reactions
of guilt, pride, anxiety or fear. Eventually, the beginnings of a forbidden act may be sufficient to provoke anticipant anxiety which
inhibits or disorganizes the act. As in other learned behavior, the
acquired anxiety reaction is likely to generalize to similar situations.
It is also likely to be aroused by incidental fragments of the original or derived situation which have no necessary relationship to
the forbidden act in terms of simple verbal logic.

(b) *Conflicts remain inaccessible because a patient cannot recognize the significance of some determining factor or factors without expert help.* The necessary help is sometimes of a simple character. Henderson and Gillespie, for instance, cite a case in which
the patient was able to clear up his conflict quickly, and get rid of
his neurotic symptoms, after the rather obvious situation had been
analyzed for him by the clinician.[16] Complex conflicts, especially
those of long standing, usually require a great deal more work than
this on the part of both therapist and patient. The therapist himself may be a long time arriving at the basic difficulties, concealed
as they usually are by a succession of defense and escape reactions.
The patient commonly cannot recognize or accept an interpretation of his conflicts unless he has had a hand in working it out himself, and this is likely to be a slow process. He may be unable to

[16] D. Henderson and R. Gillespie, *Textbook of Psychiatry for Students and
Practitioners,* 6th edition (London: Oxford University Press, 1944), pp. 163-
164.

gain lasting relief before he has lived through his conflicts with his therapist, in talk and fantasy that may precipitate emotional storms.

(c) *Conflicts remain inaccessible because the patient cannot recall, without expert help, what he has been fantasying.* This holds for very recent fantasy as well as for more remote. The free-associating neurotic patient is frequently startled by the fact that at some point in his performance he suddenly blocks. That is, in spite of his intent to cooperate, he finds that he can say nothing and think nothing further along the line his free-association has been traveling. Blocking occurs in normal everyday behavior, particularly in emotional reactions, and it plays a prominent role in certain cases of anxiety, hysteria, depression and schizophrenia. It is involved in techniques of repression which we shall discuss in the next chapter.

The free-associating patient is not infrequently startled also by what he does say or think. He may immediately disown a statement made by him in the therapeutic situation, and even accuse a silent passive therapist of putting words into his mouth and thoughts into his head. These disowning reactions, are, of course, related to normal and abnormal projection and therefore also to delusions.

(d) *Conflicts remain inaccessible if they have never been adequately formulated in language or in socially organized thinking.* Language is a powerful instrument of recall, and thinking which has been organized in its terms shares its advantages in this respect also. For most persons, the imagery of recall does not go far in recapturing past sequences unless they can fill in with talk. Talking during recall then makes subsequent recall easier, even though talking may at the same time modify recall. One of the chief reasons for the scantiness and patchy character of genuine infantile and early childhood memories [17] is that the infant and the young child lack an adequate sequential language system. This is probably also an important reason for the speed of fading in dreams and daydreams. It is not the Censor, not the Superego, but the paucity of language behavior in dream and fantasy that leaves imagery kaleidoscopic and makes recall in verbal currency meager and uncertain.

(e) *Conflicts may remain inaccessible because of their emotional components.* Personally important conflicts always include strong emotional participation which may help disorganize behavior at

[17] G. Dudycha and M. Dudycha, "Childhood memories: a review of the literature," *Psychol. Bull.,* 1941, vol. 38, pp. 668-682.

the time or later during periods appropriate for recall. The visceral contributions in emotional behavior we know are diffuse, pervasive and difficult to formulate in language and organized thinking. In deliberately recalling an emotional reaction, we can try to reinstate emotion in our own behavior, but the trouble is, again, that the visceral contribution is difficult to verbalize and communicate. Our criteria for deciding whether or not a supposedly reinstated emotional reaction corresponds to the original are at present almost entirely personal. We simply lack the socially agreed-upon equivalents in language for emotional reactions which we have for much of our other important behavior. It goes without saying that all five general reasons for the relative or complete inaccessibility of conflict, or any combination of them, may be operative in a single case.

Frustration tolerance and individual susceptibility

It is universally recognized that different individuals show marked differences in the degree to which they are able to tolerate frustrating circumstances. Wide variations also appear in the same individual at different times and under different kinds of stress. Rosenzweig has introduced the concept of *frustration tolerance* to designate these observed differences.[18] We may define frustration tolerance as *the ability to endure delay, thwarting or conflict without resorting to maladaptive reactions.* An adult may be said to have low general frustration tolerance if he is unable to endure the delays, thwartings and conflicts of everyday living, or if in adapting to them he develops other stresses that reduce his social effectiveness and his usual gratifications. He may be said to have low specific frustration tolerance if he exhibits similar maladaptation in relation to some specific kind of delay, thwarting or conflict.

Individual variations in both general and specific frustration tolerance are unquestionably influential in determining one's susceptibility to the behavior disorders. Wide individual differences have been reported among normal children in the degree and kind of stress that they can successfully withstand, and in the adequacy of the adjustive techniques upon which different children rely in time of stress.[19] We have already reviewed, in connection with person-

[18] S. Rosenzweig, "An outline of frustration theory," in J. Hunt (editor), *Personality and the Behavior Disorders* (New York: Ronald Press, 1944), pp. 379-388. The definition given above is adapted from that of Rosenzweig.

[19] J. Macfarlane, "Relationship of environmental pressure to the development of a child's personality and habit patterns," *Jour. Pediatrics,* 1939, vol. 15, pp. 142-154.

ality development, some of the effects of parental indulgence, anxiety, domination and rejection, upon the frustration tolerance and social adaptations of children. In one study, as we have seen, these effects were traceable well into adolescence. Normal adults likewise show great individual variations in frustration tolerance, both under laboratory conditions and under such special stresses as war imposes.[20] Age, sex and physiological state also affect frustration-tolerance thresholds, and so do toxins, general infections and brain damage as we shall see in our concluding chapters.

It is, however, not only the kind and degree of stress a person can endure that determines his individual susceptibility to behavior disorder. Equally important is the influence of the kind of adjustive techniques he favors, their adequacy and the ways in which he utilizes them. If, for example, a patient has been over-trained in submission, and meets frustration habitually with fantasy and passive contemplation, he will almost certainly differ in his general susceptibility from the average man. But he will also differ in specific susceptibility from the patient overtrained in the aggressive use of projection, and from the patient oversensitized to guilt. Moreover, even though these three may develop behavior pathology of approximately equal severity, the first is likely to withdraw into his familiar world of fantasy, the second to develop delusions and attack his supposed frustrators, and the third to seek propitiation in compulsive ritual or expiation in death. In short, what is sometimes called "the choice of neurosis" depends to a large extent upon the relationship which different behavior disorders bear to the unskilled or injudicious use of each special adjustive technique.

[20] R. Grinker and J. Spiegel, *Men Under Stress* (Philadelphia: Blakiston, 1945), p. 55.

6 Basic Adjustive Techniques

IF THE METHODS that neurotic and psychotic persons use in dealing with their frustrations and threats were unique for every individual, we would never be able to develop a systematic science of behavior pathology. And if their methods were really as strange and as alien as they seem to the novice, we could not account for the evolution of neuroses and psychoses from normal conduct, nor explain the gradual return to normal behavior which we so often witness in recovering patients. But the adjustive techniques we find in behavior pathology are not unique for every individual, and any of the abnormal reactions can be derived from some basic adjustive technique that normal children or adults use in everyday life. Indeed, we shall use this well-founded relationship as the bridge over which we may pass, in our analysis of behavior, from normal everyday conduct to even the most florid and the most bizarre behavior pathology.

When we speak of *basic adjustive techniques,* we mean *those habitual methods which human beings in our society use in overcoming, avoiding, circumventing, escaping from or ignoring frustration and threat.* It should be emphasized that these adjustive techniques are simply ways of manipulating situations and reducing the tensions of need or anxiety, of suspense, thwarting and conflict. They are certainly not, as at one time believed, primordial forces, well-springs of psychic energy.[1] The relative *uniformity* of these methods from person to person should not surprise us, or throw us back upon mystical speculations over a "racial uncon-

---

[1] Psychopathologists of the nineteenth century introduced the terms "mental mechanisms," "psychic mechanisms," and "dynamisms" to designate certain of these adjustive operations, under the naïve impression that they were describing psychic entities instead of human behavior.

scious." We are all built very much alike, and we all grow up in a shared social environment that presents everyone with certain inescapable problems. The *differences* we find from person to person are chiefly in the degree to which one or another technique is employed, the preferences different individuals show and the way they overplay and underplay one method or the other. These we can confidently ascribe to the differences in structural detail and rate of growth that human beings show, to status differences throughout childhood and in adult life, and to all the other factors which psychologists have found determinative in accounting for the observed individual differences in social learning.

GENERAL ADJUSTIVE TECHNIQUES

Direct aggression and the temper tantrum

One of the simplest of human reactions to threat or frustration is that of increasing the vigor of direct attack. This technique is in itself quite adequate to take care of many everyday problems. The aggressive reactions we see early in life are relatively non-specific increases in vigor. The small child cannot adequately localize or isolate specific sources of stimulation, and he suffers from a dearth of well-coordinated skills. Indeed, during the first postnatal months an infant's vigorous reactions are effective only because they happen to bring someone to the scene who does have the ability to localize and isolate difficulties in the situation, and whose skills are sufficient to correct them. Otherwise the infant could not, of course, survive. We must accept a non-specific increase in the vigor of reaction as a normal adjustive technique at the infant level of behavior.

As an infant grows into childhood his strength and coordination increase. He learns to localize and isolate specific sources of stimulation, and as time goes on he becomes more and more adequate in attacking specific objects and situations without having to enlist outside aid. But even so, direct aggression can still solve at best only a small proportion of his simpler problems. From the little child's standpoint most objects that surround him are relatively enormous or they are high out of his reach. Many situations in everyday life are much too complicated for his rudimentary skills. Moreover, the human beings among whom a child lives, and upon whose behavior he depends, are relatively very large, strong and quick, and in skill and resourcefulness they are incomparably superior. They frustrate, threaten and punish him while he is still too young to grasp the significance of what they do, and long before he has developed the means of adequate communication with them. Hence it is that, for several years beyond infancy, the normal child is repeatedly thrown back upon non-specific aggressions and continues at intervals to meet delay, obstruction, conflict and threat with temper tantrums.

Direct aggression, even ineffectual direct aggression, is employed to some degree throughout life by all normal persons. As a matter of fact, its complete absence is a great rarity, even among the behavior disorders. In some individuals direct aggression persists as the preferred and the immediate adjustive technique. Habitual direct aggression often constitutes a serious personal maladjustment which renders an individual socially incompetent. The community, which often suffers from the maldevelopment of such individuals more than they themselves do, usually retaliates with counteraggression and frustrating punishment. Indeed, our laws prescribe various forms of direct revenge upon offenders, and we still permit ourselves the expensive luxury of gloating over the sufferings of those whom we convict. Modern criminologists are beginning to realize, however, that these community attitudes reflect the same inadequacies in group adjustment which the antisocial person exhibits in his individual behavior. Because of the community's vengeful, aggressive attitudes we have not yet succeeded in carrying the evolution of our social techniques aimed at the prevention of crime and the rehabilitation or isolation of dangerously aggressive persons very much beyond the stage at which they were fifty years ago.[2] Individual illegal aggression and community counteraggression, no matter how infantile or ineffectual, both have intelligible origins and both are presumably preventable.

A common aggressive technique that looks disorganized and disruptive, but is merely explosive and relatively non-specific, is the so-called temper tantrum. The *temper tantrum* is, of course, an adjustive technique, an habitual way of meeting difficulties, but an infantile way. In most individuals it tends, like whining and

[2] For constructive proposals toward reorganizing penal codes along modern lines, see *Youth Correction Authority Act*, Amer. Law Institute, June 22, 1940; W. Healy, "A new program for treatment of youthful offenders," *Amer. Soc. Rev.*, 1940, vol. 5, pp. 610-617.

enuresis, to disappear gradually as one grows biosocially more competent. Also like whining and enuresis, the temper tantrum as an adjustive technique may persist indefinitely in persons who remain socially immature. It may return in later childhood and in adulthood under conditions of unusual stress and strain. Temper outbursts are likely to show a temporary sharp increase, for example, during the *age of resistance* and again in adolescence. In adulthood they are often prominent in marital difficulties, where adjustment on a verbal level may not carry over into non-verbal conflicts and anxieties. The same is true of many persons returning to civilian life after active military service,[3] of elderly men and women faced with new biosocial insecurity, of persons going through a grave economic crisis and of prisoners undergoing severe, continuous deprivation.

When temper tantrums occur regularly as a preferred adjustive technique in adult behavior, they are nearly always an indication of personal inadequacy or social incompetence. They are infantile aggressive techniques which, in the interest of other persons, should have been replaced by specific aggressions or by the special adjustive techniques which we shall discuss later. This characterization still holds even though the adult using temper outbursts is a prominent management or labor executive, a celebrity in the world of art, letters and science, a churchman, a political leader or a military officer. An extreme case of simple temper tantrums appeared quite incidentally, first as a diagnostic and then as a therapeutic problem, in an elderly attorney whose behavior will illustrate what we have just said.

The patient, a sixty-two-year-old bachelor, was admitted to a hospital because he was suffering from an agitated depression complicated by grave malnutrition. One day, after he had grown strong enough to be up and about, he unexpectedly fell to the floor with a yell and, still shouting and cursing, moved around on all fours and banged his head against furniture and walls. This attack recurred after a few days in apparently an identical pattern, but was reported by the nurse as a convulsion. There were medical reasons for concern over these incidents, since nothing recorded in the patient's history accounted for them. But after a careful recheck had corroborated none of the staff's conjectures, the most capable psychiatric nurse available was placed in charge of the patient with strict

[3] C. Rogers, "Psychological adjustments of discharged service personnel," *Psychol. Bull.*, 1944, vol. 41, pp. 689-696.

orders to watch and record objectively every detail of his behavior.

It was soon apparent that the attacks came only when the patient became exasperated over not having his own way. He was fully reactive to his surroundings while in them. One day, for instance, the nurse told him he was about to kneel on his false teeth, which had fallen out of his mouth. He immediately interrupted the fit long enough to place them on the table out of harm's way and then resumed the fit. Finally, a relative confessed that the patient had controlled his household all his life by what turned out to be simple temper tantrums, but of an infantile pattern seldom encountered in mature intelligent adults. This aspect of his home life had been concealed from the physicians through fear of the patient and through shame.

The story is as simple as the attacks. The patient was the eldest in his family and its only member to go after a higher education. After college, he had laboriously built up a good law practice among the poor, and with his income had for decades supported completely a houseful of grown relatives. As far back as they could remember, this professionally able man had ruled the household by his temper tantrums and by loud threats of discontinuing financial support the moment he was crossed. It was no great matter to wean him from these infantile aggressions while he remained in the hospital, by seeing to it that they were not successful while the socially mature techniques which he had heretofore reserved for purely professional contacts were. However, when he eventually left for home a well man, he gave every indication that he had no intention of changing his methods of controlling others there. For after all, this adjustive technique was fully accepted in his home environment and, infantile though it might be, it still won for the elderly attorney the complete obedience of persons who were themselves addicted to a rather infantile pattern of dependence upon him.

We frequently see pathological derivatives of simple temper tantrums in the "blind rages" of *social deviants* (the so-called "psychopathic personalities") and particularly in the outbursts of socially immature paranoid individuals. In these persons the attacks of rage are usually signs of grave social incompetence and may prove very dangerous to anyone considered to be the source of frustration or threat. Excessive fear, in individuals who have always been regarded as personally adequate and socially competent, may sometimes precipitate a blind assault on other persons or objects.

Simple withdrawal, fear and anxiety

Simple withdrawal in the face of threat or defeat can be every bit as normal and effective an adjustive technique as direct aggression. In many situations it is more appropriate, and in most situations it is more acceptable to others than aggression. Early in life, of course, reactions of simple withdrawal are relatively non-specific and inadequately executed for the same general reasons which we pointed out in relation to aggression. There his assaults met stone walls; here his pursuers all wear seven-league boots.

The inadequacy of withdrawal from threatening and frustrating situations in infancy and early childhood has an immediate bearing upon the development of fear and anxiety reactions. Inadequate withdrawal is therefore a topic of prime importance to the student of behavior pathology. For most of the special adjustive techniques which we are about to discuss are in some way or at some time directly related to fear and anxiety. We shall find that fear and anxiety are the common starting points from which exaggerations, distortions and inappropriate use of adjustive techniques lead over into frank behavior disorders.

Strong, sudden or unexpected stimulation — including the loss or impending loss of security and support — is apt at any time of life to provoke a widespread emotional reaction which in some forms we call fear and in others anxiety. By *fear* we mean *any strongly avoidant emotional reaction that culminates in flight when flight is possible*. We include as an integral part of the fear reaction, of course, the whole preliminary or anticipant phase, which begins with stimulation by the fear excitant and leads up to the actual flight.

As infants grow into childhood, and children grow into adults, the number and complexity of their acquired fear excitants also grow. Emotional displacements develop and persist, conflicts appear and multiply, and one's pursuers become rules of conduct, the neighbor's opinion and one's conscience. Direct external threats are supplemented by a person's self-reactions. These are organized through social learning into roles that once were played by parents, teachers, critical peers, policemen, priests or pastors. The more indirect, the more symbolic and internalized our fear excitants grow, the less simple it becomes to flee from them or quiet them. As adults we are able at length to run fast and hide well, but not from our self-reactions.

When a person is exposed to fear excitants and cannot flee, his immediate *overt* behavior is likely to be that of shrinking, hiding or remaining very quiet and still. His *covert* reactions, however, are not essentially different from those one sees preparatory to flight, even though flight is now impossible and may not even be contemplated. Among other changes the pulse, blood-pressure and respiratory rate increase, gastrointestinal functions alter characteristically, kidneys are overactive, tremors and other signs of skeletal tensions appear, the pupils dilate, sweating is present and the mouth goes dry. These responses are all part of the normal anxiety reaction.

We designate as *anxiety* the *predominantly covert skeletal and visceral reaction which, for an unhampered and uninhibited person, constitutes the normal preliminary phase of emotional flight, but which for some reason is prevented from going on into its consummatory phase.* In this sense, anxiety is an incomplete or amputated emotional reaction, one that becomes intelligible only when it is understood as originally the preliminary phase of an unconsummated act.

Older children and adults learn to conceal or disguise most of the *overt* components of their fear reactions, but they are usually much less successful in controlling the predominantly *covert* skeletal and visceral components which we have designated anxiety. Indeed, the very factors making for inhibition of overt flight, and of overt hiding or shrinking, are the factors most likely also to inhibit a person's admitting or even recognizing that the covert anxiety reactions are present.

For this reason, and because they are also less visible and accessible to others than overt fear, the anxiety reactions tend to remain relatively unshared. Being inadequately shared with others, they are likely even in adults to be unsocialized and private. They are not verbalized as well as overt fear, and they are therefore usually harder, even for the individual in his own self-reactions, to recognize, identify and formulate in words. Indeed, as every therapist discovers for himself, the skeletal tensions and tremors of a patient's anxiety may obtrusively persist, and the visceral reactions with them, even though the patient has inhibited his specific fear responses, and has completely lost track of the original fear excitants. The anxiety, to speak metaphorically, has lost its moorings.

Anxiety reactions whose origins have been lost, or whose origins never were recognized or formulated by the patient, were at one time picturesquely named "free-floating anxieties" and described as buoyant entities, ready to attach themselves to anything convenient in the *psyche*. However, the actual reasons for a patient's inability to identify and recognize the original excitants, as the ones responsible for a given anxiety, are much the same as those outlined for inaccessible conflicts in the preceding chapter. The misidentification and the non-identification of fear or anxiety excitants by a patient, and his ascribing his fear or anxiety to incidental, fragmentary or logically unrelated sources, are all phenomena that fall within the scope of general psychology.

A most important complication of our problem arises out of the fact that anxiety reactions develop in relation to frustrated aggression and sex excitement, as well as to fear. No one any longer questions the fact that conflict enters into a great many cases of anxiety following aggressive or sexual frustration and fantasy, and there is no reason to doubt that the conflict involved is most often the adient-avoidant one we call *guilt*. Nevertheless, it is frequently the case that even though conflict is minimal or absent a patient may still develop acute anxiety following frustrated aggression or unconsummated sex excitement. To take care of these more or less exceptional anxieties the older psychic speculators postulated the intervention, in a hypothetical psyche, of "unconscious censors" and hoodwinked or sleepy "superegos." But today there are available more plausible alternatives than these, although they remain still almost unexplored.

We have at least one promising lead in the fact that all attempts to discriminate objectively between the tensional patterns of different covert emotional reactions have so far failed. Our instruments do not yield data which enable us to distinguish reliably between the covert components of fear, aggression and sexual excitement. We have to rely upon the experimental subject himself to supply the discriminating data in words which are, of course, a part of his own self-reactions. If for any reason he is unable to make the distinction between his more or less amputated, covert emotional reactions, the distinction cannot be made at all. This strongly suggests that, under non-laboratory conditions, it might not be difficult for a patient to be misled himself in reacting to his covert emotional behavior. Without the intervention of conflict and repression, he may still mistakenly ascribe the covert consequences of frustrated aggression or sexual intent to an unknown fear.[4] We

[4] H. Murray, "The effect of fear upon estimates of the maliciousness of other personalities," *Jour. Social Psychol.*, 1933, vol. 4, pp. 310-329.

must not forget that all emotional upheavals tend to interfere with behavior analysis, even when the situation is a socially acceptable and admissible one. We shall return to this problem when we study pathological anxiety.

Of course withdrawal and fear, like direct aggression, have their constructive and socially advantageous aspects. To be lacking in fear may lead one into personal or social disaster if, for instance, one's security and the safety of others depends upon caution and precaution. Withdrawal, fear and anxiety in general put much less direct strain upon interpersonal relationships than do specific aggressions and temper tantrums. For no matter how asocial and ineffectual withdrawal may become, it is rarely anti-social or threatening to other persons. Far from inviting counteraggressions and retaliation, as chronic aggression usually does, chronic withdrawal reactions tend to make a person unobtrusive and remove his social sting.

This is one source of personal danger in reactions of withdrawal, that they are so well-tolerated by society, so easily misinterpreted as goodness and, as goodness, so often encouraged and rewarded. The shy, obedient, submissive child who likes to play alone, and can entertain himself, is looked upon by many teachers and mothers as just a "good" child. Actually he is no trouble to others because he has been made a socially submerged child, one trained to live seclusively according to somebody else's plan. Such a child is already a socially inadequate child and, unless his trends are corrected by the neighborhood and school community, he stands a good chance of growing into a socially incompetent adult.

There is evidence to indicate that infants and children can be overtrained in withdrawal and submission simply by frustrating them systematically, until they learn that striving and initiative always fail, but patience and obedience are rewarded. While such training usually develops only a profound overdependence, with or without underlying resentment, there is always a chance that it will render a child habitually apathetic in frustrating situations. Turning to a different culture, we find Bateson and Mead ascribing the observed emotional indifference and lack of striving in Balinese adults to the years of deliberate teasing frustration, to which all Balinese mothers seem to subject their children.[5] Landis and

___

[5] G. Bateson and M. Mead, *Balinese Culture, a Photographic Analysis*, New York: New York Academy of Sciences, 1942; G. Bateson, "Cultural deter-

Bolles have described acquired emotional apathy and seclusiveness in American women who for long years had met insurmountable frustration, because of their incurable physical handicaps.[6]

Such childhood training and such later influences seem to be involved in the chronic give-up reactions that one meets clinically in seclusive, withdrawn, chronically fatigued or hypochondriacal persons, in certain dependent immature hysterical patients and in apathetic, passive schizophrenics. Clinicians are continually impressed by the failure of parents and teachers to recognize early tendencies in a child or an adolescent to insulate himself from social contacts, to withdraw from the struggle, until he has developed habits of grave and often incurable social isolation.[7] His incompetence is mistaken for virtue. Indeed, the mother of a young schizophrenic is apt to say, "I just can't understand it. He was never any trouble. He was always such a *good* child — almost too good!" *Too good to be an adequate human adult,* she might have said.

The general adjustive techniques of direct aggression and simple withdrawal, which we have discussed, are gradually elaborated during every person's childhood into innumerable complex reactions, and these also generalize to a great variety of excitants. We even see withdrawal paradoxically used as aggression, for example, to defeat somebody's plans and vengefully to disappoint him. In the opposite direction we may discover persons, who have learned to prefer seclusion from social contacts and affectional ties, employing direct aggression to defend their asocial privacy from some threat of intrusion. But the task of sorting and labeling all the possible varieties and derivatives of aggression and withdrawal, like that of naming motives or emotions, is a task rather for dictionary-makers than for behavior pathologists. We shall, instead, single out for our next consideration the ten special adjustive techniques which all normal children and adults acquire, and which frequently lead to behavior disorders when they are practiced unskillfully, or used exclusively and inappropriately.

minants of personality," in J. Hunt (editor), *Personality and the Behavior Disorders* (New York: Ronald Press, 1944), pp. 714-735

[6] C. Landis and M. Bolles, *Personality and Sexuality of the Physically Handicapped Woman* (New York: Hoeber, 1942), pp. 31 and 83-91.

[7] C. Thompson, "The attitudes of various groups toward behavior problems of children," *Jour. Abnorm. Social Psychol.*, 1940, vol. 35, pp. 120-125.

SPECIAL ADJUSTIVE TECHNIQUES

Under the conditions of human group living, direct aggression and simple withdrawal have distinct limitations as adjustive techniques. Because of this, everyone is obliged to begin early in childhood to develop certain more indirect methods of reducing the tensions of anxiety and need, of solving conflicts, of substituting permissible satisfactions for taboo ones, of increasing reward from and acceptance by other persons, and of avoiding punishment and deprivation. Each of us must acquire these special adjustive techniques without foreknowledge, since at the time we lack it. In the early stages we must acquire them also without adequate language behavior, since we cannot very well wait for language to develop before adapting ourselves to the demands of our parents and siblings, and to the restrictions imposed upon our behavior by the structure of our surroundings.

The fact that we learn special adjustive techniques before we acquire adequate language behavior is a very important one in behavior pathology. These prelanguage techniques are developed, not according to verbal logic, but according to *the logic of non-verbal operations*, that is, *the logic of object-arrangements and of the apparent sequence and concomitance of events*. This is a good and valid logic, as far as it goes, for operations at non-verbal levels — the only logic available to subhuman animals, and one which human beings also use throughout life. But the great advantage human beings have is that they develop, alongside this non-verbal logic, other symbolic systems which can be manipulated differently to give them a different and, for the purposes of social operations, a far more adequate grasp of human interrelations. These are, of course, the symbolic systems of language and communication, and the derivatives of human communication which we have discussed in Chapter 4 as socially organized thinking.

We might well suppose that, as a child's language behavior grows more and more adequate, his special adjustive techniques would eventually operate always along the lines of verbal logic. But this is far from being the case. The average person goes right on meeting threatening and frustrating situations, through childhood and into adulthood, in the ways that he learned before he had acquired adequate language habits. It is obvious that if he has never verbally formulated his adjustive techniques in such situations, they will be relatively or completely inaccessible to his self-reactions. He will be unable to recall, identify, analyze or modify them, without expert therapeutic aid, because he has never learned to react specifically to them. So far as his self-reactions are concerned, his adjustive techniques in these situations operate as automatically as his adrenals or his spleen. Thus, we often find adults using inept prelanguage techniques, with inadequate prelanguage attitudes, even though their social competence is unnecessarily lowered by such use, and even though the prelanguage attitudes leave them reaction-sensitive to danger, to slights or to guilt. The incompetent adjustive techniques of an adult, like the inept social approaches of overprotected children, may persist in spite of their inadequacy for want of a better alternative.

But whether valid or invalid, apt or inept, the development and the selection of one or another special adjustive technique, as a given person's habitually preferred procedure, will depend upon the same general conditions that determine the establishment of other dominant learned skills. The success of an adjustive technique may, of course, be quite accidental and its selection therefore more or less irrelevant to the problem a person faces. If a technique brings immediate tension-reduction, it may persist as one's habitual, characteristic solution even though in the long run it leads to far more serious and resistant conflicts. It is like drinking alcohol because one's business problems are too difficult for one's business ability. An adjustive technique may persist, even though it makes a person progressively reaction-sensitive and culminates in acute panic, simply because it is the only resource the person has been able to develop to handle threatening situations. Such factors as these are alone sufficient to account for the illogical character of many maladaptive procedures. We shall introduce others as we take up the different behavior disorders.

Although variations in the acquisition, development and use of special adjustive techniques are necessarily great from person to person, there is still sufficient uniformity among them to justify our reducing the many to a basic few. These we shall divide into two groups of five adjustive methods each. They must not, however, be thought of as mutually exclusive entities. On the contrary, we shall find them often overlapping, and each of them is likely also to involve some characteristics of another. The first group is made up of the *defense techniques*. In these, the dominant reaction is more or less aggressively directed toward the difficulty or its origin, toward gaining help from others or getting oneself out of a predicament. Among the defense techniques we shall distinguish (1) *attention-getting*, (2) *identification*, (3) *compensation*, (4) *rationalization* and (5) *projection*.

The second group is made up of the *escape techniques*. In these some variation of withdrawal is prominent. The person shuts himself away, is non-cooperative, retreats from his problem, maneuvers in such a way that his problem seems to disappear, or takes refuge in daydreaming. Among the escape techniques we shall distinguish (1) *seclusiveness* or *insulation*, (2) *negativism*, (3) *regression*, (4) *repression* and (5) *fantasy*. All the special adjustive techniques, those of defense and those of escape, are potentially significant for the genesis of behavior pathology, and every one of them can be found at one time or another in the behavior of normal men and women.

Defense Techniques

Attention-getting

This is the earliest to develop and in many ways the simplest of special adjustive techniques. We may define *attention-getting* as *an habitual mode of reaction which reduces the tensions of need and anxiety by making the reacting individual the focus of other persons' behavior*.[8] Attention-getting appears so early in life and so simply that it illustrates nicely a fact of general importance in all adjustive techniques, namely, that to be effective a technique need not be planned, recognized as such, or understood by the person using it. This point is pivotal in modern behavior pathology and we must never lose sight of it. Indeed, its neglect has already led us into many speculative absurdities, based upon the opposite view, that abnormal behavior cannot become intelligible until it has been verbally rationalized according to a predigested system.

Let us take crying as our illustration. Crying is the first pattern of attention-getting to appear and become established. The reason we call it *attention-getting behavior* is simply that it does get atten-

---

[8] All of the special adjustive techniques are assumed to be reactions to tension. Unless tension-reduction can be demonstrated, or can be inferred from other behavior, we do not classify the behavior as adjustive. This specification applies equally to all of the ten definitions of special adjustive techniques in this chapter.

tion. This is a verifiable fact. We do not go further and imply that crying, or any other early adjustive technique, is a sign of infantile shrewdness, a product of unconscious fantasy, ruminative guile or racial memories. That is untestable romance, and we do not need it for the problems posed by neuroses and psychoses.

What actually happens is that internal or external stimulation arouses vigorous activity in an infant, and the crying is at first merely a part of the vigorous activity. It is a direct reaction to immediate stimulation, and not a call for help. But the crying does bring adult attention, and this corrects the situation and may also contribute a change in position, fondling, cuddling and rocking. The noise of the cry can go around corners and through walls and ceilings. It is therefore in the long run the most effective part of the general increase in vigor of an infant's behavior, from the standpoint of capturing an adult's attention. If crying reinstates adult ministrations when they have ceased, then through ordinary learning processes crying will eventually be established as the habitual specific reaction to their termination or their absence. At this stage, if not before it, we are fully justified in designating such an habitual means, which produces these results, as the infant's *attention-getting technique*, i.e., as the way in which his behavior indirectly obtains reduction in the tensions of need or anxiety.

Crying may be the commonest attention-getting technique of infants and children, but no one needs to be told that it is not their only one. Among others we may mention breath-holding, temper outbursts, wetting and soiling, thumb-sucking, nail-biting, refusal of food, slow eating, spitting out and vomiting. Older children learn more complex techniques as their general behavior grows in complexity. We find them grimacing, complaining, asking questions, acting "cute" and showing-off, boasting, teasing, fighting, talking roughly and obscenely, getting in the way, being deliberately disobedient or obtrusively attentive, lying and stealing, extravagantly giving, wasting or displaying. The most important single fact about this list, which any experienced mother could easily expand, is that every item in it is to be found in ordinary normal behavior. Indeed, we do not even dignify such reactions by calling them *special adjustive techniques* unless there is evidence that they are actually functioning as habitual methods of reducing indirectly the tensions of anxiety or unsatisfied need —

whether such a result is expected and predicted by the reacting individual or not.

Attention-getting becomes abnormal when it is excessive or inappropriately used. An excessive need for attention may come from very different prior situations. We have already found, for example, that overprotected children develop attention-getting habits on the basis of too much indulgence or too much supervision. In either case the child acquires a pattern of expectancy from his mother, at home, that leaves him uneasy and unsatisfied wherever he is, unless he can be the focus of attention. The same is true of adults and children who have at one time been much admired for their appearance, connections, possessions or achievement in any field, and who have lost this admiration. They are often unable to accept a marked-down satisfaction for their marked-up need. The *attention-getting techniques* developed by a first-born child, who is being neglected for his new sibling rival, are second to none in their variety and their persistence. The need is very great and the habits of adjustment do not become fixed in pattern until after many have been tried.

Excessive need for attention also develops in neglected persons who have received decidedly less than the average attention from others. One commonly finds exaggerations and distortions of attention-getting behavior in orphans and unwanted or rejected children, in the offspring of cold, egocentric or hypercritical parents, and in children who have never seemed attractive or worthy of esteem, to others or to themselves. In the adulthood of such children, the appearance of strong bids for attention, when attention appears objectively to be adequate, is sometimes interpreted as a defense against a return of the bleak loneliness of childhood. More often than not, however, the explanation is much simpler. Techniques that have been used for a long time tend to persist even after all need for them has passed, except the need that arises out of habitual acts themselves (Allport's "functional autonomy"). They are like the domestic ways of a retired seafarer, who continues to live in his house on land as though he were cramped for space, calls his basement the *hold* and his ground floor the *main deck*, and keeps his days divided into *watches*. Children and adults for whom the success of others has in the past brought serious threats to their own security, and children who have been continually compared unfavorably with others, sometimes show a fluctuating need for attention which tends to rise and fall with the rise and fall in others' fortunes.

Attention-getting in one form or another plays a prominent part in certain behavior disorders. Perhaps the most obvious example is the endless complaining of many hypochondriacal patients who do not, however, as a rule suspect the nature of their need. Equally unsuspecting may be the hysterical patient whose symptoms, as we shall see, sometimes appear only when conditions are favorable for attracting attention. If for no other reason, hysterical attention-getting can usually be distinguished from ordinary attention-getting by the fact that the symptoms last far beyond the limits of their direct usefulness and often bring the patient great personal disadvantage. The typical manic patient gives florid exhibitions of attention-getting behavior, particularly when he is stimulated by the presence of others. Sometimes his exhibitions seem related to anxiety and possible depression; often their origins are quite obscure.

Identification

Identifying is an habitual adjustive technique which reduces the tensions of need and anxiety by enabling a person to react to the achievements, characteristics, status and possessions of other persons or of groups as though these attributes were also his own, and to react to objects and symbols as though he shared in the virtues ascribed to them.[9] The conditions of normal group living make it inevitable that identification should arise. The child, after all, begins life as a member of the family unit. He does not enlist in the family group after he has developed social individuality, but, quite the contrary, acquires social individuality secondarily afterwards. In early infancy what he does and where he goes are determined by the activities and locomotion of others, especially of his mother. For a long time he cannot and need not distinguish his possessions from the possessions of others. From the older members of his communal family group he acquires his early tastes and interests, his ways of doing things and saying things; their characteristics he acquires as his own. His status in relation to the wider community

[9] *Identification* is frequently used in a looser sense to designate general role-taking behavior. We shall find it more helpful to confine its use to reactions that give evidence of having or of once having had, definite tension-reducing functions.

is at first the status of his family; he has no other. This is the normal, ordinary background out of which identification, as a technique of deriving indirect satisfaction and reducing anxiety, is developed by every one of us.

The small child, emerging from his home into the neighborhood community, quickly finds that he is received by other children not as a detached individual but as belonging to a certain family, with this or that standing, living in such and such a house. The older children he encounters have long ago sorted out and graded the neighborhood families, and on this basis his status is judged. The attributes of a child's parents, his home and his relatives are made to reflect one way or another upon him, and he soon discovers that he can add to his personal prestige by raising the prestige of his family and home. His reaction now is definitely one of identification. From this discovery come the tall tales, the boasting and display of children regarding the strength, occupation, income and influence of father, uncle or big brother, regarding the domestic virtues and personal attributes of a mother or a big sister. From it come also the exaggerations about family possessions and the imaginative creation of important relatives, ancestors and friends — all for purposes of competitive discourse on the porch or on the curbstone. If a child does not have a father in his home, he may invent one and endow him with attributes that will reflect credit on himself.

Through these and similar maneuvers, a child gets practice in the use of family identification as a means of gaining and defending his personal prestige. If the reactions of others to him are favorable in this respect, they will be reflected in his own self-reactions and he may develop habitual attitudes of self-esteem and security on the basis of family attributes. The same adjustive techniques generalize to admired individuals outside the family — real, fictional and historical — and to other social aggregations of which the child is, or considers himself to be, a member. Among such aggregations may be mentioned the gang, school, clubs, political and religious affiliations, majority and minority groups, and regional or civic clusters of all sizes and kinds. The child uses identifying tactics particularly when he needs their support, as when he moves to a new neighborhood, enters school, or finds himself neglected and looked down upon by his associates.

As might be expected, problems of identification often become acute during adolescence when social acceptance or rejection by dominant members in one's peer culture may depend almost entirely upon family status and national or religious origin. A good many adults seem to have made the whole structure of their social personality depend, like Ulysses' house, upon a prop that is not really a part of it. For anyone to question the integrity or worth of whatever group furnishes them their attributes is to threaten the destruction of their own personal security. This dependence is one source of the disproportionate emotional violence with which members may defend some special organization that seems trivial or functionless to outsiders.

Identification enters into a great deal of imaginative role-taking, normal and abnormal. For many persons the chief enjoyment in reading biographies and romances, in playgoing and the like, comes from the identifying with fictitious and historical characters which such activity stimulates. This is something to be remembered in evaluating a patient's tastes. Through imaginative identification, readers, playgoers and radio fans may for the moment be this person or that, with his valor and strength or her virtue and beauty. They can share with a hero or a heroine the deeds, the honors, the dangers and the triumph, or the shame, the suffering and revenge. Any alert observer can detect traces of identification with heroes, heroines, villains and comedians on the part of adults who have just attended a movie or a play, as well as of children.

Identification may also involve the inanimate object that one makes or buys, one's possessions and one's clothes. In showing off or boasting of his new car, a man reacts as though its build were his, its shine his shine, its power and speed a measure of his virility, and its cost a reflection of his personal worth. A woman in a modish and expensive gown considers herself elegant and more valuable than when she is in a bargain basement house-dress, even though the latter may be actually more becoming and in better taste. Objects of tribal, national, religious or sentimental value also stimulate individuals, in all cultures, to react as though they personally were imbued with the attributes generally ascribed to the valued object.

Identification in neuroses and psychoses appears most clearly in delusions through which a patient in his self-reactions magnifies or sanctifies himself. Identifying in mania runs mostly to strength, beauty and intelligence, the patient attributing to himself the qual-

ities of some admired or envied person — a parent, perhaps, or a
sibling or some well-known public character. The clinician often
gets a distinct impression that the manic patient does not really
believe in his identification. Paranoic persons are often quite the
opposite; they believe in the verity of their identification, and arro-
gantly or steadfastly reiterate the qualities and status which they
attribute to themselves. In schizophrenia there is frequently an
other-worldly mystical tinge to delusional identification, and the
logical analysis hangs together poorly. Foster-child delusions are
particularly common among adolescent schizophrenics and may
very well be the foundation-stone upon which identifications with
God, Jesus, the Virgin Mary and other religious or historical characters are built.

Compensation

*Compensating is an habitual mode of reducing the tensions of
need and anxiety through the substitution of some other need-satisfaction sequence for a frustrated one or for one inducing anxiety.*
Like other special adjustive techniques, compensating appears early
in life as a product of social learning. A frustrated child hits upon
some substitute activity which happens to reduce need-tensions
more quickly or more effectively than just waiting, and this activity
becomes the habitual compensatory substitute with which he meets
the frustrating situation. Of course, such substitute behavior tends
also to generalize to equivalent situations, and it will show modifications and elaborations in its pattern as the child's horizons
widen. What is true of frustration is true also of anxiety. The tensions of anxiety and of anxious anticipation can often be reduced,
and sometimes eliminated, if something else is substituted for the
anxiety-inducing activity. If this something else is a mere ritual,
like tapping, counting, making signs or thinking a magical formula,
we have compensatory substitution at a compulsive level. It reduces anxiety, but as a rule it brings no lasting satisfaction. If,
however, the substituted activity brings a person new satisfaction
and new interests, it stands a better chance of becoming established
as a more adequate and often a more constructive compensation.
This holds as well for frustration as for anxiety.

The variety of compensations found in the behavior of normal
children and adults is almost infinite. Practically any need-satisfaction sequence may substitute for a frustrated or an anxiety-inducing

one. The compensatory behavior which appears very often leads to constructive developments that make a person actually better off than if he had not been frustrated or threatened. Indeed, many of the common socially approved and rewarded activities in our culture have such an origin.[10] It is not unusual for compensatory behavior to start a person off on a lifetime hobby that is satisfying in itself and leads also to social contacts he would not otherwise have had. Biographers are fond of pointing out that famous personages, in compensating for an observed or imagined defect in appearance, special ability, personality or social background, succeed in carving out a great career for themselves in science, industry, art, politics or crime. No doubt compensation is sometimes a deciding factor in success, although biographers as well as readers are inclined to be gullible in the presence of such an attractive hypothesis and to accept conjecture as evidence. But anyone whose work is with persons at the time unhappy, and in their own eyes unsuccessful and unworthy, cannot help being impressed by the other side of the picture.

In the vast majority of instances the development of compensations is decidedly a hit-or-miss affair. Hence, compensatory behavior very often leaves a person no better off than he was before, and sometimes it only makes matters worse for him. Difficulties arise, for example, when a person who is failing in something hits upon substitute needs with substitute goals for which he is actually no better equipped. The result is then more striving and more failure, with a greater likelihood than ever that he will one day give up trying and accept a defeat which some more suitable effort might have averted. One sees this sort of thing in the dull school child who tries out for athletics or dramatics simply because others, more favored than he, have gained prestige in these. The popular fallacies that intelligent persons are usually weak, and athletes necessarily stupid, contributes to the dull child's unlucky choice. One sees the same mistake made by housewives who, unsuccessful in marriage or motherhood, attempt to become successful authors when they have no special aptitude in that direction either. Ill-conceived compensation may lead a man, already dissatisfied and

---

[10] The substitution of socially approved reactions, particularly if they have an altruistic flavor, for socially discredited or taboo reactions is sometimes called "sublimation." The term, however, has other and more technical significance which is not germane to the present discussion.

unhappy, to throw himself into an endeavor which actually does not interest him, so that even his apparent success is flavorless. Under such conditions, if the road to the goal is long and hard, the lack of satisfaction which a person finds in his phantom achievement may lead in the end to depressive or paranoid developments.

There is a no-man's land of considerable importance to us in which normal compensatory behavior overlaps with abnormal. Mothers, we know, turn to their children for more than the ordinary degree of love satisfaction when their husbands fail them or bring them much anxiety. Disappointed husbands and fathers, aside from the more direct substitutes they may seek, tend to compensate by a greater devotion to business and club activities. We have already seen that such parental reactions are important factors in producing the overprotected maladjusted child. Amorous adventures, particularly on the part of middle-aged and elderly persons whose life has not previously been adventurous, are often compensatory reactions to real or imagined loss of prestige in social or professional relationships.[11] They may also represent a more vengeful attitude to what the individual considers unwarranted personal neglect, marital inattention or filial ingratitude. Alcoholism and drug addiction develop under similar conditions for the same reasons. Normal men, women and children quite commonly attempt to compensate for loneliness, lack of affection and attention, or for failure, by eating abundantly or expensively. Many cases of otherwise inexplicable obesity, in normal persons and in persons with definite behavior pathology, have this origin and this significance.[12] Among behavior disorders, overeating as a compensatory reaction is found most commonly in schizophrenia.

The child of domineering or hypercritical parents is often unintentionally trained in self-reactions that make him regard himself as inadequate when he is not. This training usually leads a person to become reaction-sensitive to imperfections, in his person and performance, which even though actually present are quite unimpor-

[11] N. Cameron, "Neuroses of later maturity," in O. Kaplan (editor), *Mental Disorders in Later Life* (Stanford University, Calif.: Stanford University Press, 1945), pp. 143-186.

[12] H. Bruch, "Obesity in childhood. III. Physiologic and psychologic aspects of the food intake of obese children," *Amer. Jour. Dis. Child.*, 1940, vol. 59 (II), pp. 739-781; H. Bruch and G. Touraine, "Obesity in childhood. V. The family frame of obese children," *Psychosom. Med.*, 1940, vol. 2, pp. 141-206; H. Bruch, "Obesity in childhood and personality development," *Amer. Jour. Orthopsychiatry*, 1941, vol. 11, pp. 467-474.

tant. He learns to avoid painful fault-finding and ridicule at home by making light of that which he prizes and by apologizing for any appearance of virtue or success. Sometimes such an individual remains chronically discouraged by the low rating he has been taught to give his own achievement. He habitually makes little or no attempt to compensate in any other direction when he fails, although he may not lose any of his childhood attitude of anxious resentment over his insecure and undervalued status. Often he embarks instead upon a career of unsatisfied striving,[13] whose goal is a reduction in the tensions arising out of his own relentless, hypercritical self-reactions. Tension reduction in these cases is, however, seldom more than transient. Success is taken habitually as a sign that the task must not have been really difficult, and to admit frank gratification over one's achievement may be to raise the old specter of retaliation and induce anxiety. The discrepancy between goal and achievement thus tends to remain constant and to justify the person in his lifelong derogatory, supercilious self-attitudes toward his own performance.

Compensatory behavior that avoids competition, but does not renounce striving, may lead a person into lonely, eccentric ways of life which then heighten his maladaptation by isolating him from the social behavior of others. This situation is a fertile source of delusion. An individual, for example, develops needs he cannot satisfy or anxieties he cannot allay, but he has been made unusually reaction-sensitive by his childhood training or experience to possible rebuff and ridicule by others. Consequently he tries to work out his solution alone, in solitary thought. In this activity, which renders everything possible except objective verification, he acquires his compensatory tension-reducing techniques without benefit of social validation. The outcome of his asocial brooding may be almost anything from simple gaucherie to a chronic self-perpetuating personality disorganization. The following case illustrates the latter.

> An adolescent boy of impecunious immigrant stock and mediocre ability determined to overcome his socio-economic handicaps by becoming a great engineer. He enrolled in a technical high school but found it impossible to make the grade. For this dilemma he developed the solution of regarding himself as a young man of genius who could develop his own mathematical system and had no need

[13] P. Sears, "Levels of aspiration in academically successful children," *Jour. Abnorm. Social Psychol.*, 1940, vol. 35, pp. 498-536.

of the ones he was unable to master. His eccentric solution unfortunately eluded his parents' recognition for over a year. All they noticed was that he went out progressively less and less, let his friends drop, grew uncommunicative, stubborn and irritable, and finally refused to leave his room at all. Several years later he was still grinding out on paper a jumble of mathematical symbols, pseudo-engineering terms and unintelligible mechanical drawings in a state hospital where he lived as a chronic schizophrenic patient. Shock therapy brought a few brief episodes of partial rapport, but left him eventually what he had been, a useless mediocre eccentric. With a different start he might have been a contented mediocre citizen.

There is some evidence to suggest that manic attacks are often themselves compensatory reactions to a beginning or impending depression.[14] Hypochondriacal complaints, as we shall see in the next chapter, may develop in middle-age as a compensatory reaction to neglect, to loss in self-esteem and to the dwindling chances of realizing long-cherished hopes. The body's apparent ills take the place of other foci of interest, while care of the ailing body becomes a source of new and satisfying self-attention. Compulsive ritual, we have already said, reduces tension by substituting for whatever behavior induces anxiety. Hysterical inactivation and hysterical autonomy can perform similar functions. In paranoid disorders, schizophrenia, mania, and depressions, compensatory reactions in the form of delusions and hallucinations may play a prominent role.

Rationalization

Rationalizing is an habitual mode of reaction which reduces the tensions of need and anxiety by assigning to one's behavior socially acceptable motives that an impartial analysis would not substantiate. Children learn early in life, through trial and error or indoctrination, to give reasons for their conduct and to excuse failure or wrongdoing in ways that are acceptable to adults. They discover that to assign motives to their behavior other than those of which adults approve is to invite rebuke, disgrace, rejection or punishment. They learn to give what is expected of them in this respect, and they learn also to accept their own evaluations when these prove acceptable to adults. In this way a person's self-reactions go

---

[14] N. Cameron, "The place of mania among the depressions from a biological standpoint," *Jour. Psychol.*, 1942, vol. 14, pp. 181-195.

through a long course of training in the selection of motives, the socially approved receiving more and more emphasis and the condemned being more and more rejected. The child, in learning to rationalize his behavior according to the customs of his society, is learning to deceive not only others but himself as well. There is no comfortable alternative. To do otherwise would be to lower himself in the eyes of those upon whom his security depends, as well as in his own eyes.

It is easy enough to understand the prevalence of rationalizing among adults. In the first place, the origins of human acts are complex and frequently obscure. Human needs are therefore difficult to analyze and human satisfactions sometimes hard to justify. To be able to carry out motivational analysis successfully in words and verify one's tentative conclusions, one must have a rigorously detached attitude, strict impartiality, highly developed skill in suspending judgment, and an inability to be shocked, surprised or fascinated by the unusual and the taboo in any form. These are qualities that few possess who have not been professionally trained to it. Lacking them, the average person assigns to his behavior whatever probable or convenient motive has proved acceptable to himself and others in the past. Having once done so, he is unlikely to reconsider his possible motivation unless something compels him to do so; for to go back and reopen one's past behavior for an unwelcome analysis can be as unpleasant as exhuming and examining a long buried body. The general effect of rationalizing is, of course, to put one's conduct always in the best possible light. This, in turn, allows a person to develop self-attitudes far from those which expert, impartial students could justify from the objective facts, and far even from those developed toward him by his inexpert relatives and friends, unless they have a special need to believe in him.

The public tends to hold rationalization in contempt and by implication to deny using it, little realizing that in so doing they are illustrating the technique they disclaim. But rationalizing also has positive values. If it did nothing more, its function in cutting self-analysis short would still establish it as a desirable protective device. In ordinary everyday affairs, there is neither the leisure nor the necessity for analyzing out all of one's motives. As a matter of fact, the need to track down and analyze the origins and meanings of one's conduct is an outstanding compulsive symptom which has incapacitated many a patient for normal life. For routine unimportant incidents it usually does no harm to assign a socially approved but unwarranted motive, and it may make an individual happier and more self-respecting as well as more welcome to those among whom he lives. Rationalizing undoubtedly keeps down the annual crop of persons whose sense of inadequacy or guilt forces them into exaggerations of other special adjustive techniques and leaves them more vulnerable to behavior pathology.

Rationalization is one of man's chief resources in maintaining his self-confidence and self-esteem when he is so imperfect from a biosocial standpoint. A consistent and continuous analysis of his motives would break down the protection from anxiety that rationalizing affords. Indeed, we can estimate the importance of this protection from anxiety by observing the angry indignation with which motivational analysis is characteristically greeted, by patients undergoing therapy as well as by others who depend for their security upon the rigid preservation of appearances. Clinically we encounter the most serious failures to use rationalizing techniques, as protection from anxiety and denial of failure, in the depressions. Indeed, nothing can more easily convince one that rationalizing in moderation is a desirable thing than a few months spent working continuously with a dozen depressed patients.

The exaggerated, distorted and socially invalid uses of rationalization appear most clearly in delusions, a detailed consideration of which can be found in Chapters 13 and 14. Many delusions are in fact little more than unalterable or progressive rationalizations which persist in the presence of contradictions that are obvious to persons sharing the objective data with the patient. If a valued delusion is called into question, further rationalization may develop in support of it. For example, a frustrated clerk, who happened to resemble Calvin Coolidge, believed himself to be President of the United States and a man of unlimited authority. He always insisted that he had built the hospital, including the wing in which he was confined. When asked by a jeering patient why he did not leave, he declared that he had not included a door to the wing in his building plans. This rationalization he added habitually thereafter to his claim of having built the hospital.

Hypochondriacal and chronically fatigued persons often use their apparent incapacity as a rationalization for failure in realizing their ambitions or in coming up to the expectations of those close to them. This function can be a serious complicating factor in resistance to therapy. Hysterical patients present us with some striking examples of rationalization dramatized. Their disabilities are in this respect often as clearly symbolic as Indian sign language and as communicative as speech.

Projection

Projecting is an habitual adjustive technique which reduces the tensions of need and anxiety by attributing one's own characteristics, intentions, motives, thoughts or attitudes to others. The person projecting, the projector, may simply assume without valid supporting evidence that others are as he is *(assimilative projection)*. For example, it was found in an experimental study that the generosity which eight-year-old normal children attributed to others, without valid supporting evidence, correlated positively and significantly with their own degree of generosity as measured in the test situation.[15] The person projecting may, on the other hand, attribute unjustifiably to others that which is actually his own and at the same time disclaim it for himself, either directly or by implication *(disowning projection)*. For example, the business man who has shown unquestionable incompetence in a particular judgment is very apt to accuse his subordinates, some other department or service, or a governmental agency of incompetence. Whether or not his accusation turns out to have been substantially correct, if he makes it at the time because of his own anxiety over loss of prestige, position or self-respect, and without actual knowledge that those he accuses are responsible for his failure, it is disowning projection and as such closely akin to delusional developments.

Assimilative projection. In everyday life this is usually no more than an extension of the basic assumption that other people are like ourselves, an assumption without which human society could hardly operate. During infancy and childhood we are indeed molded into biosocial conformity with those around us. We learn to act and to speak in the patterns of our particular family culture, to have the family attitudes and think the family thoughts. These become for each of us the right and natural ways of living, the ones that we take for granted must be shared by everyone. When a child runs into marked divergences from his family attitudes and family ways among his playmates, his immediate reaction is likely to be

[15] B. Wright, "Altruism in children and the perceived conduct of others," *Jour. Abnorm. Social Psychol.*, 1942, vol. 37, pp. 218-233.

one of bewilderment and incredulity and even of contempt. College freshmen who are for the first time away from home show similar perplexity and disbelief concerning attitudes that are new and strange to them. It is the usual thing to expect others to be "normal" like oneself, and therefore to have the same fundamental attitudes and thoughts, the same motives, intentions and characteristics. One finds such kindred spirits easily and comfortingly predictable. One adapts to them without the effort of having to learn new and strange perspectives, and without the discomfort of trying to enter into and share these unfamiliar points of view.

The less practiced a person is in the social techniques of sharing the perspectives of others, the less opportunity he will have of finding out how different from himself other ordinary people can be. The less his opportunities for finding out and sharing in such individual differences, the more likely is he to extend assimilative projection farther than the actual conditions warrant. Inexperienced normal children and adults, who for any reason have been unable to develop adequate role-taking skills, are particularly apt to imagine that their ways are the ways of everyone else. Under conditions of unusual personal stress and strain a very common form of delusion may arise from this matrix of unwarranted assumption, the belief that everybody understands one's situation and knows about one's deeds and thoughts. The clinician in his initial consultation with such a patient may be baffled by the repeated assertion, "You know all about it; there's no need for me to say anything." One meets also depressed persons in later maturity who insist that everyone else feels as they do, the passers-by are sad and hopeless — they know what is happening — the whole world is disintegrating and growing lifeless. Correspondingly optimistic assimilative projection occurs in manic excitements and in schizophrenic ecstasy.

The assumption that animals, plants and inanimate objects or substances may have human attributes seems to occur normally in all cultures. In childhood, we are all helped in acquiring these techniques of assimilative projection by our innumerable animistic and anthropomorphic children's stories, pictures, plays and verses. We learn to ascribe human virtue and vice, human attitudes, motives and intent to animals and plants, to wind and weather, to the sea and the shore, to mountains, valleys, plains and desert, to fields and pastures, lakes and running water, to trains, ships and airplanes, to every kind of machine, toy and tool, and even to useless and meaningless things. No matter how sophisticated we become as adults, we never quite abandon these ways of regarding things. We feel more at home with dogs, cats and horses if we can ascribe human attributes to them. It is comforting to be able to look with affection upon a friendly old house or an automobile that has served us well. A man alone among mountains may feel less lonely if he can endow them with man-like or god-like attributes. Even though they seem awesome and omniscient, they can at least be thought of as reacting in ways the lone man understands. Such animistic projection is one source of the many strange ascriptions of power and influence to objects which one encounters in schizophrenia, in some depressions and among the compulsive disorders.

Disowning projection. This usually occurs in relation to the socially forbidden or the socially disdained. Normally as well as abnormally, one tends to attribute selfish motives, evil intent and stupid attitudes to others and to disclaim them for oneself, even though objectively the reverse of this may seem true to an impartial observer. Disowning projection grows out of simple childhood techniques of escaping punishment or the loss of prestige and affection. An accused small child, who has been a partner in joint wrongdoing, is very apt to deny his own complicity but not his partner's guilt. If he has been the lone offender, he may when accused try to implicate another child and clear himself. Indeed, he sometimes succeeds in persuading himself that he is innocent when his elders remain still unconvinced. A child accused by a playmate of some act, attitude, motive or characteristic which his peers condemn or ridicule commonly denies it and immediately ascribes it to his accuser — "I am not! *You* are!" — or shifts the accusation at once to a scapegoat whom everyone dislikes.

These normal childhood techniques seem shockingly immoral to many parents, who have long since abandoned them for subtler methods. But the average adult still uses direct denial and counter-accusation when he is surprised into it, and when he is frightened or angry. When a person is normally on guard and neither angry nor frightened, his denials, counteraccusations and scapegoating are carried out by indirect techniques — by implication, by stressing opposite trends, by distracting others, etc. — which frequently throw him, as well as his listeners, off the scent.[16] Both direct and

16 R. Sears, "Experimental studies of projection. I. Attribution of traits," *Jour. Soc. Psychol.*, 1936, vol. 7, pp. 151-163.

indirect disowning projection may, under unusual personal stress and strain, lead the asocial person who is unskilled in role-taking techniques into delusional and hallucinatory behavior.

Disowning projection is most likely to develop into behavior pathology when criticisms and accusations persist in coming from one's own self-reactions, from what the public calls "conscience" and "superego." Suppose that the comments, gestures and looks of others have made an asocial individual reaction-sensitive in relation to some inadequacy, guilt or inferiority of which he is ashamed or afraid. If now he broods over it, silently and alone, the reaction-sensitivity may grow progressive until his tensions become intolerable. The important point here is that it matters little whether or not his fear or shame is justified, whether or not he actually deviates significantly from the normal range in anything but his sensitiveness and lack of skill in role-taking. It matters still less whether or not the reactions of other persons were actually directed at him or had the significance his sensitiveness gave them. What does count is that for some reason he *is* reaction-sensitive, he *lacks* the role-taking skills that would enable him to be more detached about others and himself, and he utilizes preoccupation instead of discussion and socially valid checking. If, under these circumstances, the patient reacts to the self-reactions that accuse him as though they were the voice of someone else, we say he is hallucinating. If instead he reacts to the accusing self-reactions as if they were part of a plan or plot directed against him by others, we say his behavior is delusional. Both are examples of disowning projection.

Delusional and hallucinatory behavior is not always self-accusatory and self-critical. Many patients, especially among schizophrenic and paranoic persons, succeed in providing themselves with chronic praise and comfort by cultivating those self-reactions which praise and comfort them, and by reacting to their own behavior as if it were the behavior of others. They grow reaction-sensitive to acts that can be interpreted as deference and worship in others. "Everybody stands back when I walk down the street," or "They smile and nod to me as if they were telling me all is well," or "They're all saying 'Collins is king,'" or "They say I am the Blessed Virgin." This is disowning projection because the patient disavows the reactions; indeed, particularly in schizophrenia, he may be surprised and bewildered by the acclamations, the deference and the worship which he attributes to the reactions of others. We must realize that such developments arise because of need or anxiety, take the form of delusions and hallucinations because of the patient's inadequacy in social techniques, and persist because they work or simply because they are long-practiced. The importance of prevention, early diagnosis and competent therapy is self-evident.

Escape Techniques

The defense techniques which we have been discussing are for the most part adient and aggressive. If a person is neglected, he goes after attention, if he lacks attributes, he takes over those of others, and if he is blocked he changes his tack or pursues another goal. If he fails, he makes it appear to himself and others that it was not actual failure. If, finally, he stands self-accused of misdeed, inadequacy or inferiority, he may accuse others, attribute the accusations to false detractors and provide himself with comforters and sycophants in his own self-reactions, while disowning them as his. When we come to the escape techniques we find reactions which are predominantly avoidant or passive. They tend to insulate a person from the demands and threats of others or make him unable to cooperate. He abandons unsuccessful mature reactions for immature behavior that once was successful but is now no longer adequate and appropriate. He avoids tension by rendering himself unable to react in ways or in situations that arouse it. He escapes from difficulty by restricting his reactions to more or less stereotyped daydreaming, in which he can play with problems of his own choice, instead of having to work with problems forced upon him.

Insulation

Insulating is an habitual adjustive technique which reduces the tensions of need and anxiety by rendering a person or his reactions relatively inaccessible to the behavior of others. In its simpler forms, insulating is little more than an extension of the shrinking and hiding reactions normally found in frightened animals and children who cannot run away. The shy, timid, bashful child is an anxious child, one schooled in fear, or at least unschooled in social experiment and carefree exploration. The advent of strangers threatens his tenuous security; strange places take from under his feet the familiar ground he needs. Because such a child remains relatively unpracticed in the ordinary techniques of social approach and social participation, he is unlikely to succeed and find satisfaction in free cooperative and competitive play or work. New human contacts and new surroundings, instead of adding new need-satisfaction sequences that accelerate his social maturity, only bring the solitary child more frustration and anxiety. After he reaches the limits of simple withdrawal as an adjustive technique, he is likely to develop special methods of avoiding or deadening the impact of others' behavior by insulating himself.

One way of avoiding participating behavior, if it arouses intolerable tensions or threatens failure and humiliation, is to shun the cooperative and competitive situations that demand participation. This in childhood means playing and working alone whenever possible. Carried into adult life, it means choosing a vocation which avoids human contacts as much as possible, or at most permits them only in a formal, impersonal manner. It means having hobbies that are also solitary and detached. We are all familiar with the quiet, reserved, distant individual who stiffens at the friendly approach of another and shies away like a highstrung horse. Every clinician meets the apparently self-sufficient, cold, haughty adolescent or adult who complains bitterly in private of intense self-reactions of inadequacy, guilt, loneliness and tension. That such behavior is usually sustained by tension, and not by satisfaction with oneself, is obvious to anyone who has observed the effect of a social cocktail or two upon an apparently indifferent, superior adult. Extreme fear and great fatigue can have similar effects, the habitually taciturn individual letting loose an unexpected flood of personal confidences which characteristically disappear as the fatigue or fear is overcome.

The hazards of habitual insulation are many and serious. We have seen that normal effective role-taking skills depend upon adequate practice, and that without them a person cannot develop and cannot maintain socially valid behavior, overt or covert. Be the origins of insulating what they may, its practice lessens an individual's opportunities for becoming and remaining socialized, for learning to share perspectives as well as confidences, for validating what he thinks and believes in objective terms, and for learning how to turn to others when distressed and bewildered. A common product is the asocial, seclusive, "shut-in" person who seems to be surrounded by a wall and a moat, with a drawbridge that goes up the moment anyone comes close. These we shall sometimes meet in the fatigue syndromes, in hypochondria and in compulsions, but more frequently and much more dramatically among hysterical, paranoid and schizophrenic persons.

Negativism

Negativism is an habitual adjustive technique which reduces the tensions of need and anxiety by providing reactions opposed to those demanded by a situation, thus making participation impossible. Negativism is a more aggressive avoidance than insulating. It is closely related to "the sulks" and frequently culminates in a temper outburst. In childhood, negativism ranges from simple sit-down strikes to the diametric disobedience that so often exasperates mothers during a child's so-called "age-of-resistance." It seems to begin with the infant's persistent attempts to continue what he has been doing in spite of restraint and interference. This easily develops into the practice of attempting whatever is forbidden. As in breath-holding, temper tantrums and playing sick, if negativistic reactions wring favors and promises from a parent, or if they merely irritate or excite the parent, they are likely to persist and become an established mode of gaining privileges, satisfaction and entertainment.

It is easy to understand the persistence of negativism in the children of domineering, of strict and of chronically denying and punishing parents. The frustration and the tense anxieties that such handling brings to a child make some release imperative. The child gains nothing by fighting back, but his passive resistance can become a powerful weapon of revenge and an adequate tension-reducing technique as well. It is more likely to arouse guilt and anxiety in the parent than is fighting back, because it requires the parent to go to more extreme measures or give up the struggle. Some children give overt obedience but treasure secretly a covert opposition in opinion and plan, and find their satisfactions in defeating their parents' hopes even though this means losing other advantages for themselves.

In normal adolescence, as we have seen, the increase in biosocial needs often outstrips the opportunities one finds for satisfactions. Anxieties are many. Negativism as a tension-reducing technique is especially obvious in the readiness for argument and contradiction on any topic so common among adolescents. So also is the sullen refusal to comply with home regulations which seem reasonable and just to adults and have never been questioned before. There is relief in such resistance, annoying though it may be to parents and teachers. There is the same kind of satisfaction in it that a small child gets out of thwarting an adult. If negativism is a preferred adjustive technique in childhood, it will tend, as in the case of the other adjustive techniques, to remain prominent throughout adulthood. One finds many adults who react habitually to authority with a combination of resentment and obsequiousness which is closely patterned upon childhood negativism and fear. To many adults, agreeing is complying, complying is obeying, and obeying means subservience, inferiority and the insecurity of their childhood. To oppose, to disagree, to resist the assertions of superiors and competitors then means to be strong and secure. Thus, negativism persists as an escape from the threatening shadows of a man's anxious childhood.

Nowhere among the behavior disorders is negativism more impressive than in schizophrenia, where it frequently appears in obvious symbolic form. Its full significance can naturally be understood only if the individual patient is understood, and even then not always, since what starts out as a clear symbol may degenerate into a meaningless abbreviation with the passage of time. Negativism in schizophrenia may signify, of course, simple non-cooperation, a last-ditch protest against being pushed around by relatives, medical attendants or fantasied persons and influences. It may represent non-submission to imagined persecution and threat, or non-acquiescence in evil, or simply indicate that the patient does not belong or go along with those around him. Similar symbolization is found in certain middle-life depressions with aversion and resentment. Negativism also develops in cases of brain damage and deterioration, sometimes on the basis of relative cerebral incompetence. In the elderly, however, negativism is usually not a cerebral sign but a direct protest against the curtailment of freedom and reduction in satisfaction which our culture imposes upon old age. We shall discuss this further in Chapter 17.

Regression

Regressing is an habitual adjustive technique which reduces the tensions of need and anxiety by reverting to ways or objects which during earlier phases of one's development were accepted as adequate and appropriate, but which have since been replaced by other ways or other objects considered biosocially more adequate and appropriate to one's present level of maturity. Reversion to older ways we call *habit regression,* and reversion to older objects we call *object regression.*[17] The older ways are often easier than newer ways, particularly if they have ever been fixed as behavior patterns by long use or by their relationship to some important emotional satisfaction (*habit fixation*). Likewise, older objects with which a person has had long or intimate familiarity, and especially those which at one time aroused strongly emotional adient reactions, are apt to be more rewarding than newer objects (*object fixation*). The old tarnish seems warmer than the new glitter.

Some of the most clear-cut examples of regressive tactics can be found in sibling rivalry which we discussed in Chapter 2. The older of two children, whose loss of importance and parental affection has left him unsatisfied and insecure, falls back on infantile behavior of a kind that once brought him direct maternal sympathy and care. The younger child, when he is teased or frightened by his older sibling, may also revert to more infantile reactions which he had abandoned, such as crying and screaming, even though the parent from whom he could once have expected help is a hundred miles away or dead. Object regression is frequently the outcome of failure, frustration, disappointment or anxiety in relation to some new object.[18] Children who experience serious difficulties in cooperative play with neighborhood peers sometimes return to solitary play with toys they had given up and revert to a strong mother attachment against which they may have earlier rebelled. Indeed, persons in whom early patterns of adjustive reactions have been highly developed through overlong practice (habit fixation), and persons encouraged or permitted to develop unusually strong attachments to persons and objects at a childhood level of behavior (object fixation), are at any age more likely than the average to regress to them when other techniques become too difficult, or other objects and persons fail to comfort and reward them.

[17] R. Sears, *Survey of Objective Studies of Psychoanalytic Concepts.* New York: Social Science Research Council, 1943, Bull. No. 51, pp. 76-104.

[18] R. Barker, T. Dembo and K. Lewin, "Frustration and regression: an experiment with young children," *Univ. Iowa Stud. Child Welfare,* 1941, vol. 18, No. 1.

In an all too common regressive solution, when marriage proves unsatisfying and sex relationships arouse anxiety, the man or woman returns to the parental home and reverts to the once abandoned but long successful techniques of filial dependence and affection. A similar retreat often terminates what might have been a business or a college career, if a career means leaving home. The dependent socially immature young man or woman finds that the familiar comforts and protective warmth of home have been exchanged for unfamiliar, often drab discomfort and the cold appraisal of competitive contemporaries. Complaints, failures and mistakes are greeted with disapproval and derision instead of sympathy and reassurance. The homesick person grows lonely, discouraged and sad until, finally, he gives up the struggle and returns to the welcoming arms of his parents.

Even the most adequate, socially mature adult may regress when he is ill or injured and bedridden. Illness and injury force one into a comparatively childlike dependence upon others which calls out childlike attitudes with their appropriate responses. As long as a patient is quite helpless, he is likely to be obedient and grateful. However, during convalescence and returning strength the burden of frustrated need is more apt to precipitate fretting, whining and little temper tantrums. If convalescence seems unduly prolonged, one must always consider the possibility that the patient is deriving unusual satisfaction from his dependent status or that the alternative of a return to work seems threatening. The danger in either case is that of chronic invalidism. Regressive behavior is such a common reaction to frustration and threat that we shall meet it again in almost all of the behavior disorders.

Repression

Repressing is an habitual adjustive technique which reduces the tensions of need and anxiety by preventing the occurrence of a tension-provoking reaction or by inhibiting its development, in the presence of previously adequate stimulation. Repression is neither a conscious nor an unconscious force. It is simply the name we give to behavior — called out recurrently in certain situations — whose effect is to cancel, alter or deflect an impending or a developing reaction. It is essential that we adopt from the start a naturalistic, matter-of-fact attitude toward repression, and that we maintain it throughout our discussion of the behavior disorders.

Otherwise we shall almost certainly fall back upon the old confusing reifications which are responsible for the popular interpretation of repression as the outcome of a psychic struggle between
holy and unholy spirits within us.

Repression is, of course, a form of exclusion comparable with
that which we discussed in relation to behavior organization. We
said in Chapter 3 that precise and smoothly operating learned
sequences depend just as much upon what is *excluded*, in the way
of competing movements and responses to distracting stimulation,
as they do upon what is included. The same is true of organized
recall; the adequacy of recall depends upon exclusion as well as
upon inclusion. We are all familiar with the circumstantial racon-
teur whose inability to leave out the irrelevant or partly relevant
detail leads him again and again to lose track of what he started
out to say. He has not mastered the techniques of exclusion sufficiently to produce smooth-running sequential recall. Repression
is one of the techniques of exclusion involved in both manual precision and skilled recall.

Repression, like other forms of reaction exclusion, may begin as
deliberate control which requires the same special attention that
any new learning requires. We have seen that, in manipulatory
skill, the exclusion of competing movements and of responses to
distracting stimulation tends with practice to become more and
more automatic, until eventually no trace of them is discernible in
behavior. If, however, the skilled person suffers an emotional upheaval, the habitually excluded interfering responses may reappear
in his behavior to disrupt his performance. The same *return of the
excluded* occurs if the skilled person lowers the physiological competence of his brain, as an integrative organ, by drinking alcohol
or taking sedatives in sufficient quantities.

Repression as an habitual adjustive technique shows similar characteristics. With practice it, too, may become more and more automatic and it, too, may become inadequate as an incidental result
of emotional upheavals, intoxication or sedation — as well as during
periods of reduced social control, in daydreaming, sleep, hypnosis
and free association. In other words, when behavior for any reason
grows generally disorganized, the relative prepotency of reactions
in a skilled technique may be reduced to a point where the old
competing or ambivalent responses can again be aroused by the
situation. This is what is sometimes called *the return of the re-*

pressed. As Sears has pointed out, the likelihood of recurrence seems to be a function of the original *habit-strength* [19] or "fixation" of the repressed reaction.

A great many of our potentially serious early conflicts apparently disappear in much the same way that competing movements disappear with developing manual precision. As we grow more and more skilled in specific areas of self-control,[20] one of two competing reactions in a conflict drops away and is eliminated from our current repertory of behavior. In this kind of solution the settled conflict is in the same category as the skilled act. It is plain that neither in the thoroughly learned act of skill nor in the thoroughly settled conflict do we need to regard the interferences that have been overcome, and the alternatives that have been discarded, as repressed "dynamic" charges which continue to lurk malevolently in a person's unconscious psyche. In acts of skill and settled conflict a newly learned sequence simply replaces or supersedes the earlier, less well-organized pattern of behavior and, with practice it becomes established as the immediate reaction in a given kind of situation.

But if repressing as an adjustive technique is credited with reducing the tensions of need and anxiety, why is it so widely indicted for leading us into trouble? The answer seems to be that repression is so often inadequate. To be adequate and result in normally adjustive behavior, *repression* (a) *must be reasonably complete,* (b) *must not entail a disproportionate expenditure of time and effort,* and (c) *must lead neither to severe impoverishment nor to severe distortions of one's biosocial behavior organization.* These obviously are all relative criteria which stand in need of stricter, quantitative formulation before they can be usefully applied to obscure and border-line maladaptations. However, for our present purposes — for the delineation of repressive reactions in definite behavior disorder — we shall find rough, qualitative criteria actually more adequate and less deceiving than the pseudo-quantification to which, because of the paucity of dependable data in current psychopathology, we might otherwise be tempted to resort.

[19] R. Sears, *Survey of Objective Studies of Psychoanalytic Concepts,* New York: Social Science Research Council, 1943, Bull. No. 51, pp. 105-120; S. Rosenzweig, "An experimental study of 'repression' with special reference to need-persistive and ego-defensive reactions to frustration," *Jour. Exp. Psychol.,* 1943, vol. 32, pp. 64-74.

[20] For a more detailed discussion of *self-control* as biosocial behavior, see Chapter 10.

(a) _Complete and incomplete repression._ By _complete repression_ we mean simply that an otherwise adequate stimulating situation fails to elicit a reaction which is known to have been previously called out by it in a given person. Such repressing can often be distinguished from ordinary forgetting by the demonstration that, if distraction or general relaxation is introduced, the reaction will partially or wholly reappear without retraining or prompting. We assume that in active repression there appears at the moment of stimulation a tendency both to react and not to react in a certain way. If this assumption is correct, then complete repression indicates that the active inhibition is sufficient, as well as prompt enough, to prevent any significant development of the tendency to react. We shall meet with instances of extreme repression in the behavior disorders. In hysterical inactivation, for example, the patient in repressing an activity succeeds in losing completely his ability to react in certain ways or to certain situations; when he represses recall of something from the past, he may lose even the recall of who he is. Hysterical inactivation, as _overcomplete repression_, can often be set aside temporarily in the interest of diagnosis or therapy by the use of relaxation and distraction, with or without narcosis and hypnosis. In paranoid and schizophrenic disorders, one sometimes finds repression as complete as this in the service of delusional and hallucinatory developments, and in such phenomena as blocking and thought-deprivation.

The signs of _incomplete repression_ are countless. We see normal examples of these in disturbances of steadiness, strength and coordination, in gestures and mannerisms, in blanching and blushing, in odd or inappropriate comments, in slips of the tongue or pen, and in selective forgetting. Of course matters are frequently complicated by emotional displacement, the signs of incomplete repression resulting only because of a persistent emotional attitude. The initiation of this emotional attitude, as we pointed out in Chapter 3, may be logically unrelated to the immediate situation in which the signs appear, and belong, instead, to a strongly emotional reaction related to a situation that has passed and apparently been forgotten.

Incomplete repression is also a common source of behavior pathology. When inhibition is slow to appear or inadequate, a reaction tendency may develop considerable neuromuscular tension before it is headed off. If this tension persists, but the reaction is prevented from going on to completion, we have behavior which is typical of the conflict situations discussed in Chapter 5. As we saw there, such tension may reach alarming dimensions, or become chronic and pervasive, without the person's being able in the least to identify the origin or even to recognize the fact of his conflict. The conflict, we say popularly, is "unconscious" or more accurately, it is inaccessible to the person's self-reactions.[21] The effects of incomplete repression vary greatly in the degree to which they are accessible. At one extreme, they may be fully accessible to a person's self-reactions, with or without his recognition of their significance. At the other extreme, they may be noticed and suspected as possible symptoms only by an expert who is seeking an explanation for a patient's behavior.

Incomplete repression, often with emotional displacement, is characteristic of many phobias. The phobia acquires a specific anxiety excitant which the patient can designate and freely discuss; but this excitant is actually a derived, a substituted or a merely incidental one, and the original one cannot be recalled. In other words, the *origin* of the anxiety reaction has been repressed, but not the reaction itself. Incomplete repression is also prominent in compulsive disorders. Compulsive rituals, for example, frequently begin as attempts at preventing the appearance or inhibiting the development of anxiety-producing reactions. Hysterical autonomy is the result of incomplete repression. In the hysterical tremor, cramp and tic, everything is repressed in relation to an anxiety-producing situation, excepting the recurrent fragmentary movement. In hysterical seizure, which is a pseudo-convulsion with role-taking characteristics, the repression is complete most of the time, but during the attack phases it is as a rule entirely absent. The incompleteness of repression is often an important factor in the disorganization of behavior that is characteristic of schizophrenic disorders.

(b) *Time and effort in repression.* Repressing is part of reacting, and as behavior it may involve considerable expenditures of time and effort. If a reaction tendency is repressed promptly and effectively, before it has developed into an ongoing act, the repressing may be no more effortful or wasteful than the automatic control that antagonistic muscles exert in any coordinated movement. If,

---

[21] For a discussion of the origin and character of *self-reactions,* see Chapter 4, and for their relationship to inaccessible conflict, see Chapter 5.

on the other hand, repression is late in developing or insufficient, the total effort expended in the abortive reaction and its repression may be very considerable, and lead to fatigue and a noticeable reduction in the person's effectiveness as a biosocial organism. A large expenditure of time and effort may be necessitated, for example, in repressing hostile or salacious fantasying which is in itself of no value to the individual. This state of affairs one finds in many cases of chronic anxiety, in seclusive persons who complain of chronic fatigue, and in those who resort to compulsive ritual for penitence or protection from the possible evil consequences of their thoughts. In the end, the tensions developing out of incomplete repression may far exceed those which the repressing started out to overcome. The anxious tense person may grow abnormally reaction-sensitive to sound, to light, to his own dreams and daydreams, to the presence of others and his own isolation, to the possibility of insanity and to his own relative incompetence. The results of repression are then far worse than those which might have come from what was originally repressed.

(c) *Repressive impoverishment and distortion.* There are extremists in the practice of repression just as there are in dieting. Repressing becomes habitual and therefore sometimes an end in itself. It generalizes to equivalent activities, inevitably including much that is logically irrelevant, and comes to a new equilibrium only after the individual practicing it has suffered serious deficiencies and distortions in his personality organization. This is what we see in so-called "overinhibited" persons, whose restricted range of social behavior makes them seem limited, unattractive and often forbidding to others. Landis and Bolles have described moderate restrictive repression, without apparent serious personality distortion, in chronically handicapped women.[22] One finds repressive impoverishment with little distortion in a great many depressed persons and in some self-denying hysterical patients.

Repressive impoverishment may lead also to distortion, for the simple reason that what an individual excludes from his activities may very well be something essential to a well-balanced social personality. Should repression, for example, prove inadequate under conditions of normal social stimulation, but adequate when a person remains in seclusion, he may learn to cultivate a seclusive mode

[22] C. Landis and M. Bolles, *Personality and Sexuality of the Physically Handicapped Woman* (New York: Hoeber, 1942), pp. 84-85.

of life as his escape. However, seclusion for a man or woman with serious personal conflicts, such as this technique implies, is likely to encourage solutions that would prove socially invalid if they were ever put to the test. Since social validation cannot be carried out in solitude, the seclusive person runs the risk of growing progressively eccentric as his asocial solutions lead him away from the accepted paths. This is often the situation in seclusive persons with hypochondriacal disorders, fatigue syndromes, and paranoid and schizophrenic illnesses.

A paradoxical distortion develops in many sex deviants on the basis of repressive impoverishment. Earlier in life they apparently adopt a temporary social taboo, against adult sexuality for example, as their own permanent individual taboo. This leaves them only a choice between no sexuality or forbidden sexuality, and so they often end up by restricting their reactions to what is taboo for adults and run the risk of drastic social punishment.

Fantasy

Fantasying is an habitual adjustive technique which reduces the tensions of need and anxiety by restricting behavior to more or less stereotyped daydreams. The precursors of organized fantasy are easy to recognize in child's play. Children early in their second year are already able to discriminate, in their reactions, between genuine and make-believe parental threats.[23] As their strength and skill increase, children learn to participate more and more actively in make-believe play mingled with fantasy, including especially the verbal play of fairy tales and bedtime stories. Every normal child learns to use otherwise meaningless objects and situations as symbols or substitutes for persons, animals and social objects in their relational contexts, and to react to these play symbols as if they were the real thing. This play *with* objects is a training ground for private fantasy *without* them. A little boy, for example, uses and reacts to a piece of wood or paper as though it were a train, a ship or an airplane; a little girl, if she has no doll, may use and react to a towel as though it were a baby. For the one, sofa cushions become docks, stations or airports; for the other, they become cradles, tables or baby-carriages. Each child, solely through

[23] C. Buehler, "The social behavior of children," in C. Murchison (editor), *Handbook of Child Psychology*, 2d edition (Worcester, Mass.: Clark University Press, 1933), pp. 374-416.

his or her own reactions to them, has expanded the stimulating value of these play objects, which actually are meaningless so far as real-life transportation or baby-care are concerned.

Play always includes talking, if the playing child can talk, and the more adequate language habits become the more completely they can substitute for or symbolize other behavior. In fairy tales and bedtime stories the whole of play is on a verbal level. The child is told a story and in time learns to be able to tell himself the same story. He recalls it in verbal terms supplemented, of course, by those partial rearousals of the effects of non-verbal stimulation which were once called "images." As language habits and other social behavior organize his recall and his imaginative play, the child becomes gradually capable of developing favorite fantasy themes which he can repeat in solitude and enjoy or worry over, in the same way that he has learned to enjoy or worry over a fairy tale someone else tells him. According to Murphy, most six-year-old children have already elaborated their characteristic fantasy themes, and these they are likely to express in free drawing or painting situations.[24] In short, children move from building castles with blocks or snow, in which they supplement their structure with verbal and imaginative stimulation, to purely private fantasying in which they build invisible castles out of the materials of symbolic stimulation and reaction. This behavior has infinite potentialities for the remainder of a person's life.

Fantasy throughout life can be a fruitful source of relaxation and entertainment. We all go on telling ourselves fairy tales and bedtime stories, recalling the past and envisaging a future, or imagining a different present, not necessarily as things actually were or as we expect them to be, but simply in the way that satisfies us most. Many persons resort almost automatically to a favorite fantasy theme whenever they feel bored, lonely, insecure, frustrated or neglected. They use fantasying as a child uses thumb-sucking, to comfort and relax themselves. Also like thumb-sucking is the common use of a stereotyped daydream to induce sleep when one is tense. The degree to which a person develops systematic fantasying, and the ease with which he resorts to it, will depend upon how much practice in it he has had, and upon the extent of his dissatisfaction with things as they have been and promise to be. In gen-

---

[24] L. Murphy, "Childhood experience," in J. Hunt (editor), *Personality and the Behavior Disorders* (New York: Ronald Press, 1944), pp. 675-677.

eral, any circumstance in childhood or adulthood that sharply limits
one's opportunities for free overt activity and satisfying social participation is likely to increase one's practice in and addiction to
systematic fantasy. Among the common circumstances may be
mentioned long subjection to restrictive discipline and criticism,
long exposure to frustration, deprivation and neglect, protracted
disabling illnesses, the lack of adequate companionship or of satisfying achievement, and the presence of genuine or imagined personal defect and failure.

Fantasy can be a strong citadel into which the harassed person
can withdraw and escape the pressures and encroachments that
seem to hem him in. Conflict and thwarting may disappear while
the fantasying lasts, delayed satisfactions may be realized at once
in symbol, and anxiety may at least for the moment disappear. Such
escape from the din of social stimulation, into the private and more
restricted areas of fantasy behavior, give one a period of respite
and an opportunity for working out a new and perhaps more adequate plan of meeting the situation which led one to withdraw.
Indeed, a commonly experienced sequence in fantasy is first the
escape and the gradual relaxation, and then the beginnings of a
new perspective, which might have been prevented from developing for an indefinite period if the previous tensions had been kept
up by the full social stimulation. Fantasying in times of stress thus
has distinctly constructive values, just as the other adjustive techniques have.

Fantasy, even as a form of simple escape, can become very dangerous. If one learns to resort to it the moment life seems dull or
harsh, or the moment anxiety appears, fantasying may grow first
difficult and then impossible to resist. It is then a true addiction
whose potential threat to one's biosocial integrity is realized in
more than one form of behavior pathology, but especially in schizophrenic disorders. Occasionally fantasying becomes highly developed and includes a considerable part of one's biosocial behavior
repertory. If under these conditions a person acts out his fantasy
we have the appearance of the so-called secondary trance personality, whose most dramatic instances appear in autonomous
hysteria. Hypochondria and fatigue syndromes are also sometimes
the products of systematic fantasying which includes complaints of
sickness and frailty as part of the wall that helps to shut out interference with one's daydreaming by others.

Fantasy can be a scourge to the anxious and guilty, instead of

an adjustive instrument. Children are often trained by an oversolicitous or compulsive parent to be always on the lookout for
potential dangers. They are trained to analyze situations, past and
present, in terms of possible threats to their own security and to
the safety of others for whom they might conceivably be responsible. Their world of fantasy, dominated by such habitual
anticipant attitudes, will tend to become a fearsome one in which
thought sequences are forever moving toward some abyss. It is
possible that manic excitements may represent a reaction against
such habitual fantasy; it is certain that anxiety disorders, compulsions and schizophrenic reactions often have such an origin. Habits
of anxious fantasy are also engendered in the children of punishing
parents who use rejection as a favorite method of control, or who
show extreme inconsistency which makes their reactions unpredictable. Adults as well as children develop habitual anxious fantasying out of acutely dangerous situations, and out of situations
of long-standing threat to their security from any direction.

The influence of guilty and overzealous parents, clergy and teachers upon children is sometimes that of training them to fantasy
habitually in terms of guilty conflict. The finger of accusation or
suspicion is thus mounted in their self-reactions, like a compass
needle, to point always at them. Some are trained to search com-
pulsively in the rubble of their past for signs of guilt. The world
for them is a place of wrongdoing and their fantasy gives them no
escape. Out of this impasse, as we shall see, develop protective
and penitential rituals as a means of atonement for the inescapable
guilt, and depressions in which self-condemnation and self-punishment predominate. We have already indicated in Chapter 5 the
importance of fantasied conflicts, and we shall have occasion to go
further into the relation of guilt, fantasy and behavior pathology
in several of the chapters which follow. Indeed, as now we pass
to a consideration of the specific behavior disorders, we shall not
leave the adjustive techniques behind us as a finished subject. We
shall carry them right on through their pathological functions in
neuroses and psychoses to their role in contemporary therapeutic
procedures.

ADJUSTIVE TECHNIQUES AND BEHAVIOR DISORDERS

We have up to now been stressing the tension-reducing effect
of adjustive techniques, since it is this which accounts for their

almost universal presence in our culture. It would be a mistake, however, to suppose that tension reduction is the only important effect these techniques may have. They are, after all, no more and no less than learned reactions, and calling them "dynamisms" or "mechanisms" does not magically endow them with the properties of first causes. Adjustive techniques may be acquired and become established under any of the conditions common to human learning. When they are established they operate like any other learned reaction. Therefore they may be developed in a skillful or an awkward pattern and be used appropriately or inappropriately. They may help a person or injure him, solve problems or fail to solve them, and even make a situation worse than ever. The study of persons who are unskilled in using a given technique, use it inappropriately or cling to its use even when it is obviously bringing damage, does not carry us out of the realm of ordinary human behavior and into an extramundane world of psychodynamics. It is fundamentally no different from the study of the behavioral misuse of a fine razor to sharpen pencils, or of an axe to open a tin can, when either is dangerous and may be known to have previously caused serious harm.

We learn our adjustive techniques while we are still very young, when our grasp of interpersonal relationships is relatively slight and we virtually lack language. As we grow up, these techniques become important factors in our developing personality organization and help determine what we do, whom we know and the way others treat us. What we do, who our companions are and how they behave to us, in turn determine the further development of our techniques — to our benefit or our detriment. If, for example, we have learned that complaints of sickness or fatigue bring comfort and reward, we may develop this method to such a degree that we live a limited life in childhood, associate mainly with adults and learn to regard ourselves as invalid or delicate. These self-reactions may make us honestly act the role and determine the whole course of our life. If, instead, we have early learned to envy everyone and trust no one we may find others always distrustful of us, we shall have few close friends and no confidants, and our adult life will be lived in a fog of misunderstanding and suspicion. The early childhood beginnings of these two careers may seem trifling enough, but as they progress each brings the person different experiences and opportunities which make the paths of personality development diverge more and more.

What we shall next consider, as the *behavior disorders,* are frequently the end-results of such progressive maladaptation. Because their sources appear sometimes to reach back into early childhood, it has been said that the etiology of neuroses and psychoses lies in the life-history of the person. But this could be said of many cases of organ and tissue disease with equal justice, since individual susceptibilities and immunities depend upon growth factors, early nutrition, environmental conditions and previous specific illnesses. In neuroses and psychoses we must look upon anything that might influence personality development and behavior organization, whether past or present, as a potential source of behavior pathology. The immediate worry deserves the same attention from diagnostician and therapist as the remote conflict.

7   Hypochondriacal Disorders

THERE ARE in the United States today hundreds of thousands of men and women who are worrying habitually over ailments they have never had, and who will probably end up by dying of something they have never feared. Most of them prescribe for and treat themselves. Theirs is the well-stocked medicine cabinet, the vest-pocket tablet, the daily irrigation, the tonic and the laxative. They provide the chief support of the patent-medicine industry which, with its advertising media, can boast of annual receipts running into the millions.[1] A relatively small minority of these chronic worriers over health continues seeking help for their complaints from physicians. But even this minority still makes up a sizable percentage of every general practitioner's clientele, helps materially in filling the benches of out-patient clinics where the needy are treated, and presents the diagnostic specialist everywhere with some of his most difficult problems.

Contrary to popular belief, body overconcern is by no means confined to the idle and the well-to-do. It drains also the pocketbooks of individuals and families in the moderate and low income groups. Hence, even if hypochondriacal disorders were solely a matter of a reduction in income, they would still constitute a grave social problem. But far more serious than the financial waste involved is the reduction in social effectiveness which inevitably results when a person is perpetually concerned over his own health. Men and women whose symptoms persuade them that they are ill or defective are as a rule partially disabled by their own conviction. Their belief disqualifies them from entering wholeheartedly into things. They drive through life with the hood lifted, watching and

[1] B. Clark, *The Advertising Smoke Screen* (New York: Harper, 1944), pp. 66-83 and 144-200.

187

listening to their machinery, stopping repeatedly to tinker with it and discussing their signs and symptoms with anyone who shows an interest.

The hypochondriac suffers a loss in social effectiveness because he adopts the role of a sick or disabled person and excludes from his behavior whatever seems inconsistent with that role. In time his activities and interests usually undergo a progressive limitation until they may encompass little more than his own complaints and the routine which his care of them imposes upon him. If, as is too often the case, the patient harps continually on his signs and symptoms, he is sure to strain the sympathies of his associates and ultimately to tax their credulity as well. The end-result is that not only is a person's social usefulness impaired but he becomes less and less welcome among his former friends who grow weary of his repetitious complaining. Thus it is that chronic body overconcern, though it destroys no tissue and is never fatal, may nonetheless incapacitate a person and isolate him from his fellows as effectively as may chronic pulmonary tuberculosis.

Hypochondriacal disorders are characterized by *habitual preoccupation with a supposed disease or defect in an organ or body part which is actually functioning within normal limits*, or by *habitually exaggerated concern over organs or body parts which are defective or diseased.* For half a century or more there has been a rather pedantic controversy over the question, *Is hypochondria an independent disease entity or only a syndrome?* This controversy has never been settled but there is reason to hope that it has been outgrown.[2] For we all recognize today that no one of the neuroses meets the criterion of an independent disease entity. Anxiety and chronic fatigue characterize many unquestionable compulsive disorders; compulsive trends are often detectable in anxiety disorders and hypochondria; fatigue syndromes frequently include habitual worry over some normal organ; and one or all of these neurotic groups may appear during the development of an indubitably schizophrenic or depressive illness. No matter what system of grouping we select, there will always be this inescapable overlap.

Our diagnostic categories are matters of convenience; if we were omniscient and omnipotent we should presumably not need them.

[2] S. Katzenelbogen, "Hypochondriacal complaints with special reference to personality and environment," *Amer. Jour. Psychiat.*, 1942, vol. 98, pp. 815-823.

Since we are neither omniscient nor omnipotent we attempt to assemble the infinitely varied phenomena of behavior pathology into groups which we call behavior disorders. In other words, on the basis of our professional needs and our experience, we simply group those signs and symptoms together which seem to belong together, and we then designate each group by some descriptive term. What we have defined as *hypochondria* was at one time named in accordance with the organ most complained about by the patient, as *gastric neurosis, cardiac neurosis,* etc., and later these were grouped together as *organ neurosis.* But such minutely descriptive terms burden the student and the clinician with an unnecessarily redundant terminology and, what is still more important, they imply that the disorder is in the organ, or in its "psychic representation," instead of in the person, thus unwittingly falling into the patient's error.[3]

VARIETIES OF HYPOCHONDRIA

The varieties of body overconcern are endless. Almost any organ, system, part or function may be unjustifiably accused by the patient — the gastrointestinal system and its associated glands, the heart and blood-vessels, the respiratory system and the genito-urinary organs, the head and all that it includes, the neck and back, the nervous system central and peripheral, the arms and hands, the legs and feet. Diseases and disorders of every description are held to be present by one hypochondriacal patient or another — cancer, diabetes, kidney or liver disease, tuberculosis, pleurisy, anemia, heart disease, rheumatism or syphilis.

As a rule not one but several organs, parts or functions are complained about at once. For example, here are the symptoms presented by a thirty-eight-year-old married woman, without prompting or suggestion, none of which was of less than ten years' duration. She complained of headaches, frequent and severe, aches in her limbs, backaches, poor vision, floating specks before her eyes, sinus trouble and post-nasal discharge, intermittent ringing and crackling in her ears, poor sleep, dyspnea, palpitation and precordial pain.

[3] For a contemporary account of hypochondria in terms of the transfer of an hypothetical *libido,* from "intrapsychic object representations" to some specific "intrapsychic organ representation," see O. Fenichel, *The Psychoanalytic Theory of Neurosis* (New York: Norton, 1945), pp. 261-264.

She believed that her blood was not circulating freely because her arms and legs seemed to "go to sleep" too easily and because she felt sluggish. She reported a large appetite but poor digestion, much trouble with belching, sour eructations and flatus, constipation, and mucus in her stools. There were she said, nocturia, diurnal frequency, and dysmenorrhea which always sent her to bed. She complained of pains and paresthesias in many parts of her body.

This patient's work record is typical of a great many hypochondriacal cases. She gave up school at the age of thirteen without objection to help her mother around the house. At seventeen she was prevailed upon to take a job in a factory, but here she suffered from headaches, backaches, and pains in the chest and abdomen for which no basis in organ pathology could be found. She absented herself from work frequently, and at the end of two years quit her job to return home and help her mother with the housework. During the nine years following her return home, she developed an intensive interest in her symptoms and established for herself a routine of daily medication, colonic irrigation, rest and avoidance of strain. At twenty-eight she married. She disliked sex relations but was satisfied with routine housework. She had many acquaintances but no hobbies or interests, outside of keeping house and caring for her health. Her attitude toward her situation can best be described as one of satisfied resignation, without evidence of discouragement or unhappiness. She stuck doggedly to the reiteration of all her symptoms, in spite of the uniformly negative reports from extensive medical and surgical examinations and clinical laboratory studies and declined to consider any possible alternatives to her own preconceived interpretations. It was clear that body overconcern and body care had become essential sources of need-satisfaction to her.

Neither medical ignorance nor medical erudition is of itself sufficient to protect one from body overconcern. Laymen are not infrequently preoccupied and even terrified by diseases which have never existed excepting in folklore, and by supposed anatomical or physiological changes that are quite impossible.[4] Medical students, nurses and physicians are protected from folklore and the impossible by their superior knowledge of the human body, its physiology and pathology. On the other hand, they become ac-

---

[4] H. Ziegler and J. Heyman, "False concepts of diseases," *Amer. Jour. Psychiat.*, 1935, vol. 92, pp. 655-674.

quainted with hundreds of dangerous possibilities unknown to the average layman. The end-result is that medical personnel and particularly the medical student, who must master the processes of disease and death long before he learns about treatment and recovery, are fully as vulnerable to hypochondriacal worry as the most uninformed layman. In both it is the personal history and the existing status of need-satisfaction and security-insecurity that determine the outcome.

Gastrointestinal complaints

Although any of the viscera can become the focus of hypochondriacal concern, people worry most easily over functions they know about, or think they know about, and tend to implicate organs which are accessible to observation, evaluation, discussion and control. No functions and no viscera can surpass the gastrointestinal in these respects. Everyone learns very early in life to react directly and specifically to what he eats and what he eliminates. Everyone is trained to expect praise and acceptance for eating and eliminating in accordance with his elders' wishes, and to share their concern over deviations from the norms which his parents set up for him in relation to intake, digestion and residue. Since children acquire these habits in shared situations, usually with a parent, they learn at the same time gestural and verbal language habits by means of which they are able to indicate to others as well as to themselves the location, character, possible effects and probable remedies for their complaints. The goodness and badness which small children learn about, during their early training in visceral ethics, become the behavioral basis for many hypochondriacal habits later on.

There can be no doubt that some behavior pathologists attempt to account for the relatively high incidence of stomach and bowel complaints by more elaborate and romantic hypotheses than we shall present here. Indeed, a glance through the contemporary literature reveals that logical descriptions of gastrointestinal symptoms in terms of occult and psychic symbolism still abound.[5] But from a biosocial point of view the indisputable advantages which gastrointestinal functions have over other functions — anatomical accessibility, daily routine need-satisfaction sequences, quick and easy alteration, and wide cultural acceptance as a topic of free dis-

[5] Some of these will be found summarized in O. Fenichel, *The Psychoanalytic Theory of Neurosis* (New York: Norton, 1945), pp. 245-246.

cussion — coupled with their deep involvement in emotional reactions of many kinds, provide a sufficient background to account for their heading the list of body overconcern.[6] These biosocial advantages, which stomach and bowels enjoy in the individual's self-reactions, in turn make possible the rich cultural symbolism that has grown up around digestion and elimination. They make possible the early lessons in ethical evaluation of eating and eliminating, as praiseworthy or inacceptable, the childhood training in self-observation and verbal formulation of intake and residue, the high esteem in which conventional intake and residue are publicly held, and indirectly even the communal mealtime gatherings which no other visceral function shares in our society.

The symptomatology in gastrointestinal overconcern is at least as rich and varied as that in gastrointestinal disease, and since in either there may be disturbances of digestion and elimination, the distinction between them can be made with certainty only by clinicians who are equipped by training and experience to recognize both. The commoner complaints are reflected with fair accuracy in current patent medicine advertisements of antacids, cholagogues and laxatives. We may mention belching, heartburn and sour regurgitation, general inappetence or inability to eat certain foods, bad tastes and coated tongue, discomfort, distention or pain after eating. Patients sometimes begin by indicting the liver, and go on to support their indictment with a bill of particulars which includes headache, sluggishness, bilious feelings, bright spots before the eyes, and even jaundice, which is confirmed neither by daylight inspection nor by obtaining the icterus index. In most cases of gastrointestinal overconcern there are complaints of constipation, flatus and abdominal pain; in some the complaint is of diarrhea. Patients frequently betray their watchfulness and the intensity of their concern by the wealth of detail they furnish, especially with regard to diet, gastric regurgitation and eliminative residue. It is not at all unusual for the patient to read or present a written list of complaints to the diagnostician so that there shall be no oversight.

A married man of thirty-nine came to the clinic complaining, "I have trouble in my bowels and my head. My bowels just spasm on me, I get constipated and my head goes sort of toxic. It seems

6 Twenty-seven of the fifty patients in a series reported by S. Katzenelbogen, "Hypochondriacal complaints with special reference to personality and environment," *Amer. Jour. Psychiat.*, 1942, vol. 98, pp. 815-823.

to poison my system." This patient's complaints date back twelve years to an attack of "acute indigestion" in which he seemed to bloat up, pains developed in his abdomen and spread in several directions. (He traced some of these with his finger as he spoke.) He spent a month in bed at this time and on advice rested for another two months before working again. The doctors, he felt, took a very serious view of his condition, calling at the house sometimes late at night. He himself "felt sick, worried and frightened," fearing that he might never be well again. For three or four years after this attack he took enemas, three a day at first, reducing gradually to one a day. For eight or nine years he has taken laxatives and devoted constant attention to his diet. He describes variations in residue with enough detail to indicate conscientious watching. Four months before coming to the clinic he was discharged from his job as a clerk in a paper mill because of too much sick leave and an unwillingness to do anything he considered outside of his duties. Since then he has lived with his wife's relatives.

Of his childhood this man says, "My folks brought me up to feel I wasn't strong and husky, that I was not like other boys. I was always an obedient, good child." He had night terrors throughout childhood, bit his fingernails, had temper tantrums and was very "choosy" about food. He preferred reading to playing. He always disliked his one sibling, a sister four years younger than he, because his parents seemed to give in to her too easily. He lost a good deal of school because of his own "frailty" and frequent sickness. His father died when he was twelve and his mother when he was sixteen. He began work at fourteen and has never liked it. He became very dependent upon his wife, whom he married when he was twenty-two, leaving most decisions to her and taking little interest in sex relations. His attack of "acute indigestion" followed her death, five years after marriage, by three months during which he had felt lost and hopeless. He moved from the south to upstate New York three years later and soon remarried. His second wife proved less willing to assume major responsibilities for him than his first, and she made demands upon him sexually that he felt unable to meet. He became more and more preoccupied with his gastrointestinal welfare until he finally lost his position and his home. In the complete absence of community facilities for psychiatric treatment where he lived, prognosis for recovery from chronic partially disabling hypochondria was deemed poor.

Cardiovascular complaints

It is an interesting commentary upon body overconcern that, whereas cardiovascular morbidity and mortality in later maturity greatly exceed gastrointestinal, cardiovascular hypochondria is at all periods of life much less common than gastrointestinal.[7] There is not the same personal history of training in identification, formulation and control that characterizes feeding and elimination. The heart's action, pulse-rate and blood-pressure require special factors to make them matters of concern.

The chief source of disturbed cardiovascular performance in persons with normal heart and blood-vessels is the same as that in many cases of disturbed gastrointestinal and respiratory performance, namely, emotional excitement. During an emotional reaction the heart may change pace suddenly, speed up or slow down, palpitate, seem to the person to stop, skip beats, turn over or rise up and make him breathless. A pain may appear suddenly in the chest and even sometimes shoot down the left arm. The disturbed individual may complain of dizziness and faintness, of throbbing blood-vessels and feelings of pressure and fullness in the head. It is obvious here, as in gastrointestinal overconcern, that the patient's symptoms are not unlike those met in cardiovascular disease, and it is usually necessary for the diagnostician to resort to special examination procedures before he can be sure of the distinction.

If well-trained diagnosticians have even the slightest difficulty in distinguishing between cardiovascular disease and cardiovascular hypochondria, it is small wonder that so many laymen misinterpret emotional disturbance as an indication of cardiovascular pathology. Most laymen have at least a little information about the signs and symptoms of heart disease and hypertension. They have heard or perhaps witnessed how suddenly decompensation may appear and how dramatically heart disease may terminate. When, therefore, following overexertion or overindulgence, under conditions of stress and excitement, or of anxiety and prolonged conflict, the normal heart's performance is disturbed, an already sensitized individual can easily jump to the conclusion that this is the thing he has heard about — heart trouble with its threat of invalidism, suffering and early death. Now he may develop habits of cardiovascular overconcern. He watches over the heart's rhythm and rate, feels his pulse, looks out for traces of pain, avoids exertion and excitement,

[7] L. Dublin, "Longevity in retrospect and prospect," in E. Cowdry (editor), *Problems of Ageing*, 2d edition (Baltimore: Williams and Wilkins, 1942), pp. 91-110; W. Overholser, "Mental problems and their management," *Med. Ann. Dist. Columbia*, 1941, vol. 10, pp. 212-217.

examines his extremities for signs of swelling and discoloration, and perhaps for years lives the life of a semi-invalid though his heart is competent and sound. If, in addition, to have the status of a person needing and deserving special consideration, protection, care and comforting brings the frightened man unexpectedly important satisfactions, these satisfactions will tend to make his acquired status indispensable to him.

A married man of forty-two was admitted to the medical service of a metropolitan hospital because of cardiovascular complaints. Examinations, however, failed to yield evidence of systemic pathology, but there were indications that cardiac illness in others and incautious comments made to the patient might both be important factors. To the psychiatric consultant the patient said, "My heart beats too fast. I have high blood-pressure. I get a stabbing pain deep in my breast-bone but I guess that's natural. I have giddy spells. I'm not frightened any more but the doctors are." At the age of twenty-four he began having attacks of pains in his arms and over his heart which seemed worse when he lay down flat. He believed then that he had heart trouble and sometimes spent the night propped up in a Morris chair near an open window. He volunteered the information that a favorite uncle had collapsed and died, apparently of heart failure, while attending a play at the theater a few months before this. The patient could recall no special difficulties immediately prior to his own attacks at this time. These acute episodes, which were undoubtedly anxiety attacks,[8] gradually disappeared. "But," the patient added, "I've never felt secure in my life." During the ensuing years, until the onset of the present illness, he was free of cardiac symptoms.

When the patient was thirty-seven his father had the first of a series of heart attacks which terminated two years later in death. A few weeks after his father's heart symptoms began, the patient himself suddenly had an attack of cardiac palpitation and pain at the end of a strenuous week-end in the country. Although denying that he was frightened, he became shaky, felt "all in" and noticed that his head, ears, hands and knees were throbbing. "I just became conscious of my heart-beat," he said. "I never knew I had it before but I've noticed it ever since. I think I strained my heart, and I might have been suffering a nervous shock," i.e., from his father's illness. The day after this episode the patient visited a physician who, he said, told him that he had angina and high blood-pressure

[8] This case illustrates the overlap of symptomatology mentioned earlier in the chapter. *Anxiety attacks* will be defined and discussed in Chapter 9.

— "a hundred and seventy high and a hundred and twenty low," according to the patient. The druggist who filled his prescription said smilingly, "These aren't for you, I hope!" and informed the patient that one was for morphine and the other for nitroglycerin. The patient already knew that the latter was used in cardiovascular disease.

There were numerous similar incidents of cardiac pain and palpitation during the five years before the patient was finally admitted to the hospital for study. These were particularly apt to occur when he hurried, but they came sometimes when he was resting. The patient watched over his heart constantly, counted his pulse, noticed that his suspended foot moved with each heartbeat when he crossed his legs, and that his throat, buttocks, feet and fingers often seemed to pulsate. He spared himself in every possible way to prolong his life. At the time of his admission he was seriously considering retirement from a lucrative position to part-time work that would make fewer demands upon him. Psychiatric examination indicated no serious personal difficulties other than his rather strong tendencies to depend upon and identify with persons he cared for, and to develop body overconcern as a preferential reaction of insecurity. A year later, with the assistance of a family physician who was not easily stampeded by dramatic symptoms, the patient had made considerable progress toward living the life of a well man.

It is a matter of common observation that actually hypertensive persons, if told about their vascular hypertension, often suffer far more from their knowledge than their high blood-pressure. This is particularly apt to be the case if they are given only a restricted routine, medication, veiled admonitions, and hints about what to look for and avoid, or if they get a diet of indigestible facts concerning the physiology of their impairment and the contradictory suggestion that there is nothing for them to worry about. Under these circumstances the untrained, unfortified patient may develop self-reactions which threaten him at every turn with imminent death, even though for many years the actual danger to life may be almost negligible. One finds similar situations among young men and women who have been told casually, by an incautious examiner, that they have a heart murmur. The son of exceptionally oversolicitous parents, for example, was kept in bed for two years following such a diagnosis and after that forbidden to play games with other children throughout the rest of his childhood and most of adolescence. When late in adolescence the murmur was found to be absent and the heart normal, neither parents nor patient could restructure the latter's life in such a way as to enable him to participate freely in the activities of his contemporaries. He continued to sit down, stand up and walk as if his first careless move might be his last.

Respiratory complaints

Breathing, like the heart-beat, is quickly altered in emotional reactions and easily accessible to self-reactions. In excitement, whether as part of one's socially shared behavior or as part of one's private fantasy, respiration may become rapid, shallow and irregular. In anxiety it may be fast or slow, deep, shallow or sighing. Anxious patients often complain of being unable to get a deep enough breath, of feeling constricted about the throat or chest, of having something stuck in the trachea or larynx. Worried patients complain that secretory products in the respiratory passages are excessive or insufficient, that there is burning present there, or pains in the chest or throat. For any one of a variety of possible reasons, people become convinced that they are suffering from pleuritic, pulmonary, bronchial, tracheal or laryngeal disease. When the origin of respiratory complaining is in anxiety reactions, we consider it to be *hypochondriacal* if and when the patient focuses upon the complaint with the conviction that it means respiratory defect or disease. Obviously there will be a great many cases in which hypochondria and an anxiety disorder coexist.

Genito-urinary system complaints

The genito-urinary system, like the gastrointestinal system, can be checked on, evaluated and discussed, and although its performance is less subject to deliberate interference and experimentation by the patient, it is certainly far richer in folklore. Reproductive functions, in particular, are in the unique position of being at the same time surrounded by taboos and yet of the greatest practical and personal importance to nearly everyone. This paradox is more striking among men than women, for the male is much more likely to lose prestige and expose himself to ridicule by claiming sexual dysfunction than the female is. A consequence of this is that free and promiscuous discussions of personal sex symptoms are far less common among mature men than among women. The male reluctance to admit sexual inferiority may partially account for Billings' findings that reproductive system complaints are about twice as common among hypochondriacal women as among hypochondriacal men.[9] It is much commoner for women to be exempted from performing industrial and business duties on this basis than it is for men, a fact of which students of absenteeism are well aware. The woman in our culture is expected to suffer from periodic and post-partum handicaps and to gain exemptions on this basis without blame or serious loss in status as a woman.

There is no denying that female sex functions and their consequences introduce physiological difficulties and hazards to which the male is a stranger. Menstrual discomforts and pains in healthy women, the experiences of pregnancy, childbirth and lactation, apprehensions over and distress in the climacteric, and knowledge of the relatively high incidence of female reproductive system disease — all these can become fruitful sources of body overconcern. Moreover there are so many ways in which female genito-urinary complaints may be met by medical and surgical procedures that the hypochondriacal woman is particularly vulnerable to prolonged or drastic treatment of pelvic organs and related systemic functions. Of course, nothing is easier than to sit back and criticize internists and surgeons for prescribing hormones for, or performing repeated operations upon, women whose genito-urinary complaints are without basis in systemic pathology. For those who have to make the always difficult decision that remediable organ pathology is *not* present, the problems presented by hypochondriacal complaints have a very different look. No diagnostician can afford to make the mistake of assuming that, because a woman is a chronic complainer, she therefore does not have gynecological pathology. Neurotic complaints are no insurance against systemic disease and death.

Nevertheless, genito-urinary symptoms and their direct or systemic treatment play a leading role in hypochondria, in men second only to the gastrointestinal system and in women probably second to none. Exact estimates of their prevalence are difficult to make because, at least in the larger metropolitan hospitals, check-up studies indicate that considerable numbers of hypochondriacal patients are carried in urology and gynecology, just as they also are in gastroenterology. Men complain hypochondriacally of impotence, of genital aching, pain and paresthesia, of urinary and seminal

[9] E. Billings, *Handbook of Elementary Psychobiology and Psychiatry* (New York: Macmillan, 1939), pp. 125-126.

dysfunctions, and of dissatisfaction with their performance in sex relations. Women, having more difficulties on which to base their complaints, show greater variation in their symptoms. They commonly complain of pelvic and abdominal discomfort, pain or paresthesia, which may seem temporally related to sexual functions, related to strain or exertion, or chronic and more or less continual. Urinary dysfunction is also a frequent complaint and one which can easily be suggested by local after-effects of cystoscopic examinations or by comments made during cystoscopy. Headaches, nausea, dizziness, hot flashes, and other more remote complaints, which may be common in gynecological disorder or in feminine folklore, are frequently reported by hypochondriacal women and by them attributed to genito-urinary dysfunction.

Neuromuscular complaints

The importance of popular misconceptions in determining the character of one's complaints comes out nowhere more clearly than in relation to the muscles and the peripheral nerves. For although muscles actually develop innumerable fatiguing tensions, imbalances, pulls, droops and spasms, they are seldom accused of being defective or diseased by the hypochondriac, unless he has undergone unintentional but effective coaching by an interested therapist. It is true that backaches, headaches, pains in the neck, the thighs, the arms and the legs are exceedingly common complaints, but the complainer is far more likely to refer these directly to his nervous system than to the muscles themselves. Thus the peripheral nerves, although quite incapable of movement, are continually accused by laymen of quivering, pulling, clenching, drawing or knotting up. Whereas the actual changes giving rise to most of these complaints originate in local striped or smooth muscle response, for the public it is the nerves that are tensed, taut, frayed, get on edge or go to pieces. It is the central nervous system which is referred to as exhausted, debilitated, broken down, deteriorated or diseased.

This widespread tendency to interpret freely the changes in striped or smooth muscle tonus and reactivity in terms of "nerves," nervousness, neurasthenia and central nervous system dysfunction represents a serious cultural lag. During most of the nineteenth century so little was known about neurophysiology that any of the behavior disorders could be ascribed to hypothetical nerve disturbances with a clear scientific conscience. Thus even so advanced a thinker as Freud ascribed hypochondria, fatigue syndromes and anxiety neuroses to neural disorder, called them *actual neuroses* and excluded them from psychoanalysis.[10] Indeed, until recent years so inadequate has been our recognition of the potentialities for behavior pathology in situational relationships and self-reactions that, even though no lesions or physiopathology could be demonstrated in the brains of neurotics or in two-thirds of psychotics, it was still maintained on all sides that neural defect, depletion, deterioration or disease was the only conceivable basis for behavior disorder.[11] Popular thinking still persists in looking upon over-reactions to need, frustration, anxiety, guilt and disappointment as indications of nervous system disorder in spite of the large body of organized evidence to the contrary. Likewise, because of the inevitable lag in the dissemination and acceptance of new technical information, many persons today who discover in themselves conflicting or antisocial trends, who develop fear and tension symptoms, or whose thinking grows confused under stress, are left to conclude immediately that their brain is diseased, constitutionally inferior or deteriorating.

Hypochondriacal reactions in organ and tissue pathology

No diagnostician or therapist can escape the responsibility for evaluating the intensity and character of a person's complaints in relation to the more objective signs of organ and tissue pathology. With comparable pathology present, some persons appear to suffer much and some little; and even with comparable suffering, some complain more and some less. The problem of clinical evaluation is further complicated by the wide individual variations in habitual modes of reaction to pain and discomfort, by the reinforcing effects of fear, anxiety or expectation, and by the inhibiting effects of reassurance, confidence and sometimes of despair. It is further complicated by the extent to which pain and other disease symptoms are utilized, deliberately or unwittingly, to increase sympathy and affection or to gain privileges and exemptions. But regardless of the difficulties involved in diagnosis, it is well to remember that all hypochondriacal persons ultimately sicken and die, and that a neu-

[10] S. Freud, *A General Introduction to Psychoanalysis*, translated by J. Riviere (New York: Liveright, 1935), pp. 336-340.

[11] For a recent representation of this general position, see W. Alvarez, *Nervousness, Indigestion and Pain* (New York: Harper, 1943), pp. 127-168 and 230-260.

rotic individual may also house a damaged or inferior organ just as a nephritic individual may also suffer a fracture or become depressed. The following case illustrates this clinically important fact.

A married woman of thirty-four, mother of a twelve-year-old girl, came to the diagnostic clinic because, in spite of her complaints of abdominal and back pain and of digestive disturbances, her husband threatened to leave her if she had another operation. During the previous seven years she had undergone five abdominal and pelvic operations, none of which had been justified by the findings, and had dissipated the whole of her husband's savings. The first operation had been exploratory and the second for removal of possible post-operative adhesions. The succeeding three were performed each by a different surgeon, and in each case only after months of "clinical shopping" and after her vivid complaints had been supplemented by accusations of heartlessness and incompetence against those who withstood her insistence. She expressed open resentment and resistance when referred for psychiatric examination.

In taking the patient's medical history the psychiatrist found, as without doubt her surgeons had found in years past, that for practically every organ and system he mentioned she had one or more complaints. She showed by her use and misuse of medical terms that she was quick to appropriate anything she heard as a corroboration of her own conclusions. Physical examination was complicated by the patient's reporting tenderness almost everywhere. Some of her complaints pointed to one possibility, some to others, and all had to be explored with the aid of consultations and technical procedures. In the end only a small group of symptoms remained to suggest organ and system pathology. These pointed in the direction of possible gall bladder disease and a gall bladder series gave unmistakable support for this group of the patient's complaints. The husband required some high-powered assurance before he consented to her sixth operation which turned out to be highly necessary. A follow-up one year later revealed that the same galaxy of complaints was present, substantially unaltered, and that the patient had no less aversion to psychiatric treatment than she had shown before her sixth operation.

Some of the more usual varieties of hypochondriacal disorder have now been touched upon. To list and discuss them all would be to write an encyclopedia of popular medicine and folklore. For almost every imaginable complaint and combination of complaints have been developed at some time by someone and made the focus of body overconcern. Not only must the internist, the general surgeon, the gynecologist and the urologist deal continually with hypochondria in the practice of his specialty, but so also must the brain surgeon, dermatologist, laryngologist, neurologist, ophthalmologist, orthopedist, otologist, pediatrician and radiologist. The choice of symptom, like the choice of neurosis, has many possible determinants — unintentional suggestion, emotional disturbance, transient visceral dysfunction, previous illness in the patient or in others close to him, family tradition, undigested information — some of which will be taken up when we discuss the determinants of body overconcern.

BIOSOCIAL BASES OF HYPOCHONDRIACAL REACTIONS

Habitual body overconcern is an acquired reaction which most persons never develop. Therefore, to understand hypochondria we must face two important questions. One is, *From what characteristics of normal human behavior does body overconcern develop?* The other question is, *What determinants are there which seem to favor the development of body overconcern in those individuals who do become hypochondriacal?* These two questions and their answers are obviously interdependent. The first is concerned with the basic characteristics of all behavior that make hypochondria possible for anyone, and the second with the observed fact that some individuals develop hypochondria while most do not. In the present section we shall confine our discussion to a consideration of the biosocial bases that make everyone a potential hypochondriac, leaving the problem of individual differences in susceptibility for the section following.

The biosocial matrix of body overconcern

To begin with, hypochondriacal disorders could not develop if there were no physiological basis for them. Biologically considered, every human organism is a complex, interlocking system of living machinery which manufactures intermediate products and endproducts out of the raw materials it takes in. Through the use of these substances the body can perform work, maintain its own integrity in a continually changing environment, and keep its internal

milieu remarkably constant. Many of the normally occurring biochemical processes within the body are directly or indirectly stimulating. So also are the incessant pumping of body fluids, the continual changes in physiological rhythms and pressures, the intermittent ebb and flow of air, the wormlike and ringlike movements of
visceral sacs and tubes, the tightenings and relaxations of all types
of muscle, and the shifting patterns of secretory activity. It is obvious that unceasing physiological activity and biochemical change
constitute the normal background of everyone's existence. Change
and activity form a biological matrix of stimulation toward which
anyone may some time develop self-reactions of various kinds and
of different degrees of intensity.

Body overconcern is an exaggeration of the normal body care
and body concern to which everyone in our culture today is edu-
cated. As a child becomes capable of it, he is taught to observe his
body as an object, to notice some of its changes in appearance and
in product, and to report pain or discomfort to his elders. Training
in body care and in concern over health and disease is thus merely
an expansion of the early training we all get in relation to feeding,
elimination and cleanliness. In this process, every child acquires a
great variety of self-reactions toward his body's appearance and its
apparent soundness and adequacy. Many of these self-reactions are
learned in conventional language form and can thus become the
basis of public discussion and private thought. Such systematically
acquired and socially approved self-reactions form a matrix in
everyone's symbolic behavior which may become the biosocial basis
of hypochondriacal concern and hypochondriacal complaining.

Each of us is taught in childhood that pain, discomfort and unusual changes in his body or its products are to be avoided not only
for their own sake, but also because they may indicate worse things
to come. We thus learn to equate personal security with physiological adequacy, at the same time that we are acquiring our individual standards of normal body functioning. We learn that seemingly unimportant and innocuous signs or symptoms may turn out
to presage suffering, crippling, invalidism or death, and that more
blame attaches to neglect than to complaining. It is therefore to
be expected that normal children and adults, so trained in self-
attitudes and cultural attitudes, will react publicly or privately with
frank body concern when something they notice about their anatomy or physiology seems to them amiss. A person's solicitude over

his health is not considered abnormal in our culture unless it persists indefinitely in the face of contradictory evidence, unjustifiably absorbs a major portion of his attention, reduces his social effectiveness unnecessarily, or dominates his pattern of living and determines his important choices.

Hypochondriacal sensitivity

What distinguishes the hypochondriacal person from the normal is not merely that he complains more but also that he finds more to complain about. He reacts with almost hair-trigger ease to all sorts of internal and surface changes to which the normal person is a stranger. On what is this sensitivity based? Are the hypochondriac's receptors more sensitively built than those of the average person? Is his nervous system anatomically more delicate or physiologically more unstable? No one has ever presented valid evidence to show that biologically hyperacute, fragile or poorly balanced structures are at the bottom of hypochondriacal attitudes. Such pseudobiological explanations were popular during the eighties, nineties and early nineteen hundreds, and they are still occasionally reaffirmed by an authority in some field other than behavior pathology. But the continued lack of factual support and the results of modern therapy have made them even less tenable today than they were some thirty or forty years ago.

In spite of the fact that hypochondriacal persons need not have receptors of unusual acuity, there can be no question as to their hypersensitivity to certain kinds or ranges of stimulation. This superior sensitivity is, however, based upon acquired reactions. It depends upon special habits of reacting selectively to stimulus patterns that belong to the general background of physiological activity — the biological matrix which we have described above. In brief, what we call the hypochondriac's special sensitivity is actually a *special ease-of-reaction* which he has learned to give to certain kinds of stimulation. He has become *reaction-sensitive* to his body processes. For reasons which we shall shortly discuss, the hypochondriac is unable to take his physiological activities for granted and ignore their common effects. He has developed self-reactions which keep him habitually on the alert for signs and symptoms from the organs, parts or functions he overvalues or mistrusts. In his habitual self-reactions he behaves toward his body as an overconcerned mother might toward her overvalued or mistrusted child. Indeed, one finds clinically that anxious middle-aged women, when their children have grown to independence, sometimes turn to body-care and body overconcern almost as though these were substitutes for child care and child solicitude.

Persons acquire sensitivity to their bodies and grow into hypo-chondriacs by essentially the same process as that which we described under *reaction-sensitivity* and *progressive reaction sensitization* in Chapter 3. It is a learning process occurring under conditions of close attention or special motivation. The hypochondriac becomes an amateur diagnostician who makes his observations by the same general methods that a physician uses. Thus he can learn to take his pulse and watch his respirations, or feel his heart-beat with his fingers. He can use his ears to study his own wheezings, whistlings and rumblings, and his eyes to examine an accessible part of his body or his body products. If for any reason he continues to do these things, he may build up response patterns that will make him sensitive to minute and usually unimportant body changes. Body overconcern, in other words, no matter how initiated and no matter what its determinants, can become established through mere repetition like any other form of reaction-sensitivity, and grow progressive through its own cumulative effects, as in any other progressive reaction sensitization.

The hypochondriac has one advantage over the physician examining him in being able to react to physiological processes within his own body which are not directly accessible to his examiner. He can learn to count his respirations and his heart-beat from within, that is, by means of their stimulation of interoceptors, proprioceptors and skin receptors. He can acquire reaction-sensitivity, through motivated practice, to stimulation coming from any part of the ever-present physiological background of activity and change. To attend closely to something, whether inside the body or outside it, simply means to exclude from one's behavior-organization of the moment as many competing or interfering activities as possible. One's readiness to react, one's own attitude of expectancy, gives a clear channel to a special narrow range of stimulation. Anything that falls within this narrow range seems to stand out clearly and distinctly because our expectant attitude, our readiness, has reduced the number of other reactions in process at the time. The watched finger throbs, and keen anticipation whets the edge of pain.

The hypochondriac's advantage over the physician, his inside

lines of direct communication with organs and parts, is far out-
weighed by the disadvantages arising from his inexpertness and his
personal needs. The good physician has been rigorously trained to
entertain only certain criteria which have proved acceptable in the
light of the accumulating experience of thousands of other men
with a similar professional background. The hypochondriac trains
himself by a hit-or-miss unstandardized method and his background
is only that of prevalent folklore and popular medicine. More important than inexpertness and ignorance, however, are his personal
needs, his insecurities and anxieties, his habitual attitudes and gratifications. For whereas the physician can be an impartial observer,
whose dominant interest is in being accurate and competent, the
hypochondriac's self-observations are bound to be partisan. He
often believes that his security, his integrity and even his own life
are at stake. This is not the atmosphere in which sound judgments
about oneself can be made.

Emotional behavior and hypochondria

Emotional reactions often play a central role in initiating and
perpetuating body overconcern. We saw in Chapter 3 that emotional behavior is distinguished by its large and important visceral
components which are not, however, directly responsive to strictly
visceral functions, but rather to occurrences in shared behavior or
in one's private thinking. Nevertheless, these visceral changes are
essential *components* of emotional behavior and not just incidental
effects. To say, as we do in popular speech, that emotion speeds up
breathing and the heart rate, or slows digestion down, is to speak
inaccurately. If we are to understand the hypochondriacal reaction it is essential to recognize that worry and digestion share the
same stomach, that fear and blood-pressure have one heart between
them, and that the same chest sighs for air that sighs for love or
sympathy. It is essential to recognize that these emotional activities
are reactions of the organism in the same sense that walking, talking, thinking, digestion and respiration are.

Emotional disturbances often appear in such a way that the
person developing them cannot understand or cannot acknowledge
their origin. Under these circumstances a person is quite apt to
react to some striking aspect of his own emotional behavior, instead
of to what brought it on. In other words, he neglects or forgets
the thing that disturbed him and focuses upon his physiological

changes. If his stomach rebels in strong aversion, or his heart's rhythm is deranged in fear, it is the stomach or the heart to which he reacts, and no longer the situation toward which he was averse or fearful. Of course this is not a deliberately planned evasion but a displacement of anxiety. It occurs because an individual cannot single out the source of his reaction, or because the visceral change seems to him obviously the important and the dangerous thing — as indeed it would be if it really meant the disease which he believes it does. Displacement of anxiety may also occur because the visceral disturbance sometimes outlasts the stimulating situation by a very long time. This is especially the case in digestion, where each successive step depends upon the effectiveness of the one preceding it, and the whole process normally extends over many hours.

It is important to realize that, if emotional disturbances originate in personally humiliating, repugnant or dangerous situations, the interpretation of them as symptoms of disease — even of serious disease — may raise fewer difficulties for a patient than the recognition of his original predicament. This factor must always be suspected in cases which are resistant to treatment. For disease can be accepted by the patient at least as honorable, and it can be discussed openly with others. It excites sympathy and consideration instead of revulsion and contempt. Once the visceral component of an emotional disturbance has been accepted by a person and his associates as evidence of sickness, its recurrence is almost sure to be interpreted as further evidence — in this way leading toward the establishment and elaboration of habitual body overconcern.

In such reactions as these to a part of one's emotional conduct, instead of to its source, the specific visceral component that becomes established as an habitual response to stress is often called a "body protest." This term is, however, no more than a metaphor. It should not be taken to imply a separation of the body from the person, since modern conceptions of the person include every one of the body's functions.[12] The so-called "body protest" is *substitutive* insofar as it misguides and diverts the patient and his associates from the source of his emotional upheaval. "Body protests" are *symbolic* in the sense that, to one skilled in the pathology of hypochondria, they represent more or less definite relationships to a patient's original disowned or repressed reactions.

[12] See the able presentation of the modern attitude by H. Fox, "Somatic symbolism or psychosomatic dualism," *Psychiatry,* 1942, vol. 5, pp. 7-13.

Cumulative and self-perpetuating reactions

We have already seen how emotional disturbances may reinforce, build up and prolong one's reactions to difficulty, particularly through the self-stimulating organization of visceral activity. In human beings there are other sources of cumulative and self-perpetuating developments which infra-human animals lack, namely, talking and socially organized thinking. Indeed, as a topic of casual conversation, there is probably nothing but sin and scandal that can compete with illness and body complaints. Friendships over the fence, across desks and counters, on benches, trains and buses, and even through the mail, have been built up on the one foundation of a mutual interest in the visceral life.

It would be difficult to exaggerate either the prevalence or the undesirability of hypochondriacal talk. In the first place, talking incessantly about one's supposed poor health benefits no one, and least of all the talker. He will rarely meet a person who can resist giving advice, and seldom meet two who agree about it. He runs the almost certain risk of picking up new terms and new worries from hypochondriacal habitués. New misinformation and a new vocabulary give the novice new materials and tools for body over-concern. His new words and phrases make it easier for him to focus upon some fleeting characteristics of visceral performance and its products, to remember and ruminate over these in an organized manner, and to discuss them with others who are similarly engrossed. Talking and thinking about one's signs and symptoms not only aid in sensitizing one, by organizing new symbolic response patterns to set off, but they also provide a most effective means of establishing an habitual mode of response to one's physiology, and for building this up into a prominent ingredient of one's social personality.

Another important source of self-perpetuation lies in a person's learning to react specifically to *phases* or *steps* in his normally automatic visceral sequences. Viscera usually do their best work when they are not watched. A simple illustration of this can be found in the act of swallowing something. By attending closely to his swallowing, a person runs the risk of establishing a new specific reaction to some individual phase or step in the swallowing sequence. This new reaction is then quite likely to interfere with the smooth succession of automatic responses, each of which should touch off the next. It is common for persons who fuss over swallowing a tablet, for example, to develop coughing or gag-responses to contact of the tablet with the pharynx. From that time on, the automatic swallowing sequence will be interrupted by such contact, and the individual becomes one who cannot take medicines in tablet form without retraining. It is almost as easy as this to develop cardiac irregularities by watching one's pulse while worried, or pseudo-asthma by specific reactions to one's respiration. Too much attention to digestion and elimination may lead to comparable irregularities in gastrointestinal function. Through any of these specific learned reactions one may acquire new disturbances of body-function to worry over, new topics for fantasy and conversation, new reinforcements for the development of hypochondriacal attitudes.

The effects of self-treatment also aid in perpetuating body overconcern. Self-treatment focuses one's interest upon whatever is being treated. Some patent medicines capitalize upon hypochondriacal interest by inducing gross changes in body function which the patient can observe. Digestive remedies, for example, are frequently compounded so as to form or release sizable quantities of inert gas in the stomach. The patient can then belch this forth, experience relief in getting rid of what the remedy actually planted there, and then attribute his relief to the medicine instead of to his belching. Not a few chronic hypochondriacs, who try this and that medicine or procedure, do succeed eventually in damaging themselves. They may bring about disorder in the very system to which they devote their main attention, particularly if this is the easily accessible gastrointestinal system; or they may injure one system in their amateur attempts to do something unnecessary for another. It must, however, be admitted that many a chronic hypochondriac outlives his apparently more robust critics. Perhaps a lifelong interest in prolonging life spares and protects some individuals from exposure and exertion.

BIOSOCIAL DETERMINANTS OF HYPOCHONDRIACAL REACTIONS

We have just seen that all of us have the biological matrix of internal activity and change out of which body overconcern may arise, and that in our culture everyone acquires self-reactions to body activities and changes, and learns to formulate these in conventional language and discuss them. We have seen also that body overconcern is only a special case of acquired reaction-sensitivity which may develop and persist under a variety of circumstances, many of which include a significant emotional component. Now we are ready for the second question, *What determinants are there that favor hypochondriacal developments and help to account for the fact that habitual body overconcern appears in some persons and not in others?*

Adoption of the domestic pattern

When a child develops complaints of body overconcern similar to those of his hypochondriacal parent, people usually ascribe them to biological heredity. "He inherits his father's weak stomach," they say or, "He takes after his mother; her nerves have always been bad." Their recognition of the source of a hypochondriacal child's complaints may be accurate enough, but not their notion of the manner of transmission. This, of course, is through social contact in the family, and not by way of the chromosomes.[13] Exactly the same social contact transmission occurs from foster parents to their adopted children, from teachers to pupils, and among neighborhood playmates. Moreover, as every parent knows, a child can adopt whole patterns of behavior from those around him without in the least understanding what he is doing. If children acquired only those reactions which they were deliberately and intentionally taught, fathers would not have to be so careful of their language around the home, and mothers would have less occasion to regret their own outbursts of irritability and the gossip of their daytime visitors. The growing child's behavior holds up a mirror to his parents' mannerisms, attitudes and prejudices.

In the same way that they adopt family attitudes toward strangers, animals, esthetic tastes and ethical standards, children also take over family attitudes of habitual watchfulness and distrust of visceral performance. When they do, they even acquire the specific gestures and the exact expressions of concern and dismay over their own alleged malfunctioning which a hypochondriacal parent or grandparent uses. They learn to reproduce his inflections, sometimes with startling fidelity. The outcome of such a development, that is, whether or not a child retains and elaborates upon his reactions of body overconcern, will depend upon familiar factors. It will depend, for example, upon how well he learns hypochondriacal

13 E. Richards, "Following the hypochondriacal child for a decade," *Jour. Pediatrics*, 1941, vol. 18, pp. 528-537.

self-reactions and how much he practices them, upon the extent to which they become involved in other basic attitudes — such as security, adequacy and parent identification — and upon the ways body overconcern may serve him as an adjustive technique.

When a child adopts and retains or elaborates upon family attitudes of body overconcern, he unwittingly lays the foundation in his behavior for that selective reaction-sensitivity which we discussed above. He develops skilled self-reactions to changes and activities in his body machinery, with an appropriate vocabulary, and these skilled self-reactions become the instruments which for him convert his normal physiological variations into the signs and symptoms of apparent weakness or disease. A great many children, who early acquire hypochondriacal reaction-sensitivities, apparently lose them again as they grow larger and stronger, their general abilities increase, and their life outside the home expands. However, like a childhood tongue that has been forgotten through subsequent disuse, the self-reactions of body overconcern once they have been acquired can be quickly relearned later in life if the occasion favors their revival. This relative ease in relearning a neglected skill helps to account for the observed fact that, under objectively comparable stress or frustration, a minority of individuals quickly develops body overconcern while the majority does not. It also sheds light upon the so-called "choice of symptoms," that is, the tendency of certain adults to react always with symptoms belonging to the same organ or system.[14]

An interesting variant of the hypochondriacal family is the one in which there is strong and unremitting emphasis upon strength and good health. This pattern of body overconcern deserves special mention here because it is so often misidentified, particularly by the members of such a family themselves. Table-talk centers about the virtue of keeping always fit. Taking care of oneself is unmistakably regarded as a sacred duty, and daily dozens may usurp the place held in earlier generations by daily prayer. The family diet is manipulated into unusual and often bizarre designs. Alimentation is watched over vigilantly and proudly, and in some families it is the usual topic of breakfast conversation, where it is discussed as

[14] H. Woltmann points out that the elderly "neurotic" sometimes gives a history of recurrent complaints over several decades which always implicate the same organ or system. See, "Neuropsychiatric geriatrics," *Arch. Ophthal.*, 1942, vol. 28, pp. 790-801.

though it were somehow linked to the progress of civilization. It is no accident that the practicing head of many a family of health faddists is himself a former hypochondriac whose faith in exercise and diet has healed him. The danger of making such a fetish of perfect health is that it is likely in the end to boomerang. Sooner or later in everyone's life the body is sure to begin giving some poor performances. And then, whoever has built his whole personal security upon its perfection will find the very foundations of his security crumbling when he most needs them.

Anxious and oversolicitous parents

Parents need not themselves be hypochondriacal to induce hypochondria in their offspring. Parental anxiety or solicitude over the child's health can have the same outcome. The mother who worries aloud over her child's every little discomfort or pain, over his minor digestive upsets and coughing spells, and over every bump and unimportant injury he sustains, is very apt to build up corresponding self-reactions in the child's own behavior. By taking over his mother's reactions of oversolicitude to him, as his own reactions to himself, the child may acquire enduring hypochondriacal self-attitudes. He sees himself as his mother sees him, as a person whose organs, parts and functions need special care and supervision if they are to make the grade. He learns to guard and conserve his strength, to give up and go to bed at the first sign of dysfunction. He learns to exact and expect special care and consideration from everyone and to tell others, as he has been taught to tell his mother, about the variations in his physiology to which his home training has made him reaction-sensitive.

Persons whose childhood homes have been dominated by parental anxiety may develop body overconcern as one expression of their own acquired general insecurity, even though the parental anxiety was not related to health.

A man of thirty-two with many hypochondriacal complaints grew up with a mother who "worried about everything" and periodically "went all to pieces," and a father who worried continually over losing his job and told his children over and over that they would starve to death after he was dead and gone. Actually the family never was in want and the patient himself prospered in life, but he, his brother and one of his two sisters were chronically worried over not having enough to live on. One night, two years before he came for consultation, the patient was awakened by pains in his chest and upper abdomen. He thought at once that this might be a serious illness which would invalid him and beggar his wife and children. Heart disease, cancer, pneumonia, hemorrhage and a "stroke" were his guesses. He was dissatisfied with a medical examination he received and suspected that he was given a sedative only because he was too far gone for help. His complaints multiplied and he devoted more and more of his thought and attention to them. His days were spent in worry, his sleep was broken and he "found no pleasure in anything." He reacted well to a thorough diagnostic study, which seemed to impress him because he received so many different examinations, x-rays and tests. All findings were negative for organ and tissue pathology.

Not every child of anxious or oversolicitous parents will develop and maintain seriously hypochondriacal attitudes throughout his childhood. The little chronic invalid with the sound body is really a great exception. A child's most effective protection is that he has two parents whose attitudes toward him are not likely to be identical. When his father scoffs at his mother's oversolicitude, the child may resent it, but he cannot easily escape acquiring an attitude of doubt himself. If he is fortunate he will also have siblings, and siblings are rarely inclined to condone weakness and complaining in a contemporary. Even the only child of anxious parents one day joins the company of neighborhood children who have better forms of entertainment than body overconcern and a different scale of values. Of course a pattern of childhood hypochondria growing out of parental anxiety and solicitude, even though abandoned later, has the same likelihood of easy arousal in adolescent or adult life that hypochondria acquired directly from a parental pattern has.

Influence of illness or injury

Illness or injury is a frequent starting-point for the development of habitual body overconcern, in adolescents and adults as well as in children.[15] The incapacitated person is a dependent person, whatever his age. If illness or injury exposes him to the experiences of prolonged inactivity, helplessness, pain and threats to his security he may acquire habitual self-reactions of protecting, sparing, worrying and talking about his body which far outlast the need for

15 D. Levy, "Body interest in children," *Amer. Jour. Psychiat.*, 1932, vol. 89, pp. 295-315.

them. His premorbid attitudes, and the attitudes he is encouraged to develop while he is laid up, are themselves determinants of his self-reactions after he has recovered. The man, woman or child who before illness or injury has been generally insecure in relation to danger, losses, threats or deprivations — whether their sources be personal, other-personal or impersonal — is more likely than the average to show overconcern during an illness and to maintain an overprotective attitude after it is over. The same outcome may be expected in perfectionistic persons who have habitually depended upon their health, appearance and physiological integrity for their personal or social status and their sense of adequacy. Naturally, chronic illnesses and long drawn out convalescence present the patient with greater opportunities for acquiring fixed attitudes of overconcern than do acute illnesses with rapid recovery. Hence the importance of minimizing the period of inactivity in persons showing unusual anxiety or dependence during their convalescence.

During illness and convalescence the warnings, instructions and predictions given a patient, and the comments made in his presence, may have a determining influence upon the completeness of his recovery. It is often essential to the safety of a sick or injured person that he be taught to guard against certain things and to watch out for certain danger signals. The physician cannot sit with the patient twenty-four hours a day, and even if he did he would still have to depend upon the patient's verbal report for many of the most important symptoms. Unfortunately the danger signals a patient learns to notice and report are the very changes in his physiology that can become the basis for a lasting hypochondriacal attitude. Too many warnings, too much advice, and too many fragments of information and casual comments lead easily to body over-concern, and this may prove more of a handicap to the patient than any predictable outcome of body neglect. For the adult who in childhood has developed and then lost hypochondriacal attitudes, the physician's warnings are often taken too literally and his instructions followed too completely and too long.[16] Hospitalization with its unfamiliar sights and sounds, the tales and rumors supplied by other patients and by the ghoulish raconteurs who come as visitors, present the generally insecure adult or child with special hazards for his future.

[16] S. Katzenelbogen, "Iatrogenic factors in diseases," *Dis. Nervous System,* 1941, vol. 2, pp. 342-356.

Internists and surgeons meet patients who when well show only an average interest in health and disease, but who during an illness develop exaggerated, though transitory body concern. For these individuals the circumstance of being sick is apparently all that is needed to rearouse old self-reactions of vigilance, an inclination to see danger on all sides, to anticipate major operations or a fatal outcome, and to develop supernumerary complaints which cannot be accounted for in the pathology of their present illness. With clinical improvement the body overconcern dissolves, only to reappear with a subsequent illness. Similar complaints, misgivings and fearful anticipations appear in some persons during periods of reduction in general vigor, such as occurs in prolonged fatigue following unusual exertion, strain, vigil or exposure, and during recovery from injury. These individuals are unable to accept the unaccustomed physiological stimulation and the changed status of relative incapacity without suspecting something more dangerous, and then looking for signs of it. Illness in others, particularly disabling or fatal illness, may provoke hypochondriacal episodes at any age, although middle-life and later maturity seem the most susceptible periods. Any of these isolated attacks of overconcern must be looked upon as anxiety equivalents, just as are cases of transient, episodic hypochondria in persons who are acutely anxious for reasons other than illness or reduction in vigor.

Public health campaigns have their hypochondriacal victims. In holding out new hope they also spread new fear. By them people are encouraged in the interest of early diagnosis to watch out for early signs, and told what may happen if early signs go unheeded. Thus, during publicity campaigns against cancer, tuberculosis and syphilis, many thousands of persons appear in physician's offices and out-patient clinics already convinced by what they have read that they are seriously ill and in danger. Some of them are able to accept reassurance after examination, but many need more than reassurance to return them to full usefulness. It would, indeed, be a poorly conceived public health program that did not arouse neglectful persons to greater alertness in health matters. Among the potential beneficiaries of such a program are these susceptible few whose previous background or coexisting personal difficulties make their suspicions of ill-health easy to arouse and difficult to allay. They are the casualties that go with the victories.

Hypochondria as an adjustive technique

We consider body overconcern to be an adjustive technique if it originates or is used habitually as a method of overcoming, avoiding, circumventing, escaping or ignoring frustration and threat, or of increasing one's rewards and one's acceptance by others and reducing punishment or deprivation. As we have already pointed out, adjustive techniques to be effective need not be planned, identified, or even understood by the person using them. If, for example, body overconcern is successful in bringing immediate relief from tension, or in increasing one's rewards, it is likely to persist as one's habitual preferred adjustive technique until something else interferes with its practice or it fails to yield dividends. However, if body overconcern once becomes an established reaction to difficulty, there is always the danger that it may persist even though it no longer accomplishes anything useful, and even though it may lead a person into greater difficulties than it overcomes. This common outcome in hypochondria is comparable with that which we discussed in overprotected children. They continue for years to use methods of dealing with their peers which they acquired at home in the mother-child relationship, even though the methods bring them defeat, loss in prestige and serious restrictions in companionship. In both instances, long practice and secondary needs result in the perpetuation of an inadequate mode of reaction.

The use of hypochondria as an instrument of *aggression* or revenge is quite common. A child whose parents are easily frightened by complaints of illness may learn to develop complaints whenever he is thwarted or displeased, even though his symptoms make him anxious also. He is likely in adolescence and adulthood to continue using the same means of overcoming obstacles and having his own way, or to avenge himself upon those who successfully thwart him. Adults without a hypochondriacal background sometimes learn to control and punish others by body complaints through their previous success in doing so during an illness. Unruly households and straying husbands are often easier to keep in check, for example, as long as the shadow of an illness hangs over one. A man who has never been able to have his way in the home before, may likewise discover all opposition melting before the threatened return of his ulcer symptoms.

Occasionally the hypochondriacal invalid or semi-invalid grows into a household tyrant. He or she must have special food and dress, the best chair and the best bed, entertainment as desired and quiet when ordered. In extreme cases the children of a chronically hypochondriacal parent may not go out to play or choose outside friends, fall in love, marry or leave home unless it pleases the parent to allow it. These developments in our culture are difficult to combat because sick and disabled persons are given the right to expect special consideration, and in the eyes of the hypochondriacal patient he is entitled by custom to the same treatment as any other person with similar symptoms. If he is denied this right by members of his family, his indignation or his silent but recognizable reproach is likely to arouse sufficient guilt in them to overcome their opposition or indifference.

Body overconcern often develops or persists because complaints are *attention-getting*. This use of hypochondria is encountered at all periods of life, but particularly when insecurity because of rivalry and neglect are prevalent as, for example, in childhood competition for maternal affection,[17] in middle-life under conditions of marital or filial neglect, and in old age when a person finds himself losing significance and prestige. Disease, injury, an operation or a behavior disorder sometimes introduces a person for the first time in his life to the experience of being fussed over and waited upon, of having sympathetic visitors who come with flowers, gifts and the greetings of others, and who show a genuine interest in the invalid's wishes and opinions. The prospect of a return to the old status of an ordinary, unnoticed individual in a humdrum world of routine is likely to drag convalescence out into chronic body overconcern, and usually without the patient's recognizing what he is doing or why.

A not infrequent outgrowth of role-taking and *identification* is that of developing hypochondriacal complaints which correspond to the symptoms complained of by a loved or envied person. One sees husbands, for example, who develop morning sickness when their newly pregnant wives do. Indeed, there is a widespread belief that this phenomenon indicates a semi-mystical, sympathetic harmony between husband and wife. Role-taking and identification often lead to the development and recurrence of another person's symptoms in such a way as to arouse acute tensions instead of reducing them. This was obvious in the cardiovascular complaints of

[17] L. Kanner, "The invalid reaction in children," *Jour. Pediatrics,* 1937, vol. 11, pp. 341-355.

the patient, cited above, whose first hypochondriacal illness followed the cardiac death of a favorite uncle at the theater, and
whose second illness appeared after more than a decade of freedom
from complaints, when the patient's father began having heart
attacks. The maladaptive character of such hypochondria is no
less apparent than its relationship to the illness of a loved person.

As *compensation*, hypochondria is used a great deal by persons
of all ages who fail to derive adequate satisfaction from other behavior, but succeed in gaining it through excessive body preoccupation. The defeated, neglected, unhappy, disappointed or disillusioned individual may find body-care solacing and emotionally rewarding. It seems to function sometimes as a substitute both for
the care one has previously been able to give to others and for the
attention one has previously received from others. Once body overconcern has successfully replaced lost interests in a person's life, to
relinquish it might mean to give up the one thing that is protecting him from having to face his intolerable loss. Under such
circumstances a hypochondriacal patient can hardly be other than
an unjust judge who will accept only one verdict concerning a body
complaint.

The following case illustrates compensatory hypochondria in an
unmarried woman of twenty-nine whose widowed father had remarried four years earlier.

> The patient had felt very close to her father as far back as she
> could remember, and he had always called her sweetheart and
> shown her greater affection than he had her only other sibling, a
> younger brother. She had dated considerably in her late teens and
> was contemplating marriage when she was twenty-one, shortly be-
> fore her mother died, reportedly of a uterine malignancy. At her
> mother's death, she felt it her duty to give up her job and the man
> she had intended marrying, and take her mother's place in the
> home. About a year before her father remarried, the patient devel-
> oped sighing respiration, difficulty in getting a deep breath, and a
> dull ache in her chest when she tried. She could not remember
> whether she knew of her father's interest in remarrying at the time.
> Following his remarriage she moved to a rooming house and re-
> turned to work. Her complaints and her concern over them steadily
> increased, her symptoms and their treatment constituting her chief
> interest in life. She suffered from recurrent headaches, hot flashes,
> dyspnea, epigastric pain, clouded vision, aches and pains in her
> limbs and difficulty in concentrating. All clinical examinations were

negative for tissue or organ pathology, but the patient declined to consider any possibility other than a serious systemic disease. She maintained that it was the physicians' duty to find out what this disease was, and hers to keep it from growing worse and shortening her life.

We encounter compensatory hypochondria most commonly in middle and later life. Minor disturbances in one's physiological performance appear more readily in later maturity than in young adulthood. These can easily arouse misgivings in the individual who is already anxious and dissatisfied because of his changed status in society. When the limits of a person's life horizons appear and his hopes begin to fade, when his children grow into adults and leave home, when death enters the circle of his friends and relatives to make a person more and more alone, and less and less secure, he may be driven to watch constantly over his health and anxiously conserve his strength, even though his exaggerated watchfulness, anxiety and conservation disturb him far more than they comfort him.

Perhaps the best-known of all adjustive uses to which hypochondria is put is that of *rationalizing* away failure, inadequacy and humiliation. If a person is sick or in pain, it is customary in our culture to excuse his poor performance, and to reward even his mediocre achievements with praise which they would not earn if he were well. "How she ever keeps going," one hears it said of hypochondriacal as well as of other patients, "is something I can never understand!" Unforgiving attitudes in our competitive society are almost the rule toward incompetence on personal grounds but not toward cardiac, gastrointestinal or genito-urinary incompetence. An unsuccessful man can keep his own self-respect and the esteem of others if he can attribute his failures to a body that refuses to support his efforts. A neglected woman can focus others' and her own interest upon her body complaints, thus sidestepping the need for personal explanations that would certainly humiliate her without justifying her. Boys and girls, who for any reason cannot face competition with their contemporaries, can raise the complaint of ill health or frailty as a shield to protect them from taunts and self-contempt.

Hypochondria is frequently part of an *escape technique* and, as such, exposes patients to the danger of social disarticulation and the evolution of seriously eccentric, asocial behavior as a secondary development. A person's assertion and belief that he is not well enable him to remain relatively inaccessible to the reactions of others (*insulation*), or to decline or actively resist participation in social behavior (*negativism*), if accessibility or participation arouses intolerable tensions or interferes with more highly valued satisfactions.

> A thirty-two-year-old married woman complained that she had never been strong or well since the birth of her one child, eight years earlier. During her pregnancy she had suffered from general weakness, aches and pains in her legs, headaches and respiratory embarrassment. The weakness, headaches and pains in her legs persisted after delivery; difficulty in walking and burning pains in abdomen and chest were added to these complaints in the ensuing years. The patient felt less and less able to entertain visitors or go to others' homes. Her contact with the outside world had become virtually restricted to neighborhood shopping and the movies. Her husband added some pertinent data to the foregoing. The patient had been shy and retiring even before her pregnancy and probably during most of her childhood. She was frightened and shamed by her pregnancy and resented being looked over when she went out. Some time after delivery she quarreled with a neighbor woman, accusing her of throwing dirt on the baby's diapers while they were on the washline. The patient expressed fear to her husband that her neighbor would turn others against her, and later on expressed the conviction that this had actually happened. It was during this period that she began avoiding others on the basis of weakness, pain and illness. Her manner of living unfortunately drifted gradually into that of a hypochondriacal recluse with numerous delusional beliefs. In spite of her delusions and her seclusive mode of life, however, this patient managed to function quite competently in the home.

Guilty self-reactions often complicate the clinical picture. Some persons withdraw because they consider themselves unfit for the company of others, and develop hypochondria because they believe they have weakened or injured themselves, particularly if their conflicts revolve about sex fantasy and deed. Other guilt-burdened patients renounce a full life, and accept personality impoverishment, because they find *repression* inadequate unless they curb their activities strictly and thus eliminate situations that stimulate guilty conflicts. We have already considered elsewhere the appearance of *regressive* dependence upon others in hypochondria, the regressive revival of body-care as a chief source of satisfaction, and the use of hypochondria as a means of increasing one's opportunities for *fantasy* by withdrawing and thus reducing interference from without.

Hypochondria and malingering

Body overconcern often brings many advantages to the hypochondriacal person, providing him with protection, exemptions, privileges and rewards which he might not otherwise enjoy. This fact at once raises the question, *Is hypochondria often deliberately planned and carried out as a means of deceiving others, or are its secondary gains unplanned and unforeseen by patients?* Patients who flee deliberately and admittedly into hypochondria are probably few in number, and of those few, most seem quickly to forget the trail by which they have come. The great majority drift into body overconcern through genuine self-deception, rather than flee into it according to plan. They expect others to believe in their complaints because they do themselves. In making a diagnosis of hypochondria, *we exclude from consideration, as malingering, any pretended complaints in which the person examined does not himself believe at the time of the diagnostic examination.*[18] Pretended complaints may, of course, develop ultimately into body overconcern, but only if they succeed in persuading the plaintiff himself that he is ill.

We must not be so impressed by the secondary gains of hypochondria as to lose sight of the losses it entails. The freedom, pleasures and privileges of the sound in body must be renounced by anyone who plays the role of a sick person, no matter whether it is disease, injury, need or anxiety that assigns him the role. Body overconcern as an adjustive technique brings the individual peace at a price. For many hypochondriacs, as we have indicated, the stringencies, sacrifices and anxieties which their body overconcern brings in its train lead into situations even worse and less satisfying than the original ones from which their hypochondria once extricated them. And yet, in spite of the most serious disadvantages, patients remain hypochondriacal. They do not turn body overconcern on and off as the winds of their fortunes change. The envy that self-condemned chronic invalids express for the robustness of

[18] The standard work on this subject is still the text by W. Jones and L. Llewellyn, *Malingering*. Philadelphia: Blakiston, 1917.

others is just as genuine as the envy that well persons sometimes feel for the "easy" life of an invalid. Each would like to have what the other enjoys without having to give up his own status.

HYPOCHONDRIA IN RELATION TO OTHER BEHAVIOR DISORDERS

Behavior disorders, we have said, must not be regarded as mutually exclusive disease entities. Instead, they are convenient groupings of related signs and symptoms, dictated by professional need and put together on the basis of professional experience. Each disorder has antecedents, a background and a more or less characteristic course of development. Early in this development a disorder may remain for some time unclassifiable because of the variety and instability of the symptomatology or because no one group of symptoms dominates the clinical picture. Every conscientious clinician meets cases which he never succeeds in classifying satisfactorily. But usually, as behavior pathology develops, a point is reached at which maladaptive behavior patterns become sufficiently distinct and stable to make it both practicable and desirable to reach a differential diagnosis. In the following paragraphs we shall point out some of the criteria which make a distinction between hypochondria and other behavior disorders possible, and indicate the occurrence of hypochondriacal complaints as incidental components of other behavior disorders.

Hypochondria differs from *hysteria*, with which it is most often confused, in a fundamental characteristic. In hypochondria the organ, part or function complained about may be quite normal, but the patient reacts to it with exaggerated concern, focussing upon it his major care and attention. In hysteria an organ, part or function may be performing quite abnormally, and yet the patient characteristically shows relative unconcern over it. In one, the patient continually calls attention to a disability or defect which is not obvious to the clinician, whereas in the other he neglects, or accepts with little protest, a disability or defect which is. In *fatigue syndromes*, which we shall take up in the next chapter, hypochondriacal complaints are nearly always present, but they occupy a secondary position in the patient's preoccupations and are attributed by him to his general weakness and malaise.

Body overconcern is also common in *anxiety disorders*. Here as elsewhere, the differentiation must be made largely on the basis of relative dominance or relative importance of the distinctive signs and symptoms. In extreme cases the hypochondriacal patient, although exhibiting intense preoccupation with his symptoms and even building his life around them, shows little or no evidence of anxiety. On the other hand, body overconcern in extreme anxiety reactions can usually be shown to symbolize or be secondary to other, more fundamental fear excitants. If anxiety and body overconcern seem equally prominent in a given case it makes little difference to anyone but the statistician whether someone calls it anxiety reaction or hypochondria. We have already considered transient hypochondriacal complaints as possible anxiety equivalents. Body overconcern also appears in *compulsive disorders* but there, as in anxiety disorders, a differentiation can usually be made on the basis of dominance and relative importance.

Body overconcern is a common complaint in *paranoid disorders*. In some instances it amounts to a fixed delusion which is woven into whatever general pattern of insecurity, rationalization and projection may prevail in a given case. Occasionally a single, monotonous complaint becomes a nucleus around which a rigid and limited delusional system is organized (so-called "paranoia mite"). It is an old story that *schizophrenia* and *depressions* often follow upon a period of hypochondriacal complaining, and that body complaints with or without appropriate emotional attitudes are prominent in both psychoses. The hypochondriacal beliefs of *depressed* persons generally run in the direction of maladies which may be punitive, retributive, degrading, disabling or catastrophic. The hypochondriacal complaints of *schizophrenics* may duplicate depressive ones but are likely to be queer, bizarre, poorly organized and often stated without appropriate emotional reaction.

8   *Fatigue Syndromes*

FATIGUE SYNDROMES, under various names, have been the subject of lively controversy in this country for almost a century. At one time "nervous exhaustion" or "neurasthenia" was believed to be so characteristic of our nationals that it was nicknamed *The American Disease*. Beard, who first applied the term "neurasthenia" to the fatigue syndrome, maintained that it resulted from the strain of prolonged conflict. For him, however, the conflict was one arising out of life in a pioneer land where, although competition was ruthless and unprincipled, people were still held to the strict social and ethical standards of an old and stable European culture.[1] For several decades it was generally agreed that such a conflict, if long continued, might actually deplete the nerves of essential biochemical materials and thus weaken the whole nervous system.

The treatment for "nervous exhaustion," perfected in later years by Weir Mitchell, was aimed at correcting this alleged depletion of nerve structure. Complete bed rest was ordered for the patient. All visitors were excluded. Lights and sounds were muted. Soft-spoken nurses glided noiselessly about, waiting hand and foot upon the patient, who was forbidden to make unnecessary movements. Massage and mild electrical stimulation were given methodically. This regime, known as the "rest-cure" or "neurasthenic isolation," was usually supplemented by a diet rich in those ingredients of the nerve substance supposedly drained off by the exhausting life struggle.[2] In its complete form the rest-cure was necessarily an expensive luxury which few could afford.

[1] G. Beard, *A Practical Treatise on Nervous Exhaustion (Neurasthenia), Its Causes, Symptoms, Sequences and Treatment.* New York: Wood, 1880.

[2] S. Weir Mitchell, *Fat and Blood,* 8th edition. Philadelphia: Lippincott, 1900.

The public for the most part still believes in the rest-cure for behavior disorders, and there still remain a few well-equipped places where it can be had almost in its original form. But no justification for the Weir Mitchell technique can any longer be claimed. In the first place, European physicians reported that the fatigue syndrome described by Beard was by no means uncommon in the stablest of continental communities. Furthermore, in our own country it was pointed out that quite a few "neurasthenic" patients were male idlers and sheltered well-to-do women, who could obviously not qualify as struggling pioneers. Skeptics among medical men next began reporting that they were getting as good or better results in their cases without high caloric diets and rest-cures. The nerve structures were finally exculpated by the failure of improved laboratory and bedside methods to uncover any convincing evidence in support of nerve-cell depletion, or of anything else that could be labelled "nerve-weakness." The more alert clinicians soon recognized what the situation was. They had been trying to explain away a very real behavior disturbance in terms of a very hypothetical disorder of the nerves.[3] In short, they had followed the lead of their naïve patients who took it for granted that fatigue reactions were indisputable signs of overexertion or physiological defect.

As might be expected, not everyone gave up so old and accepted a tradition without first attempting to modify the now untenable hypothesis. The most popular compromises were those which shifted a part of the blame for fatigue syndromes from the nerves to other structures. The heart and blood-vessels, for example, were declared to be relatively incompetent to withstand hardship or strain of any kind, on a constitutional basis, although no valid evidence was ever provided in support of this assertion. Easy fatigability in which there was the complaint of a rapid heart rate or palpitation following mild exertion was christened "neuro-circulatory asthenia," instead of just "neurasthenia."[4] However, this compound indictment of the circulation and the nerves proved no better founded in physiology than were the older accusations

[3] For an autobiographical account of the transformation of a distinguished follower of Weir Mitchell into a distinguished heretic, see T. Ross, *The Common Neuroses*, 2d edition (London: Arnold, 1937), pp. 1-13.

[4] See for example B. Oppenheimer, "Neurocirculatory asthenia and related problems in military medicine," *Bull. New York Acad. Med.*, 1942, vol. 18, pp. 367-381.

against the nerves alone. Out of this long controversy the one fact remaining undisputed was that patients, who seemed to be medically sound, were reacting inadequately to the demands of their social environment and were ascribing this reaction to quick fatigability or chronic fatigue.

By *fatigue syndrome* we mean *the habitual preoccupation with complaints of fatigue or easy fatigability by a person who is not suffering from systemic disorder or defect, or whose systemic disorder or defect does not justify his complaints.*[5] Chronic fatigue and easy fatigability, like hypochondriacal preoccupation with disease and defect, tend to reduce a person's social effectiveness by limiting his activities and his interests progressively, as he learns to avoid situations which seem to provoke or increase his symptoms. The more the patient builds his life around his fatigue and its prevention, the less able and willing he becomes to participate in the social behavior of others, and the less likely he is to be sought after by his former associates. In the end, he may be just as badly off as the hypochondriacal recluse, just as incapacitated and just as isolated from the rest of his community.

COMPLAINTS IN THE FATIGUE SYNDROME

The dominant complaints which give the name to this behavior disorder are those of being constantly fatigued, exhausted, worn out, tired and weak, or of having to guard against comparatively mild effort and exertion to avoid these symptoms.[6] The auxiliary complaints, which vary a great deal from patient to patient, usually include headache and disagreeable head symptoms, poor sleep, hypersensitiveness to annoyances, to light and to sound, and difficulties in remembering and concentrating. As in most other behavior disorders, there may also be complaints of an anxious or hypochondriacal character, but when present these are given a relatively incidental place by the patient in his recital.

[5] Easy fatigability upon exertion, which is accompanied by palpitation or tachycardia and dyspnea in the absence of organ or tissue pathology, is sometimes also called "effort syndrome" and, in military circles, "soldier's heart."

[6] For tabular comparisons of the results of physiological reactions to exercise of normal controls and patients with fatigue syndromes, see P. Wood, "Aetiology of Da Costa's syndrome," *Brit. Med. Jour.*, 1941, part 1, pp. 845-850; M. Jones and R. Scarisbrick, "Effort intolerance in soldiers; a review of 500 cases," *War Med.*, 1942, vol. 2, pp. 901-911.

Apathetic fatigue

The following case illustrates the variety of auxiliary symptomatology encountered in fatigue syndromes and indicates the degree to which the apathetic patient may ultimately restrict the scope of his activities by building his life around his symptoms.

The patient, an unmarried woman of forty-two, was led to consult a psychiatrist out of curiosity, according to her statement, and without any expectation of getting help. She had never been engaged in gainful work, but had always helped her mother keep house. Her father, a neighborhood merchant, died of "kidney disease" when she was twenty-six, and her mother died of "cancer of the stomach" eleven years later. The patient, provided with a small life-income, lived on alone in the apartment she had shared with her mother. She complained of feeling "weak and draggy," of having no stamina, and of being obliged to conserve her strength in order to get through the day. These symptoms had been worse since her mother's death, but had evidently been present as early as her pubescence, and perhaps earlier. She complained also that for many years she had suffered from spells in which her head felt as though she were "on a Great Lakes steamer in rough weather." Her sleep had been poor as far back as she could remember, apartment and street noises awakening her at least once every night. Sometimes she seemed to be half-awake throughout the night; occasionally, but not regularly, she resorted to a mild sedative and always slept heavily when she did.

She never arose feeling rested or refreshed in the morning. Dressing was a slow process because hurrying always made her heart beat rapidly and wearied her. She prepared and ate her meals alone, did her housework in easy stages and punctuated her mornings with frequent rest periods on her bed, during which she neither read nor listened to the radio. Her afternoons were spent in sewing, reading, listening to the radio or talking with a visitor. She had a few close friends of many years' standing who dropped in frequently for an afternoon visit. If more than two were present together she found the talk confusing and felt "done up" when they left. By telephoning her orders for food she managed to restrict her trips out of the apartment to one or two a week. On her way out and on her way back, she paused at each landing until her heart beat came down to normal. She was unable to attend church or go to the movies because of her fatigability. Her evenings were spent in preparing for and going to bed, and in listening to the radio there or reading. She seldom settled down to sleep before midnight.

In addition to her head symptoms, rapid heart-rate on mild exertion, poor sleep and nocturnal sensitivity to sound, this patient complained of ringing in her ears, floating spots before her eyes, poor appetite, chronic constipation, backaches and inability to recall conversations and stories she had been listening to or reading. She readily admitted daydreaming a great deal, but asserted that this was confined to recalling the themes of recently heard or read stories, and incidents from the old days with her parents. As far back as she could remember she had been interested in romance but never, she added, in men or in marrying. She declined to consider cooperation in any form of therapy because, she said, no one knew enough to help her. She did not avail herself of the invitation given her to return at her convenience.

The case just cited is exceptionally severe, but it typifies the resigned, apathetic syndrome. In many cases apathetic fatigue seems to originate early in childhood, persists into maturity and dominates the person's whole life pattern. Sometimes the habitual fatigue reactions appear to be little more than an exaggerated acquiescence in a parental program of overtraining one in the techniques of avoiding the dangers of exertion. Sometimes they represent a costly defense against temptations, erected with the help of a parent who regards no price too high to pay for innocence. Resignation and apathy in fatigue syndromes are perhaps most often the marks of an end-stage that is reached after a long but unsuccessful tense struggle with frustration, anxiety and disappointment in adulthood.

Tense fatigue

Less clearly defined, but commoner as well as more treatable than the preceding, are fatigue syndromes which are neither end-stages nor apathetic. The patient is tense, wearied and discouraged but he is not ready to give up the struggle in which he is engaged, even though he does not understand it. The following case will serve as an illustration.

An unmarried law student, twenty-two years of age, was referred for psychiatric consultation with the complaint of chronic fatigue over a period of two years for which no basis in systemic disorder could be found. The patient first noticed his fatigue during the last semester of his pre-law course, whenever he tried to study in the evening. This difficulty persisted into his law school years where it became a much more serious matter because of the greater demands made upon his time. He could not concentrate on his work, the pages swam before his eyes, every sound disturbed him and he could not sit still. He tried going to bed after dinner and getting up later to study, but he found that he was "in a fog" and could not even understand what he was reading. Getting up early in the morning brought no better success; he could not get sufficiently awake to study. He began falling behind in his work, slept poorly and awakened every morning tired and discouraged. The light in his classrooms began hurting his eyes and distracting his attention from the interminable lectures, and the same difficulty made studying in the law library painful and ineffectual. He grew irritable and surly toward his classmates. At the end of the year he managed to get through all his courses but with the lowest grades of his career to date.

He spent the summer months vacationing at home where his condition at first definitely improved. However as September drew near he began sleeping poorly and again felt worn out. When he returned to the school situation for the fall term all of his difficulties of the preceding year reappeared. He felt exhausted and discouraged practically all of the time, slept poorly, lost his appetite, could not study and began feeling as though he had an iron band pressing on his temples and forehead. He received a "condition" in a major course and was placed on probation. On the advice of his friends he tried playing volley ball to invigorate him, and when he found that this seemed to exhaust him more than ever, he decided that he must be ill since play had the same effect on him as work. It was this conclusion that led him to seek help.

The patient was the youngest of three siblings and the only boy, earmarked from birth as a future lawyer by his lawyer father. His overprotective, dominating mother had brought him up strictly, but as a frail child who was constantly being warned against overexertion and illness by her and by his older sisters. He never questioned his future career until he went to college, away from home, and discovered how varied the plans of other men were, how much pleasure there was in spending time freely and particularly in the company of women his own age. The closer he approached to law school the less attractive seemed the three-year grind and life in his father's office. He became involved in sex adventures which conflicted sharply with his earlier acquired ethical standards, and finally he had to make the miserable choice of a law career he did not want instead of a marriage that he did. This was the setting in which his first fatigue symptoms developed. Once in the law school, he found no time for anything but study, and attempted to overcome his loneliness and disappointment by reverting to auto-erotism. This, however, failed to bring him satisfaction commensurate with the guilt it rearoused, and his struggles with it contributed greatly to his tension and discouragement. He finally decided that the only way out of his now intolerable predicament was to quit the law for a business career before failure in his studies drove him to it. He appeared immensely relieved by the actual termination of his studies and faced the prospect of a storm at home with surprising equanimity.

Auxiliary complaints in the fatigue syndrome

Auxiliary complaints such as those listed earlier may have the same origins as the dominant complaints of fatigue and easy fatigability, or they may be secondary effects of the patient's modified and usually unhygienic mode of life. Insomnia, for example, is a common outgrowth of conflict and of failure to derive adequate satisfaction and gratification in one's daily life. But insomnia is also a consequence of inadequate exercise, continual resting during the day, early retiring and late arising — all typical of the chronically fatigued patient's routine. Complaints of irritability, headache and disagreeable head symptoms may be present in any tension state and, for that matter, in normal persons who have been losing sleep for any reason whatever.

The hypersensitivity to sound and light so often complained of in fatigue syndromes is not, of course, an indication of increased receptor-cell acuity, but the result of progressive reaction sensitization. Frequently the reaction-sensitivity is acquired during tension fatigue and carried over as an established habit into a later apathetic end-stage. Patients who cannot stand the ticking of a clock may actually score below average in an audiometric test. The visual hypersensitivity in fatigue syndromes is sometimes complicated by conjunctival irritation and photalgia, secondary to prolonged poor sleep. The complaints of forgetfulness and difficulty in concentrating on a task, which are common to many of the behavior disorders, seem to be the incidental by-products of tension, conflict, aversion or preoccupation.

Fatigue syndromes in relation to organ and tissue pathology

A difficult task faces the diagnostician or therapist when he attempts to evaluate complaints of chronic fatigue or easy fatigability in relation to known organ pathology and systemic disease.

What fatigue reactions in a given case are justified by the objective evidence and what constitutes excessive complaining? Even among normal persons, under strictly comparable conditions of work and stress, there are wide variations in the rate of development, the severity and the persistence of fatigue reactions. In sick or convalescent persons complaints of fatigue and easy fatigability, like those of pain and discomfort, are often valuable indicators of systemic dysfunction or of unwise exertion. On the other hand one must not forget that fatigue reactions, whether justifiable in terms of organ pathology or not, may be increased by fear, anxiety or anticipation, and inhibited or masked as a result of reassurance by and confidence in the therapist. Moreover, fatigue complaints are utilized deliberately or unwittingly to increase or prolong sympathy, affection and privilege. Finally, like the chronic hypochondriac, the chronically fatigued and fatigable patient must one day also die, and not of his fatigue.

BIOSOCIAL BASES OF FATIGUE REACTIONS

Complaints of continual fatigue and easy fatigability, in persons not suffering from systemic disease or defect sufficient to account for them, are always acquired reactions. They occur with less frequency than hypochondriacal complaints, probably because fatigue reactions are less acceptable as excuses for inadequacy in our culture, but they confront us with the same fundamental problems. These problems are, *Out of what characteristics of normal human behavior do fatigue syndromes develop?* and, *What determinants seem to favor the development of a fatigue syndrome in a given individual?* In the present section we shall discuss the biosocial bases which make it possible for anyone to develop a fatigue syndrome, and in the section following we shall consider the determinants of individual differences in susceptibility.

The biosocial matrix of fatigue syndromes

Fatigue syndromes, no less than hypochondria, require for their development some basis in the human body, some changes around which fatigue reactions may be organized by the individual. However, as Bartley and Chute have pointed out,[7] fatigue is not a

[7] S. Bartley and E. Chute, "A preliminary clarification of the concept of fatigue," *Psychol. Rev.*, 1945, vol. 53, pp. 169-174.

simple energy concept but an expression of one's general align-ment with reference to activity, a reaction therefore of the whole person. Fatigue complaints should be interpreted as statements of unreadiness for or aversion to new or further activity, whether the attitude of unreadiness or aversion results from the effects of recent exertion or overwork, from lack of adequate rest and sleep, or from prolonged anxiety and the frustration of important needs. We are often impressed by the confusion most patients show in attributing their fatigue reactions to exertion, illness or lack of adequate rest when actually frustration and anxiety seem to us the more obvious excitants. However, so nearly universal is this confusion among normal persons, that we must regard it rather as an indication of the similarity — perhaps identity — of the self-attitudes of unreadi-ness or aversion which the various fatigue excitants elicit in every-day life.

As a matter of fact, the many needs which drive men on to work — for security and prestige as well as for food and shelter — are so inextricably intertwined that no one can say whether fatigue among normal adults develops more commonly as a result of work or of anxiety and frustration. The very work that a man must do be-cause of certain needs is bound to interfere with the satisfaction of other needs and thus become itself a condition of new frustration and anxiety. For the ordinary business man or factory worker there is the ever-present competition with one's equals, the subordination to one's superiors, and the necessity for self-control in relations with one's subordinates — all of which may impose frustrating or anxiety-provoking restraints upon free action. Men are continually meeting with delay and thwarting in the realization of their plans for personal advancement and work achievement; or, having ad-vanced and achieved, they fail to derive the anticipated satisfac-tion or to receive the expected commendation. In cooperative group living of any but the simplest kind, no one can entirely escape the nagging problems of ethical conflicts, of divided loyalties, of aggres-sion, defense and counter-aggression, the intermittent little crises of doubt, suspense, threatened failure or rejection, the flurries of resentment, envy and suspicion, or the strain of unstable ambiv-alence and incomplete repression. For the person with habitually low tolerance for frustration or anxiety the consequences of such factors may induce fatigue that is far more difficult to endure or overcome than fatigue from uncomplicated hard manual labor.

Among women, while competition may be no less important than among men, it is usually less immediate and direct because each housewife runs something approaching a separate establishment, in which she is her own boss during most of the day. On the other hand, the subordination to a husband which most women accept is subordination from which there is no prospect of promotion. Domestic routine is often fully as monotonous as work on an assembly line, while the patience demanded of a mother in dealing all day with her subordinates, the children, is of a character seldom called for under the conditions of business or industrial life. It may be true that, as often asserted, the affectional life of a mother is fuller than a father's and more directly satisfying. But, even so, the sources of a married woman's emotional satisfactions are so compactly organized around her home that she has a much less diversified and therefore more precarious foundation for her life than her husband has. When it comes to a question of anxiety and frustration in relation to fatigue reactions there is probably little to choose between the daily life of men and of women.

The fatigue complained of by neurotic patients is little more than an accentuation or elaboration of the weariness and exhaustion that often overtake normal men and women when they find themselves faced with tasks and conflicts in everyday life. There is, for example, the fatigue reaction anyone develops temporarily during monotonous and distasteful work, or while waiting indefinitely for an interview, for someone's decision, for one's wife to arrive at an appointed place or one's husband to come home after the dinner is ready.[8] There is the unutterable tedium of boring conversation, of raconteurs and unpaid lecturers from whom one cannot escape. The mere prospect of drab tasks and dreary companionship, or of approaching failure and disappointment in one's hopes, is enough to precipitate a sudden fatigue reaction. The body sags, the shoulders droop, the jaw loosens and the eyes seem weary, arms and legs go limp, and inside there is a sinking, all-gone feeling. Sometimes, instead, one grows suddenly tense and strained in a way that would be relieved by aggression or flight, but neither aggression nor flight is possible. Experiences such as these for most of us are transitory

---

[8] M. Jones and A. Lewis found that their fatigue syndrome patients showed much greater fatigability during periods of required physical exercise than during periods spent working in the carpenter shop. "Effort syndrome," *Lancet*, 1941, vol., 240, pp. 813-818.

and infrequent. But for the few, made vulnerable by previously acquired sensitivity, by habitually low frustration and anxiety tolerance, or by the severity of personal conflict or disappointment, fatigue reactions may persist and spread until they form the central theme around which the rest of life is organized.

Acquisition of fatigue reaction-sensitivity

Everyone learns in childhood to acquire fatigue reactions in relation to exertion, rest, sleep and state of health. Because small children cannot sustain activity to the same degree as an adult, they are watched over and questioned as to their readiness for continuing active behavior. Because the inexperienced small child tends to overexert himself, and is then likely to suffer consequences which are punishing to his elders as well as to him, he is deliberately trained to develop fatigue self-reactions and use these as a basis for discontinuing activity or refusing further effort. In time children learn also that the neglect of fatigue reactions may invite illness, that it is praiseworthy to protect oneself from overexertion and blameworthy to allow fatigue danger signals to go unheeded. It is from such organized normal self-reactions of unreadiness or aversion that preoccupation with fatigue or easy fatigability may develop, under special conditions, into a fatigue syndrome.

We do not consider fatigue complaints abnormal, in our culture, unless they appear too readily, persist out of all proportion to apparent exertion, impair a person's social effectiveness or form a nucleus of preoccupation around which the rest of his life is organized. In the fatigue syndrome complaints of fatigue and easy fatigability are given readily and a great many situations call them forth. Must we conclude from this fact that the patient is therefore a "constitutional inferior," that is, a poor biological product? Shall we say that the otherwise healthy man or woman who complains so often and so easily of exhaustion has actually a smaller store of vital energy on which to draw? The answer forty years ago would have been an unhesitating affirmative. The advice often given such a man or woman then was simply to quit struggling against inherent weakness and accept a sharply limited life, to avoid exertion and accept the role of a biological inferior.[9] The answer today is no longer in the affirmative because fatigue reactions have been shown

[9] This attitude has been recently revived in W. Alvarez, *Nervousness, Indigestion and Pain* (New York: Harper, 1943), pp. 230-243 and 456-466.

to have a much broader base than that of simple energy quanta and to be responsive to therapy unrelated to the patient's strength. The whole concept of a fixed store of vital energy, whether it be called *élan vital* or *libido*, is an anachronism that finds no place in modern biology.

We have already observed that the hypochondriac's acquired readiness-to-react in certain special ways leaves him selectively reaction-sensitive to physiological changes which the normal person would never notice. It is the same in fatigue syndromes. No matter how fatigue self-reactions are initiated, and no matter what their determinants may be, their mere repetition may be enough to make them easier and easier to arouse, and to increase the number and variety of the fatigue excitants. In other words, patients ultimately acquire a lowered general fatigue threshold by a process identical with that of normal progressive reaction-sensitization. The competition of other activities and other stimulation is diminished or eliminated, and the effect of this change is to increase the pre-potency, and therefore the clarity, of the fatigue reactions. As with other human behavior, the longer such reactions are permitted to dominate, the more likely they are to develop into an organized habitual technique and to become an integral part of an individual's social personality.

Cumulative and self-perpetuating reactions

At the same time a patient is developing sensitivity to specific fatigue excitants, his reactions show also the tendency to generalize to equivalent excitants with which we are familiar in ordinary learning. Likewise, as in ordinary learning, the patient seldom recognizes or identifies any relationship between original and equivalent fatigue excitants and therefore rarely understands the spread of his fatigue reactions to new situations. Under these circumstances it is almost inevitable that he will interpret his fatigue reactions as the cause of, rather than as expressions of, his unreadiness or aversion to activity. Once a person has arrived at such an interpretation, the most logical steps for him to take are those which will avoid fatigue and guard his energy reserves against further depletion. This leads, in turn, to preoccupation with questions of what fatigues one more and what fatigues one less. Thus the patient unintentionally grows expert in detecting the relatively minute precursors of his fatigue reactions and learns further avoidance and aversions. He masters the language that his muscles and tendons speak, and he learns to give them always first consideration in the same way the hypochondriac learns to heed the language of his organs and to spare them all he can.

We know that emotional excitement, whatever its character, may involve marked skeletal tensions which far outlast the original stimulation and are followed by prolonged fatigue reactions. We know also that such reactions may summate, each emotional arousal acting upon an already tense skeletal pattern. Under these circumstances, whatever arouses a patient or keeps him emotionally stimulated tends to increase and perpetuate his fatigue. Hence, even though a person complaining of chronic fatigue isolates himself from others, he is still subject to the inescapable effects of his own symbolic behavior. If his fatigue comes, for example, from an adient-avoidant conflict of guilt, though he flees successfully from the conflict situation his guilt may still be with him undiminished in his fantasies. If he escapes from public failure by retiring from public life, he will still have failure for his companion in his own self-attitudes.

So it is that a patient suffering from a fatigue syndrome need not necessarily return to tension-producing or apathy-producing situations to sustain his fatigue reactions or even to increase them. His own symbolic behavior can alone be quite adequate. And even this need not be organized and paraded in conventional phraseology or complete thought sequences in order to succeed in arousing his fatigue reactions. Any symbolic activity that can continue a conflict in the absence of its original excitants, no matter how fragmentary and condensed, will be sufficient to keep up the visceral and the skeletal tensions, to interfere with relaxation and satisfaction, to prevent or disturb sleep, and to limit a person's potential satisfactions.

Clinically and historically there are especially important relationships between sex fantasy and fatigue. It is perhaps not surprising, in view of the conventional attitudes toward thought as somehow unreal, that patients who are habitually engaged in erotic preoccupations report with complete naïveté that they indulge in little or no sex activity. They frequently express surprise that fantasy should be counted at all, for to them imagination seems as functionless as the steam drifting out of a teacup. Of course claims to an asexual existence cannot be made on the basis of one's overt behavior alone. Romantic and erotic daydreaming involves one in visceral and skeletal reactions, in definite behavior that can have far-reaching effects. Such reactions can and do promote intense desire and conflict, bring dissatisfaction or remorse, and result in an aftermath of fatigue as pronounced as any induced by overt auto-erotism. Erotic daydreaming is an important factor in perpetuating some fatigue syndromes. Unfortunately the life of relative seclusion and apparent idleness which the fatigued patient may adopt provides the very setting that is most favorable for uninterrupted preoccupation with erotic fantasy.

Of historical importance is the fact that many of the older clinicians were so impressed by the association of fatigue syndromes with overt autoerotism that they attributed them to the direct effects of masturbation. It is rather surprising to find even Freud teaching that "neurasthenia" was not so much the result of conflict as of direct injury to the nerves from a toxin which he believed was produced in excessive masturbation. This was the basis for his including "neurasthenia" among the "actual neuroses" which he considered outside the province of psychoanalysis. Today we still recognize the possible importance of erotic fantasy in the fatigue syndrome. But it is the conflict which is effective in promoting fatigue reactions, conflict between desire and opportunity, between one's needs and one's ethical self-attitudes, and not just the physiological after-effects of masturbation or its hypothetical toxins.

BIOSOCIAL DETERMINANTS OF FATIGUE REACTIONS

It is clear that fatigue reactions are not in themselves pathological, but constitute a part of the everyday behavior of everyone. Fatigue excitants range through a wide variety of stimulation, from the relatively simple and more obviously related effects of exertion, illness, injury and intoxication to the complex and more obscurely related effects of frustration, anxiety and failure. Acquired fatigue reactions exhibit the familiar characteristics of learned behavior, including generalization that does not depend upon verbal logic, emotional facilitation, interference and displacement, selective reaction-sensitivity and progressive sensitization. In our culture, individuals are usually excused for idleness, failure, low standards of achievement or appearance, inconsiderateness, and unwillingness to compete or participate on the basis of fatigue. Everyone learns in childhood to develop self-reactions to fatigue, to formulate these in conventional language and to expect exemptions and privileges on the basis of his verbal report to others. Our problem now is to attempt an answer to the question, *What are the determinants that seem to favor the development of ordinary fatigue reactions into a pathological fatigue syndrome?*

Childhood influences

As we saw in Chapter 2, almost the whole biosocial environment of the average infant and small child is made up of the members of his immediate family — parents, siblings and other close relatives or friends who live in or frequent the home. The attitudes prevailing in the home toward strength and weakness, toward work, strain, resting and fatigue, are likely to be adopted by the child as his own attitudes. If weakness and fatigue complaints are scorned by those to whom he is emotionally attached, he will scorn them also. But if fatigue complaints and weakness command respect and earn privileges he will acquire them. A feeble or chronically complaining parent or grandparent is often the direct behavior model which a child follows in gaining exemptions, rewards and special attention.[10] The complaints of his elders become his complaints and their words and gestures become his also. Through these acquired fatigue reactions he learns unwittingly to control his biosocial environment, in the same way that his parent or his grandparent does. Unless such trends are altered early by adult interference, or by the reactions of neighborhood peers, they may become a permanent part of a child's organized social behavior.

Some children who are not exposed to a domestic pattern which they adopt directly, develop a fatigue syndrome through the training an anxious or oversolicitous parent gives them. It is no accident that the patient complaining of fatigue or easy fatigability so often says, "My mother never expected to raise me." That is the picture of himself which his mother has given him; it is her attitude toward him as a constitutionally frail and delicate child which he has organized as his own self-attitude toward himself. Such a mother trains her child to avoid exertion by the same methods she uses to train him to beware of high windows, steep stairways and bad com-

[10] See the analysis of personal history in fatigue syndrome cases by M. Jones and A. Lewis, "Effort syndrome," *Lancet*, 1941, vol. 240, pp. 813-818.

panions. He acquires reaction-sensitivity to fatigue just as the hypo-chondriacal child may acquire it to his gastric function. In time he is able to detect and report degrees of fatigue which the ordinary child would never notice. He learns to give priority in his behavior to his fatigue reactions, to make them his chief criteria of ability and willingness to participate in the activities of others.

The difficulty with such training is that it leads a child, through the same confusions over fatigue excitants we all have, to report his reactions to failure, neglect, disappointment, anxiety or monot-ony as fatigue, and to interpret these reactions as danger signals calling for withdrawal and cessation of effort. Since his parents regard their child as frail and delicate too, he will learn to expect and then demand special consideration and exemptions when he so complains, and to resent as unjust and heartless the failure of anyone, inside the home or out of it, to recognize his rights and privileges. In short the child has been taught the role of the deli-cate, fragile person who controls his social environment by appeals to its sympathies for the weak. Unless later in life he finds a marital partner who is willing to adopt a reciprocal role, such an individual is likely to remain a dependent in his parents' home. In either case he proceeds from neurotic childhood and adolescence to neurotic adulthood and old age.

Many children who adopt or are trained in the role of a delicate, fatigable person are fortunate enough to have such self-reactions replaced by more adequate ones as they grow older and respond to influences outside the home. The child who regards himself early in life as weak and fragile may thus develop ultimately into a reasonably strong and competent adult. Nevertheless, in the pres-ence of severe prolonged frustration and anxiety, an adult with this childhood background may be expected to show occasional regres-sion to his once successful but subsequently discarded role of the delicate, fatigable person. As in hypochondria, so in fatigue syn-dromes, the early acquisition of a maladaptive technique leaves the individual vulnerable to its rearousal.

Influence of illness or injury

What has been said of the relationship of illness or injury to hypochondriacal developments is equally true of chronic fatigue and easy fatigability. Particularly during convalescence, the patient may be greatly impressed by the ease with which he fatigues and the unexpected slowness of recovery from slight exertion. If he has always been a relatively insecure person, or one who tends to identify physiological adequacy with personal safety, his fatigue reactions may alarm him and encourage him to take unusual precautions which continue indefinitely beyond the convalescent phase. It is often important to protect a patient during illness or convalescence against overexertion by teaching him to heed the premonitory signs and symptoms of fatigue. It is usually taken for granted, not without justification in practice, that patients will disregard these teachings even before they should. However it is frequently the case that an individual proves in this respect too apt a pupil, either because earlier experiences have prepared him in advance or because fatigue reactions serve unexpectedly as adjustive techniques in dealing with anxiety and frustrated need.

Fatigue reactions as adjustive techniques

We consider fatigue reactions to be adjustive techniques if they originate or are used habitually as a means of overcoming, avoiding, circumventing, escaping or ignoring frustration and threat, or as a means of increasing one's rewards and one's acceptance by others or reducing punishment and deprivation. As in hypochondria, it is not at all necessary that fatigue reactions be planned, identified or understood by the patient to develop and function effectively as adjustive techniques. They become established as one's preferred adjustive techniques at some period of life because they bring indirect need-satisfaction and reduce tensions or allay anxieties. Once established on such a basis, fatigue reactions like other adjustive techniques may persist because of long practice and the incidental development of secondary needs, even though they lead a person into other and worse difficulties than those from which they originally released him.

The child or adult who builds his life around fatigue reactions may also use them *aggressively* in controlling his associates, and in avenging himself upon those who resist his control. If a person is obviously fatigued by opposition or denial, and his status as a constitutionally weak or delicate individual is generally recognized, he will have little difficulty in arousing guilt and remorse in anyone who opposes or denies him. Even the skeptical can usually be shamed, or at least silenced, by the honest rebukes of believers. The resentment of the fatigable aggressor is all the more effective because he himself believes in his claims to special privilege. More rest for the semi-invalid means more quiet for the household, and more quiet means less freedom of action for everyone not resting. The household soon learns to avoid curtailment of free activity by promptly giving in to the fatigable individual who can curtail it by his complaints.

Fatigue reactions function as *attention-getting* techniques by compelling others to give time and consideration to a patient's needs. The chronically fatigued or fatigable person, whatever his age, is harder to ignore than the robust one even by those who resent him. If he is not taken into account when things are done or plans are made his fatigue may spoil the party or oblige someone to detach himself from the group, sacrifice his own pleasure and care for the neglected patient. Dependent children can increase and prolong maternal devotion by developing sensitive fatigue reactions,[11] and increased attention from one's marital partner or one's children can be stimulated similarly by an adult.

Fatigue complaints are frequently also a part of *identification*, particularly in children. The child learns to attribute to himself the characteristics and status of a fatigued or fatigable adult in his vicinity, and by so doing to avoid or circumvent frustration and threat.

Fatigue reactions become *compensatory* when self-care, or the care given the patient by others, provides substitute satisfactions for persons unable to derive adequate satisfactions from other sources, or whose other satisfactions tend to arouse serious anxieties. Compensatory fatigue reactions, like compensatory hypochondria, are most commonly encountered in middle and later life when biosocial limitations reduce the opportunities most persons have for satisfaction of their still-present needs. The universal confusion of reduced motivation with reduced strength also contributes to this development.

Fatigue syndromes seem to be utilized much less commonly than hypochondria as *rationalization* for failure, inadequacy or humiliation. This is perhaps a consequence of the fact that fatigue complaints are less generally acceptable as excuses than complaints of illness, and are more apt to be interpreted as laziness or as a mark of weakness and biological inferiority. The comparatively greater

11 W. Muncie, "Chronic fatigue," *Psychosom. Med.*, 1941, vol. 3, pp. 277-285.

readiness of women than of men to use fatigue reactions as rationalization can be explained on the basis of sex differences in the
pattern of cultural expectation. Weakness in women is expected in
our culture and to some extent condoned. If a woman's complaints
of chronic fatigue or fatigability are interpreted by others as the
direct consequences of womanly functions to which society attaches
high value, fatigue reactions may actually enhance rather than
diminish a woman's prestige.

Throughout our discussion of fatigue syndromes it has been
apparent that fatigue reactions are commonly a part of *withdrawal,*
occurring in response to the tensions of prolonged anxiety or frustrated need. The unreadiness or aversion which characterizes
fatigue is easily mistaken by the patient for an indication of systemic disease or constitutional weakness, and acted upon as a
warning against further effort. The most serious consequence of
such withdrawal is the one exemplified by our first case, namely, the
insulation of the patient from his social environment and the erec-
tion of *negativistic* barriers in his mode of life, which resist social
participation to the point of virtually disarticulating the individual
from his society. In isolating themselves, patients lose much of
that everyday give-and-take with others which helps to keep a
person's attitudes and his fantasies in touch with the attitudes and
happenings of those around him. As we have seen, in the extreme
case the patient shunts himself off the main track and spends the
rest of his life ineffectually resting on a siding. This outcome in
fatigue syndromes is, as we might expect, closely related to and
sometimes immediately antecedent to the development of schizophrenic withdrawal and subsequent disorganization.

Fatigue reactions, as we have said, frequently represent *regression* to a previously satisfying relationship of dependence upon and
protection by another person.[12] Adolescents and young adults who
find the conditions or demands of adult life unpalatable utilize their
unreadiness or aversion as the basis for such a regression, turning
back to parental domination if it is available as an escape from the
threats and stresses that confront them. Other adolescents and
adults succeed in establishing relationships with a contemporary
whose reciprocal needs make him welcome the acquisition of a
socially immature dependent.

[12] E. Wittkower, T. Rodger and A. Wilson, "Effort syndrome," *Lancet,*
1941, vol. 240, pp. 531-535.

The development and persistence of fatigue syndromes bear the same general relation to inadequate *repression* that we described for hypochondria. Patients who are unable to handle frustration or anxiety otherwise, particularly patients in whom adient-avoidant guilt conflicts are prominent, may progressively eliminate those situations, contacts and activities which seem to increase their fatigue symptoms. Patients addicted to *fantasy* likewise develop aversion and unreadiness for any activity that interferes with their fantasy. These reactions of aversion and unreadiness they report accurately to others and to themselves as fatigue, but they inaccurately ascribe it to constitutional weakness, frailty or an obscure systemic disorder. In some fatigue syndromes the development and persistence of fatigue reactions are further complicated by the fact that inadequate repression and unconsummated sex fantasying often tend directly to increase tension, and therefore to aggravate and perpetuate the patient's fatigue symptoms in ways that have no direct parallel in hypochondria.

FATIGUE SYNDROMES IN RELATION TO OTHER BEHAVIOR DISORDERS

We have designated as fatigue syndromes those behavior disorders whose most prominent or serious symptom is the complaint of chronic fatigue or easy fatigability. In *hypochondria,* as we have seen, the patient's chief preoccupations focus upon specific organs, functions or parts. In fatigue syndromes, by contrast, the characteristic fatigue reactions are unlocalized and non-specific. They represent an alignment of the whole person with respect to continuing activity or engaging in new activity, an alignment which is described as one of aversion or unreadiness.[13] As in other behavior disorders, hypochondriacal complaints may be present in fatigue syndromes, but when they are they occupy a relatively incidental place in the fatigue syndrome.

The non-specific character of fatigue reactions distinguishes the fatigue syndrome also from *hysteria.* Hysterical complaints refer to specific inactivation or to autonomy of function that has no counterpart whatever in fatigue syndromes. The patient in fatigue syndromes, like the hypochondriacal patient, is concerned and preoccupied with his disorder in ways that are foreign to the typical hysterical patient.

[13] S. Bartley and E. Chute, "A preliminary clarification of the concept of fatigue," *Psychol. Rev.,* 1945, vol. 53, pp. 169-174.

Fatigue reactions are usually present in *anxiety disorders*, and often also in *compulsive disorders*. This is easy to understand in view of the severe tension characteristic of the prolonged anxiety behavior in both. A differentiation between fatigue syndrome on the one hand, and anxiety disorder or compulsive disorder on the other, must frequently be made on the basis of which symptoms are most prominent, since anxiety and mild compulsive behavior may both be present in fatigue syndromes. An apathetic fatigue syndrome is sometimes the end-stage not of prolonged tense fatigue but of an acute or chronic anxiety disorder, or of a prolonged compulsive conflict. It is, in a sense, the patient's solution of his difficulty which substitutes relative inactivity and incompetence for the intolerable tensions of the anxiety reaction or compulsive disorder.

Fatigue reactions frequently precede the development of recognizable *depression* and often constitute an important part of the fully developed depressive complaint picture. Aversion and unreadiness in relation to further activity or new activity are prominent characteristics of both depression and the fatigue syndrome. A distinction between fatigue syndromes and depressions is often a matter of relative importance of the presenting symptoms, the former showing marked fatigue reactions and mild or absent depressive reactions, the latter showing definite depressive reactions with fatigue complaints of secondary importance. This relationship between depression and fatigue syndromes illustrates the difficulty, and in some instances the uselessness, of attempting to divide the behavior disorders into mutually exclusive disease entities. Of course a fully developed depression, with or without prominent fatigue reactions, seldom presents a serious problem in differential diagnosis. The slowing or agitation, the direct or indirect mood statement of sadness or hopelessness, the suicidal trends and the commonly present delusions of a self-derogatory or apprehensive nature are characteristics of depressive illnesses and not of the fatigue syndrome.

Fatigue reactions frequently precede the development of recognizable *schizophrenia* also, and they may continue as a prominent constituent of the fully developed complaint picture. Fatigue in both schizophrenia and the fatigue syndrome represents a reaction of unreadiness or aversion in relation to new or continued activity, and in both this may stem from insecure, dependent attitudes on the part of socially immature persons. It seems probable that certain schizophrenic developments are little more than the disorganized result of withdrawal and insulation, which has begun as a fatigue syndrome, but has gone much further because of other inadequacies in the individual's social personality. In any case, even though both tension and apathy are common in schizophrenia as well as in fatigue syndromes, there is seldom serious difficulty in making a differential diagnosis between them. Fatigue syndromes lack such typical schizophrenic symptoms as bizarre delusions, odd posturing and gesturing, verbal vagueness and scattering, hallucinations, inappropriate smiling, giggling, grimacing and other indications of autistic fantasy.

Fatigue reactions accompanied by complaints of difficulty in remembering and concentrating are prominent early symptoms in cases of toxic, infective, post-traumatic or deteriorative brain damage. A differentiation between these cases and fatigue syndromes can usually be made on the basis of the presence or absence of other signs and symptoms of cerebral incompetence. The fatigue reactions and the thinking difficulties may be diminished in both cases of brain damage and of fatigue syndrome by introducing effective motivation, but in the former the improvement is generally short-lived and less marked than in the latter. The reason for this difference is, of course, that in brain damage complaints arise on the basis of relative incompetence of the cerebral machinery, whereas in the fatigue syndrome the brain is normal in structure and the patient's complaints arise because of personal attitudes and habitual preoccupations which interfere with his readiness to engage in other activities.

9   Anxiety Disorders

ANXIETY is probably the commonest symptom in behavior pathology, but we reserve the diagnosis of anxiety disorder for those syndromes in which anxiety reactions are dominant and other symptoms clearly incidental. Anxiety is common in behavior pathology because it is exceedingly common in normal behavior.[1] As we have seen in Chapter 6, the conditions of ordinary group living in our culture expose all of us to innumerable emotional excitants but provide us with relatively few opportunities to carry emotional reactions through to their consummatory phases. The result of this cultural denial is to make unsatisfied emotional tensions an everyday affair for almost everyone.

Anxiety is common in behavior pathology for other reasons which we have discussed earlier. As an emotional reaction it is slow to die down once it is aroused, it is diffuse and pervasive, apt to acquire new excitants while it persists, and likely to influence the outcome of logically unrelated behavior (*emotional displacement*). Moreover, anxiety reactions are for the most part covert, and in conflict situations they are usually unshared and often unverbalized as a result of strong inhibitory components. Covert, unshared and unverbalized behavior cannot be as easily subjected to the processes of analysis, recognition and formulation in one's self-reactions as can overt, publicly shared behavior. Hence it is that if anxiety reactions become habitual and obtrusive, the patient is usually unable to dispose of them effectively because he cannot identify their specific excitants and eliminate or modify these. The superiority of analytic therapy over reassurance, explanation or conditioning alone is that it directs the patient's efforts toward gaining con-

[1] Anxiety is defined, and its implications for normal behavior discussed, in Chapter 6.

246

trol over the anxiety reactions by identifying, formulating and controlling the anxiety excitants.

It will help us to understand anxiety disorders if we first sketch the development and recession of normal anxiety behavior, in which most of the classical symptoms of chronic anxiety reactions and acute anxiety attacks can be found, but for which we need assume no hidden personal conflict. Let us suppose that a mother has been thoroughly alarmed by her child's sudden illness and her pediatrician's insistence upon immediate hospitalization. At the hospital the mother, instead of being able to pitch in and do something about it, must simply sit and wait alone while further examinations are completed. When at last the threatening diagnosis is confirmed, she may react at once with rapid, shallow breathing, dilated pupils, sweating, a palpitating heart, symptoms of pressure in her head and a sinking in her epigastrium. This illustrates the occurrence of acute anxiety under the usual conditions of an emergency which provides the frightened person with no adequate emotional outlet. The mother, although tense and ready for direct action, is obliged to leave her child unwillingly in the hands of strangers and go home.

Back at home once more, without her child, the mother will have lost her acute anxiety but she will show clearly the indications of a persistent anxiety attitude. She remains tense, preoccupied and restless. Her hands are tremulous and she is not as well coordinated as usual in her movements. She exhibits exaggerated and inappropriate responses to petty annoyances, the telephone and the doorbell make her jump, her appetite disappears and she may suffer other visceral disturbances. When she tries to converse or read the evening paper, she reacts selectively to frightening things, to illness, accidents and death. She cannot seem to concentrate, plan or think clearly. She forgets easily and misplaces things. At night she falls asleep with difficulty, sleeps lightly and tends to dream of tense and dangerous things, some of them connected with the day's events and some perhaps reflecting distortions of her earlier experiences.

Once the child is out of danger, his mother's tense background of anxiety attitude will fade, and with it will go also the tremor and incoordination, the startle, and the overreaction to annoyances. Her visceral life will return to its usual level of function. She will recover the ability to relax and sleep soundly, with perhaps an occasional anxiety dream or none at all. She will be again able to think clearly, to plan, concentrate and remember.

Anxiety attitudes such as this need not be preceded by acute anxiety. They frequently arise in situations where danger is conceivable but not imminent, and they may be present in a person's behavior without his even suspecting it. A normal man walking alone through a cemetery at night, for example, may believe himself to be quite unaffected by his surroundings. But a sudden noise or a moving shadow is almost sure to startle him, speed up his heart and make him sweat with a readiness which he would not have shown if he had been walking down Main Street at noon. Merely entering a cemetery at night rearouses in the average man, sometimes without his taking note of it, the old anticipant attitudes which he once acquired in childhood by going to funerals, or hearing and reading about ghosts, corpses, murders, premature burials and body-snatchers. His anxiety attitude then makes him reaction-sensitive in these terms.

Normal anxiety attitudes are not without useful functions. The moderately anxious person is ready for prompt and vigorous action when the need for it appears. As a watcher he is more apt to remain vigilant, cautious and reaction-sensitive to slight stimulation than a relaxed person. Moderate anxiety may actually increase endurance and forbearance during an emergency. However, when anxiety attitudes grow protracted and severe they may become instead a serious liability. This is especially apt to be the case if the individual's status in society or some specific personal conflict in thought and overt conduct gives rise to his anxiety, whether he recognizes the source or not. As soon as the point is reached at which a person's tensions interfere seriously with his satisfactions, reduce his competence, disturb his rest and transform everyday tasks into Gargantuan labors, we consider his anxiety attitude to have assumed the proportions of an anxiety disorder.

ANXIETY DISORDERS

Among the anxiety disorders we may distinguish three degrees of intensity. The *chronic anxiety reaction* is a protracted attitude characterized by tension and frequently punctuated by anxiety attacks. The *anxiety attack* is an acute episode which is much briefer in duration, but decidedly more severe, than the chronic anxiety reaction. The *panic reaction* is a hyperacute anxiety attack, the end-result of cumulative tension, which sometimes terminates in permanent behavior disorganization. The *phobia* is an anxiety reaction which the patient habitually attributes to specific, though to him often inexplicable, excitants.

Chronic anxiety reactions

The chronic anxiety reaction is characterized by the presence of persistently heightened skeletal and visceral tensions, which disturb a person's habitual rhythms of living and predispose him generally to give exaggerated and inappropriate responses on relatively slight provocation. In well-developed cases the patient's complaints and the examiner's findings together give a consistent clinical picture that is not difficult to recognize. The patient usually complains of tightness, aching or pain in his head, neck, shoulders, back and limbs which indicates increased muscular strain, particularly but by no means exclusively in the main postural groups. The generally increased reactivity of skeletal muscles can as a rule be clinically demonstrated in the brisk phasic stretch reflexes, the initial resistance to passive flexion and extension, and the fine to moderate tremors in fingers, tongue and sometimes lips and eyelids. The patient usually looks or acts strained in walk and posture, in facial expression, verbal reaction, gestures and other movements, and especially in response to intense or unexpected stimulation.

The common visceral complaints are those which we would expect from our knowledge of the visceral components of ordinary anxiety reactions. Thus, the patient tells us of loss of appetite or continual hunger, of difficulty in getting food down, nausea and regurgitation, abdominal discomfort, spastic constipation or chronic mild diarrhea, of urinary frequency and urgency, cardiac irregularities, breathing difficulties, secretory changes and cold, clammy extremities, of menstrual disorders or changes in sex pace, of dyspareunia or relative impotence.

The chronically anxious patient usually states that he cannot think clearly, concentrate or remember as he once could, and that he cannot seem to stick to any one task for long. Although these claims are seldom corroborated objectively by ordinary test procedures, one is not justified in concluding that therefore they are unfounded. Most test situations call for a relatively brief period of application to a task set by someone else, who also provides special social motivation. The patient's difficulty is in setting his own tasks and providing sufficient motivation himself to keep at them until they are completed. He is usually irritable, fatigued, worried and discouraged. In his thoughts he may return repeatedly to problems facing him or ruminate in a mildly compulsive manner over his possible errors of omission and commission. Many of his choices and decisions are made actually in response to his tensions rather than to factors in the objective situation.

It is obvious to an observer that the patient cannot let go and relax. His tensions contribute to his restlessness and interfere with adequate satisfaction in anything, and his restlessness and frustration contribute further to his tension. He falls asleep with great difficulty and only after a long period of tossing in bed; he awakens easily and once awake finds trouble in getting to sleep again. His sleep is often disturbed by anxiety dreams, sometimes of awesome or horrible predicaments, sometimes of his daytime fantasies and conflicts, which he carries over into the sleeping phases of his life in more or less recognizable forms. With this general background of unrelieved tension and strain, the patient is prone to develop anxiety attacks now and then, occasionally in response to stress which he can identify at the time, but more often not. If this occurs during sleep, and the patient awakens to find his heart thumping, his breathing difficult, his hands trembling and his body damp with perspiration — but no remembrance of a dream to guide him — he can scarcely be blamed for concluding that his end is near.

Chronic anxiety reactions, like fatigue syndromes and chronic hypochondria, tend in time to restrict and distort a person's pattern of life. The anxious patient begins by avoiding people, activities and situations that seem to increase his tensions, and choosing whatever seems to reduce them. This commonly leads to his giving up friends and recreations, which are needed for relaxation and diversion by everyone, but particularly by the person suffering from unusual tension. The end-result, as in other neuroses, may be that the patient makes self-protection his chief career and subordinates everything else to it.

Few patients with chronic anxiety reactions understand the significance of their complaints. Anxiety signs and symptoms are so varied, and their determinants may be so complex and obscure, that no amateur with a stake in the outcome of his self-analysis should be expected to work out the relationships successfully without expert aid. Other well-known factors, such as emotional displacement and the operation of special adjustive techniques, raise difficult problems for even the highly trained and experienced behavior pathologist or therapist. What the patient usually does is to blame incidental and often irrelevant fragments of an originally disturbing situation, to focus his avoidance reactions upon these, and thus to impose needless limitations upon himself and others without, however, eliminating his abnormally heightened tensions. The following case will illustrate many of the common characteristics of the anxiety disorders, acute as well as chronic.

The patient, an American oil geologist for many years resident abroad, aged thirty-two and unmarried, was referred by his company for diagnosis because of numerous complaints which he believed meant that he must be insane. For five or six years he had been suffering from intermittent attacks of dizziness, blurred vision, weakness and unsteady gait, for which no satisfactory explanation had been found by his medical examiners. For three years the patient had been bothered by almost constant "nervous tension," irritability, increased sex pace with incomplete satisfaction, inability to relax, poor sleep and frequent troubled or terrifying dreams. His neck seemed always strained and he frequently rubbed it and made rotatory head movements to relieve the pull. For about a year the patient had been so restless that he could scarcely sit still and stand still in the daytime or lie still at night. He walked so vigorously that he tired everyone else out and himself too. As long as he kept on the move he felt in reasonably good spirits, but he was intolerant of delay and opposition no matter from what or whom it came. The moment he let up in overt activity his symptoms increased, his legs ached, he felt "jumpy" and he could get no satisfaction unless he drove himself on to further activity, even though he felt worn out. He began to rely more and more on whiskey to steady him during the day and on barbiturates to get him to sleep at night.

One day, about eight months before his referral for diagnosis, while the patient was dressing to go out for an evening's entertainment, he felt something in his head suddenly snap, everything around him looked unnatural, and he seemed to be about to faint. He lay down on his bed for a long time, his heart pounding and his breathing labored, while the thought kept recurring, "I'm dying, I'm dying." Eventually he managed to sit up, weak and shaky, to drink about a pint of whiskey and take a double dose of sedative, after which he slept through the evening and the night. Following this, the patient had frequent recurrences of anxiety attacks which consisted of "queer head sensations," weakness, sweating, coarse tremor, palpitation and the conviction that something terrible was happening to him. He had only one repetition of the snapping in his head but he dreaded its return more than anything else. He stated that, from the time of the first snapping to the present, he had never regained his previous ability to think clearly, concentrate or remember.

From the character of the patient's complaints and the outcome of thoroughgoing diagnostic examinations, it was obvious that we were dealing with chronic anxiety of long standing which had been reinforced by innumerable acute anxiety attacks. During the course of a two-months' distributive analysis in office consultation a great many factors emerged to account for the development and perpetuation of the anxiety disorder, a few of which may be mentioned here. The patient was the youngest of four children, brought up strictly and with as great emphasis upon avoiding the appearance of evil as upon avoiding evil itself. He had been trained, in his self-reactions, to search each night at bedtime through the happenings of the day for unworthy thoughts and deeds which needed forgiveness. He learned early in life to fear the consequences of concealing a misdeed from God and his mother more than death itself. He suffered from frequent night terrors as a child and recalled one in which he saw the flames of hell so clearly that it frightened him even to think of it afterwards. In his home the sinfulness of sex and the inviolable sanctity of marriage were first principles; and the patient learned that his one great duty was to honor his father and his mother.

When this child was fifteen, his mother, without prior warning, told him that she was separating from his father at once and instituting proceedings for a divorce. He was allowed to choose between his parents, which one he would continue to honor. He chose his mother, but found he could forgive neither parent, particularly when he learned that the divorce would not be contested by his father. This, he still felt, amounted to collusion. He considered that his parents had swindled him with their fine talk about marriage and concluded that women were untrustworthy, and his mother a hypocrite as well as a sinner. After two years with his mother, during which he became uncommunicative in the home and felt ashamed before others when away from it, he left home for college.

In his freshman year he felt lonely, deserted and in continual conflict over the moral and ethical matters discussed by his associates. His childhood training had given him too narrow a base for anything new to stand on, and no base at all for the contradictions of his young adolescence. On the pretext of making up a deficiency, but actually to avoid the pain of returning home, the patient attended summer session at another college after his freshman year was up. Here he had an unexpectedly gay time and was introduced to attitudes and techniques with which he had until then been unfamiliar. As a result of his experiences and the discussions he entered into with other summer session students, he decided upon a complete change in his mode of life, his goals, his standards and his choice of companions. Everything else was to be henceforth subordinated to financial success and self-aggrandizement.

Accordingly, when he returned to his old college in the fall he began selecting his new friends entirely on the basis of their influence or affluence. By making separate demands upon his parents he assured himself of an income that was unusually large for a college student. He bought a sporty car, was pledged to a prominent fraternity and began dating freely at a girls' college in a nearby town. Although at the time prohibition was in force, he began drinking quite heavily at parties so as to be known as a regular fellow. It is, however, significant that for a long time the patient despised himself for what he was doing, hated his new friends and felt contemptuously superior toward the girls he dated. During his college career he had numerous sexual adventures, all of them heterosexual.

Following graduation the patient spent a year of graduate study in geology at a famous university for the sole purpose of getting a commercial offer. After two years more, working in American oil fields, he accepted a lucrative position abroad. Here he found the work taxing and the climate hot, but the living conditions provided were far more comfortable and elaborate than anything he could have afforded in the United States. Social life was everyone's chief avocation and intrigues of all kinds flourished, as they always do in small in-group communities. Local customs restricted social intercourse almost wholly to Americans and Europeans with the result that everyone within this group knew everyone else, and all saw a great deal of each other. The patient, as an unmarried man who was not without charm, soon found himself entangled in a succession of minor affairs with the bored, dissatisfied wives of other men. One of these affairs finally became so serious that the patient asked for a six months' vacation in Europe to get him out of the situation. Shortly after his return, however, he found himself again entangled with the same woman. This period coincides with the increase in symptoms, listed at the beginning of the case history as appearing three years before his referral for diagnosis.

It was quite clear that the patient did not at the time see any connection between his personal difficulties and his symptoms, but free association and distributive analysis led to the demonstration of multiple relationships. His simplest conflict arose from the fact that his mistress was his close friend's wife. He recalled this in giving his personal history with sardonic contempt, but his behavior changed during free association to anger, first at the therapist and then at the woman. She, he felt, had reinforced his distrust of women by her own faithlessness to her husband and had therefore pushed a normal married life farther from his own grasp, at the same time that she compromised him in his friendship with her husband. The acute anxiety attack, in which the patient thought he was dying, followed by a few weeks his discovery that others knew the details of their affair. From that point on, the patient had reason to expect exposure and retaliation at any moment, and realized that he was at the mercy of anyone he offended. As his fear mounted, so also did his guilty self-reactions. This was the situation which led him to report sick for a return to the United States. The outcome of his treatment was that he lost his anxiety attacks completely and considerably reduced his chronic tension. Four years later he wrote that he was still virtually symptom-free but his distrust of women seemed to be undiminished.

Many persons manage to adapt themselves moderately well to chronic anxiety without seriously distorting their biosocial behavior or limiting their range of action. Some take out their tension on others, plunging energetically into family or neighborhood troubles, into business and professional problems, or into civic, political, religious and other more or less impersonal controversies and conflicts. It is sometimes possible to detect, in the public pronouncements of certain officials, executives, reformers, journalists, clergymen and scientists, at least presumptive evidence of personal anxiety which has been successfully displaced but presumably not recognized. Nevertheless, to adapt to anxiety is not to lose it. The person with a chronic anxiety reaction, whether partially compensated or not, is more susceptible than the average to an occasional acute anxiety attack which he may then misidentify as overwork, devotion or impending death.

Anxiety attacks

The anxiety attack is an acute episode of emotional decompensation, usually appearing in the setting of chronic anxiety, and exhibiting to an exaggerated degree the characteristics of normal fright.

As a rule the anxiety attack climaxes a long period of mounting tension, to which the patient has been progressively adapting, but with ever-increasing difficulty. Finally he reaches the limit of his tolerance, he can compensate no farther, and the continuation or an increase of the stress precipitates the acute episode.

In extreme cases, the anxiety attack resembles sudden violent uncontrollable alarm. The patient grows restless and agitated, his pupils dilate, his face changes color, he breaks out into a sweat and his mouth goes dry. His breathing quickens, he complains of choking or suffocating and tugs at his collar or jerks it open. His heart beats rapidly and develops irregularity, with sometimes a chest pain referred down one or both arms, the attack then resembling *angina pectoris* (*pseudo-angina*). Acute nausea and salivation, with or without vomiting, and urinary urgency or diarrhea are other common incidents. The patient is tremulous and may walk or stand unsteadily. He complains of feeling dizzy, faint or weak in the knees, of numbness and tingling in his extremities, of hot flushes or chilly creeps. He is overwhelmed by the anticipation of impending danger, of heart failure, death, insanity or some unpredictable disaster. He may implore those around him to get help at once, and rail at them for their indifference or incompetence if they do not share in his alarm. After a period of from a few minutes to an hour the attack gradually subsides to a comparatively unobtrusive level, or it disappears completely.

The following case illustrates some of these features.

> The patient, a twenty-nine-year-old married stenographer, was referred by an internist after his examinations failed to reveal signs of organ pathology. She complained of sudden attacks which first made their appearance a year earlier and a few hours after she had been reprimanded by her employer. It was toward the end of a hot, tiring day during which she had been more than usually annoyed by the petty, domineering manner of her immediate superior, a female secretary. "My heart suddenly stopped. Then it came up in my throat and turned over and quivered so fast you couldn't count it. I had a pain in my chest and down my arm. I was like in a tight vise, I couldn't breathe. It seemed like I was going to die." She was given a week's vacation, which she extended to a month by using her accumulated sick-leave. Three months after her return to work, she had another attack, and during the month immediately preceding her referral she had been having one every three or four days. The chief etiological factor seemed to be her conflict over

having to go on working to help a husband whom she loved but who, she was beginning to recognize, was dependent and incompetent. She said, "I guess I'll just have to go on working like this 'till I die."

Anxiety attacks are not always as severe and dramatic as this. Often they are relatively brief episodes of moderate intensity which frighten the patient but do not disable him. There may be considerable variation in symptomatology from person to person, depending in part upon the specific situation in which the attack develops, in part upon events preceding the attack and in part upon individual differences in a person's habitual patterns of reaction in fear and excitement.[2] One patient, for example, felt suddenly dizzy and faint while walking along the street, things went black and he held on to a railing for support. After a minute or two he pulled himself together, got some spirits of ammonia at a drugstore and went on with his business. Between attacks he felt cheerful, but during them he was afraid that he would collapse or yell. Another patient, sitting quietly working at his desk, felt suddenly nauseated, grew pale and tremulous, perspired freely and a few minutes later vomited with considerable relief. Subsequent attacks ended either in vomiting or evacuating. In neither case was there organ or system pathology and both improved when therapy was directed toward the behavior disorder.

Patients sometimes suffer momentary disorientation in an anxiety attack, become paramnesic, or complain that things and people around them seem unreal and that they themselves seem unreal or changed. They may report disturbances in perception, of various kinds and in various fields, or temporary impairment of locomotion, coordination, speech and thought, superficially resembling attacks of *petit mal*. Anxiety attacks are occasionally ushered in by what the patient describes as an explosion in his head, as his head cracking open or as the sudden "snapping" of which our oil geologist complained.

Panic reactions

The panic reaction is a maximal anxiety attack, an episode of extreme emotional decompensation which may include violent aggression, headlong flight or suicide. The clinical picture is one

[2] D. Cameron, "Autonomy in anxiety," *Psychiat. Quart.*, 1944, vol. 18, pp. 53-60.

of excessive fear. If the patient feels trapped, he is apt to behave as though he were and attack persons near him, or attempt to kill himself. Misinterpretation of the social environment, sometimes amounting to disorientation, delusions of persecution, particularly of impending sexual assault, and auditory hallucinations of a threatening, taunting or reviling character, are common in panic reactions.

The duration of a panic reaction may be brief or last as long as several months, during which the intensity of reaction fluctuates. The eventual outcome of prolonged or recurrent panic reactions cannot safely be predicted.[3] If the patient is given adequate protection and support, in a situation which allows him complete seclusion but does not force seclusion on him, the panic patient can usually be expected to recover. Even in recovering cases, delusions may persist for weeks, and milder suspicion for months, after the panic reaction has subsided. On the other hand, in prolonged excessive fright there is always the possibility that some permanent distortion of personality organization will result. Sometimes the partially repressed but never accepted or understood conflicts, which the patient carries into his overt behavior during acute emotional decompensation, cannot afterwards be disposed of by the patient when the acute phase passes. The sequel to acute panic may be a chronic paranoid reaction or schizophrenic disorganization, as in the case of emotional decompensation cited in Chapter 3.

Phobias

Phobias are anxiety disorders in which the immediate anxiety excitants are specific and can be identified by the patient, but which he usually regards as inexplicable. The phobic patient, because he is able to identify the specific excitants, can of course avoid his anxiety reactions if he succeeds in avoiding whatever arouses them. Since, however, the excitants are usually found in normal everyday life, it is practically impossible to escape at least occasional contact with them unless one chooses to live abnormally. Moreover, the typical patient learns that his phobia seems absurd or ridiculous to others. It therefore represents for him a continual source of embarrassment and humiliation, which causes him to develop special techniques for concealing or rationalizing his anxiety, in addition to those directed toward avoiding its excitants.

[3] O. Diethelm, *Treatment in Psychiatry* (New York: Macmillan, 1936), pp. 191-194 and 251-252.

Theoretically any object or situation may become an excitant in phobia. Among the commonest are the following: animals, germs, dirt and poisons; small rooms, elevators, alleyways, trains and other closed-in places; wide-open spaces such as public squares, parks and fields; public gatherings, street crowds and theaters; storms, high places and the dark.[4] Conversation, reading or imagining may effectively substitute for the object or situation symbolized. Thus, some persons develop acute anxiety reactions at the thought of being trapped, drowned or buried alive when no such danger is imminent, while others react similarly to the mere thought or mention of disease or behavior disorder. Certain individuals, who often give other indications of social immaturity, suffer acute anxiety over sexual discussion, fantasy or temptation and may ultimately adopt a celibate way of life and cultivate compensatory satisfactions, as their solution.

The first case indicates a relationship, often cited, between anxiety reactions to height and punishment for guilt.[5]

> The patient, an unmarried woman of thirty, came with the complaint that for a year she had been suffering from an inexplicable fear of going higher than the second or third floor of any building, even on an errand. She gave her complaint with shame and embarrassment, stating that, even though she considered her fear ridiculous, she succeeded only in provoking acute anxiety whenever she tried to overcome it. One result of her predicament was that she had been reduced in one year from a confident, well-paid secretary to an anxious, inefficient, poorly paid saleslady in a store which occupied only a first floor and basement. She had become morose, seclusive and dissatisfied with life, had lost appetite and weight, grown restless and sleepless, and had begun to think she must be losing her mind.
>
> The patient recalled readily that her difficulty began one evening while she was working alone late at the office. She was suddenly seized with terror lest she fall or jump out of the eighth floor office window. She was so frightened that she crouched down behind a

[4] It was once customary to classify *phobias* on the basis of their excitants and to assign a different name to each, as, for example, *achlophobia, acrophobia, agarophobia, claustrophobia, misophobia, nyctophobia,* and *zoophobia.* This practice, in addition to the burden it places upon students of behavior disorders, gives the impression that the excitant is the most important thing in the situation, whereas it is often quite incidental.

[5] See, for example, O. Fenichel, *The Psychoanalytic Theory of Neurosis* (New York: Norton, 1945), pp. 195-214.

file for some time before she could trust herself to clear the desk hurriedly, gather up her things and leave for home. She reached the street level still perspiring freely, her heart pounding and her breathing rapid. After this the patient found she could no longer attend properly to her work because of the anxiety which overcame her as soon as she reached the office. Her mornings were spent in counting the minutes to noon, when she could return to the street, and her afternoons in counting the minutes to closing time. By the end of two months her dread of each day's ascent had reached such proportions, and the criticism of her growing incompetence had become so outspoken, that she was obliged to give up her position. A period of unemployment followed, in which she attempted unsuccessfully to accustom herself to high places, and then her need for income drove her to take what she could get within the limitations imposed by her phobia. This was the situation when she went for help to her gynecologist, who referred her for psychiatric treatment.

As a result of distributive analysis it soon became apparent that the patient had been deeply involved in an affair of long standing with a married man who had left his wife but because of religious scruples could not get a divorce. The patient herself had been caught in a severe conflict. She had felt hopelessly guilty over her own conduct, too much in love to break off the liaison, and unable to give up the belief that one day the man would marry her. The crisis came when she was told that she was pregnant. There followed a succession of tense conferences between the pair, in which the patient grew more and more insistent that they marry while the man remained obdurate, until finally she threatened to expose him.

A few days before the initial anxiety attack in her office, the patient had received a farewell letter from the man and discovered on checking that he had left town. She had felt degraded in having to beg and threaten him, and disillusioned by his attitude of irresponsibility. But this desertion overwhelmed her. She concluded that she had been living the part of a prostitute and that her only solution was suicide. The acute anxiety over falling or jumping out of the window appeared in this setting as a climax to mounting tension and an impulse to punish herself and escape from her situation by a violent death. As is so often the case, her acute anxiety attack left her with inadequate recall of what had immediately preceded it in her thinking, and focused her attention upon the anxiety reaction and the height rather than upon what was impelling her toward suicide. Consequently, when she learned later that she had actually not been pregnant, the news did nothing to relieve her phobia. Under treatment she recovered from her phobia completely and was able to return to secretarial work, but after a year, although considerably improved, she was still mildly depressed over her experience.

The second case illustrates the not infrequent development of anxiety reactions to crowded places and to the possibility of illness or accident in the street, from antecedent repressed anxiety reactions over the danger of public exposure.

A twenty-two-year-old unmarried man was referred with the complaint that for several months he had been unable to attend moving-picture shows, concerts or plays because he felt suffocated, and feared he could not get out in case of illness or a fire. He was also experiencing anxiety when riding in elevators and crowded busses, and had recently begun to feel frightened in downtown city streets. In the course of distributive analysis, the patient at first interpreted his most recent symptom as the fear of falling ill among strangers who would not know him, and therefore might fail to give him the help necessary to save his life. Later on, however, it developed that his anxiety reactions to downtown streets had followed upon the thought of his being injured or falling ill and losing control of himself. What frightened him was the possibility that in a fit or when injured he might shout something, or talk without realizing what he was saying.

This discovery made the patient suspect that his basic difficulty was anxiety over giving himself away in public, and led ultimately to a reconstruction of the origin and development of his phobias. Several months prior to his referral, while sitting in a theater, the patient had suffered an acute anxiety attack, touched off by a homosexual theme in the play he was attending. He himself had shortly before this been sensitized by a threat made to expose his own homosexual activities. He became even more frightened, not only by his own violent palpitation and dyspnea, but also by the possibility that he would attract the notice of others around him who might guess at the source of his agitation. As soon as the curtain fell, he left the theater feeling weak, tremulous and nauseated.

After this experience the patient found himself unable to sit in a theater unless he was very near a regular exit. Even then he was so unrelaxed and watchful of his own reactions that he could no longer enjoy the play, and finally stopped going altogether. The anxiety reactions generalized to moving-picture shows and to concerts, in the latter case obliging him to surrender a season ticket. The factors common to these situations and to the crowded busses and elevators were, of course, the fear of exposure, the proximity of other persons and the difficulty of escape. Indeed, the success of the patient's analysis depended upon his realization that the specific situations eliciting his anxiety reactions were only incidental background, while his personal conflicts were central to his disorder.

Anxiety disorders in cases of organ and tissue pathology

The patient is indeed rare who does not react with at least mild anxiety to the discovery that he is ill. In some patients the anxiety reaction to this discovery is decidedly more disturbing than the direct systemic effects of the organ pathology. The individual differences which one finds in the intensity and the duration of such anxiety behavior can usually be related to differences in habitual tension and in habitual dependence upon personal vigor and good health for personal security. Equally important in many cases are individual differences in the degree to which a particular illness seems to the patient to put his life or his biosocial status in immediate jeopardy, or to threaten those dependent upon him with the loss of his care and his emotional or financial support.

Although the verifiable objective evidence for it is still very meager, there is today a widespread belief that anxiety reactions may influence significantly the development and recession of tissue pathology, particularly in viscera whose activities are considerably altered in emotional behavior. A great deal of interest is currently focused upon the possibility that chronic or recurrent anxiety disorders may induce tissue damage which local conditions then render self-perpetuating or progressive. This relationship is postulated most frequently for gastric and duodenal ulceration, colitis and cardiovascular pathology. So far the most convincing positive evidence for this hypothesis has been obtained by Wolf and Wolff.[6] They succeeded in producing an ulcer experimentally in exposed human gastric mucosa by abrading the surface during an anxiety reaction, and continuing to abrade it slightly thereafter. The gastric mucosa becomes engorged, succulent and friable during anxiety reactions and may conceivably be injured under these conditions by food abrasion. Injured gastric mucosa which is not protected by the normal mucinous coating is subject to irritation and further

[6] S. Wolf and H. Wolff, "Evidence on the genesis of peptic ulcer in man," *Jour. Amer. Med. Assn.*, 1942, vol. 120, pp. 670-675; S. Wolf and H. Wolff, *Human Gastric Function, an Experimental Study of a Man and His Stomach.* London: Oxford University Press, 1943.

damage by the digestive juices constantly present. Thus a cycle might become established in which visceral responses to general organismic reactions sustain and aggravate local tissue pathology.

Further research of this caliber should carry us a long way in the direction of determining what effects the visceral responses in anxiety disorders may have upon the evolution of tissue pathology. There are, unfortunately, important obstacles to progress in this field at present. One is the stubborn refusal of many experts to entertain even the possibility of an effective relationship between what the whole organism does and what its tissues locally do. To them tissue pathology is something you study under a microscope and emotion is something you leave to neurophysiologists and philosophers. This negativistic attitude is found principally among persons whose one-sided training makes it seem inconceivable that the human organism can operate as a biosocial unit. An equally important obstacle to steady progress in this field is the uncritical enthusiasm of those whose hypotheses stand in urgent need of physiological props to hold them up. This group, on the basis of theoretical exigency, begins with the preconception that first causes are to be found in emotional reactions, and therefore tends to underestimate the importance of objective verification.

In the case of cardiovascular pathology there is the special difficulty posed by all systemic diseases that begin unnoticed by the patient or an observer, progress slowly over a period of decades, and are found sooner or later in a large proportion of the populace. We do know, however, that when the heart beats rapidly and irregularly in cardiac pathology the patient is likely to become acutely anxious. His self-reaction to his cardiac dysfunction may thus further overwork the damaged heart and contribute to its irregularity. In short, the patient's anxiety over his heart inevitably includes a cardiac response which may prevent the cardiac rest needed for recovery. Thus it is that the cardiologist directs a large share of his effort toward the reduction of anxiety in his patient.

Something similar to this occurs in respiratory disorders, and particularly in bronchial asthma. In the following case we see a respiratory disturbance, developing on the basis of demonstrated protein allergy, reinforced by anxiety reactions which involve the same organs. This case also illustrates the dramatic and lasting improvement in the overall clinical picture which may follow upon the patient's learning to control the anxious self-reactions.

ANXIETY DISORDERS 263

The patient was a fourteen-year-old girl, the only child of anxious and devoted parents. She was transferred to psychiatry from the medical ward when it became evident that, although she had bronchial asthma on the established basis of bacterial protein sensitivity, her own anxiety and that of her parents were contributing to the precipitation and persistence of her respiratory attacks. The nurses on medicine reported that on admission the patient entered the ward flanked by her frightened parents, her mother on one side supporting the girl, her father on the other side carrying a syringe loaded with adrenalin ready for instant use. This entrance typified the attitudes which all three had developed in relation to the patient's asthma. At home the father had been devoting himself after work entirely to the task of diverting his daughter so as to minimize her attacks. Actually, however, her attacks had increased in frequency and severity following his arrival home, but neither parents nor child had suspected the possibility of any connection between these events, other than simple concomitance. In this situation the psychiatrist's task became that of treating all three persons, and not the patient alone, of working on parent-child relationships, on overdevotion and overdependence as well as on protein sensitivity.

While, therefore, the patient was having her chronic sinusitis directly treated, she was being desensitized to the bacterial proteins by autogenous vaccines, and being desensitized to her asthmatic attacks also — by a retraining of her self-reactions and by emotional reorientation in relation to parental and filial dependence. When she began having an asthmatic attack on the psychiatric ward, she was not exposed to the anxiety reactions of her parents, or of anyone else, and she was not rewarded with extra attention beyond the requisite minimum of nursing care. The importance of the last-mentioned factor may be illustrated by the following incident. The psychiatrist observed that the patient showed a regular increase in attacks on protein clinic days, when she went for her injections, and the nurse reported that the patient received a great deal more attention there than on the psychiatric service. Arrangements were accordingly made with the allergist to have the vaccines administered by psychiatric nurses on the psychiatric ward. The patient was told only that the change was one of convenience, but her attacks from this point on showed no increase on injection days.

As the patient's attacks grew less severe, she was given ephedrine in place of adrenalin and the ephedrine was then progressively decreased — always without any indication by direct comment, innuendo or manner that a change was being made or a dose diminished. Before her admission the patient had suffered a reduction in permitted activities to a level appropriate for a person in imminent danger of collapse and sudden death. Therefore, while the psychiatrist continued direct therapy, the girl was placed on a schedule of increased activity until she had regained the self-confidence that her training in anxiety had taken from her. During the early part of the patient's stay in the clinic her parents were permitted to visit her only at infrequent intervals, but they were encouraged to discuss their own anxieties freely with the psychiatrist. At the end of four months the girl was discharged, and seen thereafter regularly by the psychiatrist in office consultation. Asthmatic attacks continued infrequent, and when they did occur both parents and daughter were successful in handling the situation without excitement or alarm.

BIOSOCIAL BASES OF ANXIETY DISORDERS

If at this point we pose the question, *From what characteristics of normal human behavior are anxiety disorders derived?* the answer is simply that anxiety disorders are derived from commonplace normal anxiety reactions and these, in turn, are merely variants of emotional behavior. Indeed, so fundamental are anxiety reactions to an understanding of behavior pathology that we have been obliged to anticipate this section in our discussions of personality development, behavior organization, conflict and the basic adjustive techniques. There we saw that in our society the human organism is often tensely poised, as if for vigorous action, but at the same time prevented by some factor in the total situation from going on into an overt consummatory phase which would terminate the tension. Under these circumstances a variety of possible consequences present themselves of which we shall discuss the five most pertinent to our study.

(1) As in all emotional behavior, the unconsummated tensions of anxiety may gradually die down, with the help of interfering activities and of other satisfactions, until the organism regains its usual level of relaxation. (2) The tensions of anxiety may be sustained or become cumulative, still without transcending normal limits, through reaction-sensitization, language behavior, thinking, role-taking and self-reaction. We have already given these factors detailed consideration in Chapters 3 and 4, and discussed their specific relationship to fear and anxiety in our chapter on the basic adjustive techniques. (3) If the sustained or cumulative tensions

of anxiety develop beyond the limits of individual tolerance, we then have a *chronic anxiety reaction* as defined earlier in the present chapter. This, as we have seen, may be punctuated intermittently by acute *anxiety attacks* in which the patient may or may not identify some object or situation as his anxiety excitant. (4) In exceptional cases there is no clear evidence of chronic anxiety reaction, but the patient shows reaction-sensitivity to certain anxiety excitants which he may not be able to identify without behavior analysis. He suffers occasional *anxiety attacks,* but between them appears to lead a normal life. (5) The anxiety tensions may mount progressively higher and higher, until finally they exceed the limits of an individual's ability to adapt further, and an episode of acute emotional decompensation is precipitated. This we have already described as the *panic reaction.*

Anxiety reactions, then, are the bases of anxiety disorders and no one can help developing them under the normal conditions of human society.[7] To the direct cumulative and self-perpetuating effects of the visceral and skeletal tensions of emotional behavior, to which all mammals are subject, the human being adds the effects of talking and thinking about dangerous things, about shameful and forbidden things. Through these symbolic reactions, and their organization as role-taking and self-reacting, he is able to build up and sustain anxiety behavior in ways that are foreign to other mammalian forms. As in other learned activity, a person's anxiety reactions tend to generalize and acquire new excitants, so that potentially almost anything may come to stimulate anxiety, whether its relationship to the original excitants conforms to language organization or to what we have earlier described as the logic of non-verbal operations. And finally, everyone has limits to his anxiety tolerance beyond which he is likely to suffer emotional decompensation. We are now ready to proceed at once to the problem of individual differences in relative susceptibility to and immunity from anxiety disorders.

BIOSOCIAL DETERMINANTS OF ANXIETY DISORDERS

If it is true that anxiety reactions are normal and universal in our society, and that we are all potential candidates for anxiety

[7] D. Cameron, "Observations on the patterns of anxiety," *Amer. Jour. Psychiat.,* 1944, vol. 101, pp. 36-41.

disorder, we must next account for the observed fact that under objectively comparable conditions some individuals develop anxiety disorder and others do not. This brings us to our second fundamental question, *What are the determinants which seem to favor the development of ordinary anxiety reactions into a pathological anxiety syndrome?*

The hypotheses which ascribe differences in the frequency and intensity of anxiety reactions to congenital biological differences in emotional lability have as yet been insufficiently tested. The impression is quite widespread among those working with infants and young children, however, that important individual differences in emotional reactivity do appear which cannot be completely explained in terms of learning.[8] Considering the complexity of human structure, and the relative directness and simplicity of anxiety reactions, it would be surprising if structural variations were shown to play no part in the observed differences in individual susceptibility to anxiety disorder. Nevertheless, the fact remains that adequate physiological and behavioral data in support of congenital differences in emotional lability are still lacking. We shall have to leave this aspect of our problem to the investigations of the future.

Adoption of the prevailing pattern

Anxious adults make anxious parents and help to create an atmosphere of uneasiness in the home. The child, long before he is able to identify or understand what is upsetting him, tends to react to the prevailing insecurity with his own anxiety reactions. Thus, adults who are continually starting, exclaiming, ducking, cringing or crying, when danger seems to threaten them, are likely to have children who do the same. Indeed, domestic animals also develop anxieties in the presence of anxious adults, so that an habitually apprehensive master is likely to have an apprehensive horse or dog. Likewise the anxious attitudes, gestures and inflections of an adult in relation to darkness, fire, animals, lightning, sex, high places, hospitals, sin and a hundred other topics, favor the acquisition of corresponding behavior in the child who is ex-

[8] L. Murphy, *Social Behavior and Child Personality* (New York: Columbia University Press, 1937), pp. 35-41 and 149-150; G. Murphy, L. Murphy and T. Newcomb, *Experimental Social Psychology*, 2d edition (New York: Harper, 1937), pp. 330-331.

posed to these reactions. This was brought out dramatically in the 1940 London air raids when it was found that adult anxiety reactions were more effective anxiety excitants in children than the terrific barrage of noise, fire and destruction.[9]

In the following illustration an anxious, insecure child grows to womanhood, runs into serious personal difficulties, and reacts to them with an anxiety pattern which she has witnessed in her mother all her life.

The patient, a widow aged thirty, had always as a child seemed "nervous" and apprehensive, had slept poorly and cried easily. "If you just looked at her, she'd cry," her mother reported. As far back as she herself could remember, the patient had lived in daily dread of her mother's sudden death and the breaking-up of the home. The mother, from the time of the patient's birth, had suffered from heart attacks and shortness of breath which doctors had "never been able to diagnose properly," i.e., as heart disease. When she was upset the mother often said that one day she would be found dead, "Just like your grandmother was." The grandmother's death had made a profound impression on the patient and this threat of her mother's never failed to disturb her. This, then, was the specific pattern of insecurity in which she grew up.

The patient lived at home, helping with the housework until she was twenty-two, when she married a stable and responsible older man. He died four years later, a year after they had lost their only child of tuberculous meningitis. Following this the patient nursed a brother through a year of pulmonary tuberculosis until he recovered. She learned during this period of the dangers of contact infection and evolved the not unlikely hypothesis that her child had died as the result of exposure to her brother. She found herself thinking that the brother could have kept away from them, or himself died, instead of being the cause of her only child's death. She began hating the sight of her brother while she nursed him, and blaming herself as well as him for letting her child die. In this setting of marked ambivalence and guilt she suffered her first nocturnal heart attacks with dyspnea, which made her afraid of her own death just as she had feared in childhood that her mother would die. She recognized that her attacks duplicated those of her mother, but she was unable to explore their origins in her conflicts further.

[9] A. Freud and D. Burlingame, *War and Children*. New York: Medical War Books, 1943.

Childhood training in anxiety

Children may be trained in reaction-sensitivity to danger by parents who are not necessarily themselves anxious persons. The overprotective parent, for example, may by sudden preventive lunges and repeated warnings train the small child to be habitually apprehensive. Older children are sometimes taught systematically to ferret out in imagination every hidden danger that might conceivably lurk in an apparently innocent situation. They learn to think always in terms of the future but never to have confidence in it, to cross bridges before coming to them and imagine each bridge collapsing the minute they give it their full weight. By such procedures growing children gradually build into their social personality habitual attitudes of tense, uneasy anticipation which often interfere with their seeking the activities necessary for social maturity.

Parents frequently make the mistake of trying to foster social maturity in their child by parading adult problems, adult uncertainties and adult disillusionments continually before him — doubts concerning food and shelter, financial uncertainties and business worries, adult social strivings, and parental discords that divide his loyalties and threaten the fundamental security of his home. The child has many difficulties of his own to work out that belong to his own age. He needs protection from adult uncertainties, which are too complex for him to grasp and lie far beyond his limited resources to remedy, so that he may be free to build his security in relation to childhood responsibilities among his elders and his peers. Otherwise the child grows into adulthood prematurely frightened by its threatening aspects. He has learned adult apprehensions before acquiring the strength, social skill and emotional independence needed to meet and overcome adult insecurities.

Perfectionistic training is apt also to be training in anxiety. Many chronically anxious persons have been reared in homes dominated by incessant demands for better and better conduct, more and more achievement, higher and higher aspirations.[10] They have been urged on to adopt ambitions and set goals which require for their realization aptitudes or inclinations they do not have, and a combination of fortunate circumstances they have no good reason to expect. If a person is taught always to strive beyond and above

[10] B. Beverly, "Anxieties of children: their causes and implications," *Amer. Jour. Dis. Child.*, 1942, vol. 64, pp. 585-593.

what is possible for him, to expect of life or himself nothing short of perfection and completeness, and to regard any compromise as defeat, he can be certain of only one thing, that no matter what he accomplishes or what he is given, it will never bring him lasting satisfaction. The discrepancies he is bound to find, between his imperfect attainment and his perfect goal, will always be for him the measure of his own inferiority or of others' malice, and in either case a source of frustration in the present and the future.

Anxiety and chronic insecurity

Some domineering parents deliberately keep their child dependent by keeping him chronically insecure. By giving him emotional support only when he conforms completely to their wishes, and withholding it entirely at the first hint of rebellion, parents can train a child to remain habitually in subjection. He learns that submission is easier to tolerate than the anxieties of ostracism which come to him the moment he asserts himself. He may have his periods of resentment and half-smothered filial hate, but in the end he penitently gives in.

Submissive children are emotionally dependent children and make anxious, insecure adults. When they attempt in adolescence to break away from parental domination, as they must do if they are ever to make a successful adult alliance with a mate, their habits of submission and their deeply ingrained anxiety over parental disapproval become really formidable obstacles. For many young men and women the obstacles prove insurmountable and they remain unmarried children in their parents' home forever. Some find their solution in an emotionally mature or older marital partner who can take over the parental role of providing emotional support.

In their courting and marital relationships overdependent adults typically show exaggerated reactions to signs of acceptance and rejection in the partner, often little different from their habitual reactions to parental acceptance and rejection. If the marital partner dominates them, exacts submission and rewards it adequately, the relationship established may be reasonably successful even though it be punctuated by periodic revolt, like the childhood rebellions. But if the partner demands emotional parity or, as in the case of many normal women, prefers to be under moderate protective domination herself, the relationship is unlikely to bring either person satisfaction. The demands of dependent adults for emotional support are seldom limited to a marital partner. Usually they include the expectation that one's children will render unceasing devotion or homage, and that even one's business or social equals and superiors will express continual appreciation. The perpetually insecure adult may be likened to a ball held suspended in the air by fountain jets; he must have never-failing streams of reassurance and approval from all sides to keep him up.

It must not be assumed that anxiety disorders develop only in adults with an unusually insecure childhood. Childhood insecurity certainly predisposes many adults to react to personal and situational difficulties with anxiety, but if the stress or strain is severe and prolonged enough almost any adult will begin to show pathological anxiety behavior. For example, an unlooked-for success or the proddings of an ambitious wife may raise unrealistically high levels of aspiration in a mature man, and secondarily induce chronic tension with its low anxiety threshold. Anxiety disorders may appear for the first time in a person's life following prolonged uncertainty over the loyalty of a marital partner or justifiable concern over the welfare of a child, from unexpected moral and ethical conflicts, unaccustomed economic insecurity or even from a much-desired increase in vocational responsibility which one is not equipped to handle ("promotion panic").

The middle-aged and elderly, because of their insecure status in our society, are particularly vulnerable to anxiety disorders, and for some of them pathological anxiety is a completely new experience.[11] The inevitable reduction in biological competence that comes with ageing is for most persons matched by a loss in personal significance and socio-economic security. In men decreasing strength, endurance, skill and sexual prowess are common sources of anxiety reactions, and in women the loss of attractiveness and fertility. Men and women accustomed most of their lives to unquestioned or privileged status may unexpectedly discover, when they begin to lose it, that it is the keystone of their personal security and significance. The sudden recognition of resentment and hostility toward those who supersede or rival them often gives rise to serious conflict, particularly when the rival or successor is a close

[11] N. Cameron, "Neuroses of later maturity," in O. Kaplan (editor), *Mental Disorders in Later Life* (Stanford University, Calif.: Stanford University Press, 1945), pp. 143-186.

relative. If by way of compensation the neglected person turns to other satisfactions, such as autoerotism or sexual adventures, he may further damage his waning status and arouse guilt and the fear of social retaliation.

Punishment, anxiety and guilt

The anticipation of punishment is fundamental to the development of guilt reactions. Children learn early in life to suspend or reverse a response, to withdraw, cringe or cry when an adult makes a movement, a grimace or an exclamation which originally preceded or accompanied punishment. The child's reaction is, we say, anticipant; it is a reaction to the early phase of a developing situation, the warning signal, in a way that is actually appropriate to the final phase, interference or a slap. Laymen witnessing such an anticipant reaction are likely to say, *"The child knows he is being naughty!"* and to mean that he recognizes what he is doing as misbehavior. But all that we really have in such a situation is a reaction anticipating punishment, in the restricted sense that it was originally learned in direct relation to punishment. We can witness the same anticipant reaction in domestic and trained animals, most of which certainly give no very convincing evidence of having evolved a system of ethical scruples.

By the familiar processes of reaction sensitization, role-taking and self-reaction, which we discussed in Chapters 3 and 4, every child acquires a selective readiness to react to things taboo in his society, and learns to play the part of his disapproving, threatening and punishing elders toward his own forbidden trends. Thereafter he can and does develop conflicts and suffer anxieties as the direct result of his self-reactions to his own behavior, and in the absence of anyone else. A cycle of reaction and self-reaction is thus established from which the child can never again wholly escape. He has, in other words, acquired anxious self-reactions to his own behavior and laid the behavioral groundwork of secret guilt and conscience.

For such cycles of reaction and self-reaction to operate, and operate effectively, it is, of course, unnecessary that the child understand the full implications of what he is doing or to be able to say how he does it. These are techniques which in the early stages of their development are not even verbalized. Originally a child reaches or manipulates and suffers interference and punishment.

From these he acquires inhibiting and punitive self-reactions to his own reaching or manipulating. At first he reaches and manipulates, let us say, simply and directly with his hands. But later on he learns the techniques of *reaching* and *manipulating* more complexly and indirectly in his symbolic behavior or, as we usually say, he learns the techniques of *wishing* and *daydreaming*. He also punishes, threatens and passes judgment on his wishing and daydreaming, develops adient-avoidant guilt reactions and, if the cycle continues on without relief, his tensions grow to the proportions of anxiety disorder.

As we have seen in Chapter 4, all children learn to react to their own behavior as others react to it, and gradually acquire self-attitudes derived from the dominant attitudes of others toward them. Hence the child whose conduct is continually scrutinized and depreciated by hypercritical, rejecting, guilty or unforgiving parents will usually develop correspondingly exaggerated self-reactions to his own conduct. Through these self-reactions he then arouses in himself the anxious guilt which his parents have been arousing in him. If the sinfulness of stealing or ingratitude has been his elders' favorite theme, he may throughout his life show marked anxiety over honesty or gratitude which makes him take extreme precautions to avoid guilt and even the appearance of guilt in these directions. If sex misconduct was his parents' favorite topic, the anxious guilt reactions that sex interest touches off in him may reduce or destroy his competence in this important area of human life, or at the very least leave him unusually reaction-sensitive to sexual topics, and therefore less able to find ease in sex relations.

The person who in childhood has been made reaction-sensitive to sins of omission or commission is not likely to confine his sensitivity to his own behavior. The shortcomings and misdeeds of others come also under his critical scrutiny and make him anxious as well as indignant. Conversing, reading, thinking or dreaming about forbidden things provoke anxiety with relative ease in a person sensitized to sin. This possibility must always be considered in analyzing the motivation of unusual public protests, letters to the editor and reform programs aimed at increasing cultural taboos. Some of these appear to arise from an urgent need to eliminate something in the behavior of others that excites severe anxiety and guilt in the complainant. Some seem to represent an attempt to gain control over one's own conduct or to absolve one's own guilt by restraining or punishing similar behavior in others. Such motivation is seldom easily accessible to one's self-reactions.

It is well known that persons trained in guilty self-attitudes as children may react to all authority with anxiety as adults. The mere approach of a policeman on his beat makes them uneasy. Being called to a superior's office becomes a major crisis and the habitually guilty individual anticipates a dressing-down even though his superior has always maintained a neutral or friendly attitude toward him. On the witness stand such a person often feels more in peril than the man on trial even though he is not implicated in the crime. Authoritarian sermons and lectures or plays based upon moral conflicts frequently arouse intense anxiety and fear of punishment in individuals whose lives have involved perhaps less than average peccancy but who have been trained to suspect themselves of every possible sin. When anxious, guilt-burdened persons grow also confused and disorganized, we find them confessing to crimes they have heard about or read about but never committed. This possibility is known to all experienced criminologists and law-enforcement officers who sometimes find greater difficulty in exculpating the innocent, anxious schizophrenic than in convicting the actual culprit.

Anxiety disorder as an adjustive technique

We consider anxiety disorders to be adjustive techniques if they originate, or are used habitually, as a means of overcoming, avoiding, circumventing, escaping or ignoring frustration and threat, or as a means of increasing one's rewards and one's acceptance by others or reducing punishment and deprivation. It is obvious that anxiety disorders, which are themselves so directly threatening and punishing to the patient, must have serious limitations as adjustive techniques. Nevertheless, we find both anxiety attacks and phobias used *aggressively* in controlling others and gaining special privilege. One of our patients, who had been suffering repeated anxiety attacks, recalled deciding at one point that he would never again do anything he did not want to, and from that point on, his anxiety attacks became his stereotyped reaction to all opposition, disappointment and neglect. They were utilized similarly in the clinic and this proved an important aid in the patient's distributive analysis.

Our asthmatic girl gave some good examples of the utilization of anxiety attacks as an *attention-getting* technique. Her case illustrates also how effectively such a technique may operate without the patient's planning, identifying or understanding what she is accomplishing and what her methods are. The relationship of her success in gaining attention to the frequency of her attacks was neatly demonstrated by the coincidence of bad days with protein clinic days, and by the immediate effect of discontinuing her protein clinic visits altogether.

Anxiety disorders are sometimes used in *rationalizing* one's failures and inadequacies in much the same way as hypochondriacal disorders are. The sudden attack, the chronic "nervousness" or the inexplicable phobia, which incapacitates the individual, is also considered by the patient as beyond his control and therefore not his own responsibility. The patient in such situations is reducing the tensions of anxiety over one difficulty by presenting an anxiety disorder, developed originally perhaps on some other basis, as his excuse for poor performance. Anxiety disorders may also compel a person to isolate himself from others and decline to participate in cooperative enterprises. These are, however, simply direct avoidant reactions and do not represent the use of anxiety as an adjustive technique.

On the other hand, anxiety disorders may be of considerable importance in *repression*. Acute anxiety produces remarkably effective amnesia, often retroactive, even in normal persons. Its operation in rendering patients amnesic for personal conflict, fantasy and wish is familiar to everyone who has treated anxiety disorders. In the typical phobia, for instance, we see repression appearing in a somewhat different relationship. The habitual anxiety excitants are often derived or incidental substitutes which enable the patient to designate, to himself as well as to others, an acceptable even though unintelligible origin for his anxiety. Recall or recognition of the original stimulation may thus be repressed to the point of making it completely inaccessible to the patient's self-reactions.

ANXIETY DISORDERS IN RELATION TO OTHER BEHAVIOR DISORDERS

The prevalence of anxiety reactions in normal life and in behavior pathology is attested to by their appearance as topics of discussion in every chapter of this book. But anxiety reaction does not necessarily imply anxiety disorder. On the contrary, we find that intolerable anxiety reactions are met successfully in normal behavior through adjustive techniques, and dealt with successfully also, even if at a very high cost, in such behavior disorders as hypochondria, apathetic fatigue, compulsions, hysteria and mania. We find anxiety fended off sometimes in schizophrenia and depression where the patient retreats from threat and conflict into a protective shell of incapacity. In other words, the presence of uncomplicated anxiety disorder indicates that, in the face of mounting anxiety, the patient has neither successfully utilized his normal adjustive techniques nor developed other behavior disorders instead.

As we have seen, anxiety reactions appear in most cases of *hypochondria* and *fatigue syndrome,* while body overconcern and complaints of chronic fatigue are common events in anxiety disorders. We make our differential diagnosis on the basis of the relative prevalence and importance of one or another group of signs and symptoms. Some hypochondriacal and chronically fatigued persons have apparently adopted or been trained in attitudes of body overconcern, and in habits of guarding themselves against effort, without ever having suffered unusual anxiety reactions. They have developed topical reaction-sensitivity in these directions by the same methods which lead other persons, for example, to become reaction-sensitive to sports news or fashion. Transient hypochondria is sometimes an anxiety equivalent, the patient recurrently focusing concern on some organ, part or function, during a period of severe stress, from any source, and recovering quickly after relief comes. The origin of hypochondria in anxiety disorders, and of both hypochondria and apathetic fatigue syndromes as maladaptive solutions of anxiety disorder, have already been discussed.

Anxiety reactions are among the commonest symptoms in *paranoid disorders.* Paranoid patients often report typical anxiety attacks, and few of them are free from some degree of chronic anxiety reaction. In well-developed cases the differentiation raises few difficulties, since more or less systematized delusions dominate the clinical picture of paranoid disorders, whereas delusions are absent or fleeting and incidental in anxiety disorders. Pronounced anxiety reactions are also characteristic of a considerable proportion of *schizophrenic disorders,* especially during acute episodes. Indeed, there is good reason to believe that the disorganization of behavior in schizophrenia is often the direct result of prolonged acute anxiety, such as that which occurs, for example, in panic reactions. Anxiety disorders can be distinguished from schizophrenia by the absence of serious lasting behavior disorganization, including bizarre delusions and hallucinations.

The likelihood that *mania* often represents the outcome of severe anxiety has already been mentioned. Some behavior pathologists look upon the manic attack as an escape from insupportable anxiety into overt action, or, as it has been expressed by metapsychologists, an escape "into reality." Typical mania is not easily confused with anxiety disorders, however, for anxiety disorders lack the overweaning, aggressive self-assertion of mania, its elation and distractibility, and its characteristically lively stream of talk with quips, puns, rhymes and flight of topics. *Retarded depressions* likewise raise few problems of differential diagnosis, although, of course, a person suffering from long-continued severe anxiety may secondarily develop a retarded depression. But in the uncomplicated anxiety disorder one does not find fixed sadness, slowing of movement and speech, or well-developed delusions.

Agitated depressions, on the other hand, raise serious diagnostic difficulties. In fact, if marked sustained anxiety progresses without dramatic emotional decompensation the point may finally be reached where the clinical syndrome can no longer be distinguished from agitated depression. In the anxiety disorder one does not find outspoken delusions of overwhelming guilt, unworthiness or impending punishment. The patient, unless actually in or recovering from an acute attack, can usually go on with his work, and he does not seriously plan suicide or exhibit the signs of despair so prominent in agitated depressions. If these depressive characteristics begin to appear in an anxiety disorder, the patient's treatment must be modified to that appropriate for an agitated depression, since that is what his behavior has become. In *brain damage,* anxiety disorders may develop on the basis of delusions, disorientation or the failure of previously adequate adjustive techniques as a result of relative cerebral incompetence. In mild or early cases the possibility of brain damage is sometimes overlooked, while in elderly persons anxiety disorders are frequently blamed upon brain damage which cannot actually be demonstrated.

Of all the behavior disorders, *hysteria* and *compulsions* give the clearest evidence of being maladjustive techniques which reduce and sometimes eliminate otherwise intolerable anxiety tensions.

Anxiety disorders are seldom difficult to distinguish from *hysteria*, since when one syndrome is prominent the other is usually absent. Indeed, hysteria often represents the price a person has had to pay, in terms of losing control over some function, for getting rid of an insupportable anxiety reaction. His unaided attempts to regain control of the function he has lost, if he makes them, usually defeat themselves by reactivating the anxiety disorder from which the disability protects him. Similarly, in *compulsive disorders,* to which we shall next turn, the fruit of resistance to the compulsion is mounting anxiety, while the reward of indulgence is a temporary respite.

10   *Compulsive Disorders*

IT IS IMPOSSIBLE to study compulsive rituals without being struck by a remarkable resemblance between the functions they serve in the individual patient's life and the functions performed by the rituals of various social institutions in the life of the community. Indeed, there are significant relationships between these two groups of phenomena which we as behavior pathologists cannot afford to miss. For unless we recognize that something more than superficial resemblance is involved in the comparison, compulsive disorders with their rigid uniformity of procedure and design, and their systems of taboo and penalty, must remain for us no more than isolated and therefore unintelligible curiosities, instead of what they are — the abnormal variants of a universal biosocial trend.

If we begin by looking at the organized play of normal children — for example, at a group of girls playing "hopscotch" in the street — we are at once impressed by the participants' intense devotion to inflexible rules of procedure, exactitude in repetition, and observance down to the minutest detail of fixed formulas and ceremonies. There seems to be a general principle implicit in their code that deviations are not to be treated simply as mistakes, but as transgressions to be met with penalties and ostracism from the participating in-group. True, the patterns and rules of play are culturally transmitted from older to younger children. But this fact alone does not account for the intense moral indignation that sweeps an organized play group when one child deliberately alters or omits a step in the traditionally fixed sequence — stands on the right foot instead of the left or turns to the left instead of the right, even though one way is as good as the other so far as the next move is concerned.

Nor are these ritualistic childhood attitudes confined to organized group play. Children individually and collectively give similar reactions to every inadvertent change or omission by an adult who is reading or telling a fairy tale with which they are familiar. They greet the most trivial alteration with passionate and irritated opposition, and insist vehemently upon exact repetition and inviolable order. The unsanctioned innovation and the unfilled gap interrupt the expected flow of the familiar, bring tensions of frustration to the child, and cheat him of his anticipated closure. The old ways, the complete and ordered ways, become sacred in a child's life when they bring him the fulfillment of expectation and therefore satisfy his aroused need.

Normal adults likewise impose arbitrary strictures upon their own social behavior, not only in games and other recreation, but throughout their social institutions. Moreover, we find in adult society an ardent and obdurate insistence — much like that shown by normal children in relation to their play and folklore — upon maintaining innumerable compulsory self-limitations for decades and centuries after these have become meaningless, and even after their original significance has been forgotten. In legal formalities, in parliamentary procedure, in religious and club ritual, in military, social and business etiquette, there is overwhelming evidence of the common man's conviction that some special virtue attaches to repetition and uniformity, to uncompromising regulation and unvarying sequence.

If, for example, any man hopes to accomplish a certain thing in the public interest, he must proceed meticulously step-by-step according to the rule. Never mind how urgent the need may be for speedy action. Let him not omit a single station, lest someone make him start his pilgrimage all over again. If a bride wishes her wedding to be a "good wedding," she must on no account walk to the altar with the man she is about to marry, even though she expects to walk beside him through the rest of her life. Suppose a man has the signing of his will witnessed by two honest and competent witnesses in one of the localities where the rule calls for three. The will may be declared invalid, and the beneficiaries disinherited, even though everyone agrees that the will represents the intent of the deceased. Or if a witness at a hearing, who is judged able to raise his right hand as tradition requires, will raise only his left hand, it matters little how much his testimony is needed and how honest he is known to be, his oath is irregular and the testimony may be sacrificed to the rule.

There is no denying that, whatever its origins, man's devotion to order, repetition and ritual has played an essential part in the evolution of modern society. We tend to emphasize change and improvement so much in the history of the arts and sciences that the equally important factors of uniformity, exactitude and repeatability are often overlooked. Technological, ethical and esthetic developments have depended always upon man's ability to hold on to successful techniques, or techniques that he believed were successful, and to build them through cultural transmission into a lasting tradition.

In the course of this progression, carried through millennia, man has repeatedly evolved techniques for prediction and control long before learning to analyze his own methods and sort out the essential from the incidental components. Even in ancient times he exhibited an avid appetite for explanation and the same love of premature conclusions that he shows today. As a result, in order to account for his successes and failures, he has over and over again adopted plausible hypotheses which have later proved irrelevant.

Unfortunately, a great many of these discredited hypotheses, in the form of magical practices and superstitious folklore, have remained remarkably tenacious in our culture.[1] Thus, in contemporary America, one of the most highly developed technological civilizations of all time, magic and superstition flourish everywhere. Famous hotels and hospitals have no thirteenth floor; prominent business and political figures consult occult sources for prediction or for personal strength; charms, signs and amulets are worn or carried to bring safety and good fortune; amateur and professional gamblers rely upon a tie, some antic, a coin or a rabbit's foot; magic formulas are repeated which often include words having no meaning whatever for the superstitious speaker.

This is the cultural and historical backdrop against which compulsive repetition, order, ritual, penance, magic and superstition must be viewed. With such a perspective, we shall see that compulsive techniques are little more than individualistic variations, exaggerations and distortions of the techniques used in our contem-

---

[1] Compare G. Caner, "Superstitious self-protection in psychopathology," *Arch. Neurol. Psychiat.*, 1940, vol. 44, pp. 351-361.

porary culture by normal children and adults in the practice of magic, science and religion. Moreover, the goals of compulsive patients closely parallel the goals of normal men and women. For both normal and compulsive persons try to increase their control over events, or over their own conduct, by increasing uniformity; both evolve favorite techniques with which to anticipate and hold off danger; both believe that guilt can be absolved or nullified by penalties and formulas. The compulsive disorders thus take their place beside the other neuroses as exaggerations, distortions or socially inappropriate developments of common, normal human trends.

Compulsive disorders are characterized by irrepressible tendencies to do, say or think something in a particular way, which are initially opposed by tendencies to resist such behavior, and are accompanied by anxiety reactions whose periodically rising intensity leads to indulgence, followed by relief. The acts, words and thoughts involved in compulsive disorders are often ordinary and trivial, such as snapping the fingers, tapping, counting, saying a set word or phrase, recalling or imagining a prescribed sound or a scene. Compulsive acts, words and thoughts may also be horrifying, painful, blasphemous, humiliating or disgusting to the patient. The relief from anxiety tensions, which a patient may obtain through indulging in his resisted tendency, is always incomplete or temporary relief. Sooner or later the tensions begin again to mount until the patient is obliged to give in once more in order to reduce them. As with other adjustive techniques, the compulsive reaction tends to generalize, and may in time become a stereotyped mode of meeting all kinds of difficulty, whether these involve mounting anxiety or not. It is usual for the compulsive patient to be ashamed of his compulsion; often he is perplexed by it and resents it as absurd and burdensome.

VARIETIES OF COMPULSION

To bring the vast array of compulsive patterns within the compass of a brief discussion, it will be necessary to reduce their variety to a few main groups, and to confine our illustrations to the most common and important forms. Accordingly we shall distinguish *compulsive repetition, serial compulsions, compulsive orderliness, compulsive self-restraint and coercion, compulsive magic* and *anti-*

social compulsions. These groupings must not be thought of as constituting mutually exclusive "types" of compulsive disorder. On the contrary, the clinical case is rare which shows no overlap whatever from one group to another, and any or all of these varieties may appear together in the same person's compulsive behavior.

Compulsive repetition

All compulsive behavior is to a certain degree repetitious, but in some disorders repetition dominates the whole clinical picture. We do not, of course, consider habitual repetition a compulsive disorder unless it interferes with a person's social effectiveness and his satisfactions, makes him expend disproportionate effort upon everyday activities, or leads him into behavior that is inappropriate or inexplicable. Many cautious householders, for example, insist upon making sure every evening before they retire that doors and windows are fastened, water faucets, gas jets and lights turned off, and the children all safely tucked in bed. Their insistence upon this routine may demonstrate personal insecurity but it does not constitute a compulsive disorder. There are, however, cautious householders who must habitually return again and again to check on what they have already done, because they remain restless and anxious over the possibility that something in what they have done is wrong or incomplete. Even though these rituals of nocturnal verification become burdensome to the individual, disturb his rest and bring him into conflict with others, he cannot as a rule resist repeating them because of his increasing anxiety. Such a householder is no longer merely cautious; he is suffering from a repetitive compulsive disorder.

Many of the milder degrees of compulsive repetition are hardly more than expressions of generally insecure, doubting, overconscientious and perhaps guilty attitudes. Thousands of persons who unmistakably exhibit such tendencies are able to keep them within moderate bounds under favorable conditions. If, however, they get into situations which seem to threaten their relatively precarious security, or if their usually mild compulsive trends are directly reinforced, a compulsive disorder may develop. The following case illustrates the growth and recession of compulsive repetition as a situational reaction.

> A young man, with a background of mild childhood and adolescent compulsions, was led to obtain employment as a bank teller by

learning that if he proved satisfactory the bank would make his future secure. His vision of a secure future, however, turned out to be a mirage. He soon found himself obliged to count and recount, check and recheck, always doubting his results and day by day getting more anxious, until finally it became utterly impossible for him to keep up with his work. He grew afraid that others would notice his repetitive and often furtive behavior and misinterpret it as an indication of malfeasance. After work he was unable to relax or to gain restful sleep, because of frightening imaginations and dreams that he had slipped up somewhere and would be disgraced or imprisoned. He was referred for psychiatric consultation by the family physician in his home town.

Because the patient's home was distant from a city with psychiatric facilities, and because the patient and his family resented the implications they read into his referral, extended psychiatric therapy could not be planned. Nevertheless, a change of position to one with fewer details and little risk brought some improvement at once, and the alarming anxieties for which he had originally sought medical aid subsided after a few sessions of brief therapeutic analysis. When the patient discontinued treatment he still had his old doubts and insecurities, but these he preferred to accept as immutable components of his personality. In view of his own and his family's prejudiced attitudes, and the lack of facilities in the region where his home was situated, this characterization of his inadequacies by him was undoubtedly correct.

Among the more severe syndromes of compulsive repetition none is more illuminating than that classical aberration of a normal human habit, the syndrome of compulsive handwashing. The following case will illustrate the development of such a compulsion in an insecure person who suffered from lifelong tendencies to feel inferior and inadequate, to resent preference and attention given to others, and to develop strong guilt and anxiety in relation to her own reactions.

The patient, an unmarried female government clerk of twenty-seven, complained that she had been obliged to break off an engagement of three years' standing because of ungovernable outbursts of rage, continual preoccupation with thoughts of contaminating others, and irresistible impulses to wash her hands in spite of a painful chronic dermatitis. Her difficulties plainly reached back into early childhood. She had always been compared unfavorably with a younger brother, the family favorite. She could recall brooding a great deal over her parents' preferential attitudes and developing hostile ruminations concerning her brother and resentment toward her parents. She often felt unwanted, inferior and guilty. As a child the patient had frequent severe temper tantrums, particularly when her younger brother teased her, and she experienced many fearful dreams in which she had several times jumped out of bed and run into the lighted hall before awakening. She was an unusually fastidious child, even in the pre-school years, liking everything around her to be in perfect order, her person meticulously neat and clean, and her dresses without a crease or a touch of dirt to mar them. Her parents had brought her up to have a strong sense of moral responsibility, and she had never lost the anxious, ambivalent fascination for unpardonable sin that she acquired early through her religious indoctrination.

During perhaps two years, when the patient was between ten and twelve years of age, she became involved in occasional episodes of mutual sex arousal with girl friends. This made her feel wicked at the time, but seemed not to have given rise to serious conflict between episodes. For several months, around the age of twelve or thirteen, the patient developed the practice of counting parked automobiles and passing automobiles in groups of seven. She kept the counts of the parked and the passing cars separate, and felt that if she made a mistake something terrible might happen — she did not know what. She completed high school creditably at the age of eighteen and, after a year of special study in Washington, obtained civil service employment with a federal agency. During her civil service course and her first year of work the patient had a great deal of trouble performing repetitive acts, particularly in relation to cross-filing, indexing and the proper use of forms. At home she showed her tension in marked irritability, temper outbursts, poor sleep and crying spells; both the temper outbursts and the crying spells were typically followed by tension-reduction.

Between the ages of twenty and twenty-seven the patient had three serious love affairs. At twenty she began going steadily with a dignified, reticent man of thirty-five for whom she felt great admiration. Religious differences, however, raised so much opposition on the part of her family, and so much uncertainty in her, that she found herself growing more and more tense in his company. After a series of misunderstandings over trivial matters, there was a final quarrel in which the patient burst into a violent rage and told the man never to return. She was then nearly twenty-two. Her second serious interest in a man, some six months later, ended disastrously for her. After a few uneventful dates, her escort unexpectedly commenced sex play and she as unpredictably reacted to the experience with an upsurge of guilt, not so much over the contemporary situ-

ation as over her girlhood sex misdeeds. Back home, she went at
once to her mother and in a spirit of self-abasement confessed her
childhood and adult iniquities, saying that she had sinned against
God and that her hands were unclean. No handwashing compulsions, however, appeared at this time.

Following this episode and her confession, the patient remained
for several months seclusive and self-depreciatory, declaring to her
mother that she felt unfit for human company. She talked a great
deal about right and wrong, and told her mother that she had for
years been troubled by pelvic sensations which came with sex
tension, with visceral distention, and with guilty thoughts. She had
frequent crying spells and her sleep and appetite were poor, but
there were no temper tantrums, and the patient managed through it
all to stay at work. When summer came she obtained a ninety-day
sick leave and spent it on a farm. It was here in connection with
her use of commodes, whose daily redistribution was quite hap-
hazard, that the patient's first preoccupations over contaminating
others appeared, and it was here that she began her repetitive
handwashing.

She returned from her sick leave much improved in spirits but
with an established compulsive disorder. At home she insisted upon
having yellow laundry soap for her hands, she scrubbed her hands
and forearms up to the elbows with a nail brush, and sometimes
added lysol to the water. With this routine the patient was not long
in developing a chemical dermatitis of the hands and forearms,
which was disfiguring as well as painful, the dorsal skin of her
hands sometimes cracking and oozing serum. But whether painful
and disfiguring or no, she was compelled to keep on washing and
scrubbing. For if she delayed or resisted, an acute anxiety attack
appeared, with palpitation, mounting tension, dyspnea and perspiration. She found that, under penalty of acute anxiety, she could
not use a towel twice without laundering or a dress twice without
cleaning. Her bureau drawers were gradually filled with discarded
brushes, combs, powder puffs, gloves and handbags which for her
had become instruments of possible contamination, and therefore
were untouchable.

At work the patient became meticulously careful about the
records she kept, copying whole forms over if they seemed untidy.
In erasing and eradicating she felt obliged to eliminate every trace
of the wrong entry and to restore with great exactitude the column
and cross lines. These were no more than exaggerations of her
usual techniques, but to complete them now meant relief from
anxiety tensions which gave them still greater impetus than had
her former simple satisfaction with good order alone. Her diffi-

culties were further increased by the inevitable discovery of her handwashing routines by her fellow-workers and their open recognition that something was wrong with her.

When she was twenty-four the patient fell in love with a man her own age of whom her family approved. Within a short period they became engaged, but her irritability, temper outbursts, handwashing rituals and continual preoccupation with contamination repeatedly raised barriers to their intended marriage. She proved unreasonably jealous of her fiancé, accused him of not appreciating her worth or giving her enough attention, and devoted a great deal of the time they were together to discussions of the injustices committed against her and against others whom she liked. The tensions she developed while with him often culminated in a violent scene, and this bore a direct relationship to her compulsive handwashing.

The patient stated that whenever she developed tensions as a result of feeling jealous, unappreciated, neglected, frustrated or sexually stimulated, these regularly included the pelvic changes of which she had complained to her mother several years before. As soon as she gave vent to a temper outburst, however, the relief which always followed it also included anal sphincter relaxation. She now had two sources of anxiety, the one that she might contaminate someone after her relaxation, and the other a remorseful reaction over the unmerited hostility she had shown her fiancé. The situation led each time to a vigorous cleansing ritual. She frequently found that hurting herself was pleasurable, telling herself in her self-reactions that she had it coming to her, and gloating when the smarting made her wince and whimper. After the ritual was over she usually felt relaxed and gratified.

Meanwhile the patient found that some of these reactions had generalized to less directly related situations and activities. If she compared herself in her thoughts with other persons whom she admired, the reactions of inadequacy, resentment and guilt which were aroused would lead her to another painful ablution. Thinking about taboo subjects, hostile or jealous ruminations over anything, and the feeling that she or anyone else was being unfairly treated, had the same effect. Even ordinary tensions developing from delay, from having to stand in line at the cafeteria, or from having to hurry, eventually made handwashing seem imperative. It is noteworthy that if ablution was impossible at the time, the patient's anxiety gradually subsided, but whenever handwashing seemed to her at all possible, she could not resist it. She said that something in her appeared to dominate her choices; it seemed to have two sides, one saying, "Yes" to a contemplated decision, and one saying, "No," and the outcome depended upon which side triumphed. There was no hint of disowning projection in the patient's reaction to this "something"; she regarded it as mysterious and irresistible, but still as a part of herself. This was her situation when she finally broke off her engagement in desperation over her own plight and her fiancé's growing coolness. Extended therapy succeeded in improving the patient's adaptation to her anxieties and in reducing her compulsions, but it did not make her well.

This case points up certain important characteristics, common to many varieties of compulsive disorder, which will enter into our discussion of the bases and the determinants of compulsions. For one thing, it is clear that the patient's ritual is not an isolated, meaningless habit in her life, but rather a direct outgrowth of serious, long-standing conflicts and anxieties in which techniques learned earlier in life became symbolic of moral cleansing. Moreover, each indulgence brings the patient relief, even though relief so obtained is both transient and costly. The handwashing ritual showed generalization to other excitants, and it tended to grow cumulative and self-perpetuating. A division appeared in the patient's behavior — one that she recognized herself and, fortunately, did not project and disown — into a permissive aspect and a forbidding aspect which, she said, seemed to dominate her choices. Finally, the patient showed great concern over guilt, obvious self-punitive attitudes, and peace following expiation. And in attempting to cleanse herself of sin, she performed a ritual whose pattern has appeared and reappeared in our cultural traditions for thousands of years.

When Pilate saw that he could prevail nothing, but that rather a tumult was made, he took water and washed his hands before the multitude, saying, I am innocent of the blood of this just person: see ye.

Serial compulsions

The serial compulsion requires a person, in carrying out certain sequences of acts, to adhere at any cost to a preconceived invariable order. The normal man or woman, for example, follows an habitual preferred order in such routine matters as dressing or undressing, and as we pointed out in relation to ambivalence and ambitendencies in Chapter 3, this organization of routine means economy and freedom for such other simultaneous activities as conversing, daydreaming and making music. But normally the serial order is not rigidly fixed. If one is in a hurry, or preoccupied with daydreams and conversation the habitual, preferred order may change without arousing anxiety and usually without being so much as noticed. Not so in the serial compulsion. In compulsive dressing, for example, a certain shoe, sock, stocking or glove must always go on before the other, and the upper garment always before the lower, or vice versa. Buttoning and unbuttoning become important matters of procedure in which the order must remain invariable. If by accident the prescribed sequence is not followed, the garment concerned or all one's garments must be removed and the act repeated correctly. Undressing may have to be done in an order exactly the reverse of that prescribed for dressing, with corresponding penalties for deviation.

The tyranny of serial compulsion sometimes dominates the whole pattern of a person's life. To be absolutely certain that a fixed order of procedure is always rigidly followed, and not a single step omitted or left incomplete, the patient must pay undivided attention to every detail of his compulsive routine. He must be able to look back, if need be, and check each step to make sure it has been carried out perfectly and in the proper place. But suppose he does not clearly recall each step afterwards. Was the fixed order followed with complete fidelity to the last detail? Has everything been done exactly as it must be to bring complete security to the anxious, doubting patient? Suppose a misstep or a mistake has been made somewhere in the process. What shall he do?

The compulsive patient who is suddenly unsure of what he has completed in his ritual is in the same predicament as the downtown shopper who suddenly recalls starting the bath water at home, but cannot remember turning it off. In either case the anxiety that arises may make a check imperative. For the compulsive this usually means repeating the sequence from start to finish, watching his every move and perhaps calling each shot as it is made, in order to be doubly sure. No matter if somebody is waiting downstairs, or there is an important appointment to meet, or a train to catch. A few experiences with the mounting anxiety that appears, when the compulsive tries to ignore his doubts, are quite sufficient to cure him of his incipient rebellion. The following case will illustrate these points.

   The patient, a forty-one-year-old childless married woman, complained that for six years she had felt compelled to adhere strictly to a rigid routine of bathing and dressing before going out and that, during the year past, her serial compulsion had grown more insistent than ever. The beginning of her difficulties followed her marriage by one year, and developed in a setting of three-cornered bickering between her husband, her mother and herself. She was an only child, brought up without assistance by her widowed mother whose goals for a daughter were obedience and perfection.

A year after the patient's marriage at the age of thirty-four, her mother had come to their home in the country to spend the summer. A tug of war soon developed between her husband and her mother. When in the daytime the patient listened sympathetically to her mother's grievances, she felt guilty of disloyalty to her husband. When at bedtime she heard her husband's none too gentle comments on her mother's character, habits and probable future, she found herself growing hateful and indignant toward him. It was soon plain to her that they were all three skating on thin ice, and she became haunted by the fear that at any moment she might do something to precipitate an open row. She began anxiously watching every little thing she did and said, in order to maintain the precarious balance for the remainder of her mother's stay.

Although the patient was never able to identify a directly precipitating incident or to recall exactly when compulsive dressing started, the events of the summer of her mother's visit were unquestionably its background and it was well under way before her mother left. In its complete form the ritual prescribed every movement, from the moment the patient disrobed for her bath to the moment she was dressed for the street. Shower cap and curtain, soap, bath mat, towel and body powder had all to be arranged beforehand in their appointed places, and then used according to rigid regulations. Dressing to go out was the next ordeal, its every step governed by rules of procedure, even to the point of prescribing the hand in which a garment must be held, and which foot must go before the other. If at any phase of this elaborately controlled sequence the patient became unsure of an earlier phase, her mounting anxiety compelled her to start the dressing over, and sometimes the bath also.

About two years after the onset of her symptoms the patient underwent psychotherapy in a private sanatorium for several months. She was discharged greatly improved but still with her serial compulsion. Three years later a new development made her condition worse than ever. Probably as a result of increased anxiety over financial reverses, and the specter of living again with her mother, the patient began perspiring profusely after her shower. This she attempted to meet by using lukewarm water, moving

slowly and applying large amounts of anaphoretic deodorants. However, if while dressing she felt hurried, if she became uncertain
about the ritual, if she thought of something unpleasant or annoying, or even if she recalled having left something undone that ought
to have been done, she would break out into perspiration at once
and then have to start all over again with another bath.

As a result of this recent exacerbation of her symptoms she and
her husband, an habitually sociable person with many lifelong
friends, had become more and more isolated from the companionship of others. In a community where hospitality among the old
families was perhaps the most important surviving tradition, this
couple was obliged to delay dinners, come inexcusably late or not
show up at all, because of the patient's enslavement to the service
of her ritual. On one occasion she undressed and bathed herself
five times in succession, while her husband sat waiting to go out
with her to dinner. It was only after she had given up hope, and
he had presented to their expectant hostess their apologies for not
being able to come, that she managed to complete her dressing in
preparation for an unhappy meal at home. The patient gained considerable insight in the course of analytic therapy, this time reveal-
ing ambivalent attitudes of dependence and hostility toward her
husband, which threw light upon her use of the ritual as an instrument of spite against him and of punishment against herself. She
was discharged greatly improved but still compulsive.

Any ordinary habitual succession of acts may be frozen into a
serial compulsion as a reaction to anxiety. Many compulsive patterns are caricatures of the normal person's dependence upon routine. Everyone derives comfort, security and satisfaction from going through or witnessing familiar sequences — at home, at business
or in church, on the parade ground, at the ball game, watching a
familiar plot unfold at the theater, or listening to musical sequences
one has heard a hundred times. In these habitual successions even
the normal adult is likely to react to unauthorized changes in procedure, no matter how trivial the changes may be, with dissatisfaction, uneasiness and sometimes open indignation, like children in
the presence of a violation of their game or fairy-tale sequences.
For the compulsive patient the habitual routine, whether a caricature or not, has for one reason or another become the behavioral
foundation of his personal security. A change in this means for
him disruption, and therefore a direct threat to his integrity.

Compulsive orderliness

Mammals seem to operate most effectively in surroundings whose design is relatively stable and familiar. The unchanging context supports their routine activities and provides a dependable background against which to cope with new elements entering the behavioral field. Human beings exhibit, in more ways than any other mammal, a preference for straightness, symmetry, uniformity and completeness in their surroundings, the origins of which are still the subject of lively controversy.[2] For example, in our own culture, we find that circles, ellipses, triangles, squares, straight rows and balanced pairs prevail indoors as well as out. There are, for example, the endless lines of packaged merchandise, the ranks of marching men or dancing girls, the avenues of evenly spaced trees, all alike, the design of parks and gardens, pictures on walls, balanced windows and matched furniture, stamp collections, rows of identical books and the rigid symmetry of tables set for dinner. In all of this we see the evidence of normal human satisfaction, in our culture, with an orderly arrangement of human environment. We do not consider such a trend abnormal unless it dominates an individual's behavior to the virtual exclusion of other usually cogent considerations, or is so intimately bound up with his security that the slightest variation precipitates unbearable anxiety.

Compulsive orderliness is usually concerned with simple everyday arrangements. Shoes, for example, must be lined up exactly against the baseboard and ranged according to slight differences in size or color. Every doily on a table must be straight to the thread; paired military brushes or perfume bottles on a dresser must precisely balance each other to the quarter inch; each chair must be in place and at some exact angle in relation to other furniture or to a corner of the room. The slightest deviation from a prescribed design engenders immediate dissatisfaction, restlessness, annoyance and anxiety. The compulsive person's relaxation, his pleasure, even his going to sleep, must then wait upon the restoration of his accustomed stereotyped pattern.

Overmeticulous housekeeping is a common form of compulsive orderliness which is frequently mistaken for virtue by one's neighbors. Some interiors look like furniture advertisements because everyone is restrained from making normal use of them. Nobody

[2] See for example R. Linton, *The Cultural Background of Personality*, New York: Appleton-Century, 1945; B. Malinowski, *The Dynamics of Cultural Change*, New Haven: Yale University Press, 1945; J. Whiting, *Becoming a Kwoma: Teaching and Learning in a New Guinea Tribe*, New Haven: Yale University Press, 1941.

is free to do as he pleases, to relax and lounge, to get articles out and leave them around, to shift furnishings for comfort or convenience — in short, to do all the untidy things that make houses into homes. The place is ruled over by an irascible domestic tyrant who cannot allow the slightest disarrangement of furniture or knick-knacks, who cannot tolerate a speck on the rug or a spot of water on the kitchen linoleum, a pillow or a cushion slightly askew, a bed-cover with even the hint of a wrinkle, or window shades at heights that disagree by an eighth of an inch.

The compulsive household tyrant is, of course, herself under the relentless tyranny of her own anxiety reactions. It is because the most trivial departure from perfect orderliness makes her acutely miserable that she develops attitudes of annoyance and resentment toward those who disregard her injunctions. In one such instance the patient obliged her husband and three children to spend all their evenings in a bleak kitchen, although this had been the pattern of neither her husband's nor her own parental home. On those rare occasions when guests were entertained in the living room, the whole family found itself next day engaged in a rigidly supervised campaign of housecleaning and restoration which made each visit seem to everyone a visitation. Under these circumstances the patient and her husband were more and more isolated from the rest of their community, and their children took the earliest marital and business opportunities to get away from home. The patient developed toward her former friends an attitude of proud, injured aloofness, and toward each child as he left home a feeling of resentment at the desertion. Her husband recognized the pathological character of the domestic arrangements, but as he considered the situation irremediable, he found it easiest to acquiesce.

Compulsive self-restraint and coercion

There are, of course, elements of self-discipline and the coercion of others in most varieties of compulsive disorder. But the lives of some compulsive patients seem overshadowed by an irresistible need to hold themselves or someone else in check. Many behave as if their wishes were wild horses to which they dared not give free rein. Some play the role of unforgiving parent in their self-reactions, formulating needlessly strict rules of conduct for themselves and imposing harsh penalties for the least infraction, as though they were punishing the misdeeds of a rejected child. The roles of vengeful, punitive critic and punished malefactor may be wholly acted out in fantasy, or, as in the following illustration, part of the play may be enacted on the public stage.

A college woman of eighteen complained that during three months she had frequently felt compelled to place herself in a humiliating and somewhat dangerous situation. On several occasions in the night she had actually gone outside half-clad and made herself lie in the snow with arms outstretched in an attitude of crucifixion. She would then experience a confused mingling of spiteful pleasure, ecstasy, martyrdom and cold misery, while the possibility of discovery both alarmed and fascinated her. She recalled without difficulty that this behavior first developed after she had been listening to some of the girls in her dormitory discussing sex relations. They pictured the female as playing a sacrificial role, and this at once reminded her of stories she had heard of the crucifixion of women by Nero.

The patient said at first that she used her ritual simply as self-punishment for sexual fantasy. However, as therapy proceeded she found that it represented her ambivalent attitudes toward the adult woman's sex role, and that fulfillment as well as penance entered into the compulsion. For if she resisted going out, she became breathless and anxious, but after she had given in, and gone through with her ordeal, she always returned to her room relaxed, satisfied and ready for sleep. In other words, the patient acted out the role of punishing parent in her self-reactions to her own sexually stimulating fantasies, and she submitted to the punitive ritual in the role of erring child. At the same time, however, the hazardous situation in which this self-discipline placed the patient excited her still further. After the wet cold had punished her sufficiently, and her excitement had died down, she could return to the comfort of her bed in the dual role of penitent, forgiven child and satisfied adult.

Compulsive patients do not usually confine their disciplinary behavior to themselves, and some appear to work out their personal problems entirely upon others. Prisons, orphan asylums, boarding schools and other institutions, where restraint and discipline can be openly practiced, inevitably attract a few individuals who derive needed satisfaction from these functions. The situation permits these persons to play the role of the strict, unforgiving parent without having to be also the apprehensive child. Denying and punishing remove their own need and divert them from their guilt; they regain peace through being strict with others. Some fanatical, ascetic reformers seem to belong on the fringe of this group. They gain relief from their own conflicts and frustration by violence toward others — who are thus scapegoats for their own guilt — and they succeed in transforming their private compulsions into a public career.[3] Similar in origin, but much less dangerous in implication, is the compulsive restraint in the behavior of great numbers of rigid and demanding business men, nagging housewives, pedantic teachers, stern librarians, rigid secretaries, perfectionistic staff physicians, inflexible public servants and legal Pooh-Bahs, whose fervent devotion to routine, procedure and detail spreads resentment and despair in all directions.

Compulsive magic

There is no disputing the fact that normal children practice magic. They openly declare their faith in charms, signs and incantations, in ritualistic antics, and in the meaning of chance concomitance. In their play they frequently maintain that even the most trivial omission, addition or other change, cancels out the efficacy of what they are doing. This is a step beyond the simple conservatism of childhood which we mentioned earlier. Children employ special phrases and gestures, whose original meaning has usually been lost, to validate certain procedures, to protect themselves or others from harm, and to reverse or nullify harmful influences that may be imminent. Without this mumbo-jumbo the enterprise will fail or do somebody damage. Even when alone, children play little games of magic in which they arbitrarily link good or bad luck, sickness or health, with some completely irrelevant concomitance. For example, a child walking down the street tells himself that it will not rain tomorrow and spoil the picnic, or that such and such a sick relative will not die, provided a certain automobile passes a certain lamp-post before the bus at the corner starts up. Another child may imbue the outcome of a solitary game of horseshoes or jacks with similar magical influences.

The magical practices of childhood become compulsive disorders when non-indulgence or a break in technique brings persistent anxiety, interferes seriously with a child's effectiveness or happi-

---

[3] This has been brought out in connection with the public and private guilt aroused by a highly publicized disaster. See H. Veltfort and G. Lee, "The Cocoanut Grove fire: a study in scapegoating," *Jour. Abnorm. Soc. Psychol.*, 1943, vol. 38, pp. 138-154.

ness, and leads to behavior which is inappropriate or exaggerated in terms of the child's peer culture. For example, a boy on his way to school who avoids every crack and groove in the pavement is usually playing a little game. Even if he says, "Step on a crack, break your mother's back!" and goes through ridiculous contortions to keep his record perfect, he may still be playing a game and nothing more.

When, however, a child finds that he cannot step on a crack or groove without severe anxiety which forces him to glue his eyes to the pavement, and drives him irresistibly back to correct even the possibility of a misstep, regardless of the cost — that child is no longer merely playing. One such boy could not cross a crack or groove without stepping squarely on it. If he suspected that he might have missed one, or that he might have stepped on it in such a way that it ran under the arch of his shoe so that the shoe had not actually come in contact with it, he felt compelled to return and step on it again. Whenever his mother tried to interfere with his ritual, or with his backtracking, the patient showed rapidly mounting anxiety behavior which terminated in a violent temper tantrum. His sidewalk compulsion was only one of many rituals used by him to ward off dangers.

Normal adults in our culture practice magic also, putting their faith like children in signs, charms, rituals, incantations, concomitance and stereotyped procedure. It is important for the student of behavior pathology to realize that, in dealing with matters of deep personal concern, even the most sophisticated and socially mature adult makes little or no use of scientifically objective methods. Rigorous logic is a negligible factor in one's private fantasies and in the determination of one's personal attitudes, even in the private fantasies and attitudes of a scientist. Therefore the adult compulsive who relies upon magical performance is neither getting childish nor going primitive. He is simply giving unusual prominence to methods already present in our contemporary culture, and showing anxious dependence upon them for his personal safety. It is this exaggerated use and this relation to extreme anxiety that distinguishes the compulsive from the normal magic. The following case, for example, bears an unmistakable resemblance to the normal play of children and adults. But its function and its influence upon the patient's life were far removed from those of play.

A young unmarried woman developed an irresistible need to think of a different person with each separate act she performed in a given series, until she finally reached a point at which gainful employment and marriage were both out of her reach. This magical practice began originally as a technique of distraction from sex preoccupations, which had induced severe anxiety reactions in the patient as she walked each morning to work. She established a rule that each step on or off the curb at a corner must be accompanied by the thought of some adult she knew, the adult must be a different one for each step on or off the curb, and she must have one clearly ready in her imagining ahead of time. If she thought of the same person twice on the same street something terrible might happen. The provisions of her ritual made a frequent change of street convenient and this obliged her to start to work earlier and to shun company, both because talking interfered with preparation for the curb crises, and because her changes of course were hard to justify to someone else.

Because her anxiety over possible lapses continued, the patient's magical practice spread to other situations. As she put on or took off each article of clothing she had to think of a different person, and the same rule eventually applied to eating, to washing and drying dishes, dusting and tidying the house, inserting typewriter paper and carbons at work, opening and sealing envelopes or filing letters. She had to give up her job, finally, when the ritual crept into her typing in spite of everything she did to prevent it. She could not help daydreaming as she typed, and sooner or later forbidden thoughts would start up her protective device. This first cut her speed down and later destroyed her accuracy also. Of her complicated ritual, she said, "For a long time I couldn't break it, and now it just seems easier to go on."

Anti-social compulsions

Among the commonest of anti-social compulsions is the impulse to commit violence against someone. Fortunately the compulsive thought is rarely carried into overt action. One patient, for example, when halfway through her pregnancy, began imagining herself burning up her child after it was born. This fantasy, although it always precipitated severe anxiety and guilt, continued to be irresistible for several years. In middle life the patient developed an insistent need to choke her husband in his sleep. At times the need seemed so imperative, and her tension grew so unbearable, that she would have to get up and leave the bedroom. Her husband knew of this compulsive intent but refused to consider himself in danger. At last reports she still had her compulsion and he was still alive.

The development of anti-social compulsions such as these can sometimes be traced to their source in some transitory episode of anger and resentment toward the person in question, or to a momentary thought of ridding oneself of an unwelcome responsibility that is present or in prospect. Often the compulsive reaction originates in relation to someone or something else, but as a consequence of repression and emotional displacement a substitution of another referent for the original one occurs.[4] Anti-social compulsions are often compared to the amoral violence expressed, and sometimes carried out, by young children before their socialization has toned down their aggressions. They are similar also to the amoral violence that occurs in many dream fantasies.

In general, the more conscientious and scrupulous a person is the more intensely emotional will be his self-reaction to a momentary impulse or thought of anti-social violence. Inflexible overscrupulous persons, who are habitually intolerant of themselves and addicted to solitary rumination, are less able to pass over so serious a contravention of their own rules of ethical conduct. They are startled and alarmed by what seems to them a monstrously unnatural wish and in keeping with their habits of ruminating they brood anxiously over the incident. Thus it is that the overconscientious person, who lives by rigid standards, keeps alive and builds upon an episode which a less scrupulous person would hardly notice and quickly dismiss.

Compulsive thoughts of suicide and self-mutilation, even in the absence of depression, are by no means rare. A compulsive patient, for example, who drove a long distance for psychiatric consultation, reported that on the way he fought at every curve against a powerful urge to drive off the road. He gripped the steering wheel so tensely by way of resistance that he was obliged to stop driving every now and then to rest his aching arms. Another patient, a business man in middle life, complained of an impulse to cut his throat when he shaved, of anxiety over resisting and of fright over some day giving in. Both patients were wrestling with serious personal conflicts involving a great deal of anxiety and guilt. Their

[4] For a discussion of *emotional displacement* see Chapter 3, and of *repression* see Chapter 6.

compulsive thinking bore the same kind of relationship to their anxiety as the phobic reactions which we discussed in Chapter 9.

Of course compulsive thoughts of violence sometimes do go on into compulsive overt violence, with the same anxiety preceding climax and the same after-reaction of relief. An old tendency still survives among behavior pathologists to look upon persons who merely think compulsive violence as quite different from persons who both think and commit it. This separation is sometimes justified on practical grounds, since compulsive overt violence may threaten the public safety whereas compulsive thoughts of violence usually remain a personal problem. However, the student of behavior pathology should not allow the traditional distinction between anti-social thinking and anti-social doing to blind him to their fundamental similarity, and thus to divert him from the important unsolved problem of determining what factors are responsible for the differences in outcome.

Among the common anti-social compulsions that appear as anti-social acts, none has more important implications for behavior pathology than compulsive stealing. A relatively uncomplicated example can be found in certain forms of habitual shoplifting. Department store managers, magistrates and bewildered husbands come face to face with apparently inexplicable stealing on the part of women who have been carefully reared, are comfortably off and have no great need of what they take. When picked up by a store detective the culprit is typically frightened, humiliated and penitent. She is usually as much at a loss for an explanation of her strange conduct as are the merchant, the magistrate and her husband. All she can say is that the temptation seemed to sweep over her, that she tried to resist it, but that she felt driven to do it in spite of herself.

In many such cases warnings, fines, disgrace and even imprisonment have at most a temporary deterrent effect; sooner or later the urge reappears and the stealing is resumed. Stores sometimes enter into a secret agreement with the husband. When the patient is detected in the store she is trailed and her observed thefts are charged to her husband's account. For the behavior pathologist it is most significant that, if a compulsive shoplifter suspects collusion of this sort, she may at once move from the place where she can safely steal to one where she is once again in danger.

It is generally agreed that in compulsive stealing the danger and suspense, the furtive excitement, the wrongdoing and the deception are the important ingredients of the act. Sometimes the character of the object stolen is significant and sometimes not, but in either case merely getting an article is not enough. The thing must be done dangerously and by stealth, and once done it must soon be done again. The resemblance of compulsive stealing, as well as compulsive assault and arson, to sexual excitement and satisfaction has impressed behavior pathologists for many decades.[5] It is often reported that the irresistible urge seems to rise more or less periodically, even though fairly specific objects and situations always arouse it. Patients sometimes report that with the anti-social act there may be flushing, rapid breathing and heart-beat, fine tremors and tinglings, and the sense of letting oneself go on, regardless of consequences. Some patients report orgasm at the moment of crisis, followed by a sudden let-down with guilt, remorse and fear of consequences. There is evidence of sex differences in the prevalence of one or another form of anti-social compulsion, women being greatly in the majority when it comes to shoplifting, and men when it comes to arson and assault. Such variations are presumably related to biosocial differences in degree and kind of aggression in the two sexes.

Men seem to predominate also among those who acquire and collect sexually stimulating objects or *fetishes*. Since the fetish is usually a part or a possession of a woman, compulsive fetishism frequently brings the patient into open conflict with the law. The choice of objects involved in fetish-stealing is as a rule more limited than in compulsive shoplifting, and the manner of acquisition may be more rigidly prescribed. For example, a woman's handkerchief to be valued must be taken directly from a woman's person; hair must be cut from a woman's head and without her knowledge; shoes must be snatched directly from a strange woman's feet. In most cases of compulsive fetishism a relative, a friend, or even an acquiescent stranger will not do. For some patients the theft itself is all that seems to count; for others the theft is still cardinal, but the patient also hoards and counts his stolen things in secret.

Another group of anti-social compulsions, in which men are again the chief but not the only offenders, is that which includes sexual peeping, gazing, exhibiting, eavesdropping, touching and investi-

[5] F. Alexander and W. Healy, *Roots of Crime, Psychoanalytic Studies* (New York: Knopf, 1935), pp. 77-123.

gating. These compulsive activities seem to represent fixations upon the preliminary phases of normal sex behavior which then usurp the place of adult sex goals, or at least attain to a position of equality with adult sex goals. It is generally believed that early mishaps, misinterpretations and compensations for severe repression in relation to childhood sex curiosity play the determining roles in developing such compulsions, and that they are therefore to be regarded as distortions of biosocially immature sex behavior. In all forms of compulsive sex substitution, not only does the patient place himself and others in hazard, but he tends also to suffer a reduction in his range of normal sex activities and frequently distortions in his non-sexual interests as well.

Obsessions, ruminations and doubts in compulsive disorders

Obsessions, ruminations and doubts, although by no means confined to compulsive disorders, are so commonly found in them that various other terms have been proposed from time to time so as to give these symptoms greater prominence. Thus, Adolf Meyer always used the compound term "obsessive-ruminative-tension states" in place of compulsive disorders.[6] Henderson and Gillespie have attempted a compromise by distinguishing between "obsessive-ruminative states" and "obsessive-compulsive states," the principal clinical difference being that in the former the preoccupations are not followed by compulsive acts while in the latter they are.[7] The French at one time recognized as a sub-group those cases in which doubt and indecision were dominant symptoms and called them *la folie de doute.* However, as we pointed out in Chapters 3 and 4, thinking forms a behavior continuum with saying and doing; it is not a separate kind of reality. Indeed, one is more apt than not to find compulsive thoughts, words and acts appearing together in a single compulsive syndrome, and to find them all involving the same kind of symbolic substitution, penance and protection in the patient's reactions to anxiety.

A further source of confusion in our field is the ambiguous use of the term "obsession" — a result of that term's confused history. Thus, thinking, even though it be apparently unrelated to anxiety

[6] A. Meyer, "Leading concepts of psychobiology (ergasiology) and of psychiatry (ergasiatry)," *Proc. Fourth Conf. Psychiat. Educ.,* 1938, p. 282.

[7] D. Henderson and R. Gillespie, *A Textbook of Psychiatry for Students and Practitioners,* 6th edition (London: Oxford University Press, 1944), pp. 200-209.

and compulsive disorder, is commonly called "obsessive" when actually it is only repetitive or stereotyped. For example, everyone is annoyed at some time or another by a catchy tune, a slang phrase or a meaningless imagining that keeps recurring even though it is neither entertaining nor satisfying. Most of these recurrences seem to have no special significance for the individual, although of course it is always possible to argue that if one probed deeply enough a special meaning would emerge. But whether or not the recurrence turns out ultimately to be personally significant, we should still begin by designating such thinking as repetitive or stereotyped, and then proceed from this descriptive start to investigate it for the presence or absence of those behavior characteristics which make it compulsive.

Similar considerations apply to rumination and insistent doubting; they are common symptoms in compulsive disorders, but they are common also in other behavior disorders and in normal behavior. Everyone is familiar with the fruitless ruminations so prevalent in pubescence and adolescence for which there are no final answers. *What is the meaning of life? Why is this thing or that the way it is? Where is it all leading? What am I?* Questions, puzzlings and anxieties over such matters as eternity, endless space, the hereafter, the infinitely large and infinitesimally small, seem to be a normal part of the often difficult transition from the life of a dependent child in a child's world to that of an emancipated adult in an unfamiliar adult world.

For most adolescents these preoccupations are gradually crowded out by more immediate practical problems, which the maturing individual through his growing experience and new social skills is able to meet with increasingly practical solutions. It is not unusual, however, for normal adults to revert occasionally to ruminations over unanswerable and often meaningless abstract questions in times of personal catastrophe and disillusionment. Some persons never succeed in giving up their adolescent ponderings but carry them over into their adult life, along with other indications of relative social immaturity. Of these a few become progressively immersed and finally drowned in their fathomless cosmological rumination, and these we group with the socially disarticulated schizophrenics.

We saw earlier in this chapter that an excessive need for certainty as to the correctness or completeness of what one has done helps to establish and perpetuate compulsive rituals. If doubt arises, the thing must be done over again or a protective formula of some kind must be invoked to guard against harm. In some patients insistent doubts habitually arise before every personally important decision can be made, and for the occasional patient almost every move raises serious doubt. When the compulsive person is faced with a choice to be made, he may be assailed by unconquerable doubt concerning the rightness, wisdom or feasibility of every possibility that presents itself. Whatever he does, he must know beforehand where it leads; he must always choose the most right, the best, the surest and the most complete alternative. Therefore, when the need for a final decision looms up ahead, the patient may have to suspend action while he mulls over every conceivable course and carries it through in fantasy to its probable outcome. But this procedure usually brings in unexpected subsidiary choice-points, and he may have to go on to explore the potentialities of these alternatives also. The following incident, taken from the narrative of a compulsive patient, illustrates the extremes to which such trends often lead.

> A young man, uncertain as to whether or not his calling up a well-to-do girl for a date would advance his cause with her, spent an anxious, miserable hour in a telephone booth, able neither to put the nickel in the slot and call, or to pocket it and go home. Each time his hand approached the coin box he developed anxiety lest his calling her might ruin his chances with her; each time he let his hand fall again he developed anxiety over the possibility of his throwing away a golden opportunity. He matched every good positive argument with a good negative one, going into all the intricate ramifications of his contradictory motives, imagining everything the girl and members of her family might think about his attentions to her and about his neglect of her. He fantasied in detail, as he sat there, every possible consequence of his decision, to him and to her, on and on into remote contrasted futures. This patient was, in fact, caught in a common compulsive dilemma. He needed a far greater degree of certainty than the ordinary person before embarking upon a given course of action. But his technique of guarding against every conceivable mischance, by imagining it as it might occur, actually drove him farther and farther from his goal the longer he employed it. In the end he had to give up the ambivalent debate and go home, feeling exasperated, chagrined and worn out. He later developed the conviction that, in not making

the telephone call, he had missed the chance of a lifetime for gaining happiness and security.

Compulsive disorders in organ and tissue pathology

One of the most interesting areas of overlap between the sciences of neuropathology and behavior pathology is that occupied by the compulsive disorders. Just as in the case of hysteria, it is often exceedingly difficult to differentiate between syndromes originating in neural irritation or destruction and syndromes arising out of intolerable anxiety. Superficially they may appear identical even to experts in both fields, and the differentiation must then wait upon further investigation or the test of therapeutic response.

Repetitive and stereotyped behavior, as we have said, does not constitute a compulsive disorder unless it is a reaction to periodically mounting anxiety and brings temporary relief to the patient. In acute, chronic and progressive brain pathology the appearance of repetitive and stereotyped activity is quite common. The patient may show annoyance and irritability over interference with such activity, but it will be no greater than or different from the annoyance and irritability he shows over any other frustrating intervention. If, on the other hand, the patient because of cerebral incompetence becomes easily angered or made anxious, and for the same reason over-reacts emotionally when he is, it may become impossible as well as useless to establish a differential diagnosis.[8] Pathology in organs other than the central nervous system may give rise indirectly to repetitive and stereotyped behavior if it results in a serious disturbance of brain metabolism. As in direct brain pathology, such behavior may or may not have the essential characteristics of compulsive disorders.

BIOSOCIAL BASES OF COMPULSIVE DISORDERS

We have seen in previous chapters that the chief complaints in *hypochondria, fatigue syndromes* and most *anxiety disorders* refer to the functioning of the patient as an organism, rather than as a biosocial person. In other words, patients with these disorders tend to identify the origin of their difficulties with the dysfunction of some organ or part, to excuse social inadequacies and non-participation on the grounds of poor health and fatigue, or to focus

[8] For further discussion of this differentiation, see Chapter 17.

their self-reactions upon internal tensions and the symptoms of acute emotional decompensation. It is only when we come to *panic reactions* and *phobias* that we encounter chief complaints whose referent is frequently expressed by the patient in terms of his relationship with his biosocial environment. Indeed, this is one source of the difficulty which classifiers have always found in deciding where to put the phobias, whether to group them with anxiety disorders, as we have done, to give them separate status, or to include them with compulsive disorders, as Janet did in his "psychasthenia."

The moment we turn from these to the *compulsive disorders,* it is at once apparent that the chief complaints of the patient refer primarily to his relationships with his biosocial environment. In terms of the distinction we developed in Chapter 4, the patient is clearly reacting to himself as a social object rather than as an organism or physical object. For he speaks in terms of social innocence and guilt, of the vulnerability of himself and others to reprisal and punishment, of chance, luck and magic involving the social influences of persons and forces, real or imagined. Even when the compulsive person's anxiety is focused upon questions of health and disease, one finds that the *techniques* he employs in meeting his anxiety are derived from the techniques of normal self-control which he learned as a child in connection with good and evil, or social right and wrong.

Normal self-control

For our purposes, we shall restrict the meaning of *self-control* to *the regulation of an incipient or developing reaction by an organized self-reaction, both arising in response to the same stimulating situation, or the self-reaction resulting from stimulation provided by the incipient or developing reaction itself.*[9] In this sense self-control is obviously a form of social skill, the acquisition and operation of which can profitably be compared to the acquisition and operation of a mechanical skill.

Simple manual precision, for example, depends upon the operation of an exact balance between antergic muscle groups which work simultaneously against one another. As flexors and adductors contract, extensors and abductors pull against them sufficiently to prevent wobbling and rebound. In eye-hand coordinations, the

[9] For a discussion of the development and the characteristics of *self-reactions,* see Chapter 4.

retinal stimulation and eye-muscle tensions also help control the manual movements, while the manual tension and torsion patterns in turn reciprocally control eye-movements. The more unified and smoothly integrated such balanced reaction systems become, the less guidance they require from one's other behavior systems, the more easily they lead to satisfaction, and the freer they leave one for other activities. Thus, the skilled butcher or bicyclist can carry on a conversation while he works without reducing the accuracy of his performance. The woman who, when she was learning to dance, needed the contributions of her eyes and her tongue, now glides by with her partner, her eyes upturned and her tongue engaged in topics other than the timing of her steps. But let doubt, hesitancy or conflicting trends enter into any of this skilled behavior and the individual again needs every available source of control in his reaction systems to carry through the once self-sufficient, balanced skilled act.

What we have been describing in the preceding paragraph is self-control operating at the level of manual precision and locomotory coordination. It represents regulation of the action of a synergic muscle group by the simultaneous action of an antergic group, and the guidance of such a balanced, coordinated system by another system — here the guidance of the manual and locomotory activities by ocular and verbal responses. Nevertheless, such self-regulated skilled behavior involves principles which are substantially the same as those involved in other self-control, both as regards its acquisition and its maturely coordinated operation. We may illustrate various stages in the acquisition of social self-control, simultaneously present, by taking as our example the behavior of hungry children and adults at an old-fashioned Thanksgiving dinner. The objective feeding situation and the visceral response we may assume to be roughly equivalent for all, but the social behavior of the different age groups is noticeably different.

The smallest child reaches directly for the food; only distance and the restraint of his high-chair prevent his eating at once. His reactions, even though asocial, are still unified. The older children's reactions, however, are not unified but overtly ambivalent. The dinner situation arouses incipient reaching responses, just as it does in the smallest child, but it also arouses antagonistic withdrawal responses which are still incompletely learned. These older children are obviously under considerable strain, for they are tense, excited, noisy and easily quarrelsome. One child may make little darting hand movements of approach and withdrawal from time to time, while another sits with his eyes fixed on the food, as motionless as a pointer scenting game. When the elders give the signal there is a dramatic release from the tension of these competing ambivalent reaction systems — to grab and not to grab — and the children suddenly give way to what they have been resisting. It would be difficult to miss the similarity between this outcome and the dramatic release that a tense, anxious patient shows when, after long resistance, he finally lets go and indulges in another compulsive ritual.

The behavior of the hungry well-trained adult at our Thanksgiving dinner table exemplifies the full development of mature, skilled self-control. His competing tensions have become knit into a poised readiness-to-react at the appropriate moment, like the balanced tensions of a good golfer preparing to tee off. When the moment arrives he begins eating, vigorously perhaps, but without the burst and rush of a suddenly released tension system. His behavior has become secondarily unified through the acquisition of balanced self-control, the dinner situation stimulating him to behave in a manner that he has learned is expected of him as a biosocial adult. This is self-control operating at the level of public good manners.

Publicly shared behavior, we have said, stands a better chance of reaching social maturity than private. Hence, we should expect to find a relatively high incidence of immature, asocial techniques in self-control operating at private and socially taboo levels. It is, of course, by no means impossible for self-control to develop along adequate lines in private and taboo behavior. But this development requires that within the family group an effective behavioral relationship be maintained, between a child and his elders, which encourages the free interchange of attitude and information, the sharing of perspectives, and opportunities for role-taking in matters individual as well as social.

Such a relationship within families is, however, comparatively rare. Under the usual conditions of family life, self-control in areas of behavior which are traditionally subject to strict taboo therefore raises special difficulties, and is an important source of behavior pathology in general and of compulsive disorders in particular. As outstanding examples may be mentioned the rigid taboos currently in force against overt filial and sibling hostility, and those against overt interest and manipulation in relation to perineal functions which, as Freud long ago pointed out, are usually confused in the self-reactions of little children. In sex behavior especially, the almost universal lack of free interchange of attitude, information and perspective between children and their parents seems to be largely responsible for the socially immature, costly and relatively ineffectual techniques of self-control that prevail in our culture. Compulsive rituals, as we have already seen, represent one of the personally most expensive of these techniques.

Normal self-criticism and conscience

By *self-criticism* we mean an *evaluative self-reaction to one's own behavior or its product, occurring while the behavior is in progress or after it has been completed.* Human beings are continually reacting evaluatively to their behavior and its effects. The man who, after sawing a board or turning a metal shaft, holds it up for inspection is practicing self-criticism. So is the girl who, while dancing, thinks to herself or says to her partner, "I'm not doing this well tonight," or who hours later reacts one way or another to what she remembers as her performance on the dance floor. For while the acquisition of verbal and other symbolic reaction systems increases the complexity and the range of self-criticism enormously, self-criticism in the form of talk or thinking operates fundamentally in the same way that a self-evaluative glance does. And regardless of whether the self-criticism be in glance, word or thought, its influence is exerted in a manner similar to the interaction of other behavior systems which we discussed in the preceding section as forms of self-control.

The term *conscience,* although loosely and often ambiguously employed in popular speech, seems usually to refer to what we would designate as *an individual's reactions of self-control and self-criticism in relation to his ethical and moral conduct and to its effects.* The implication is also commonly present that these reactions influence one's individual behavior in the direction of coinciding with the group mores. A person's conscience, in this sense, is rarely a completely consistent and coherent system of behavior. The unity which is popularly ascribed to it is as a rule only terminological unity, the arbitrary result of restricting the term to moral and ethical problems. The degree of coherence and consistency that any person achieves in the group of self-reactions which he calls his conscience will depend largely upon the degree of coherence and consistency present in the behavior of his parents — the chief interpreters of a child's culture — toward moral and ethical matters. This holds not only for parental reactions to a person's own childhood conduct but just as much for parental self-control and self-criticism.

What the public calls conscience, and we call an individual's reactions of moral and ethical self-control and self-criticism, is not born in us but must be individually acquired. For the human infant at first is neither clean, orderly, restrained nor considerate; he is neither good nor bad, moral nor immoral, ethical nor unethical, righteous nor sinful. Indeed, such characterizations of behavior are themselves derived from social evaluations and depend upon particular group mores rather than upon universal truths. We expect nothing along these lines from the newborn baby because we can get nothing from him. When later on ethical and moral conduct does appear, it is the outcome of deliberate improvements made by the parents upon their original model. As we have indicated in Chapter 2, parents begin by imposing a predetermined schedule upon their infant, they prescribe limiting conditions within which he may operate, and they inaugurate as soon as possible an expanding system of *do's* and *dont's* that carries him along a straighter and narrower path than he might otherwise choose to tread. This is, of course, control and criticism by others rather than self-control and self-criticism, but we have already seen in Chapter 4 that the former are the indispensable behavioral foundations upon which the latter must be built.

An intermediate phase in the development from the discipline and correction of others to self-control and self-criticism is obviously related to compulsive ambivalence. We see it in the attitudes of hesitant, anxious expectancy that the young child shows when he is about to repeat an act which previously has brought him punishment (*adient-avoidant conflict*). Thus, for example, the hand that has been slapped hesitates on its way to a forbidden goal, and the child's eyes are fixed on the punishing mother or on the doorway through which she usually comes. This is the normal childhood prototype of the abnormal hesitancy and indecision which adult compulsives show at comparable adult levels of ethical conflict. In both normal child and compulsive adult, the socially derived self-control has not been adequately unified into an integrated act, and the individual is left to struggle between his developing positive and negative reactions — neither dominating over the other, neither subordinated.

A later developmental phase, the immature remnants of which can be recognized in many compulsive disorders, is a simple but highly significant form of role-taking that is derived directly from parental correction. The child, reaching toward a forbidden object and hesitating, instead of waiting expectantly for his mother's intervention, now supplies his own. He reacts to his own behavior with "No-no!" or restrains his reaching hand, and even slaps it, with his other hand. He is a house divided. The mouth that speaks is the child's mouth and the restraining hand is his also, but the words and the act of restraint are his mother's. His mother, in his left hand, knows what her child, in his right hand, is doing. It is important for us to understand that the child in this way begins to take over the control and guidance of his own behavior in his mother's name, and through her in the name also of society. It is equally important for us to realize that toward these self-corrective and self-restraining reactions the child can and does still respond with objecting and unwilling attitudes — which, too, are the normal prototypes of compulsive behavior in conflict situations.

As the child's socially organized talking and thinking grow in effectiveness, they tend more and more to become the preferred forms of self-evaluating reactions. At the same time, of course, talking and thinking enter forbidden channels and become the stimulus for self-correction and self-criticism. The ultimate development in private but accessible conflict is that in which a solitary person gives critical, restraining, permitting or encouraging reactions in symbolic form to what he is thinking in secret. Now he is alone with his self-evaluative attitudes and responses, which he has derived from the evaluative reactions of others, or as we usually say, "He is alone with his conscience."

Compulsive self-control and self-criticism

Sometimes compulsive self-control occurs in a form that is at once recognizable as a caricature of parental discipline. Thus one of our patients, up to the age of twelve years, used to slap her own wrist painfully whenever she had a temper tantrum — a simple, infantile mode of self-control which she had taken over early from her mother's correction of her. Another patient would tape up his mouth if he said or thought obscenities. A third compulsive patient with beginning behavior disorganization, a boy of twelve who later became schizophrenic, used to say, "Shut up!" to his sexual thoughts and to thoughts about the cosmos and the nature of God.

We have already discussed the less simple but more usual compulsive development of self-reactions into the dual roles of critical, domineering, vindictive parent and anxious, submissive, guilty child. In compulsive patients, these originally distinct roles give little evidence of having progressed toward the integrated organization that marks normal biosocial maturing. Instead they may remain remarkably distinct, each role perhaps growing more complexly organized in its own way, but both perpetuating the wasteful and inadequate fiction of a parent-child struggle. There is incontrovertible evidence in many such cases that the patient has developed his alternation of parent-child roles into an important need-satisfaction sequence which becomes therefore self-perpetuating. The need-satisfaction often goes back to childhood situations in which the excitement of wrongdoing, the stimulation of restraint and punishment, and the comforting aftermath of childhood repentance and parental acceptance, may all be determining factors. Sometimes frank erotic components are obvious in the clinical picture, even to the unaided patient.

We have already pointed to the general significance of ritual in compulsive disorders. It should be added here that ritual is also used in them as a technique of self-control. Even normal men and women lean heavily upon rigid, socially immature ritual in moral and ethical matters that touch upon their personal security. Thus they guard themselves from the danger of witting or unwitting lapses by replacing the fluidity of choice with the crystallization of fixed habit. Compulsive ritual as self-control represents an exaggerated development of these same techniques and for similar reasons.

The compulsive patient is usually a person who has been allowed or encouraged to develop habitual attitudes of severe anxiety and overscrupulosity. As a result of this, his life is overshadowed by needs for absolute security and absolute certainty which nothing can ever wholly satisfy. By adopting ritualistic devices he succeeds at least in reducing the variety of his possible reactions, thus eliminating the necessity for decisions he cannot face and reducing the range of anxiety-producing stimulation to which he is free to respond.[10] The effect of compulsive ritual may thus be to simplify a world with which the patient is unable to cope in its full, dangerous complexity.

In compulsive orderliness, for example, the more invariable one's pattern of living can be made the less chance there is for an irregularity to slip in unnoticed and the fewer things there are to watch. Ordinary preferences for straightness, symmetry and familiarity of design become elevated to the level of absolute necessities, often on the basis of semantic confusion. Thus things straight, symmetrical and "as they should be" are tacitly assumed to form the necessary background for a moral life deserving similar adjectives — straight, upright, well-balanced, harmonious, conventional and proper. Undoubtedly these verbal confusions spring in part from childhood experiences with the imputation of wickedness to the crooked, unbalanced, disorderly and unconventional. Indeed, in some families and in some schools, children are still punished as severely for having a disordered room or rumpled clothes as they are for cheating, stealing, lying or assault. To dress immaculately and with the utmost correctness of detail means, for some adults, to appear above reproach to the world, to be without error or blemish in every respect.

In this section, and in the case material used to illustrate the varieties of compulsion, we have indicated some fundamental relationships between normal behavior and compulsive disorder. It is evident that all of us show tendencies in our everyday childhood and adult life which, if exaggerated and continued under the influence of anxiety, might make anyone compulsive. This brings us inevitably to the equally important question, *What are the determinants of compulsive behavior?* In other words, what are the conditions in childhood and adulthood that seem to be responsible for its development in certain individuals and not in the others?

BIOSOCIAL DETERMINANTS OF COMPULSIVE DISORDERS

The view was at one time prevalent that persons who developed compulsions did so because they belonged to a peculiar class of

10 L. Woolley, "Studies in obsessive ruminative tension states. Etiology, dynamics and genesis of psychasthenia," *Psychiat. Quart.*, 1937, vol. 11, pp. 654-676.

human beings, known as the "compulsive type," which was distinguished by starting life with an inherited "compulsive constitution." This hypothesis has proved scientifically sterile, being in effect a restatement of the problem in terms of untestable assumptions, and has been generally superseded by the more adequate hypothesis that compulsions are biosocially determined. According to our approach, compulsive disorders result from the selective action on human organisms of certain special conditions in the biosocial environment and in the individual's socially-modified behavior. To these special conditions we shall now turn.

Adoption of the prevailing pattern

As in other behavior disorders, the pattern of abnormal behavior found in compulsive children is sometimes the direct product of prolonged contact with a compulsive parent or other adult. The child takes on the prevailing techniques used by the adult with whom he is identified, and the attitudes which support these techniques, in the same general way that the average child may adopt as his own the timidity or truculence, the particular preferences and prejudices of his elders. When a child adopts a parent's anxieties, and with them also the parent's exaggerated need for certainty and his use of stereotyped ritual, he has become a compulsive child, and unless these techniques and their supporting attitudes are radically altered, he will grow into a compulsive adult.

> For example, a certain woman had suffered behavior restriction and distortion through developing severe compulsive scrupulosity over confession around the time her puberty began. She gave the typical picture of dissatisfaction and mounting anxiety over possible omissions or inaccurate statements, and she became continually preoccupied with sin and penance. Her daughter, admittedly reared in an atmosphere of openly expressed anxiety over guilt and expiation, developed almost identical compulsive scrupulosity following her first confession at the age of seven. It was the daughter who came to the clinic for treatment when she was nine. She showed improvement during her stay. However, when they were visited twelve years later in their home, mother and daughter after some reluctance said that they were both dominated by the same concern over sin and religious practice, by an almost irresistible need to repeat confessions and to fence their lives around so as to diminish the opportunities for error. They made a statement comparable to the one made by our government clerk, namely, that they

experienced a reduction in the need for repeating confession when this was forbidden by the parish priest.

Childhood training in compulsive behavior

The child of parents who are not themselves pathologically compulsive can, of course, be trained to develop compulsions just as under other circumstances he might have been trained to watch over his organs or to avoid exertion. Children of non-compulsive parents may become compulsive through having been reared with too heavy a sense of responsibility acquired too early, with too much emphasis upon detailed procedure and the importance of precise end-results, or with too much dread of sinning and fear of retaliation. Some children are encouraged, for example, to weigh every pro and con before a decision and to ruminate over possibilities, even in decisions they do not make. Spontaneity means risk and they are taught not to take risks.

Training such as this denies a child the actual practice in making clean-cut decisions which he needs if he is to learn that one way of gaining maximal satisfaction out of having or doing one thing is to give up the alternative completely. The child is made to lay so much emphasis upon procedure, certainty and rigid standards that he develops severe anxieties in relation to choice, frustration, conflict and temptation while he is still too young and inexperienced to have acquired adequate techniques for handling anxiety. One consequence of his prematurely intensified needs and anxieties is to drive him into compulsive ritual which, as we have seen, is a relatively inadequate substitute for the biosocially more mature adjustive techniques. If the rituals he develops succeed in allaying his anxieties and satisfying his needs they are likely to become dominant and permanent in his behavior repertory.

Training in guilty attitudes

The old-fashioned practice of constantly impressing upon little children the gravity, prevalence and terrifying fruits of worldly wickedness, long before they are capable of understanding adult problems, is still a common source of compulsive behavior. Children who believe that they are perpetually in danger of plunging into mortal sin can hardly avoid being dominated by attitudes of guilty anxiety. From this perspective the ice seems much too thin for pleasure skating; one must be constantly on the watch and take every precaution to stave off personal disaster. Some children become fascinated, as well as frightened, by the process of imagining the possible consequences of all their actions, including even the innocent and thoughtless little things they do. To gain control over things and protect themselves from the dangers of unwitting sin, children are likely to employ the naïve techniques of compulsive ritual with which they have grown familiar in folklore, fairy-tale and play.

Our society lays so much stress upon sex behavior in relation to right and wrong that guilt over sex problems inevitably takes the lead from pubescence on. Pubescent and prepubescent children usually learn far more about sex guilt than they do about sex functions and sexual self-control. They therefore develop attitudes of guilty anxiety over their sexual misunderstandings, conflicts and misdeeds long before they acquire mature perspectives or adequate self-reactions in relation to sex. If they become intolerably anxious, they will use whatever techniques they have available — penitential and protective ritual, self-reproach or self-punishment — and since sexual attitudes are seldom genuinely shared, these may become the individual's fixed adjustive techniques. In late adolescence and early adulthood, when sexual interests are rather abruptly encouraged by society to develop into mating and family formation, the person who has learned compulsive ways too thoroughly in childhood may be unable to get rid of them and lead a complete adult sex life.

Compulsions and parental criticism

Compulsive behavior may also develop as the result of a child's failure to establish adequate emotional relationships with his parents or parent surrogates. The stern, austere and unforgiving parent, for example, makes it very difficult for a growing child to develop mature emotional attachments. What the child learns in later life to call love and admiration might look to an observer at the time like fear and awe, with relief from severe anxiety as the sorry substitute for a more positive satisfaction in parental approval. In extreme cases the child is made to follow exactly his elders' dictates as the price he must pay for minimal emotional acceptance. His slightest deviation from the narrow path set for him is punished at once by a complete withholding of parental affection. Young children, as we pointed out in chapter two, can seldom withstand the pressure of emotional rejection. If they find themselves plunged into lonely isolation for trivial mischances and misdeeds — many of which they are too young and inexperienced to foresee and avoid — they soon learn to be forever on the lookout for little storm signals of parental disapproval.

For us the important thing about this situation is that the child as he grows to adulthood tends to develop these unfortunate child-parent roles as his own. The chasm between him and his hyper-critical parent he carries over into maturity as a chasm between a fearful childlike role and the role of a vindictive parent. If as a child the compulsive patient has learned propitiatory and self-abasing rituals in dealing with his critics he is likely to continue using these immature techniques in dealing with himself as an adult. In the case of a young woman who practiced self-punishment and self-abasement, for example, a humiliating ritual imposed upon her in childhood was one of the chief determinants of her compulsive behavior. Whenever, as a child, she was adjudged naughty by her parents she was made to ask them for punishment and to thank them afterwards for inflicting it. In adolescence and young womanhood she found excitement, satisfaction and gratification in playing the double role of indignant parent and guilty child whenever she developed unusual tension, and this farce, acted out in her self-reactions, became her substitute for a mature heterosexual adjustment.

Compulsive disorders as adjustive techniques

The compulsive reaction is by definition a special adjustive technique. It is, in other words, an indirect method of reducing the tensions of anxiety or need, of solving conflicts, of substituting permissible satisfactions for taboo ones, of increasing reward from and acceptance by other persons, and of avoiding punishment and deprivation. Compulsive reactions fail as adjustive techniques because the tension-reduction which they effect is transient, and because the compulsive pattern results in impoverishment and distortion of the patient's life. Moreover, the patient provides himself with a new sequence of mounting anxiety and ritualistic relief which eventually develops its own need and satisfaction as an habitual reaction. We have already indicated the aggressive and vengeful uses of compulsive behavior, as well as the relationship of compulsions to attention-getting, identification, compensation, negativism and regression, as these were defined in Chapter 6.

When it comes to *repression* the problem is somewhat more complicated. We have already seen that the compulsive ritual begins usually as an attempt at preventing an anxiety-provoking situation from arising, or at inhibiting the development of anxiety-inducing behavior. The use of ritual is, of course, repressive in character. But the patient, by focusing upon his ritual, succeeds also in repressing recall and recognition of the original anxiety excitants in relation to which the ritual developed. The ritual, on the other hand, is a *consequence* of incomplete repression as well as an inadequate repressive *technique.* For if repression were complete, there would not be the recurrent phases of mounting tension which demand repetition of the ritual for their relief. As we shall see, this outcome of incomplete repression, although quite different in pattern, has some points in common with hysterical autonomy, which is also a result of incomplete repression.

COMPULSIVE DISORDERS IN RELATION TO OTHER BEHAVIOR DISORDERS

The compulsive disorder is most closely related to *anxiety disorders* for which, indeed, it may be considered in some respects a substitute. A differentiation between the two can usually be made on the basis of the relative severity and importance of the compulsive symptoms present. The frequent association of compulsions with *phobias*, which we prefer to regard as anxiety reactions with specific manifest excitants, has long been recognized as an intimate one. Janet, it will be recalled, placed both compulsions and phobias within the framework of his "psychasthenia." However, there is an interesting contrast in the uses made of repressive techniques in the two disorders. In compulsions the patient focuses upon a substitute reaction, his ritual, whereas in phobias the patient fixes upon a substitute stimulation. A clinical distinction between the two syndromes, when it is necessary to make one, rests upon the relative importance and prominence of compulsive and phobic symptoms.

The same distinction holds for the differential diagnosis between compulsive disorders, on the one hand, and *hypochondriacal disorders* or *fatigue syndromes* on the other. Difficulties arise only when components of neither disorder seem dominant, and then a differentiation is of significance only to the statistician. While compulsive symptoms may occur in any of the other behavior disorders, they are most commonly encountered in *schizophrenia,* and in *agitated depression.* Not infrequently they precede or usher in schizophrenic and depressive attacks. In schizophrenia the originally compulsive symptom may lose its significance as a defense against anxiety and persist simply as a stereotyped, perseverative movement or routine which has a history but no function.[11]

Compulsive disorders are distinguished from *hysteria* in general, as we define both, by the prominence of recurrent mounting anxiety in one and the relative lack of anxiety evident in the other. Forms of *hysterical autonomy,* such as the tics and cramps we shall take up in Chapter 12, are sometimes called compulsive; but they are more accurately designated as merely repetitive or stereotyped, since anxiety is minimal or absent in the patient's report. Moreover, these tics and cramps exhibit a semi-independent character which is missing from compulsive symptoms. When we turn to *hysterical inactivation,* which is the subject of our next chapter, we find a reaction to anxiety that is in some ways the very antithesis of compulsive behavior.

[11] E. Stengel, "A study on some clinical aspects of the relationship between obsessional neurosis and psychotic reaction types," *Jour. Mental Science,* 1945, vol. 91, pp. 166-187.

11   *Hysterical Disorders*

I. Inactivation

BEFORE A CASE of hysterical disorder has been carefully examined, it is likely to be mistaken for the product of specific neurological disease, and after neurological disease has been ruled out, it is in danger of being dismissed as fraud. The demonstration that hysteria is neither fraud nor a product of neurological disease is one of the great achievements of the past three-quarters of a century. For in working out new interpretations of hysterical symptoms and in devising more adequate therapeutic techniques, the neurologists and psychiatrists of the recent past succeeded not only in resuscitating active interest in other neuroses, but also in resurrecting the psychoses from their burial place under the headstones of binomial classification. The ancients, of course, were conversant with some of the problems of hysteria, and so were moderns even before the nineteenth century, as, for example, in the battle over witchcraft and in Mesmer's early magnetic theories and practice. But it was the Paris-Nancy feud that began the psychiatric renaissance.

During the latter half of the nineteenth century, a violent but important controversy broke out in France over the relationship of hypnosis to hysteria. The Parisian school, led by Charcot, maintained that only persons who were potentially hysterical could be hypnotized; the Nancy school, led by Bernheim and Liébault, insisted that practically everybody could be. The Nancy group had a great advantage in having devoted itself to hypnotic therapy for years prior to the opening of the feud. On the other hand, Charcot, who according to Janet had never hypnotized anyone, was unquestionably the world's most eminent authority on hysteria. In the end, Nancy turned out to be right in claiming that almost anybody

318

could be hypnotized, and Paris in holding that hypnosis and hysteria are closely related.

By all odds the most important product of this academic squabble was that it focused the attention of the chief contestants and their associates upon behavior pathology, its origins, characteristics and treatment. Two men who came under the personal influence of Charcot during this period became themselves internationally famous in the field of behavior pathology. Pierre Janet, who succeeded Charcot as professor at the University of Paris, began a series of important publications with his books, *L'automatisme psychologique* (1889) and *L'état mentale des hystériques* (1893-94). Sigmund Freud, then a young Viennese neurologist, was so stimulated by his year with Charcot in 1885 that upon his return to Vienna he translated Charcot's works into German and championed Charcot's views among his medical colleagues. Freud did not, however, blind himself to the other side of the Paris-Nancy controversy. In 1889 he spent a few months with Bernheim and on returning home translated into German the latter's classic on suggestive therapeutics. Freud's first papers, published in part with Breuer in 1893 and republished with additional material in 1895, were also on the mechanisms of hysteria. They give unmistakable evidence of the effects of these professional excursions and clearly presage Freud's daring originality.[1]

The term *hysteria* is of great antiquity. It is derived from the Greek word for uterus (*hystera*), just as is *hysterectomy*, the surgical term for removal of the uterus. Judging from their writings, the ancients evidently recognized that sexual problems often play a leading part in maladaptive behavior. However, in both theory and practice they seem to have made the same mistake that moderns still tend to make — that of interpreting biosocially determined disorders as the misbehavior of a single organ and therefore treating only a part when the difficulty lay with the whole person. They said that in hysteria it was the uterus or *hystera*, wandering about the body like an animal within an animal, which produced local disturbances of functions wherever it went. On the basis of this dynamic hypothesis, a therapeutic procedure was developed which apparently was successful in curing patients. The ancients argued

---

[1] J. Breuer and S. Freud, *Studien ueber Hysteria*, 1895. Translated by A. Brill as *Studies in Hysteria*. New York: Nervous and Mental Disease Publishing Company, 1936, *Nerv. Ment. Dis. Monog. No. 61.*

that the wandering uterus, since it was feminine, might be repelled by bad odors and attracted by fragrance. Accordingly, they ordered fragrant oils to be applied to the patient's genitals and foul-smelling substances placed under her nose in order to coax the uterus back where it belonged and end the disorder.[2]

The Greeks' *hystera hypothesis* is probably an important source of a widely accepted and at one time almost universal fallacy, namely, that hysteria is found only among women. Freud related that, when he returned from Charcot's clinic in 1886, his Viennese colleagues refused to believe his stories of having seen male hysterical patients in Paris. Indeed, so firmly established in modern medicine was this ancient error that even after Freud had found and publicly demonstrated hysteria in a man, some of those witnessing it were reluctant to accept the testimony of their own eyes.[3] Of course there is no denying that in civilian life today, for reasons still unclear, the incidence of minor hysterical complaints is much higher among women than among men — according to Billings, five times as great.[4] However, their unmistakable prominence in male industrial compensation cases and military disabilities has given hysteria a recognized place as a behavior disorder of considerable importance in both sexes.

Hysterical disorders are characterized by the development of persistent inactivation, or persistent autonomy, which resembles superficially the inactivation or autonomy produced by neurological damage or disease, but lacks an adequate basis in organ or tissue pathology. For example, one finds loss of speech in patients whose biological machinery of speech shows no impairment, paralysis which contradicts anatomical and physiological fact, and skin anesthesia that does not correspond to the known cutaneous nerve distribution. There are amnesias, in the absence of head injury or systemic disease, which are peculiarly selective or remarkably complete.

Autonomous movements appear and persist in hysteria which, whether or not they resemble the effects of nuclear lesions, respond

[2] J. Whitwell, *Historical Notes on Psychiatry* (London: Lewis, 1936), pp. 76-77.
[3] S. Freud, "The history of the psychoanalytic movement," in A. Brill (editor), *The Basic Writings of Sigmund Freud* (New York: Random House, 1938), pp. 931-977.
[4] E. Billings, *Elementary Handbook of Psychobiology and Psychiatry* (New York: Macmillan, 1939), p. 122.

to diagnostic and therapeutic procedures in ways that the automatic movements of neurological disease do not. The activities which have disappeared from the hysterical patient's repertory, or have become autonomous and out of control, may reappear or lose their autonomy temporarily during sleep or under suggestive therapy, with or without hypnosis. Occasionally the organization of social skills emerging in hysterical autonomy is so large and inclusive that it alternates in dominating behavior with what remains of the premorbid personality organization, or even replaces it. This is essentially the situation in *alternating* and *double personality* which we shall discuss in the next chapter.

Under ordinary conditions of civilian life, hysteria seems nowadays to flourish in an atmosphere of ignorance, naïveté and superstition. The marked reduction in the major hysterical reactions encountered in our clinics during the past fifty years has therefore usually been ascribed to such factors as progressive urbanization and the wide dissemination of medical information among laymen. Another factor of first-rate importance concerns the medical profession. Diagnosticians have learned that the patient being questioned and examined may unwittingly develop and retain complaints to meet an examiner's apparent expectations. In other words, we know today that minor hysterical symptoms can be rounded out into major hysterical disorders by leading questions, unguarded comments and incautious manipulations. We have fewer major hysterical disorders today because physicians are wary of providing the obliging patient with blueprints for their development.

VARIETIES OF HYSTERICAL INACTIVATION

By *hysterical inactivation* we mean *a persistent selective reaction-insensitivity, which involves a loss in activity related to need or anxiety, but lacks a background of organ or tissue pathology adequate to account for it.* Symptoms of slight and transitory hysterical inactivation are of relatively frequent occurrence in general medical practice and in the general hospital or clinic. However, the symptoms, like those in other minor or incipient behavior disorders, are characteristically vague and unstable, while their variety is almost limitless. Therefore, in the interest of clarity and brevity, we shall confine our discussion to the far less common but more instructive major hysterical disorders. And because some of our most significant biosocial behavior is organized around talking and eating, seeing and remembering, and using the arms, legs, hands and feet, we shall in what follows devote special attention to the hysterical inactivation of these important functions.

Hysterical aphonia and mutism

By *hysterical aphonia and mutism* we mean *the persistent partial or complete loss of the ability to speak as a reaction to need or anxiety, in the absence of organ or tissue pathology adequate to account for it.* Aphonia, the inability to speak aloud, and *mutism,* the inability to speak at all, are not far removed from everyday life. For example, the child facing an audience from a platform for the first time, the shy youth introduced to an attractive girl, the clerk in the presence of a stern executive, the private suddenly addressed by a reviewing general — any of these may be unable to speak above a mumble or even to say anything at all. Almost anyone can be rendered literally speechless by unexpected bad news and by frightening or shocking situations. But although it might be justifiable to call all such inactivation hysterical, we arbitrarily reserve that designation for aphonia and mutism which persists well beyond the immediate precipitating situation.

Hysterical aphonia and mutism seem to be precipitated in the same general way as is momentary loss of voice; that is, by surprise, sudden fright, anxiety, frustration, conflict and disappointment. A minor injury or an infection of pharynx or larynx may also be effective. One of our patients could not speak at all for a month after an uncomplicated tonsillectomy and then was suddenly all right. The stress of war, both in military service and outside of it, has given us innumerable examples,[5] but civilian life in peacetime also bears a sizable crop. In the following case bitter disappointment, frustration and humiliation all played a part.

> A somewhat histrionically inclined girl of fifteen was competently adjudged to have "a very promising voice," but she was denied vocal training, on which she had set her heart, by an unsympathetic family. Her father said jeeringly at the dinner table, " 'Promising,' yes! But promising what?" — a stab which her younger sibling was

5 L. Clerf and F. Braceland, "Functional aphonia," *Ann. Otol. Rhin. Laryng.,* 1942, vol. 51, pp. 905-915; J. Greene, "Functional speech and voice disorders," *Jour. Nerv. Ment. Dis.,* 1942, vol. 95, pp. 299-309.

allowed to repeat to everyone. After a few days of mourning over
her dead hopes, the girl finally gave up not only her career but her
phonation also; she could not speak above a whisper. The father
was sufficiently alarmed to agree to a vacation for the girl away
from the hostile family environment, during which the disorder
disappeared without direct therapy.

In another case, the part played by anxiety, conflict and sudden
fright in preparing the ground for and precipitating hysterical
inactivation is clearly illustrated.

The patient, himself scrupulously honest, suddenly found himself
innocently involved in an unethical business venture which had
brought ruin to members of his community. The prosecution persuaded him, in the interest of justice as well as in self-interest, to
testify against his one-time associates. The patient knew that his
own good standing had been fraudulently employed by the accused
as a screen for their manipulations. Nevertheless, he could not escape a sense of deep guilt, since it was almost certain that his
testimony would lead to a conviction. On the other hand, his
alternative was to accept undeserved disgrace for himself and his
family, to be pilloried before his friends as a thief, and to run a
good chance of winding up in the penitentiary.
    While in the midst of this conflict, and after it had been reported
that he was turning state's evidence, the patient was one day accosted in the street by two fellow-members of the indicted board of
directors. He was loudly accused by them of deliberately throwing
them to the wolves to save his own skin, and then an attempt was
made to give him a public beating. After bystanders had intervened,
the patient discovered that he could not utter a sound, and when
examinations had demonstrated normal neurophysiological function,
he entered a psychiatric clinic. Here he remained mute and unresponsive to therapy, but apparently in good spirits, until some time
after the date set for the trial, when he suddenly recovered.

Hysterical inactivation represents the selective loss of a function
or activity which is *biosocially* determined. In hysterical aphonia
and mutism this means that verbal communication has been partially or completely lost. The organs of speech in other activities,
as, for example, during the clinical examination, will therefore
usually not be immobilized as they might be in neurological disease
or damage. Thus, one ordinarily finds the lips, tongue, uvula, epi-
glottis or vocal cords performing normally in some other relation-

ship, as, for example, during inspiration and expiration, or during eating and swallowing. The onset is usually sudden, and all sounds may be equally or completely lost. On the other hand, the impairment of complex behavior, which would almost certainly appear if such losses were the product of cerebral damage, is conspicuously wanting. The patient frequently communicates well by gesture or writing, and shows none of the disorders commonly accompanying aphasias of central origin. Finally, the inactivation usually clears up abruptly and completely.

Hysterical anorexia

A few decades ago it was not rare for young women who had gone on a restricted diet, ostensibly for reasons of health and beauty, to succeed in starving themselves to a point where some intercurrent disease brought a fatal termination. Long after they had reached their apparent weight-reducing objective, and even after progressive emaciation had made a low food intake extremely hazardous, certain patients proved incapable of overcoming their acquired inappetence. Some of these found that they could scarcely swallow, and when they did swallow, reflex vomiting promptly nullified their efforts. It is, of course, always difficult to evaluate the medical records of past eras, particularly in the field of behavior disorders where basic attitudes and techniques have undergone radical changes. Nevertheless, we can be sure that many such cases would today have been regarded as hysterical. Modern diagnosis, the great strides forward in the science of nutrition, and our more adequate methods of artificial feeding make a fatal outcome from self-starvation nowadays unlikely, but the problem of hysterical anorexia as behavior pathology is still a matter for grave clinical concern.

By *hysterical anorexia* we mean *a persistent partial or complete inappetence as a reaction to need or anxiety, in the absence of organ or tissue pathology adequate to account for it.*[6] Inappetence, under conditions that ordinarily stimulate one to eat, is one of the commonest of normal reactions in persons who are excited, anxious, disappointed, sad, confused or in conflict. We have already indi-

---

[6] Thus defined, *hysterical anorexia* is a less inclusive term than *anorexia nervosa*. See the discussion of the latter in J. Masserman, "Psychodynamisms in anorexia nervosa and nervous vomiting," *Psychiat. Quart.*, 1941, vol. 10, pp. 211-242.

cated, in Chapters 2 and 5, the many social implications that hunger, eating and the after-reactions of gratification normally acquire, through the concomitance of interpersonal reactions during feeding. Indeed, if eating had no meaning for human beings other than that of satisfying hunger, hysterical anorexia would never develop. But eating together means sharing, and sharing means a degree of acceptance which may vary from toleration to profound emotional approval and identification. Hence, to be banished from the table or excluded from a dinner celebration means social rejection, and implies social unworthiness or unimportance that no amount of eating alone can eradicate.

We have also pointed out that, in religious ceremonies, spiritual acceptance into the community of believers — and in some societies this means virtually the whole community — is marked by the periodic communal eating of a consecrated animal, a man, or the symbol of some deity whose characteristics one worships. Thus, the Hawaiians reported that among the chieftains who ate the flesh of Captain Cook were those who held him in the highest esteem and wished in this way to partake of his inherent virtues. In our own society, besides similar more devious cultural attitudes, we must never forget the backlog of frankly cannibalistic tales on which we have all been reared (e.g., Jack and the Beanstalk, Hänsel and Gretel, and watered down versions of Sinbad the Sailor and the Odyssey), or the stories we have been told about love potions, poisonings and magical body changes resulting from food or drink (e.g., Alice in Wonderland, Cinderella, Snow White and some of the Shakespearean themes).

This is the biosocial background from which persistent inappetence may emerge and the basis for much of its intricate and often confused symbolization. At the same time anorexia, like other hysterical inactivation, is an adjustive technique, a maladaptive reaction to need or anxiety. The ground is sometimes unwittingly prepared for its later development when a child is allowed to use food refusal as a technique of expressing displeasure and rejection in general, and as a means of controlling others through arousing their anxiety. This broad use of a specific inactivation raises the possibility that, as in the following case, the child growing into adulthood may reject this development symbolically in his well-practiced way — by refusing and indeed becoming unable to eat.

A socially immature adolescent schoolgirl had learned as a child to alarm and control her parents by rejecting food whenever she was crossed. The parents were mystified by her apparently occult ability to lose weight rapidly when punished, even though they forced her to remain facing her meal until she had eaten it. What they did not discover was that throughout her childhood the patient had practiced the common deception of concealing her food at the table and later flushing it down the toilet. Like many children of overprotective, domineering parents this girl did not welcome the approach of biosocial maturity with its anatomical and physiological changes, its new social responsibilities and particularly the prospect of playing an adult sexual role.

She began her rebellion by attempting to delay her growth by drastically curtailing her food intake. This brought her immediately into sharp conflict with her oversolicitous parents who made the mistake of using coercion, and were rewarded by the paradox of increased eating with decreasing weight. Just as the eating had come to symbolize her growth into adulthood, so now the patient's contest with her parents represented for her the struggle, not only against her own approaching biosocial maturity, but against their whole domination of her. In public she appeared to accede to their demands that she build herself up, and then in private, like Penelope, she proceeded to undo her work. She went further than she had in childhood and not only concealed food to throw away but regurgitated much that she had swallowed. Eventually she reached a point where she could ingest only small amounts of food, with considerable coaxing, and even these she could seldom retain. She complained of inappetence and disgust with food, but not of hunger.

She was finally admitted in an emaciated condition to a general hospital and treated for the vomiting and malnutrition. It soon became obvious to the staff physicians, however, that she and her parents were primarily in need of psychiatric attention. Through the coordinated efforts of internist and psychiatrist the vomiting was brought under control and normal feeding was re-established. When the patient was given bathroom privileges she began again to conceal and dispose of food according to the old pattern, and expert psychiatric nursing had to be introduced to prevent her thus evading the fundamental issues which feeding symbolized for her. After three months she was discharged in good general health and without the symptoms for which her admission had been sought, but also without full acceptance of the role of an emancipated, biosocially mature adult.

Hysterical anorexia, like hysterical aphonia and mutism, represents the loss of an activity having far-reaching social implications. The inappetence develops initially because anxieties, or needs other than hunger, are more imperious or more important to the individual than the need for food. Unlike the self-dieting hypochondriac, who restricts his intake because he believes that he is suffering from a digestive disturbance and worries over it, the patient with hysterical anorexia is usually the least worried person in the situation. The digestive system, unlike that in gastrointestinal organ or tissue pathology, reacts well to food when it is introduced, provided that reflex vomiting has not become secondarily established as an habitual technique of rejection. Recovery from hysterical anorexia does not, of course, occur with the dramatic suddenness of recovery from aphonia or mutism, since starvation leads to the breaking-down of tissue whose rebuilding takes time.

Paralysis and anesthesia

Hysterical paralyses and the hysterical loss of cutaneous and mucous membrane sensitivity are found nowadays most often among persons of meager education and limited background. Laymen, we said, have themselves grown more sophisticated and skeptical toward what they consider "imaginary ailments," and physicians are more adroit in avoiding the suggestion of symptoms to impressionable patients. Nevertheless, one still runs across classically complete paralyses and anesthesias in civilian and military practice.

By *hysterical paralysis* we mean *the persistent partial or complete loss of specific motor activity as a reaction to need or anxiety, in the absence of organ or tissue pathology adequate to account for it.* By *hysterical anesthesia* we mean *the persistent partial or complete loss of response to stimulation of a surface area as a reaction to need or anxiety, in the absence of organ or tissue pathology adequate to account for it.* Hysterical paralysis and anesthesia, whatever the reason, seem more mysterious and unnatural to the average layman than do aphonia and anorexia. Actually there is nothing commoner in everyday life than transient disturbances in motility, in posture and in the ability to respond to cutaneous stimulation.

People, for example, get so frightened that they not only say they cannot move, they show it; they are "scared stiff" or "paralyzed" by impending danger that calls for action. During sudden anxiety, severe conflict or in fascination a person may remain "rooted to the spot," and after the crisis crumple up as though he had been struck on the head, but without losing his ability to speak. In happy as well as unhappy excitement people momentarily do not respond to ordinarily painful stimulation; when startled or profoundly disappointed, they speak of "feeling numb all over" and give evidence in overt behavior that some inactivation of their usual responses to cutaneous stimulation is present. It should be said that verbal behavior and thinking are no less capable of producing transient normal inactivation than the non-symbolic reactions which they supplement, or for which they substitute.

Hysterical paralyses and anesthesias are precipitated in ways that appear to be identical with those involved in corresponding normal inactivation.[7] The statement is generally made that hysterical anesthesia and paralysis always develop on the basis of a preexisting conflict. This assertion would be exceedingly difficult to disprove, for no one is entirely without conflict. Certainly the presence of chronic anxiety or intense unsatisfied need at the time of fright, excitement or a mishap should make the development of some hysterical disorder more likely, since hysteria is a technique which disposes of the tensions of need and anxiety. But neither the precise character of the hysterical reaction, nor its timing, can be completely understood without including the influence of the precipitating situation, as the following case shows.

> The patient, daughter of a ranchman whose means and education were both very limited, was in early adolescence when her hysterical disorder had its onset. While she was alone in the ranch house one afternoon, according to her story, a relative entered and threatened her with rape. She screamed for help, her legs gave way and she slipped to the floor, where she was found unharmed a few moments later by her mother. She was carried to her bed and waited upon there with unaccustomed devotion for several days. When, however, attempts were made to get her up, it was discovered that her legs buckled under her and she could not stand. The family physician attributed this reaction to fright, in which he was probably right, and advised keeping her in bed until her legs grew strong again, in which he was unquestionably wrong. The family added confusion to the situation by relating her illness to an epi-

---

[7] J. Sutherland, "A survey of one hundred cases of war neuroses," *Brit. Med. Jour.*, 1941, part 2, pp. 365-370; R. Grinker and J. Spiegel, *Men Under Stress* (Philadelphia: Blakiston, 1945), pp. 104-105; R. Grinker and J. Spiegel, *War Neuroses* (Philadelphia: Blakiston, 1945), pp. 28-32.

demic of paralysis among ranch animals which had appeared in the neighborhood.

As it became evident that the girl was not recovering, she was allowed to displace her father in the parental bedroom, which opened into the living room. Her mother slept with her at night. Neighbors paid frequent visits, brought her homemade things to eat and to wear, and discussed her disability over and over. As an invalid and a victim she received the best of food and attention. Her mother massaged the paralyzed legs morning and evening. The patient spent her time in sewing, conversation and reading. Attempts to get her to stand and walk were finally abandoned, as she showed no improvement and the effort required to encourage and support her was too much for the hard-worked family. She did not lose the ability to move her legs around in bed, and she could reach for things with her toes and pull them toward her.[8]

The patient would probably never have come to the attention of neurologists and psychiatrists but for the intervention of a newcomer in the neighborhood ten years later. The newcomer recognized the possibility that the paralysis might be hysterical in character, but made the mistake of arousing hopes of a medical miracle among relatives and friends of the patient. Upon the patient's admission to the hospital, it was obvious that her relatives expected something to be done immediately which would make her well. It was equally obvious that the patient herself resented the whole move and regarded the physician's questions and examinations as covert accusations against her honesty. She, her family and the neighbors appeared to believe completely in her illness as "a paralysis," which to them was in the same class as "infantile paralysis," the paralysis of a "stroke" and the epidemic paralyses occurring in ranch animals.

On clinical examination the neuromuscular reactions appeared normal. The patient's legs and thighs showed less atrophy than one finds in the average bedridden person with normal legs. The absence of secondary contractures and vasomotor disturbances could be attributed to unusually devoted nursing on the mother's part or to movement of the legs by the patient in bed. Whenever she was supported in a standing position, her legs became limp, whereas when she lay in bed they were not. She leaned with her entire weight upon the nurses supporting her and let her feet drag when the nurses tried to help her to walk. Both she and her relatives expressed frank disbelief when it was suggested to them that their interpretation of the disorder might be mistaken. The mother said,

[8] This is similar to the classical *astasia-abasia* syndrome of Blocq.

"It's you and not her that's supposed to do the curing." At the end of a month the patient was removed against advice, even though her stay cost the family nothing, and returned to her home to resume her life-role as the community's invalid girl.

This case illustrates some of the complexities of motivation in hysterical inactivation that help to account for the exaggerated development of what in Chapter 3 we called *overexclusion*. There is no disputing the effect of the threatened assault in precipitating the disorder and in determining its location and general pattern. Because of the patient's uncompromising hostility toward her would-be therapists, we know nothing about her premorbid conflicts. We do know that after the onset of her disability she expressed definitely ambivalent attitudes toward the aggressor which may very well have been present before it. The coincident animal epidemic undoubtedly helped to fix the disorder, since it provided, not only a reasonable and honorific origin for the girl's illness, but also the topic of endless conversations in which the two were linked together. The patient, when finally studied, gave every sign of preferring her status as a chronic invalid to the alternatives otherwise open to her, any of which would certainly have left her a less privileged and less important person. She had developed new needs and new satisfactions which in a normal woman's way of life would find no place. By the time she reached the hospital, she had behind her a decade of idleness and dependence to justify — to herself as well as to the community.

It was plain that there were secondary gains for the patient's family also in this situation. They occupied a position of considerable prestige in the community because of their daughter's strange affliction. Because of it they also received many more and much longer visits than would otherwise have been the case, and visits are prized on isolated ranches. From other sources it was learned that within the family circle there had been a great storm over the original incident, and that a concerted effort had been made in the early days to divert the attention of relatives and others from it by emphasizing the epidemic. All of these factors entered into the attitudes of patient and family toward the inactivation and toward those who threatened to interpret it differently.

In hysterical inactivation an arm or a leg may be even more completely excluded from participation in the patient's life than in the case of our ranch girl who, after all, could move her legs in bed and reach with them. Indeed, as we shall see later in the chapter, patients with hysterical paralysis become actually incapable of taking the anticipant attitudes upon which the responses of an affected part depend. These individuals, without successful therapeutic intervention, may be just as incapable of performing inactivated functions as is the victim of poliomyelitis or cerebral accident, sometimes developing secondarily contractures and atrophies of disuse which are indistinguishable from those of uncorrected neurological disease.

Hysterical anesthesia, which may develop alone or with paralysis, is sometimes equally impressive. One applies ordinarily painful stimulation to a cutaneous or mucous membrane surface that is hysterically anesthetic and there is no visible result other than perhaps pupillary constriction. When, for example, a needle is stuck into the affected area, the patient neither winces nor withdraws; he reports that he feels nothing, and his other behavior seems to corroborate his report. Notwithstanding these facts, there are inconsistencies and contradictions in the details of hysterical anesthesia and paralysis which rule out the possibility that they can be accounted for in terms of the straightforward logic of neuroanatomy and neuropathology.

If, for example, a hand loses skin sensitivity on an hysterical basis, the whole hand up to the wrist may be involved and all the cutaneous sensitivities equally excluded as instigators of response (*glove anesthesia*). The adjacent skin of the forearm, which unknown to the patient has some of the same nerve supply, will nevertheless lead to normal responses when stimulated. Moreover, the boundary line between normal and anesthetic areas in hysteria is typically sharp, whereas in neural damage or disease the boundaries are indistinct because of partial overlapping in the cutaneous nerve supply. The same holds true for the leg, whose area of hysterical inactivation may end sharply just above the knee (*stocking anesthesia*), even though this contradicts the neurological facts. Likewise in hysterical hemianesthesia, the area of inactivation stops at the midline of the body which is not the case in disease of the nervous system. In short, we are dealing here with anesthesia of the layman's hand, leg or body-half, and not with that of the anatomist.

It is much the same with hysterical paralysis. A leg, as we have seen, may be useless for standing or walking and yet some of its otherwise inactivated muscles participate normally in other functions. Shoulder muscles that are limp and functionless as part of an hysterically paralyzed arm may behave quite normally in movements of the head, neck and thorax, or in general postural adjustments of the trunk. In neurological disease and in myopathies it is the muscle that becomes disabled, whereas in hysterical paralysis it is a specific activity or group of related activities.

Hardly less noteworthy than these characteristics of hysterical symptoms is the patient's attitude of relative unconcern toward them (Janet's *la belle indifférence*). This attitude contrasts strangely with the attitude of an average person who, through accident or disease, has suffered sweeping losses in skin sensitivity or become paralyzed. Often the hysterical patient seems quite satisfied with his predicament even though it seriously restricts his freedom, bars him from gainful employment, and puts most forms of recreation out of his reach. The hysterically paralyzed individual, instead of compensating for his disability by using auxiliary muscle groups and postural changes as other paralytics do, apparently makes no special effort to overcome his handicap. On the contrary, he may display and exaggerate the defect. If he complains, he seems to be complaining defensively, and only with his mouth. The patient's attitudes and the peculiar character of his symptoms, as we shall see later, give important clues for our understanding of the origin and the persistence of hysterical inactivations.

Hysterical amblyopia and amaurosis

Hysterical amblyopia or amaurosis is the partial or complete loss of response to visual stimulation as a reaction to need or anxiety, in the absence of organ and tissue pathology adequate to account for it. Disturbances of vision which may form a basis for hysterical disorders are exceedingly common in everyday life. The eye is continually exposed to minor direct and indirect injuries because of its position and structure, to corneal and conjunctival irritation, and in our society to overstimulation and overuse both at work and during recreation. Moreover, the changes which normally occur in iris, ciliary body and extraocular muscles as part of emotional reactions, including anxiety, make everybody familiar with blurring, loss of accommodation and double vision in the absence of ocular injury or disease. But the normal antecedents of hysterical amblyopia and amaurosis most often overlooked are the inactivation of peripheral vision that develops when one looks intently at a specific object, and the complete exclusion of response to stimulation of the unused eye which anyone may quickly learn in shooting, or in working with an ordinary monocular microscope.

The precipitating factors in hysterical *amblyopia* (reduction in vision) and *amaurosis* (loss of vision) are no different from those already discussed in other hysterical disorders. The tensions of anxiety and unsatisfied need may prepare the ground, while a trivial injury or irritation, an acute emotional episode or the products of eye-strain and sleeplessness provide the incident.[9] Bilateral hysterical amaurosis is rare. When it does occur, the pupillary reflexes and extraocular movements are unaffected and the patient usually avoids obstacles placed in his path, just as a sleepwalker does, indicating that retinal function is still present.

In monocular hysterical amaurosis the pupillary reflexes and extraocular movements are also unaffected. Nothing more clearly indicates that hysterical inactivation is an extravagant form of *over-exclusion*, a selective *reaction-insensitivity*, than the test performance of hysterical monocular amaurotics. If the normal eye is covered by a magnifying lens and large letters are exposed at a distance, the unsuspecting patient may read them off, even though they are actually blurred beyond recognition for the normal eye by the convex lens used. If each eye is covered by a different colored lens the patient may read off words printed in a color that cannot be seen by the normal eye. In the pseudoscope test, the image opposite one eye is deflected by hidden prisms to fall only on the other eye. The patient is likely to report that he sees only the image opposite his normal eye and not the other, whereas actually he is responding to light falling on the hysterically amaurotic eye and excluding responses to stimulation of the normal eye.

The hysterical patient falls down on these tests because his blindness depends upon his inhibiting all responses to the stimulation of one eye and thus excluding its visual activities as factors in his behavior. This he continues doing, as well as he knows how, in the test situation. The patient's test failure is not a sign of his insincerity, as it is often taken to be, but rather the consequence of

---

[9] R. Ironside and I. Batchelor, "The ocular manifestations of hysteria in relation to flying," *Brit. Jour. Ophthal.*, 1945, vol. 29, pp. 88-98; V. Mahoney and W. Linhart, "Amblyopia in hysteria: report of thirteen cases," *War Med.*, 1943, vol. 3, pp. 503-507.

a deliberate fraud perpetrated upon him by the examiner. Clearly his inactivation is not just a matter of retina or visual cortex, but involves also the patient's biosocial reactions to what seems to him the stimulation of a blind eye.

A common form of hysterical amblyopia is contraction of the visual field for one or both eyes. The patient may respond normally to stimulation directly in his line of regard but show reduction or loss of reactivity to more peripheral stimulation. Hysterical contraction of the visual field may superficially resemble that found in retinal and central nervous system damage or disease, but closer and longer observation will reveal inconsistencies. Thus, the contraction in one eye may be quite different from that in the other. Variation from one perimetric examination to the next often exceeds the usual margin of error, or there is a large increase during a single examination if the examiner seems to expect it and repeats the process. In hysterical *tubular* or *tunnel vision* the area of an object seen does not usually show a proportionate increase as the object recedes, yet the patient may read or drive through city traffic without difficulty.[10] Hysterical amblyopia or amaurosis, like the inactivation of other hysterical disorders, represents a disturbance in the biosocially determined response to stimulation and not damage or destruction of receptor or nervous system.

Hysterical amnesia

Hysterical amnesia is the persistent partial or complete loss of response to stimulation normally leading to recall or recognition, as a reaction to need or anxiety and in the absence of organ or tissue pathology adequate to account for it. We have already indicated some of the factors responsible for normal amnesia or forgetting in our discussion of *accessible and inaccessible conflicts* in Chapter 5 and of *rationalization, projection* and *repression* in Chapter 6. We shall have occasion to go into them further in the present chapter and the next one. As a matter of fact, the inability to respond with recall or recognition in the presence of usually effective stimulation appears to some degree in most hysterical syndromes. Janet used to call all hysteria the great forgetfulness. Sometimes, however, hysterical forgetting is the outstanding symptom while the other symptoms are secondary. The amnesia may vary in degree, from the selective forgetting of a few fragmentary inci-

[10] R. Hammill, "Tubular vision," *Arch. Ophthal.*, 1934, vol. 12, pp. 345-351.

dents, to the disappearance from one's repertory of whole episodes which superficially resemble the effects of brain concussion. The following case illustrates the dramatic suddenness of both onset and recovery so characteristic of hysterical attacks.

A man, dressed in working clothes and apparently in his early thirties, appeared one Saturday morning at the main entrance of a general hospital with the complaint that he had lost his memory and did not know who he was. There was nothing on his person by which he could be identified. On admission, physical examination disclosed no signs of injury, toxic process or systemic disease. The patient's neurological status was essentially normal and clinical laboratory studies were negative. His formal behavior, including his speech, was also normal except for the fact that he appeared dazed and could recall nothing about himself — his name, age, occupation, home, relatives or friends. He could not remember where he had been that day, what he had been doing or how he had come to the hospital. His manner was not evasive, and he asked repeatedly to be helped. However, he proved unexpectedly resistant to hypnosis, and sedation yielded nothing but profound sleep. He spent Saturday and Sunday on the psychiatric service as John Doe, going through the usual routines of an ambulatory ward, without observable change in the clinical picture.

On Monday morning, when the patient awoke, he was greatly disturbed at finding himself in a hospital, told the nurse at once who he was and where he had come from, and said that he must leave to attend a coroner's inquest. To the psychiatrist he gave the following story. He was a vegetable farmer living in a neighboring town. Early Saturday morning he had been driving a truck loaded with his produce to market. While entering the outskirts of the city, at that period of dawn when the light is still poor and headlights help vision very little, he had run down and killed an elderly man who had stepped out suddenly from between two parked cars on a hill. The police assured the patient that he would be exculpated, but ordered him to send in a report of the accident and hold himself ready to appear at the inquest.

Very much shaken, he left the scene and went to the home of friends in the city, where he filled out the legal form for reporting accidents to the state commissioner which the police had given him. His friends' excited comments, warnings and coaching intensified his anxiety and frightened him particularly concerning his own responsibility and his ultimate fate in court. The last the patient could recall was going out alone and putting the report in the mail box. It turned out later that he had been brought almost to the door of the hospital by a stranger who had probably noticed his dazed appearance.

Certain aspects of this case deserve further comment in relation both to amnesia and to hysterical inactivation in general. The sudden onset followed a period of intense anxiety which had been aggravated by the conduct of the patient's friends, and it was immediately preceded by an irrevocable act of self-accusation — dropping into the letter box a formal report which designated the patient as a killer. His reaction to this irrevocable act was an exaggerated form of *insulation* in which he made himself as a social person, not only inaccessible to the behavior of others, but inaccessible also to his self-attitudes and self-responses. In ridding himself of the now intolerable anxiety, he excluded, not only every possibility of recalling the fatal accident and his predicament, but everything else that would identify him, to himself or to others, as the man who had just killed someone. A person with different habits might have achieved the same oblivion and loss of personality by going to a tavern and getting dead drunk.

Normal self-identification depends upon a person's ability to take certain organized self-attitudes and to give the responses appropriate to these attitudes when the situation calls for them. This man's technique of *overexclusion* barred the recall of an otherwise unforgettable tragedy, and of himself as a participant in it, through inactivating also his whole system of self-attitudes which enabled him to react to himself as a social object in relation to his community. *We* could not identify him because we could get no useful answers to our questions; *he* could not identify himself because he could no longer give answers in his self-reactions to his own questions. As a biological organism he seemed to be all there, but his social reactions to his own past behavior and status, which made him a certain social person, were virtually absent from his repertory. We shall have occasion to refer again to the behavioral analysis of this case when we take up the problems of fugue and multiple personality in the next chapter.

Hysterical amnesia is rarely as complete as this. It is not unusual for patients to lose recall and recognition for whole episodes without losing their reactions of self-identification.[11] The commonest

[11] See the report on Dunkirk evacuees by W. Sargent and E. Slater, "Amnesic syndromes in war," *Proc. Roy. Soc. Med.*, 1941, vol. 34, pp. 757-764.

form of hysterical amnesia by far is that in which personally significant fragments of an otherwise remembered episode remain inaccessible. The gaps in recall may simply be treated by the patient as unimportant forgotten details, or they may be filled in by manufactured incidents which in effect disregard or directly contradict what has actually happened. Such techniques are, of course, not far removed from those used daily by the normal person — particularly when to recall means to be anxious, guilty, humiliated or disillusioned. In the modern history of behavior pathology, it has been the challenge of hysterical amnesia which, more than any other single phenomenon, has stimulated the development of investigation, theory and therapy in the neuroses.

Hysterical inactivation and organ or tissue pathology

In our historical introduction to this chapter and in connection with each major hysterical disorder, we have made certain distinctions between the symptoms of hysterical inactivation and those of neurological disease and myopathy which need not be repeated here. In actual practice, the task of differentiating one group from the other is sometimes one that demands the utmost in skill, ingenuity and patience. It is true that hysterical symptoms as a rule are relatively inconsistent and often unstable, while their patterns usually do not correspond exactly in character or design with the symptoms to be expected in neurological disease. But even in the clear-cut cases of *major* hysterical disorders which we used as illustrations, the task of differentiation was not simple, particularly with those patients who had acquired some orthodox neurological symptoms through previous examinations and hearsay. Most cases of hysterical inactivation are not at all clear-cut, and the symptoms of neurological disease and myopathy sometimes show a surprising degree of instability and inconsistency. Moreover, there are hysterical patients with medical knowledge, and symptoms that show it, while there are patients with indisputable neurological disease who develop new symptoms following an examination, or show sudden unexpected remissions.

As for *minor* hysterical disorders, not only are they much commoner than major ones, but they tend also to be more unstable and inconsistent. They are harder to detect and harder to identify, and just because they are less dramatic and complete than the major disorders we have discussed, they are less likely to arouse the suspicions of the examiner. When a minor atypical hysterical inactivation follows or accompanies some other illness or an injury — which may itself involve inactivation — we have a situation that can become a major diagnostic challenge. There is today, partly as the result of the recent war, a rapidly spreading realization that mild atypical behavior disorders are present on every ward of every general hospital, and that they merit competent active therapy quite as much as do other illnesses. To treat the results of organ or tissue pathology adequately, and then to brush off behavior pathology with a dose of common-sense advice and reassurance, is simply to show expertness in one-half of therapy and incompetence in the other.

We have now taken up the commoner major varieties of hysterical inactivation. Before proceeding to the closely related syndromes of hysterical autonomy, however, it will repay us to consider in greater detail the relationships between normal behavior and hysterical inactivation. Indeed, we shall find later on that an understanding of these relationships sheds light, not alone upon the nature and development of all hysterical disorders, but also upon delusions and hallucinations, and therefore upon paranoia, schizophrenia, mania and the depressions.

BIOSOCIAL BASES OF HYSTERICAL INACTIVATION

We have long ago concluded that, in attempting to understand the origins of hysterical inactivation, it is neither necessary, nor in the long run profitable, to turn away from the facts of normal human behavior and seek to build our working hypotheses out of rationalistic metaphysics. For to do so is to exile our theoretical problems to a speculative "unconscious world" where they become by definition inaccessible and unreal. We shall therefore begin with the fact that hysterical inactivations are maladaptive modes of reacting to unsolved personal difficulties, occurring in the same universe of human behavior. As we have clearly indicated in Chapters 4 and 5, this universe includes a person's public social behavior, where hysterical symptoms appear, and his private individual behavior where severe conflicts and anxieties may have long been active. If, now, we pose the usual question, *From what characteristics of normal human behavior is hysterical inactivation derived?*

the answer is that it is derived from normal exclusion, one of the commonest and most important characteristics of normal skilled acts.

Inactivation in normal organized behavior

So common and important a characteristic of normal behavior is inactivation that we have not been able to wait until this point to introduce it. In discussing behavior organization and behavior pathology we said that, in both the acquisition and performance of skilled acts, as much depends upon what is excluded as upon what is included. For maximal effectiveness it is essential that the irrelevant, the competing and contradictory tendencies be excluded from participation in the act, or, in other words, *inactivated*. This holds true whether we are considering manual skill, close attention, problem-solving behavior, consecutive speech or logical thinking. Merely to sit and read, for example, means to inactivate innumerable potential responses to the stimulation of exteroceptors, proprioceptors and, often, interoceptors also. The sense-organs one does not respond to are normal, the nerves are intact, and we can be quite sure there is no central nervous system lesion. But as far as the man reading is concerned, there might just as well be no stimulation at all beyond that within the narrow range of his reading.

The reading man has learned to become, in effect, deaf and blind to stimulation which nevertheless may at the same moment be activating the dog or cat that shares his surroundings, but cannot share his reading. Even his competing fantasies and the recall of things undone must be kept out of his present occupation. The act of reading, if the book has a strong personal appeal, may exclude the smell of burning food, the discomfort of heat, cold or pressure, hunger contractions and the call to dinner. The moment any of this excluded stimulation intrudes and dominates a man's behavior, the reading activity is in its turn excluded; the man's eyes may scan lines, but for him they have no meaning. In short, one system of reaction becomes dominant at the expense of other reactions, and for the time being these latter cannot be called out by the same stimulation which, under other conditions, would be fully effective.

Everyone is familiar with the appearance of temporary inactivation in the behavior of normal persons under stress. We have already mentioned *aphonia* and *mutism* in normal excited, frightened or awestruck individuals. The loss of ability to eat (*anorexia*) under similar conditions is too well known to deserve elaboration. The same might with justice be said of *paralysis* and *anesthesia* but for the fact that their significance is for some reason more often overlooked by the public than in the case of emotional inappetence. Many normal men and women go weak in the legs under the stress of overwhelming emotional stimulation, whether it is welcome or abhorrent. The ranch girl whose legs buckled under her, for example, was not reacting abnormally under the circumstances. It was the perpetuation of her inactivation into an enduring disorder, in spite of the severe restrictive distortions this produced in her life pattern, that made the reaction pathological.

During intense emotional reactions the normal transient exclusion of cutaneous and special sense-organ stimulation from a person's response system is a common occurrence. For the moment, the normal individual fails to see what is all around him; he does not hear what is said directly to him or feel the hand placed upon his shoulder. One sees this phenomenon at funerals, in court, and in the partings and reunions at railroad stations. Less common but more impressive is the temporary inactivation that accompanies violent activity as, for instance, in street fighting, in battle or during a fire panic. The dominant behavior often completely excludes responses to stimulation as intense as any that are employed to test hysterical inactivation. Severe contusions, lacerations and fractures, if they are not immediately disabling, may go completely unnoticed, a finger may be lost or a hand mangled, one may sustain a bullet or stab wound and discover it only afterwards when someone else exclaims or he notices blood. Here, as in hysterical forms of inactivation, we need not turn at once away from the data we have, and begin rummaging around for the undercover work of a hypothetical shrewd, unconscious *psyche* which will explain away the fact of overexclusion. The place where explanations for normal and hysterical inactivation must be developed is where inactivation occurs, that is, in the field of biosocial operations.

Normal *amnesia*, except for its profound importance in relation to hysterical disorders, would need no special mention here. It is common knowledge that people get so absorbed in conversation and in doing or watching something, that they cannot remember appointments or routine time-bound duties, and forget where they are going or what they have been doing. Excited persons show the same signs of temporary loss of recall and recognition, even failing to recognize acquaintances or familiar places and to recall names, dates and events which, when they are calm, appear immediately in their response repertory. Again, it is the *persistence* and *spread* of amnesia in spite of its severely limiting or distorting one's behavior that makes us label it hysterical amnesia, rather than normal forgetting.

But what about *selective* reaction-insensitivity? Is this a part also of ordinary exclusion or is normal inactivation always non-selective? Selectivity is certainly evident in normal inactivation, and nowhere more clearly than in forgetting, as Freud so brilliantly demonstrated.[12] It is harder to recall the unpleasant than the pleasant,[13] easier to misname or fail to recognize a disliked than a beloved person, commoner to forget a dental appointment than a theater engagement, and one's failures than one's achievements. Indeed, the success of many important human relationships, including friendship and marriage, depends quite as much upon one's habitual unthinking skill in what is selectively forgotten as in what is selectively recalled. In other forms of exclusion it is much the same. There are things a person learns to endure by learning not to react to them at all — not to see, feel or hear them, not to develop the anticipant attitude which can lead only to tension without hope of consummation.

How completely and for how long certain reactions are kept inoperative will depend to some extent upon how much of a person's behavior is involved in a given dominant habit system, and how tightly organized that system is. The consistent well-integrated role, for example, is one that is so organized that whatever reactions tend to disrupt it, or to introduce serious conflict, are entirely excluded. Consider the average college man who decides in the face of an impending difficult examination to be a devoted student. If he is throughly successful in adopting this role as his own, the attitudes set up in his now dominant behavior organization will rule out most of the usually effective stimulation in his surroundings and make many of his customary activities impossible during his self-imposed

---

[12] S. Freud, *Psychopathology of Everyday Life*. New York: Macmillan, 1914.
[13] For a review of this topic see R. Sears, *Survey of Objective Studies of Psychoanalytic Concepts* (New York: Social Science Research Council, 1943), Bull. No. 51, pp. 110-115.

period of abstention. Sights, sounds, fatigue, mild hunger contractions, dry throat, and the antecedents of recall and fantasy — any of which, if responded to, would interfere with the activities belonging to the selected role — seem for all practical purposes to have vanished from his world. The organization of an adopted role, that has for the time being a high personal significance to the individual, keeps all of them inactivated.

In the more lasting and culturally more important role of the mother we again find that exclusion plays an indispensable part. The young woman who undertakes to make the role of the conventional mother her own, willingly and wholeheartedly, is the most likely to become a consistent mother in terms of her society and to find her role personally rewarding. But to take the role of the conventional mother, skillfully and consistently, a young woman cannot stop at *including* the cultural components which she has learned in childhood and adolescence. She must also *exclude* permanently all reactions and reaction-tendencies to be negligent, cruel, selfish, irresponsible, footloose, capricious and immoral. For if a woman must be forever wrestling with incipient and developing reactions that contradict her chosen role, she will inevitably be in perpetual conflict, tense, anxious and dissatisfied. To take roles such as this, completely and with minimal wasted effort, one's behavior organization must permanently inactivate the anticipant attitudes which make contradictory, competing and inconsistent responses possible. This is permanent inactivation that is not pathological because it is neither personally distorting in terms of one's own society, nor personally expensive in terms of effort and reward.

Hysterical inactivation as biosocial behavior

There was a time when it was generally believed among clinicians that the only conceivable explanation of hysterical inactivation lay in occult lesions of the nervous system. But this belief was continually contradicted by the unyielding facts of clinical examination. For not only was the typical onset of inactivation peculiarly sudden, but the symptoms failed to correspond to the known patterns of neural distribution, they were inconsistent and shifting, and the manner of recovery was often completely unorthodox from a neurological point of view, the patient losing his symptoms when he was not supposed to, or under influences that cannot remedy the effects of receptor and neuromuscular damage or disease.

Let us take hysterical anesthesias and paralyses as our examples. From the perspectives of neuroanatomy and neuropathology their patterns have always seemed irrational and unintelligible. Glove anesthesia, we have pointed out, violates all the rules of peripheral nerve distribution, while the leg that is completely flaccid when walking is demanded may execute movements in other situations which a comparably flaccid leg in ventral horn disease could never manage. It is easy to understand the exasperation of the less imaginative clinicians who in the old days pronounced judgment on hysterical patients and called them frauds. It is easy also to understand the temptation that nineteenth-century dualism offered to the more imaginative clinicians to reformulate the patient's complaints in such a way as to carry them out of the soma and into the psyche where the rules of neuroanatomy and neuropathology need not be observed.

The nineteenth-century dualists were right in rejecting the rules of neuroanatomy and neuropathology for hysterical inactivation. The logic of organ and tissue pathology is relevant and effectual only where the disorder involves organ and tissue pathology. In hysterical anesthesias and paralyses the logic of neuroanatomy and neuropathology may be just as irrelevant and ineffectual as would be the logic of social operations if we used it to explain away *myasthenia gravis, syringomyelia* or *hemiballism.* When a disorder can be shown to arise out of anxieties, frustrations, conflicts and disappointments in interpersonal relationships, we must be ready and able to study the patient, not just as a biological organism but as a biosocial person, whose activities include important self-reactions derived from social behavior. Thus, the particular character and location of hysterical inactivation usually has considerable significance. But this significance can be understood only if the patient's past behavior, his anxieties, frustrations, conflicts and disappointments, the origins and effects of his habitual symbolism, and the character of his self-reactions are all included when his case is studied.

The nineteenth-century dualists and their disciples were wrong in abandoning the biological organism for the psyche, as their unsuccessful attempts to join the two together through *psychosomatic interactionism* has demonstrated. From a biosocial point of view hysterical anesthesias and paralyses are neither irrational nor unintelligible, and they occur in our familiar everyday world of human behavior. But the hand that becomes insensitive or paralyzed is not merely the hand of the brachial plexus, or the cortical hand; it is the hand which the patient normally uses as a tool and by means of which he works and plays, loves, fights, eats and sins. It is the hand the patient can see, touch and hold — in short, the *social hand*, to which he can react as to any other social object, and in the same ways that others react to it.

To insist, as some still do, that "the only scientific approach" to the problem of hysterical inactivation is one that begins and ends within the nervous system seems as unrealistic as it would be to insist upon restricting studies of *acrophobia*, acute anxiety in high places, to a hunt for lesions in the optic and vestibular organs and their central nervous system end-stations. Indeed, one might just as well argue that the only scientific way to study fatigue is to limit oneself to the physiology of the adrenal cortex. No human being operates wholly in terms of his internal machinery; even if he just falls down a flight of stairs, we have to find out about the steps, the landing, where it was, what he was doing, where he had been and what he was carrying. The physician is no scientist who sets a fractured arm without inquiring into the biosocial facts. The only scientific approach that can be defended on an empirical basis is one that begins with whatever evidence is available and closes no avenues of investigation, even though they lead into new and scientifically less reputable fields.

In hysterical anesthesia and paralysis it is the biosocial activity, we have said, and not the sense-organ, muscle or neuron as a physiological unit that has been inactivated. The same is true of other hysterical inactivation. Speaking is important only if it stimulates the speaker or others; aphonia and mutism arise because speaking is involved in one's difficulties or because its momentary loss is a part of one's reactions during acute anxiety. Eating and swallowing, we know, are not completely understood in human beings if we stop with the facts of seizing, biting and deglutition; eating and swallowing occur in a complex social field whose characteristics often give us the key to otherwise meaningless disturbances. The eye in human affairs is a most important social organ, participating actively in interpersonal relationships to a degree rivaled only by the hand and tongue. Moreover, the pleasures directly or indirectly attributed to the eye are many and so also, therefore, are its opportunities for sinning, in commission and in unfulfilled anticipation. It is the same with recall and forgetting. What the human being re- members or forgets may be far more effective in perpetuating hysterical amnesia than what is happening at the time of clinical examination.

Development and persistence of hysterical inactivation

Throughout this chapter it has been evident that the biosocial behavior matrix, out of which hysterical inactivation develops, is not peculiar to some human subspecies with an inherited hysterical constitution. Every symptom so far discussed is obviously derived from the normal inactivation occurring in everyday life as a reaction to unusual need or anxiety. Indeed, we have seen that when activity is violent, or excitement extreme, normal temporary inactivation may reach an intensity that rivals anything encountered in the hysterical disorders. Here as elsewhere among the behavior disorders, the distinction between normal and pathological is made largely on the basis of the persistence and spread of maladaptive patterns, and on the basis of the degree of ineffectuality and distortion that these patterns impose upon biosocial behavior. We shall therefore turn now to a consideration of three important influences in the development and persistence of hysterical inactivation, those of *overexclusion, disuse* and *role-taking.*

The *overexclusion* in hysterical inactivation is, of course, a form of *overcomplete repression*. The patient reduces his tensions of need or anxiety, as in all repression, by preventing the occurrence of the tension-producing response, or by inhibiting its development, in the presence of previously adequate stimulation. But he carries the technique to extremes. For not only is the specific response with its supporting and immediately anticipant attitudes repressed, but all responses to certain kinds of stimulation are abolished or drastically curtailed — as in the cutaneous and special sense-organ anesthesias — and whole groups of related biosocial activities are eliminated, as in the various paralyses. The patient, in other words, gains secure protection from the rearousal of tension by excluding from his behavior repertory everything that might lead to rearousal, even at the expense of being permanently disabled.

A difficulty with these extreme repressive reactions is that, as learned behavior, the hysterical inactivation is bound to generalize to equivalent excitants and therefore take in situations not originally implicated. Moreover, in this process the logic of non-verbal operations, including such factors as simple space-time proximity, must be considered by the behavior analyst on an equal footing with verbal logic. The patient's extreme repression extends, as we have indicated, to the anticipant attitudes which would otherwise prepare a behavioral background in advance of the appropriate responses. With these attitudes excluded from a person's behavior organization the patient cannot possibly begin certain responses.

Thus, the patient with complete hysterical paralysis cannot take the anticipant attitude leading to movement; it is no good urging him to try because his trying must include the appropriate anticipant attitude which he has lost by his overcomplete repression. He is like a man standing relaxed in front of a four-foot fence — jumping it remains an impossibility as long as the anticipant attitudes of postural tension, preliminary flexion and oculomotor adjustment are absent. Some hysterical patients report that they are unable even to imagine a lost activity. They cannot think it because the thinking belongs with the preliminary anticipant attitudes which have been repressed; they are like the normal person who cannot imagine strongly taboo acts which have been excluded from his repertory by repressive inactivation early in life.

Hysterical inactivation develops initially, as we have seen in our case material, because it disposes of intolerable need or anxiety, and it persists partly because it continues to perform this function. If hysterical inactivation becomes reasonably complete, it may provide the patient with a workable solution which lasts as long as the symptoms last. This may mean a matter of days, as with our amnesic truck farmer, or weeks, as with the mute business man, or even years, as with our pseudo-paraplegic girl. But as long as the patient remains selectively unresponsive to stimulation that once aroused specific need or anxiety — whether such stimulation originates outside the organism or inside it, whether it comes from the overt behavior of others or from his own overt and covert behavior — he cannot suffer rearousal of his unsatisfied need or his unbearable anxiety.

In addition to the influence of overcomplete repression in perpetuating hysterical inactivation, we must consider two important effects of *disuse,* one of them direct, one indirect. As every physician knows, the protracted disuse, sparing or overprotection of a part sometimes leads to an ineradicable secondary disability which may seriously reduce the residual function left after injury, operation or corrective immobilization. Similarly, in hysterical inactivation it sometimes happens that, simply because the hysterically disabled part is not used, secondary atrophies and contractures develop which are identical with those resulting, for example, when fractured limbs are kept too long inactive in a cast. The indirect result of disuse arises from the fact that the part excluded from participation in behavior suffers from being left out of the patient's biosocial organization, like renounced affection or a neglected skill. An hysterically disabled hand, for example, cannot be included in whatever new things the patient learns, and as for the old things which the hand used to do, they are omitted entirely from the patient's life or done in a new way. In short, the disabled member by the very fact of disuse acquires no new excitants and loses all the old.

The influence of *role-taking* is as important in organizing and perpetuating hysterical inactivation as it is in organizing normal behavior. We have seen the effects upon normal behavior of adopting the role of a devoted student or a conventional mother. If circumstances lead a man to adopt the role, let us say, of a disabled person as his own, then the close organization of his behavior into a culturally defined pattern will exclude whatever seems to contradict it. Once he has taken such a role publicly he has committed himself, in others' eyes and in his own, to renounce every inconsistency which he or others recognize. Moreover, if he gains privileges and exemptions in the role of a disabled man, he cannot abandon the role without endangering his community status and his self-respect — unless, of course, he is publicly cured, and this is one of many explanations for the miraculous public cure.

What has been said about the adoption of a culturally defined role applies equally to the rejection of one. In Chapter 3, for example, we alluded to the development of amnesia in relation to inacceptable wifehood and motherhood. A woman who is in fact a wife and mother can become to herself no wife and no mother if she succeeds in developing amnesia for whatever contradicts a childless virginal role. Through such overcomplete repression the patient becomes incapable of recognizing her husband or her child, and cannot accept them therefore as her own. She is unable, in spite of prompting, to recall her pregnancy or delivery, and she disavows marriage. In extreme cases of role-rejection the patient develops supporting delusions and then, if these lead to serious behavior disorganization, what may have begun as hysterical inactivation becomes a schizophrenic disorder.

There is no evidence to indicate that factors predisposing certain individuals to develop hysterical inactivation under stress differ from those which seem to favor hysterical autonomy. Presumably whatever increases need or anxiety in susceptible persons leads to the acquisition of hysterical reactions that dispose of it, whether these reactions merely inactivate behavior or produce autonomous activity which is out of the social person's control. We shall therefore consider the determinants of both hysterical inactivation and autonomy together, toward the end of the next chapter, and discuss there also the relationship of both inactivating and autonomous symptoms to the other behavior disorders.

12

Hysterical Disorders

II. Autonomy

WE HAVE JUST SEEN how people sometimes succeed in disposing of behavior that arouses the tensions of need or anxiety by developing a persistent selective reaction-insensitivity. Through such a development the person renders himself incapable of certain specific activities, or unable to respond to certain kinds of stimulation. The result is that the tension-producing reactions cannot occur; they are excluded from participation in the rest of the patient's biosocial behavior. This is the form of reaction-insensitivity which we have called *hysterical inactivation*.

We shall now consider another form of reaction-insensitivity, called *hysterical autonomy*, which involves overexclusion on a basis somewhat different from that of simple inactivation. In one variety of hysterical autonomous behavior, which includes *tremor, cramp* and *tic*, the tension-producing reactions are not completely eliminated from the patient's repertory; they continue to appear, but only as isolated fragments which are not in keeping with the shared environmental context. In a second variety, the patient rather suddenly develops an alteration in his dominant behavior organization, and an autonomous episode or phase appears in which previously excluded behavior is present in its entirety, as in *hysterical seizure* and in one form of *multiple personality*. Or else, the alteration disposes of tension-provoking behavior by excluding it from the newly developed autonomous phases, as in *hysterical fugue* and in another form of *multiple personality*. The striking thing about this second variety is that the patient, in getting rid of his troublesome reactions, also eliminates a great many other related activities and suffers, as we shall see, a definite break in the continuity of his environmentally oriented behavior.

VARIETIES OF HYSTERICAL AUTONOMY

By *hysterical autonomy* we mean *the appearance of an isolated behavior fragment or behavior episode, which is out of keeping with the shared environmental context or with the person's prior behavior organization, and which develops as a reaction to the tensions of need or anxiety in the absence of organ or tissue pathology adequate to account for it.* Hysterical autonomy, like hysterical inactivation, occurs in countless minor varieties which often complicate the diagnosis, treatment and course of other medical and surgical disorders. But hysterical autonomy also occurs as the chief or only presenting symptom in a series of maladaptive reactions, ranging all the way from little localized movements to complex multiplications of the personality organization. As in the preceding chapter, we shall confine our discussion to those major hysterical disorders which, although less common than the minor ones, provide us with clearer and more instructive illustrations of principles that hold for major and minor varieties alike.

It is most convenient to discuss the major varieties of hysterical autonomy by arranging them in the order of ascending complexity and increasing involvement of overt behavior. Accordingly, we shall begin with the simplest and most limited movements, the *hysterical tremor* and *cramp*, and proceed to the more versatile and expressive *hysterical tic*. From there we shall go on to the *hysterical seizure*, which is not only more involved and complex than the tic, but also introduces the break in behavior continuity mentioned above. This prepares us to understand the similar but less narrowly circumscribed episodes which constitute *somnambulism, hysterical fugue* and *multiple personality*.

Hysterical tremor

Hysterical tremor consists of autonomous oscillatory movements, ranging in rate from four to ten oscillations per second, which develop initially in relation to need or anxiety, and recur or persist in the absence of organ or tissue pathology adequate to account for them. Hysterical tremor usually appears when a certain movement is made (*intention tremor*), but it is sometimes found when the part is at rest (*rest tremor*), particularly when the patient's self-reactions are directed toward the part. Although found most frequently in the extremities, the face and the head, it is possible for hysterical tremor to develop in any region of the body.

Tremor constitutes one of the most commonplace reactions of the normal person under conditions of stress, anxiety, frustration, eagerness and delight. It appears also, without these conditions, after prolonged sleeplessness or intense exertion, and during illness, convalescence and transient toxic states. Following an argument, a fight or an accident, the receipt of bad news or exciting news, many normal persons develop tremor of the fingers or hand which usually increases in amplitude when the part is used. Such normal tremor tends for some hours, and sometimes days, to recur with relatively mild emotional stimulation, even though this is unrelated to the original incident. Tremor may also normally recur for some time whenever the person recalls the precipitating incident, its antecedents or its sequelae. Moreover, the tremor often interferes seriously with the execution of habitual skilled acts while it persists. A man, for example, finds that he cannot drive competently after he has witnessed or been involved in a near-accident or has just received an humiliating lecture from a policeman; a woman sitting absorbed in a daydream has to stop her sewing because of the tremor that comes with her recall of yesterday's quarrel.

The hysterical tremor may differ neither in pattern nor in manner of precipitation from normal tremor. What earns for a tremor the designation *hysterical,* in addition to its origin in need or anxiety, is its indefinite persistence or incessant recurrence, its continued interference with normal performance, the attitude of acceptance or display which the patient shows toward his symptom, and his inability to recall or recognize its beginnings. Hysterical tremor, like the symptoms of hysterical inactivation, may occur only when some specific act is attempted and not when other acts are performed which involve the same muscles and even the same movements. It may appear when the patient tries to do something in certain special situations, whereas in all other situations he can do the same thing without a tremor. Sometimes the tremor develops and persists in a specific act, not because that act is necessarily related in any other way to the precipitating incident, but merely because it happened to be in process during a period of severe emotional disturbance.

Among the economically most important of these hysterical symptoms is the so-called "occupational tremor." The name does not, of course, designate a special kind of movement, but refers only to the fact that the symptom interferes with the patient's earn-

ing his livelihood, recurring or increasing in amplitude whenever
the patient begins a movement or a postural tension upon which
his occupational status depends. Thus, one finds clerks, housewives,
artists, writers, skilled mechanics, professional men and machine
operators who have become incapable of carrying on the work
with which they are identified because of hysterical tremor. The
mode of origin of "occupational tremor," and the significance it
may have in an individual's life, are well illustrated by the following case.

> A nineteen-year-old unmarried woman was brought for consulta-
> tion because of an intention tremor in her left hand which had com-
> pelled her to give up her job. A year earlier she had obtained em-
> ployment as an elevator operator in a department store for the
> purpose of saving money toward her marriage. Her fiancé, who at
> that time had moved to a better job in another city, had begun by
> writing her twice weekly and visiting her once a month. After a
> few months, however, his letters grew cooler and less frequent; he
> kept putting off visiting her on various plausible pretexts, and when
> he finally did come he behaved in a strained and preoccupied man-
> ner. In response to her worried promptings, her fiancé agreed that
> his changed behavior was the result of business cares, but a few
> days after he had left, he sent the patient a letter which stated
> bluntly that he had decided to marry someone else.
>
> The patient was very much shaken by this sudden collapse of
> her life-plans. She felt deeply humiliated at being rejected after
> she had so confidently told everyone whom she could, almost daily,
> of her marital plans. Back at work she found that she could no
> longer reach for and hold the elevator clutch because of a coarse
> intention tremor which appeared each time she tried. The symptom
> received strong reinforcement from the reactions of her fellow-
> workers to it. With their genuine sympathy they mingled the
> inevitable frightening anecdotes which people in all walks of life
> seem to save for such occasions.
>
> The patient responded well to brief therapy which, in addition to
> personal reorientation, included an immediate change in vocation,
> and a move to another neighborhood where her adversity would
> not be known. Her initial resistance to any interpretation of the
> tremor other than that of a "palsy" gave way as treatment pro-
> gressed. She succeeded in recalling that the trembling in her left
> hand was originally not an isolated phenomenon, as it later became,
> but had been part of a generalized trembling which immediately
> followed her receipt of the bad news. She remembered that, after

reading the letter, she had found considerable difficulty with the manipulations involved in eating and in putting on her things before going to work. "I was shaky all over," she said. However, the other tremors diminished, while the one in the hand upon whose steadiness her job depended grew worse. In the course of therapy, the patient gradually lost her symptom as she worked out the factors precipitating and perpetuating it, and as she recognized its significance as a public statement of her inability to go on any longer with her plans.

Hysterical cramp

Although quite different in pattern, the hysterical cramp is practically identical with tremor in origin and significance. By *hysterical cramp* we mean *a persistent autonomous contraction of a muscle group, which develops initially in relation to need or anxiety, and lacks a background of organ or tissue pathology adequate to account for it.* In normal life sustained muscular contractions, coming on suddenly and painfully, are familiar events. They frequently follow overstretching of muscles, prolonged overexertion, overcooling or excessive heating. Cramps represent a serious occupational hazard in those vocations which necessarily involve such direct peripheral effects (e.g., *stokers' cramp*).

Hysterical cramp is also a serious occupational hazard. It develops, however, on the biosocially more complex basis of personal need or anxiety and it persists, like "occupational tremor," as a public statement of disability. Thus, we have *writers' cramp, violinists' cramp, typists' cramp, watchmakers' cramp, telegraphers' cramp, seamstresses' cramp* and a score of others. They all have in common this one characteristic — that the symptom makes it impossible for the patient to carry on his vocation, even though he may be able to perform similar movements, without cramp, in activities unrelated to his work.[1] The neuromuscular machinery remains undamaged, unless of course the cramp is severe and of long duration, in which case secondary changes may lead to a contracture that requires surgical correction.

In *writers' cramp,* for example, an unsuccessful author who is unable to accept or rationalize continued failure may develop a painful contraction of the muscles used in writing. Each time he

[1] See, for example, the report on telegraphers' cramp by M. Smith, M. Culpin and E. Farmer, "A study of telegraphists' cramp," Industrial Fatigue Research Board, 1927, No. 43.

tries to write thereafter the cramp returns, and there is nothing for him to do eventually but give up trying — which means give up writing. Real as this cramp is, and painful as it is, it can be shown to involve muscles which the patient uses without the least difficulty in activities other than writing. The origin of the symptom is in the would-be writer's ambivalent attitudes toward his endeavor — for instance, a desperately tense perseverance coupled with hopelessness and loathing for the work. The patient, who cannot admit to himself or others the implications of his ambivalence, continues to repress his loathing and hopelessness. He cannot, without expert aid, recapture the referent of his symptom, the attitude to which it belongs, and therefore to him it is socially meaningless. He and his associates are likely to accept the cramp as a partially disabling disease, the socially irresponsible behavior of a biological organism and nothing more.

Hysterical tic

In many ways the tic is similar to the tremor and the cramp, but as overt behavior it stands much higher on the scale of complexity and is, as we have said, more versatile and more expressive. By *hysterical tic* we mean *an autonomous organized repetitive movement or sequence of movements which develops initially in relation to need or anxiety, and lacks a background of organ or tissue pathology adequate to account for it.* The hysterical tic is closely related to the countless little manneristic movements that normal children and adults make, many of them annoying and most of them functionless. These include sniffing and throat-clearing, smacking the lips and clicking the tongue, grimacing, eye-blinking and head-nodding, stereotyped hand and finger movements, shrugging, twitching, tapping, jiggling and squirming.

There are few places in behavior pathology where it is more difficult to make a clear distinction between normal and abnormal than in the area of overlap between mannerisms and tics. Were we to adopt one extreme view, we should have to consider all adventitious movements hysterical, while the opposite extreme would lead us to omit the tic entirely from hysterical autonomy. If, however, in each case we investigate successfully the origins of the movement, the conditions of its recurrence, its effects upon normal performance and the significance of amnesia, if it is present, we shall then have criteria which make differentiation feasible.

The list of reported varieties of hysterical tics is very long. We may mention, by way of example, twitching, jerking, nodding, rotating and wagging of the head; twisting, flexing and extending of the torso; postural changes in neck, shoulder, back and pelvis; tongue-clicking, sniffing, grunting, barking, throat-clearing and swallowing. Of especial interest to the behavior pathologists are the endless varieties of facial grimaces, extraocular responses, and movements of fingers, hand, forearm and arm, in which the remnant of a common act — often a communicative gesture — is discernible.[2] There are also, of course, toe, foot, leg and thigh movements, genital and anal tics, and a host of movements related to or derived from special skills and other habitual sequences, some of which reach a high degree of complexity.

But whatever the pattern, hysterical tic is usually the remnant of a once useful adjustment to need or anxiety, the residual fragment of an incompletely repressed act. It may also be a symbolic assertion of incapacity and non-participation not unlike the symbolic assertions we have seen in anesthesias and paralyses. The beginnings of a tic are often simple. For example, an upward movement of the chin, accompanied by platysma contraction and facial grimace, may have its start as the reaction to a tight collar, discomfort from which has been made acute by concomitant anxiety. However, if the reaction generalizes to other anxiety excitants, restraints and discomforts, it may eventually become established as an autonomous movement which the patient cannot control and does not understand.

The complexity of many hysterical tics, on the other hand, gives them greater latitude as autonomous sign language. A single tic pattern, for example, may represent denial of a role that once was dominant in behavior, and at the same time be a contradiction of the currently dominant role. We sometimes encounter such ambivalent representation in the well-known *hysterical spasmodic torticollis*. This tic consists of a recurrent elevation of the chin with simultaneous rotation of the head — a movement which sometimes raises diagnostic difficulties because its pattern closely resembles

[2] Compare M. Krout, "Autistic gestures: an experimental study in symbolic movement," *Psychol. Monog.*, 1935, vol. 46, No. 208; "The social and psychological significance of gestures (a differential analysis)," *Jour. Genetic Psychol.*, 1935, vol. 47, pp. 385-412; "Further studies on the relation of personality and gesture, a nosological analysis of autistic gestures," *Jour. Exper. Psychol.*, 1937, vol. 20, pp. 279-287.

the product of an irritative central nervous system lesion. For instance, in a patient of ours whose neurological status was normal, the symptom turned out to be a gestural remnant of deep-seated reactions of aversion and disdain, which the patient had disowned and incompletely repressed. In his current behavior, however, this tic was often the patient's contradiction of his dominant role in which amiability and rather submissive attitudes of cooperation prevailed. His torticollis was observed to increase whenever it was discussed, when therapy became at all aggressive, and when his opinions or preferences were disregarded. The symptom was diminished by distraction and when others were acquiescent, and it was abolished in hypnosis. Eventually it disappeared in the course of therapy which was aimed, not at the tic or at the undamaged nervous system, but at the patient's unsettled conflicts.

The following case illustrates a somewhat different state of affairs in which, although the pattern of the tic was highly complex, the motives resulting from behavior analysis turned out to be remarkably simple.

> The patient, a schoolboy of twelve years, was brought for consultation to a children's hospital. His worried parents stated that, despite negative pediatric and neurological examinations, the boy continued having "fits." He was able to demonstrate these so readily that it was decided to take a moving picture of them, an arrangement to which the boy at once agreed. In the presence of half a dozen physicians and his parents, the patient gave us the shots illustrated (Figure 1).
>
> The sequence of movements always followed approximately the same pattern. After an expiratory grunt or two, the boy would suddenly clap his hands to his abdomen and stiffen up. This he usually repeated two or three times, with little expectant pauses in between, and then proceeded to execute a remarkable series of stooping and forearm flexing motions that looked more like school calisthenics than a fit. After this was over, he would stand panting heavily for a few seconds, again in an expectant attitude, and go into another similar sequence, or abruptly relax and behave quite normally again. It should be noted that when the photographer asked him to move from his place under the awning out into the light, the patient complied without hesitation, even though at the moment he was in the middle of another attack. When the photographing was over, the boy left the terrace, walking and talking quite normally, his father patting his shoulder and comforting him as they went.

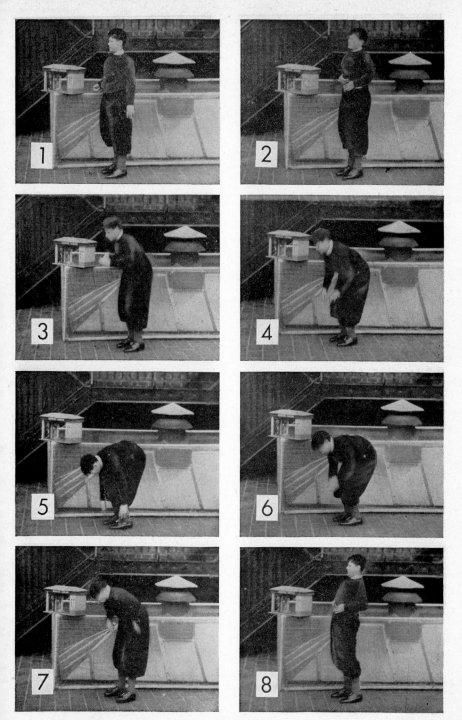

Figure 1. Elaborate hysterical tic in a school-boy. The patient remained in adequate touch with his biosocial environment throughout the sequence, which was sometimes repeated.

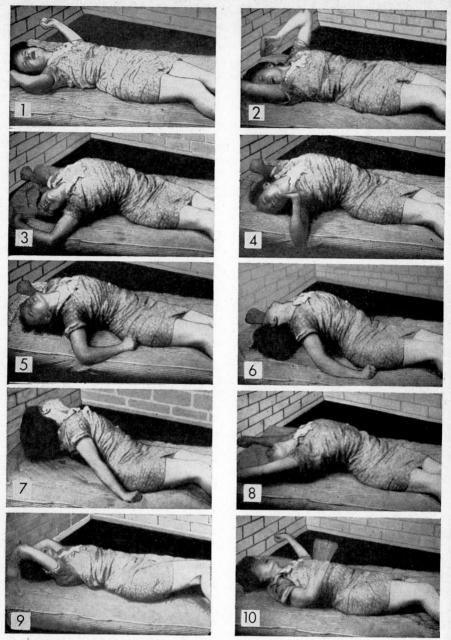

Figure 2. Hysterical seizure in a young woman. The patient remained out of contact with her biosocial environment throughout the sequence which was repeated many times in a single attack.

This elaborate tic seems to have developed initially in a setting of extreme parental anxiety when the patient was suffering from attacks of abdominal pain of undetermined origin. It became firmly established because it brought the boy many privileges and kept him constantly in the limelight as an extraordinary "case," the focus of everyone's interest and speculation. An important aspect of the attacks is that, while one was in process, the patient was in adequate touch with his biosocial environment — even to the point of suspending an attack temporarily on demand — and after it was over he had no amnesia for the period of the attack. This is in sharp contrast to the hysterical seizure which we are about to discuss. Needless to say, the boy and his parents believed the "fits" to be evidence of a strange disease and the repeated negative diagnoses signs of medical ignorance. Under the direction of a competent child psychiatrist, who turned his major efforts toward the difficult task of re-educating the anxious oversolicitous parents, the tic disappeared and the boy became well again.

The variegated gesture and posture language to be found in tic and seizure together form an unmistakable bridge connecting hysterical autonomy with those schizophrenic disorders in which grimacing, mimicry, signaling, pantomime, posturing and bizarre role-taking are the chief symptoms. Of course hysterical tic, like tremor and cramp, may become quite functionless and still persist as an habitual response, as meaningless and unnecessary in the patient's current behavior as a normal mannerism often is.

Hysterical seizure

In turning now from *hysterical tremor, cramp* and *tic* to *hysterical seizure,* we pass from autonomous movements whose occurrence is unaccompanied by serious disturbance in the patient's general orientation, to circumscribed attacks which include a disruption in the patient's immediately previous relationship to his environment. No longer do we find, as in the elevator girl and the boy with the calisthenic tic, that patients maintain effective contact with those around them during an hysterical episode, respond to ordinary requests in the usual manner, and recall easily the events of one phase while they are in the other. On the contrary, the most impressive things about the autonomy we are about to describe are the break which seems to divide the period of hysterical attack from the rest of behavior, and the comprehensive character of the amnesia in one phase for events belonging to the other.

By *hysterical seizure* we mean *an autonomous, circumscribed behavior episode which resembles superficially a convulsive attack, develops initially in relation to need or anxiety, and lacks a background of organ or tissue pathology adequate to account for it.* The hysterical seizure has a well-defined beginning and, as a rule, a well-defined ending. Its onset is marked by a clear break in behavior continuity; the role taken during the circumscribed episode, and all recall of it, are absent from the patient's everyday repertory. When the seizure is over, the patient may resume whatever he had been doing before it started, as if nothing had intervened, or he may appear for some time poorly oriented. In some cases, like the one we shall describe shortly, the seizure is followed by a trance-like episode (*twilight-state*) whose duration varies from a few minutes to several days. During this after-period the patient seems dazed and preoccupied, allows himself to be led around and usually gives limited, rather passive cooperation in ordinary dressing, feeding and toilet routines.

The pattern of the hysterical seizure may vary greatly from person to person, but for a given individual it is frequently stable and predictable. Some seizures are simple in design, amounting sometimes to little more than jerking, thrashing or tic-like movements that are difficult to distinguish from attacks of *petit mal*. Others are more elaborate and better organized, so that they give the impression of being an "act," which may easily be mistaken for mere display or simulation.

Of course it can be shown that during the period of a typical hysterical seizure, which may last a few minutes or several hours, the patient is almost completely out of touch with his social environment. His autonomous behavior, far from being supported by the social context, goes on in spite of it just as if he were daydreaming. Indeed, as we shall see, the seizure may represent overt role-taking of a kind that ordinarily belongs in covert fantasy; the patient acts out his repressed reminiscences, his unrecognized needs and unacknowledged satisfactions as though he were in a fantasy ballet. The seizure in such instances is an attack of intense imagining which, like profound preoccupation, excludes nearly all stimulation from the social context while it lasts. As in ordinary recall, the seizure can be precipitated by words, daydreaming or some incident which functions as an equivalent of the original incident. The following case illustrates many of these fundamental points.

The patient, an unmarried woman of twenty-three years, was admitted to a psychiatric hospital while apparently having a generalized convulsion, the pattern of which was obscured by her being strapped to a stretcher. She was taken to a private room and placed unrestrained upon a floor mattress, attended by a nurse, where she soon became quiet. She remained, however, completely unresponsive to questions and examination procedures, staring ahead of her with a perplexed look, or rolling her head from side to side and sighing deeply. As physical examination and laboratory studies proved negative, the patient was kept under observation during the ensuing twenty-four hours.

The next day the patient seemed normally responsive and, when brought to the physician's office, she at first cooperated well in giving her medical and psychiatric history. When she came to her adolescent difficulties, she began describing a sexual assault upon her because of which, she asserted, her mother had driven her out of the home. As the patient proceeded with this story, she appeared to grow increasingly preoccupied and her account became more and more vague, as though she were going into a schizophrenic stupor. Suddenly, however, she slid from the chair to the floor, let out a scream and commenced another seizure.

The seizure began with well-coordinated struggling, writhing and rolling movements of the whole body and extensor responses in the arms (Figure 2). These continued for several minutes and were punctuated by occasional screams and sobbing without tears. Then came a rest period during which the patient's eyes were open and her brows furrowed, while she slowly rolled her head from side to side in what appeared to be sorrow. Her face shone with sweat and at first she breathed heavily. In a few minutes a scream and more tearless sobbing ushered in another sequence whose pattern was, in general, like the first. The seizure was not interrupted by the manipulation involved in transferring her to her room, and it continued for several hours afterwards. The fact that this patient rested between periods of struggling reminds one immediately of the schoolboy's calisthenic tic. However, unlike him she remained unresponsive to her social surroundings throughout her seizure and its aftermath.

After her seizure had subsided the patient remained in a typical twilight state for a day and a half. She was not cataleptic, but she stood or sat wherever she was placed, staring ahead without appearing to see anyone present, knitting her brows and occasionally shaking her head slowly from side to side as she had done in the seizure. She neither spoke nor responded to speech. She took the food and drink that was put to her lips, and she required neither reminding nor coaxing to chew and swallow, as stuporous depressed and schizophrenic persons so frequently do. But she chewed and swallowed in the mechanical way that normal persons do when they are grief-stricken. In the hospital routines the patient cooperated slowly and heavily but without much urging. She could safely be led up and down stairs or outside the building; she avoided obstacles, waited motionless for doors to be opened, got through doorways unguided, and did not stumble on the uneven ground out-of-doors. She wakened on the second morning, once again normally responsive to her social environment, but with amnesia for the seizure and the twilight-state.

There were several repetitions of this sequence during the next few weeks, and it was soon evident that any discussion of sex, home or mother was sufficient to precipitate another seizure. Attacks were also favored by protracted lonely daydreaming and by the patient's need for sympathy and comfort. On two occasions, for example, when the patient was kept in her room alone in the evening, she came out into the corridor, screamed and sank to the floor in a seizure which lasted the rest of the night, and was succeeded by her usual twilight-state.

This young woman presented a difficult therapeutic problem. She was a grade-school graduate who was not above average intelligence, and she came from a slum environment where she had gained the reputation in her early teens of being seriously delinquent. Furthermore, the seizure which originally brought her to the hospital had been undoubtedly precipitated by difficulties she was having with the police. In the hospital she reacted to anything that bordered on her personal problems as she had reacted to questioning by the police — with a seizure and a prolonged twilight-state. Direct therapy was finally abandoned, and a program of work was set up for her, which provided limited ground privileges and a pleasant room as long as she performed her duties and had no attacks. Under this regime she soon became symptom-free and was discharged four months after her admission. Two years later she was readmitted because of similar seizures, similarly provoked, and was again discharged with symptomatic recovery but presumably nothing more.

The unmistakably theatrical display in this case, and the transparent use of hysterical seizure as an escape technique, might mislead the impatient or inexperienced observer to jump to the conclusion that the whole episode was mere pretense and our patient a simple fraud. But to do this would be to behave like a policeman toward a person whom the police had already recognized as a patient. Moreover, there are certain behavior peculiarities about the hysterical seizure that should make anyone hesitate to begin his study of them with an indictment. It is a fact, for example, that the person is rare who can develop hysterical autonomy in this form, no matter how pressing the need or how overwhelming the fear. The skeptical student should find out for himself how great a difference there is between pretending to take a role and actually living the same role; that is to say, between being a fraud and being hysterical.

The hysterical patient in a seizure is acting through or re-living a special, circumscribed role with a constant theme. The seizure is not just any random act; it is an act having particular significance in the patient's life. The patient cannot as a rule come out of the episode until it has been lived through; and during the attack he remains completely in character. He seems to be as much alone with his fantasy, even though it is overt fantasy, as is the normal man who lives through a reminiscence while he sits alone smoking his pipe.

Our patient was, of course, acting through the role of being assaulted, a role toward which we had reason to believe she maintained strongly ambivalent attitudes. Her seizure was pantomime reminiscence, overt recall, a re-enactment in which her fantasy sequences dominated all her activity, and excluded responses to stimulation from the social environment. As far as secondary gain is concerned, this patient could have obtained as much sympathy, comfort and protection by a ten-minute attack as by the two or three days of bleak isolation which her seizure and trance state brought her. But she demonstrated over and over that, once she slipped into the seizure, she could not bring it to a close until it had run a long course. If, as we have suggested, hysterical tic often represents a form of fragmentary recall in gesture language, then hysterical seizure must be complete recall in the language of a solitary drama.

Once an hysterical seizure has been developed, it is likely to be repeated; and with repetition it may become a preferred, habitual mode of escape from conflict, monotony and punishment — as in the case we have described. The organization of the attack develops reaction-sensitivity in the patient toward stimulation that sets it off, with the usual tendencies toward generalization which we have discussed in relation to normal reaction-sensitivity. As the seizures are repeated, they may also become more and more stereotyped, so that the behavior pattern of the attack can be accurately predicted even, as in our illustration, for recurrences of the disorder years later.

Hysterical somnambulism and fugue

By *hysterical somnambulism* we mean *autonomous behavior, resembling and related to normal somnambulism, which develops initially as a reaction to need or anxiety, and lacks a background of organ or tissue pathology adequate to account for it.* Taken literally, the term *somnambulism* means no more than sleep-walking, but in practice its meaning has expanded to include any coordinated biosocial act performed in sleep or sleep-like states. Normal somnambulism, in this sense, is far commoner among children than among grown-ups, but it appears in the night behavior of a great many adults also.

The normal forerunner of normal somnambulism is the vivid action-dream in which a sleeper tosses, twists, moves his limbs and head, makes sounds and says words belonging obviously to some context other than that of the shared social environment. The change from the common action-dream to somnambulism is essentially the product of an increase in the amplitude and range of the sleeper's reactions to his own fantasy. For, as a person's dream behavior grows more and more overt, it comes into more and more effective relationship with objects and persons in the surroundings. This change in the situation, if it does not awaken the sleeper, modifies his dream behavior in the direction of increasing his responsiveness to these objects and persons. The dreamer who manages to carry out routine coordinated acts without awakening — sitting up, arising, putting things on, talking and walking — already has the bases of hysterical somnambulism in his repertory. If he repeats such performances, he is likely to come into contact with more and different situations, as he moves about in his sleep, and to develop greater complexity and adequacy in his somnambulistic performance.

Most persons who have lived in dormitories, camps or interns' quarters have at some time been disturbed by a somnambulist who wanders around at night, rummages in dresser drawers, valises or closets, asks questions and gives more or less irrelevant answers, and awakens then or in the morning with amnesia for the episode. Somnambulism that reaches this degree of complexity and persistence should be considered hysterical, even though it leads to nothing more serious.[3] On the basis of the relatively few cases which have been adequately studied, the presumption is justified that somnambulism does not become as resistant as this to interruption unless, as with seizure, persistent strong need or anxiety has led to exceptionally well-developed autonomy.

By now it has become obvious that the patient in hysterical somnambulism is decidedly more responsive to his biosocial environment than one in hysterical seizure, and that his behavior, even though at times fumbling and hesitant, is much less stereotyped. On one somnambulistic excursion the sequence and character of responses may differ considerably from those of the preceding one. It is by no means rare for a somnambulist to exchange a few words with a sleepy roommate, dress or half-dress, go downstairs, unlock the front door and walk down the street without awakening. If the sleep-walker is accosted by a policeman, or if he tries to gain entrance to a strange house and arouses the occupants, he may suddenly come out of his autonomous phase with amnesia for its events. The hysterical somnambulist can sometimes be persuaded to return to his bedroom, undress and go to bed without awakening; when he gets up in the morning he, too, is amnesic for the autonomous episode, like the normal dreamer for most of his dreams.

For convenience of exposition, we have introduced hysterical somnambulism in its *nocturnal* form, which evolves from the vivid action-dream. But hysterical somnambulism may also be *diurnal*, occurring in persons who are not asleep but intensely preoccupied with private fantasy. This origin in need or anxiety, the characteristically sudden onset, the break in behavior continuity and the amnesia in one phase for events of the other, all indicate the close relationship between diurnal somnambulism and hysterical seizure. But the outcome is quite different. For in spite of the amnesia and the break in behavior continuity, the somnambulist makes sufficiently adequate use of his biosocial environment to enable him to move around among others, often without his attracting special notice for some time. Occasionally a person in a diurnal attack, in

---

[3] In military establishments the danger to the patient who fails to halt at the guard's command must also be considered. See S. Sandler, "Somnambulism in the armed forces," *Ment. Hyg.*, 1945, vol. 29, pp. 236-247.

spite of amnesia which may include the loss of personal identity, is able to carry out difficult manipulations, enter into biosocial activities that demand complex role-taking, including conversation with strangers, without arousing the least suspicion in others that something is wrong with him.

When a somnambulist, diurnal or nocturnal, actually takes to his heels and flees, we call the episode an *hysterical fugue.* Almost everyone says at one time or another, "I'd like to go away and forget it all!" The somnambulist in an hysterical fugue acts out this role literally. Our amnesic farmer who ran down the pedestrian with his truck had the beginnings of an hysterical flight in his behavior. But he landed in the secluded and protected environment of a hospital almost immediately, and this circumstance may have been all that prevented his developing a full-blown hysterical fugue. Quite often the flight from a situation comes first, and then anxiety over the possible consequence of fleeing results secondarily in somnambulism, which breaks with the immediate past, as in the following case.

> An impoverished male graduate student, aged twenty-two and unmarried, received an invitation to dinner at the home of an instructor whom he scarcely knew. When the day and hour for the dinner came, the graduate student failed to appear, nor could he be located by telephone, although it was ascertained that he had started for the instructor's house in plenty of time. Two days later he was picked up by the police in a neighboring state, at first unable to identify himself, but able to recall traveling on a freight train, talking with people and sharing their food. The contents of his pockets identified him and he was fetched home by relatives.
>
> Eventually the patient was able to recall the events both prior to and during his fugue. He had been dreading the prospect of dining out, partly because his clothes were exceedingly shabby and partly because the attitude of his host had seemed to him decidedly condescending. He had spoken to his roommate of withdrawing his acceptance of the invitation by telephone, but he never got around to doing it. Finally, when he was on his way to dinner, a passing freight train held him up at a railroad crossing, and he impulsively decided to escape from his miserable predicament by boarding it. The onset of somnambulism, which converted his simple flight into an hysterical fugue, seems to have followed his taking the decisive step of getting on the moving train. As in most cases of hysterical fugue, the patient retained nearly all of his manipulatory and locomotory habits, and behaved in general as other adults behaved who were reared in the same cultural environment.

It is quite possible that, had this patient escaped detection as a vagrant and lacked the means of self-identification, his fugue might have led him to acquire new self-reactions and a new vocation without his recalling the old, in which case he would be said to have developed *multiple personality*.

Multiple personality

By *multiple personality* we mean *hysterical autonomy in which, as a reaction to need or anxiety, two or more organized systems of biosocial behavior develop, with complete amnesia in one system for activities of the other, and in the absence of organ or tissue pathology adequate to account for the development.* In spite of the compendious literature on the subject, multiple personality is a comparatively rare syndrome, a recent estimate by Taylor and Martin placing the total of acceptable cases reported at around one hundred fifty.[4] It will be found convenient to distinguish between two main varieties, *alternating personality* and *double personality*, even though many cases fall into both categories.

By *alternating personality* we mean *multiple personality in which two or more organized systems become dominant, one at a time, and each system is amnesic for activities of the other.* This mutually amnesic variety seems, in most of the cases reported, to develop suddenly and at first under conditions of severe stress. As the alternation is repeated, however, it tends to occur with greater and greater ease and to acquire new excitants, like other learned reactions. Alternating personality occasionally begins as a fugue, but usually it does not. It resembles fugue in that the patient, as he passes from one phase to the other, retains fairly adequate responsiveness to the social environment. On the other hand, alternating personality resembles hysterical seizure, both in its manner of onset and in the mutual interrelationship of amnesia between its alternating phases.

By *double personality* we mean *multiple personality in which there is one dominant organized system of behavior with one or more subordinate systems, and the dominant system is amnesic for activities of the subordinate systems.* The dominant system is an

4 W. Taylor and M. Martin, "Multiple personality," *Jour. Abnorm. Soc. Psychol.*, 1944, vol. 39, pp. 281-300. This article contains an excellent bibliography and a table summarizing the characteristics of seventy-six reported cases.

incomplete organization because of amnesia which is typically serious and sweeping in character. However, a great deal of what is missing from the recall of the dominant system may be recovered indirectly by employing such techniques as automatic writing and hypnosis. The subordinate system is not amnesic for activities of the dominant organization. The situation in double personality is somewhat analogous to that in hysterical tic, for the subordinate behavior system is fragmentary, it may appear simultaneously with activities of the dominant system, and because of repression it functions as though it did not belong to the person who is the patient.

When indirect techniques are employed in cases of double personality, the reactions obtained, which constitute the subordinate system, often include comments, criticisms, advice, sympathy and derision — all directed toward the behavior of the dominant system — as though they referred to another person entirely. This relationship reminds one forcibly of the critical self-reactions so characteristic of dual role-taking in certain compulsive disorders. Indeed, some of the reported cases involve so much of the self-punitive, self-ridiculing attitude, and betray so many signs of childish immaturity in the subordinate personality,[5] that we may assume an origin for them also in conscience, as we defined it in Chapter 10. Of course, the relative lack of anxiety, and the serious amnesia of the dominant organization, differentiate double personality clearly from compulsive self-criticism.

Where more than two autonomous systems of biosocial behavior develop in multiple personality, certain of them may be mutually amnesic, as in alternating personality, while certain others in the same patient may be amnesic in one direction but not in the other direction, as in double personality. Moreover, the subordinate, submerged organization of a typical double personality may, while the patient is being studied, become suddenly one phase of an alternating personality. In this case, also, the subordinate system may develop little or no amnesia for the dominant system as a result of its metamorphosis, but continue to criticize and sometimes to tattle on the reactions in the dominant organization.

[5] An interesting example of this may be found in "Sally," the BIII personality, as described in Morton Prince's classical work, The Dissociation of a Personality. New York: Longmans, 1905.

Hysterical autonomy in relation to organ and tissue pathology

When it comes to distinguishing them from the products of organ and tissue pathology, the symptoms of hysterical autonomy pose the same general problems as do those of hysterical inactivation. Indeed, hysterical tremor, cramp and tic often resemble so closely the signs of neurological disease that to look anywhere but in the nervous system for their sources may seem at first glance absurd as well as unscientific. Such marked resemblance is, of course, not difficult to understand. For, no matter what may start a movement off and sustain it, the pattern of the movement will still be determined by the origins, insertions, planes of action and nerve supply of the synergic group of muscles executing it. This is so whether the movement is a direct result of an irritative lesion, a gestural response to verbal stimulation from another person, the outcome of one's private thinking, or an overt part of otherwise covert fantasy. In all four situations the movement may appear identical to an observer who lacks the auxiliary information upon which a differentiation can be made.

Although what has been said applies with especial force to *tremor* and *cramp*, whose patterns are relatively limited in variety, it is also true of a great many *tics*. The *spasmodic torticollis*, to which we have referred, may result from the stimulation provided by an irritative lesion of the central nervous system, and still the movement may resemble exaggerated aversion and disdain. The human being's direct response to something repulsive near his face is that of hyperextending the neck and rotating or averting the head; other animals, if similarly constructed, make a similar coordinated movement under the same circumstances. It is this coordinated movement which is thrown into action by certain neural lesions. In man the movement becomes a gesture, a language reaction, when it is given in response to stimulation that substitutes for something repulsive near the face — for example, to the stimulation of a repulsive word, recall or fantasy. If such a gesture becomes autonomous and its original stimulation cannot be recalled, as in hysteria, we then have a tic which is like that of neurological disease, not only in pattern but also in being beyond the patient's control.

Hysterical tic, as well as hysterical cramp, may lead eventually to irreversible secondary changes in muscle, tendon, ligament and even bone. Clonic spasmodic movements, for instance, overexercise the muscles and make them hypertrophy. Long-continued tonic contractions keep one set of muscles under tension and its antagonists relaxed, so that the former hypertrophy and the latter atrophy. Moreover, the tendons of chronically relaxed muscles may undergo progressive shortening which makes normal extension eventually impossible. Ligaments in cases of hysterical cramp sometimes develop anatomical thickening and form adhesions to produce typical contractures, while bones, through long disuse and unusual muscular stresses, are likely to undergo rarefaction and distortion. Thus, in extreme cases of hysterical autonomy, through prolonged disuse or overuse, the machinery of skilled coordination becomes irreparably damaged and the end-result is much the same as in disorders arising from organ or tissue pathology.

Hysterical seizures, even though they are regarded from a neurological standpoint as pseudo-convulsions, create many diagnostic difficulties. They are by no means always as clear-cut, obvious role-taking as in our example, nor always as prolonged. Moreover, there is a wide variety of patterns among the convulsive disorders of known neuropathological origin, and to complicate matters still further, hysterical patients who have witnessed or read carefully about any of these may unintentionally give a good reproduction of it in their hysterical seizure. Finally, one must never overlook the possibility that an hysterical patient, like anyone else, may develop convulsions on the basis of concomitant organ or tissue pathology, while a neurological patient may react to his difficulties by having an hysterical seizure. The same observations hold for *twilight-state, somnambulism, fugue* and *multiple personality,* all four of which have, for example, been reported as following *grand mal,* severe head injury and blast concussion.[6]

BIOSOCIAL BASES OF HYSTERICAL AUTONOMY

In the preceding chapter we pointed out that the biosocial bases of hysterical inactivation are readily discernible in everyday nor-

[6] See K. Bowman and A. Blau, "Psychotic states following head and brain injury in adults and children," in S. Brock (editor), *Injuries of the Skull, Brain and Spinal Cord,* 2d edition (Baltimore: Williams and Wilkins, 1943), pp. 294-341; E. Stengel, "On the etiology of fugue states," *Jour. Ment. Science,* 1941, vol. 87, pp. 572-599; E. Stengel, "Further studies on pathological wanderings (fugues with the impulse to wander)," *Jour. Ment. Science,* 1943, vol. 89, pp. 224-241.

mal behavior. We stated that consequently there was no need to begin our study of hysterical inactivation by turning away from our natural world to manufacture explanations out of the mythical dynamisms of a mythical *psyche*. The same is true of hysterical autonomy. If we ask the question, *From what characteristics of normal human behavior is hysterical autonomy derived?* the answer is simply that it is derived from normal autonomy, by which we mean the relative isolation of one behavior system from other simultaneously active behavior systems.

Autonomy in normal behavior organization

There has long been a tendency, especially noticeable in essays on human personality, to magnify the importance of unity and integrity in biosocial behavior. One result of this overemphasis has been to make the obvious disunity and fragmentation of behavior in hysterical autonomy seem weird, capricious and altogether unlike normal conduct. Actually, however, it is the unusual thing for a human being to react all in one piece, to perform one and only one grand function. Most of the time he is engaging simultaneously in a diversity of activities, some of which bear little or no relationship to others beyond the fact of their occurring in the same organism.

Normal autonomy is at once a reflection of the multiplicity of environmental stimulation and an expression of the human organism's extraordinary versatility in dealing with simultaneously present discrete demands. An experienced person can drive a car, reacting continuously to the demands of steering, and intermittently to traffic, road signs and pedestrians, while he keeps up a running conversation with a companion or listens to the radio and daydreams. Almost any housewife is able to stir food cooking on the stove and fasten a loose strand of hair with her other hand, while she listens to a radio drama and watches her child at play in the yard. Some of these activities can be reported by the auto driver or the housewife while some cannot.

It was once fashionable to ascribe reportable activities to the cerebral cortex or to the conscious mind, and unreportable activities to subcortical structures or to the unconscious mind. But there is no support for this dichotomy, either in the character of the reactions involved or in the physiology of the central nervous system. The unreportable overt act, word or thought — whether forgotten because unimportant or repressed because of need and anxiety — is behavior in the same sense as is the reportable; and as for the nervous system, everything we know about it speaks against the identification of conscious with cortical and subconscious with subcortical.[7]

The general principle of behavior autonomy was, of course, implicit in our earlier exposition of personality development and behavior organization, and in our discussion of emotion, symbolic behavior, role-taking and self-reactions. It was somewhat more explicit in the account of self-control and self-criticism with which we introduced the bases of the compulsive disorders. From what has already been said in these presentations, it must be evident that autonomous behavior is a product of learning, and that it improves with practice, tends to generalize and acquires new excitants. Moreover, autonomous behavior normally occurs without arousing self-reactions to it, so that during and after its performance, the autonomous act may remain inaccessible or, as we say in popular speech, "unconscious."

Indeed, in many skilled acts autonomy is an essential condition for optimal performance. We need only mention the highly complex behavior involved in typewriting from copy. Here the activity depends not only upon retinal stimulation, but also upon coordinated eye-movements, intraocular adjustments and the maintenance of a particular posture. The intricate play of finger, hand and wrist movements must be continually changing in response to retinal, proprioceptive and auditory stimulation. Yet, in the presence of such widespread and complex involvement, it is a well-known fact that the experienced typist finds irrelevant daydreaming a definite aid in sustaining speed and accuracy. For these two activities, typing from copy and daydreaming, to progress smoothly — each autonomous with regard to the other, and both unquestionably sharing the same organism and the same cerebral cortex — it is only necessary that neither one become dominant. Should difficulties arise because of defect in the manuscript or in the machine, the daydream is immediately interrupted; should the daydreaming raise disturbing conflicts, the typewriting suffers. Autonomy, then, is a

[7] See the discussion in J. Masserman, *Principles of Dynamic Psychiatry* (Philadelphia: Saunders, 1946), pp. 16-17. Also R. Grinker, "Hypothalamic functions in psychosomatic interrelationships," *Psychosom. Med.*, 1939, vol. 1, pp. 19-47; S. Ingham, "Some neurologic aspects of psychiatry," *Jour. Amer. Med. Assn.*, 1938, vol. 111, pp. 665-668.

normal characteristic of ordinary behavior and is often necessary for the smooth performance of well-practiced, skilled acts, even though such acts involve continually varying complex adjustments within them.

When the autonomous movement that appears in normal behavior is fragmentary and seems unrelated to or contradicts the context, we can infer the occurrence of incomplete repression, just as in the case of autonomous hysterical fragments. This is most obvious in situations which compel an individual to take a role in public that runs counter to certain of his strongly emotional attitudes. The person, for example, who is obliged by custom to congratulate his successful rival publicly after losing a vitally important contest may not recognize an incompletely repressed tendency to strangle him. But a close observer notices the loser's stiffly restrained posture, a trace of pain or snarl in his smile, or a tightly clenched left fist that does not match the friendly clasp of his other hand.

The point of importance to an understanding of the hysterical fragment is that these normal dissident behavior fragments — the postural stiffness, the tight or curled lip and the clenched left fist — are the incompletely repressed remnants of an otherwise abandoned role. The vanquished, in his moment of frustration and public humiliation, does actually take the required role of the good loser, but he does not succeed in eradicating all traces of the persisting combatant role. These traces continue in his behavior out of the shared social context and along with the responses belonging to his official, dominant role which the situation elicits. The clenched fist, for example, is the normal beginning of a blow which, under different circumstances, a man might give his opponent for defeating him — as untrained children often do. In this sense, it is a symbol of the taboo reaction of aggression which has been publicly rejected and disowned in the friendly handclasp. The unsuccessful contestant is not likely to react to these fragments, to identify them or to recognize what they signify, any more than patients do in relation to hysterical symptoms. Indeed, were the stiffness, the lip response or the clenched fist to persist as a cramp or recur as a tic, we should not hesitate to call the fragmentary reaction hysterical autonomy.

Hysterical autonomy as biosocial behavior

By now it has become clear that the biosocial behavior matrix, from which develop the symptoms of hysterical autonomy, is to be found in normal autonomy with which we are all familiar. Hysterical autonomy, like hysterical inactivation, is biosocial behavior which cannot be made intelligible if its investigation is limited to a study of the organism in isolation. The autonomous symptom says something to the person who understands its background, its evolution and its significance in the patient's life. If the symptom is a fragment — as in tremor, cramp or tic — it is the fragment of a biosocial act, and not merely a coordinated contraction. If it is a phase or episode — as in hysterical seizure and fugue — it is a biosocial phase or episode, with a background in the patient's interpersonal relationships from which it derives its meaning.

The overexclusion in hysterical autonomy, like that in hysterical inactivation, is a form of inadequate repression. The repression in hysterical autonomy, however, instead of being overcomplete is always in some way *incomplete*. Indeed, as we have seen, the autonomous symptom in *tremor, cramp* and *tic* is the fragmentary remnant or substitute which is left over from an otherwise repressed episode. The patient has succeeded in repressing enough of the anticipant and supporting attitude to deprive the response of biosocial meaning in his life, but he has not succeeded in repressing the whole reaction. As a result, whatever might formerly have elicited the intact tension-producing reaction now elicits only the residual fragment or fragmentary substitute. Through this subtotal repression of anticipant and supporting attitudes the patient loses control of the symptom, and this helps to explain the effects of therapeutic measures which rearouse the repressed attitudes in the patient's behavior organization. For if he completely recovers the anticipant and supporting attitudes, he regains control of the autonomous symptom belonging to them.

Repression is also incomplete in *hysterical seizure, somnambulism* and *fugue*. But here the patient, instead of exhibiting residual fragments as his symptom, develops autonomous episodes or phases in which either all of a repressed role is present or all of it is absent. The repression, in short, is an all-or-nothing affair. In seizure, for example, the episode that is kept repressed most of the time consists of a closely integrated succession of related acts, which intermittently supplants and excludes in its turn the previously dominant role. It makes no essential difference in the outcome what terminates the repression and starts the seizure — whether increased stress, fatigue, the facilitating suggestion from another person or the patient's own daydreaming. Once the recall begins in overt pantomime, all response to the social context is inhibited, and the sequence develops wholly in terms of its supporting fantasy context. The patient in the seizure is then socially inaccessible in the same sense that a normal person, while he is dreaming, may be unresponsive to social stimulation.

This overexclusion of response to the social context during hysterical seizure has its homologue also in the waking life of normal individuals. The person who, for example, becomes enraged, sexually aroused or extremely frightened may develop a behavior sequence that goes on irresistibly to completion. While this behavior sequence lasts, the person is relatively inaccessible to interruption from others, and the controlling self-reactions usually characteristic of him are absent. We say he is "not himself" or "beside himself." There is usually discernible also a certain degree of behavior discontinuity which appears to involve a discontinuity in repression. A person may go into a normal emotional episode quite suddenly, remain more or less unresponsive to social stimulation while the attack lasts, and afterwards resume his usual role. Sometimes, when his emotional storm has subsided, he cannot recall what he has done, and is genuinely incredulous when others tell him. The similarities to hysterical seizure are unmistakable.

Both the normal emotional storm and the hysterical seizure share their common characteristic of irresistible sequence with the recurrent compulsive crisis which we discussed in Chapter 10. The compulsive patient, it will be recalled, grows increasingly resistant to interference with the performance of his ritual as his emotional tensions rise. Once the episode gets under way, particularly in self-punitive and anti-social compulsions, the patient may also become reckless of consequences; and after the crisis has passed, he is at a loss to account for what he has done and often shows partial amnesia for his behavior. It is clear that, as far as the irresistibility and emotionality of ongoing sequences are concerned, the recurrent compulsive ritual has much in common with the recurrent hysterical seizure.

In stressing these similarities between compulsive and autonomous hysterical reactions, however, we must not lose sight of the equally important differences. It is true that both the compulsive patient in his ritual and the hysterical patient in his seizure suffer a recurrent loss of inhibition, but there is a fundamental difference in what the loss of inhibition involves. The compulsive loses his ability to inhibit repetition of the ritual, but in giving in to it he does not recall, in pantomime or in any other way, the original anxiety excitants. In hysterical seizure, as we have seen, there is recall in a re-enactment of the repressed anxiety-inducing behavior. On the other hand, the hysterical patient when the seizure phase is over has complete amnesia for it, whereas the compulsive suffers no amnesia at any time for the fact or for the character of his ritual.

Furthermore, the intense emotional reaction so characteristic of the compulsive ritual is a displaced emotional reaction, for the ritual is a form of substitutive behavior which has developed originally in response to some still repressed anxiety excitant. In hysterical seizure, on the other hand, the profound emotionality belongs to the patient's recall of a repressed episode and is therefore directly appropriate to it. And finally, in compulsive crises the degree of behavior discontinuity and unresponsiveness to the social context is decidedly less than in hysterical seizures. This difference is probably correlated with the fact that the emotional crisis in compulsions does not occur with a complete *return of the repressed,* whereas in hysterical seizure it does. For we have pointed out that the dramatic discontinuity in shared social behavior, and the accompanying social unresponsiveness, are in hysterical seizure a product of a sudden failure in repression.

We have indicated earlier that in *hysterical somnambulism* and *fugue,* the symptomatic or attack phase replaces a previously dominant role, as it does also in hysterical seizure. There is, however, this important difference: that reactions in terms of the social context are not nearly so drastically excluded by the developing repression. In consequence, the general behavior of a somnambulistic patient — particularly in the fugue — is apt to be much more effective and appropriate than that of the seizure patient in an attack. It is true that the exclusion of self-identifying and vocational behavior from the somnambulistic or fugue role prevents the patient from reacting to a great deal of his social environment, but his continued responsiveness to the rest of it allows him to develop new culturally defined roles out of his remaining social skills.

In *multiple personality* the characteristics of the repression differ in the two chief varieties. The situation in *alternating personality* is in certain respects like that in hysterical seizure, as we have said earlier. There is the all-or-nothing operation of the repressive technique; one phase is present or the other is; no compromise appears. The transition is abrupt, with discontinuity of the social behavior in one phase when the other becomes dominant. Each phase is amnesic for the other. Of course, in alternating personality neither phase is a simple recall pantomime, and in both phases behavior takes the social context into account much more adequately than in seizure phases. Repression in *double personality* is less apt to show the phasic character of seizures and alternating personality. The incompleteness of repression, which we have earlier compared to that of hysterical tic, is revealed in the autonomous self-reactions which, together with repressed recall, constitute the subordinate organization.

BIOSOCIAL DETERMINANTS OF HYSTERICAL INACTIVATION AND AUTONOMY

The hysterical patient, like the compulsive, was at one time supposed to belong to a peculiar class of human beings. Individuals in this class were thought to begin life with an inherited "hysterical constitution" which left them susceptible to the development of hysterical inactivation and autonomy. Such assumptions are, of course, part of the hypothesis generally accepted in the nineteenth century that persons developing behavior disorders did so because they were constitutionally inferior. This hypothesis appears deceptively simple and comforting. It says, in effect, that people are different as adults because they were born different. Its principal defects are that it virtually ignores the whole period of biosocial development from birth to maturity, that it encourages students in the field to regard the question of individual susceptibility a settled one, instead of one in great need of investigation from all directions, and that it has so far proved resistant to test and relatively unfruitful.

From what has been said in this and the preceding chapter, the hypothesis seems more tenable and scientifically more promising that most, if not all, human beings have in their behavior repertory the bases from which develop hysterical inactivation and autonomy. This assumption neither excludes the possibility that adequate evidence may be found in support of biological inheritance as one of the determining factors, nor diverts our attention from the influence of general cultural differences and specific childhood influences, about which a great deal more is known today than half a century ago. But if we adopt this as our preferred hypothesis, we must pay for its advantages by facing at once the incontrovertible fact that relatively few individuals actually do develop an hysterical disorder as their way out of personal difficulty. *Why is it,* then, *that certain persons show relative ease in developing persistent hysterical symptoms as a reaction to need or anxiety, while others exposed to comparable stress and strain do not?* In other words, who are the hysteria-prone, and what factors in their acquired behavior organization seem to predispose them to develop hysterical inactivation and autonomy?

Adoption of the prevailing pattern

One important source of differences in individual susceptibility seems to result from cultural differences in credulity. We have said that major hysterical disorders are most commonly encountered in an atmosphere of ignorance, naïveté and superstitution. A child reared by adults who are uninformed, credulous and superstitious about human physiology and human behavior is more likely to acquire hysterical symptoms, other things being equal, than is a child whose elders are in this respect sophisticated and informed. For the first step in developing an hysterical symptom is the acceptance of normal inactivation or autonomy as evidence of an impersonal disease or disability, as a strange visitation or as a sign of magical powers. If a person learns in childhood to accept hysterical symptom, sudden visitation and miraculous cure in this light, he will have acquired the first prerequisite for developing a major hysterical disorder — unquestioning credulity, or, as it is usually called in this connection, *hypersuggestibility.*

Even without such a cultural background, a child may develop hypersuggestibility to his own inactivation or autonomy on the basis provided him by a parental model. For example, the child whose parent has hysterical symptoms may exhibit similar complaints in childhood or adulthood, and thus give the superficial impression of being a victim of biological rather than cultural inheritance. The parent who is given to exaggeration and emotional display in controlling the home environment, even though devoid of hysterical symptomatology, may unwittingly provide his child with attitudes and techniques that result secondarily in hysterical disorder. Children in prolonged contact with a seriously handicapped individual sometimes develop hysterical symptoms on this basis. For whether the handicap is itself hysterical or not, the behavior of the disabled person may provide the child with attitudes and techniques that leave him more vulnerable than the average to hysterical role-taking later in life.

Childhood training in social immaturity

Children whose elders provide them with no models of hysterical behavior, or of behavior favoring hysterical developments, can nevertheless be so trained in social immaturity that they become as susceptible as though a model had been given them. Parental anxiety and oversolicitude may, for example, lead a child to develop disabling hysterical symptoms in the same way that they lead children to develop hypochondriacal overconcern and fatigue syndromes. If a specific disability or an autonomous symptom enables a child to avoid effort, responsibility and punishment, or merely keeps him in the focus of attention as something unusual — like our schoolboy — he is likely to develop such a reaction as a preferred adjustive technique. If his parents accept the reaction as the basis for exemption and privilege, the child will also accept it, and in his adult life he will expect others to treat similar manifestations in him with comparable respect and consideration.

It is customary to point out that many hysterical patients seem to be playing for audience-effect in a shallow, insincere, theatrical and egotistical manner. But this clinical name-calling, however accurate it may be, must not divert us from the fact that such behavior has a background and represents a difficulty. An excessive need to hold the center of the stage, to impress others and gain their emotional support is always a difficulty; and its background is frequently in a childhood spent with an overprotective, indulgent parent, such as we described in Chapter 2. A child so reared develops the expectation that he will be noticed, admired and applauded for everything he does; if his expectation is not met, he cannot help being dissatisfied and uneasy. To be treated as just one of the crowd, without special attention and praise, means to him that he is considered a nobody, that he is rejected or even actively discriminated against and disliked.

Hence it is that the roles taken by adolescents and adults with such a childhood background are carried through rather for audience-effect — for the satisfaction of being considered unusual and important — than for satisfaction in the role-taking itself. Work, leisure and recreation become opportunities for seeking applause and thus satisfying needs that cannot otherwise be met. The socially immature techniques involved in seeking continual audience-support are closely related to hysterical symptom display.

We know, now, that symptoms of hysterical inactivation and autonomy are derived under conditions of unusual need or anxiety from their normal counterparts. The unhappy, dissatisfied or frightened person who notices momentary inactivation or autonomy in his behavior may be impressed by it, and reinforce it through his own self-reactions to it. If others are also impressed, his need for their attention and sympathy may lead to the persistence of his response as an hysterical symptom. And if in this way he at last achieves the satisfactions he so strongly needs, we can understand his self-attitude of unconcern toward the symptom — Janet's *la belle indifférence*.[8]

The domineering, overprotective parent, unlike the indulgent, admiring parent we have just discussed, does not allow anyone else to hold the center of the stage, for he has the need himself always to hold it. Nevertheless, his child may also be trained in the techniques of social immaturity and dependence, which leave him vulnerable as an adult to the development of hysterical disorders. The dominated child learns that for him there is but one great commandment, *Whatsoever thou doest, see that it please thy parent, the giver and denier.* He finds that the only way he can secure his satisfactions and avoid intolerable anxiety, rejection and retaliation is to behave always in such a way as to elicit signs of parental approval and acceptance. He is schooled to watch for these signs in everything he does, to wait expectantly for them, and to feel comforted and secure when they appear. Acquired reactions such as these generalize, of course, from parent or parent-substitute to other adults and to the child's contemporaries. Once established, they tend to persist as habitual techniques even though they may be relatively ineffectual.[9]

[8] Compare the account given of paratroopers in R. Grinker and J. Spiegel, *Men Under Stress* (Philadelphia: Blakiston, 1945), pp. 104-105.

[9] An important factor in the production of telegraphers' cramp, for instance, is the continual presence of a potential critic at the other end of the line. See M. Smith, M. Culpin and E. Farmer, "A study of telegraphists' cramp," *Industrial Fatigue Research Board*, 1927, No. 43, pp. 15-19.

In this way the child develops through his training in submission, not only a need to subordinate himself, but also an expectation of receiving in return the protective acceptance, approval and affection with which his parent has rewarded his dependent ways. Of course, such a child, in growing to adulthood, may give up this dependence and submission. But if for any reason he is temporarily incapacitated so that he is placed in a dependent relationship with other persons, he is much more likely than the average person to develop symptoms that prolong or perpetuate his incapacity. Thus, in the end the person who has been trained to need sheltering affection, and who is most secure in a subordinate relationship, may exhibit the same hysterical symptomatology as the person needing to be in the spotlight as an unusual individual deserving prominence. The submissive patient's self-attitude toward his symptom, if it leads to a reduction in his need or anxiety, will as we might expect be also one of satisfaction or unconcern — again, *la belle indifférence.*

It would be a mistake to suppose, however, that only those children whose parents are oversolicitous or overprotective become hysterical adults. As we pointed out in Chapter 6, neglected and rejected children also develop exaggerated attention-getting techniques, and carry these into their adulthood along with the other social skills they learn in childhood. Habitual insecurity and excessive need leave such individuals similarly vulnerable to the development of hysterical symptoms if the symptoms allay anxiety and bring them satisfaction. Likewise, adults whose childhood includes neither oversolicitude, overprotection, neglect nor rejection, may nevertheless develop the same symptoms, on similar grounds. If for any reason they have, as adults, enjoyed great admiration or deference, special privilege or a comfortable, protected status, and the conditions upon which these depend are suddenly swept away, only their own informed or skeptical attitude may stand between them and a major hysterical disorder.

We come now to the part played by excessive daydreaming in hysteria. As a source of need-satisfaction, daydreaming becomes of the greatest significance when other sources are not available. Thus, the child of domineering, denying or rejecting parents, who reduce his activities and deprive him of the acceptance and reassurance he must have, frequently is driven to daydreaming for his chief satisfactions. In his daydreams he gives himself the things he needs

— reassurance and acceptance, freedom of movement, security and importance. In them he also learns that acts may be fantasied and situations manipulated fearlessly in scene or symbol which, were he to try carrying them out in overt shared behavior, would be severely punished. Provided that he does it all in daydreaming, the child finds he can be good in ways of his own choosing, that he can be strong and proud of it, or bad and enjoy it.

Of course, if the recall of such covert behavior, when the child is with other persons, leads to guilt and anxiety reactions in him, he is likely to repress it until he is alone again and the opportunity comes for indulgence. In this manner, a child may develop a well-practiced fantasy life, which is reserved for private use, and a public shared social life in which his private fantasies have no place. This situation is a normal forerunner of certain hysterical developments, particularly amnesia and the autonomous breaks in the continuity of shared social behavior which we encountered in seizure, somnambulism, fugue and multiple personality.

Influence of illness and injury

Illness and injury predispose some individuals to develop hysterical inactivation or autonomy in the same general way that they lead others to develop hypochondriacal disorders or fatigue syndromes. The incapacitated person, as we pointed out in Chapter 7, is a dependent person. For the individual who has long had unsatisfied needs to be in a dependent relationship to someone, an incapacitating illness or injury carries with it special hazards which the patient is unlikely to recognize.

There are endless opportunities for developing hysterical symptoms if one is prepared to accept inactivation or autonomy as evidence of disease or defect. For example, any bedridden patient is likely to produce a transitory numbness and weakness in an arm by lying on it while he is asleep. Under conditions of unusual need or anxiety the patient may immediately accept his symptoms as evidence of paralysis, and lose the use of his arm. His faith has made him ill. Fracture patients occasionally present the same clinical problem when a cast is removed. Even though the part is neurologically and röntgenologically normal it cannot be moved. Likewise, convalescent patients when they first get up may be unable to support their weight even though physical examination reveals no justification for the weakness. While the need to be sick dominates his behavior, the convalescent patient will continue unable to stand and walk; if his need can be abated, his legs will quickly recover.

We have already indicated the frequent origin of tremor and cramp in occupational injury or fatigue; anesthesias and paralyses, aphonia, mutism, amblyopia and amaurosis often begin in comparable ways. For example, a person suffers a minor industrial, domestic or street accident which results in pain, numbness and temporary impairment of movement, speech or vision. If the accident frightens a person badly, his reaction to such symptoms may intensify and perpetuate them. To this the excitement, anxiety or indignation of other persons also contributes — at the scene of the accident and in the inevitable discussions afterwards, when there is the usual talk of disabling injuries to others, of financial compensation and revenge.

Catastrophic situations in war and peace have similar results.[10] A man is thrown to the ground under terrifying circumstances, buried under debris, trapped or pinned down by wreckage; and afterwards he finds he cannot walk, use an arm or see, even though the organs and parts involved — as organs and parts — are normal. Hysterical amnesia, seizures, fugues and even multiple personality may begin with an illness or injury which provides the patient with a pattern for the adjustive technique he needs.

Hysterical disorders as adjustive techniques

Hysterical disorders, no matter how maladaptive they may eventually prove to be, are by definition adjustive techniques, since they reduce or dispose of the tensions of need and anxiety. Hysterical symptoms are often developed and used *aggressively* against other persons as spite reactions in which the patient, through his disability, is able to deprive others of their freedom of action and their opportunities for relaxation and pleasure. Symptoms are sometimes developed and used aggressively by a patient in relation to himself. Thus, through his disability a patient may punish his own guilt by barring himself from many rewarding activities. More commonly, however, the hysterical symptom is developed and used primarily as a technique of withdrawal or *escape*, as indeed we have already seen.

[10] See the report on Dunkirk evacuées by W. Sargent and E. Slater, "Acute war neuroses," *Lancet*, 1940, part 2, pp. 1-2.

Throughout our discussion of hysterical disorders the use of symptoms as an *attention-getting* technique has been obvious. The patient, without necessarily planning it or recognizing what he is doing, makes himself the focus of other persons' reactions through developing his symptoms. What usually happens is that inactivation or autonomy occurs in response to a specific situation, which may not be related to the patient's difficulties.[11] The patient, however, because of intense need or anxiety at the time reacts to the change as to something of special significance, and leads others to react in the same way. A similar development is frequently seen on the wards of general hospitals. If the patient gains in personal significance by displaying symptoms to physicians on rounds, to nurses and students, to other patients and visitors, his symptoms may multiply and persist as hysterical inactivation or autonomy.

Hysterical symptoms also develop on the basis of *identification*, the patient reacting to the characteristics and status of a sick or handicapped person as though they were his own. He adopts, in other words, some part of the role of an envied or emulated personage — an invalid sibling, parent or spouse, for example, or a martyr, a hero or a saint — and includes in what he adopts the disability from which that personage suffered. Hysterical symptoms are *compensatory* in function when they substitute for some other need-satisfaction sequence. For example, a patient may seek and accept care and privilege on the basis of an hysterical disability, in place of love and protection on the basis of sexual desirability. The same general principle applies to achievement in non-sexual fields; the patient gains satisfaction from the needs presented by his hysterical disorder which substitutes for other unattained satisfactions. The use of hysterical symptoms as *rationalization* has already been sufficiently discussed, particularly in relation to occupational tremor and cramp. As we said in Chapter 6, hysterical disabilities may in this respect be compared with sign language and sometimes even with speech in what they symbolically represent. But more often than not the patient cannot recognize, through his own self-reactions, what it is that his symptoms indicate.

Hysterical symptoms quite commonly serve to *insulate* the patient; that is, to render him or his reactions relatively inaccessible to the behavior of other persons. This is achieved in hysterical

[11] E. Wolff and G. Lachmann, "Hysterical blindness in children: a report of two cases," *Amer. Jour. Dis. Child.*, 1938, vol. 55, pp. 743-749.

inactivation through the development of a persistent reaction-insensitivity, as a reaction to need or anxiety. Anesthesias and paralyses, for instance, render the patient inaccessible to certain kinds or sources of stimulation by others, and sweeping amnesias make him inaccessible to past events through eliminating his recall of them. In hysterical autonomy certain restricted behavior — such as in tremor, cramp and tic — becomes inaccessible to the behavior of other persons as well as beyond the patient's control. The patient in such phasic or episodic autonomous reactions as somnambulism, fugue and multiple personality, may become wholly inaccessible as a social person to the behavior of certain other individuals. Finally, we have seen how insulated is the patient in hysterical seizure; by acting out a dramatic role in his fantasy context he puts himself out of everybody's reach.

The use of hysterical symptoms as *negativism* follows along similar lines. Participation in activities with other persons is made impossible by the development of inhibitory and autonomous reactions which are opposed to those demanded by shared social situations. We have already pointed to the *regressive* character of some hysterical symptom development. Persons accustomed in childhood to receive special consideration, affection or exemption by exhibiting signs of disability or forgetfulness may in adult life revert to these immature, but once successful techniques (*habit-regression*). Reversion to this technique rather than to some other is frequently the result of long practice in childhood, or of involvement of the technique in important childhood emotional satisfactions (*habit-fixation*). In adulthood the regressive relationships inevitably set up by injury, illness, poverty, prolonged idleness or arbitrary discipline may favor the development of hysterical symptoms also. The important part played by *repression* and *fantasy* in the development and perpetuation of hysterical disorders has been discussed earlier in this chapter and in the preceding one.

HYSTERICAL DISORDERS AND MALINGERING

We began our consideration of hysterical disorders in Chapter 11 by observing that hysterical patients are always in danger of being misjudged as frauds. Throughout our discussion of the varieties of hysterical inactivation and autonomy this point has come up, again and again, because there is no differentiation more difficult to establish than that between hysterical symptom and malingering. The reasons for this are obvious. The motivation that we extract from the behavioral relationships may be identical in the two biosocial reactions — that is, both are adjustive techniques which are developed and used in the same situations. Moreover, hysterical disorder and malingering have many characteristics in common, as we have already indicated, and both may be present in behavior at the same time. The patient may, for example, deliberately dupe others by tampering with his thermometer, in order to persuade them of the verity of an hysterical disorder in which he himself believes. Or the patient may begin by pretending that he is disabled in some way and end up by convincing himself of it, thus falling into the trap that he had set for others.

No matter what symptoms are being investigated, the differentiation between hysteria and malingering must finally rest upon the criterion of self-deception. If the patient accepts and believes in his symptom as evidence of disability or disease, we must accept and believe in him as an hysterical patient; if he does not, we must consider him a malingerer. The trouble is that, while there are many cases which are either one or the other, there are many others in which pretense and self-deception are so intermingled as to make clear distinction impossible.[12] It is frequently said, for instance, that in malingering the patient resents being examined and that his symptomatology is apt to be unstable, inconsistent and subject to bizarre modifications induced by deliberate suggestions on the examiner's part. But all of these characteristics of malingering can also be found in the patient, who is indubitably hysterical, but feels unjustly suspected and overplays his hand in defense of his own convictions. Indeed, a distinction can sometimes be made only by watching the course and outcome of therapy. For whether a patient is considered hysterical or a malingerer he stands in need of therapeutic help.

HYSTERICAL DISORDERS IN RELATION TO OTHER BEHAVIOR DISORDERS

We have said elsewhere that it is typical of the patient suffering from hysterical inactivation or autonomy to be relatively or com-

---

[12] D. Parfitt and C. Gall, in a study of amnesia, state that the difference between hysterical amnesia and malingering is only one of degree. "Psychogenic amnesia: the refusal to remember," *Jour. Ment. Science,* 1944, vol. 90, pp. 511-531.

pletely unconcerned over his serious disability. This attitude, in addition to the more detailed symptomatology, differentiates hysterical from *hypochondriacal disorders*. For the hypochondriacal patient is characteristically overconcerned, and he is frequently convinced that organs or parts of his body are diseased or functioning defectively when they appear normal to clinical examination. A further distinction rests upon the degree to which biosocial behavior is implicated in the chief complaint. In hysteria the activities affected by the complaint are primarily social activities, whereas in hypochondria the patient's emphases are primarily upon a supposed disease of some internal organ or system at a physiological level. Hypochondriacal preoccupation is often a substitution of visceral interest for personal dissatisfaction or conflict. Hysterical 'symptoms are less a substitution of disease interest for dissatisfaction and conflict than they are a demonstration, to the patient himself and others, that the activities involved in conflict are absent (*inactivation*) or out of the patient's control (*autonomy*), and in either case outside his range of responsibility.

In the *fatigue syndrome* there is not the specificity of complaint which characterizes hysterical disorders, and the attitude of the chronically fatigued patient is typically one of overconcern — more like that seen in hypochondriacal disorders than in hysterical. The distinction between hysteria and *anxiety disorders* is not difficult to make in well-developed cases, since the hysterical symptom is fundamentally an adaptive reaction to the tensions of anxiety or need. However, it is not uncommon for this adaptation to be incompletely successful, with the result that anxiety symptoms will be found in company with hysterical symptoms, sometimes one group and sometimes the other dominating the clinical picture.

Although there are many points of similarity between the behavior pathology of hysterical and *compulsive disorders*, the distinction between them is usually not difficult to make. Hysterical disorders lack the successive phases of mounting anxiety, indulgence in ritual and transient relief, so characteristic of the compulsive syndrome. Both are reactions to anxiety and both primarily involve serious disturbances in social behavior; but the techniques employed in one differ fundamentally from those employed in the other — hence the contrasting attitudes one finds between them. The compulsive is, so to speak, a frightened man who prays in a lightning storm to keep from being hit, whereas the hysteric is a man who solves the same problem by going blind.

The distinction between hysterical tic and the so-called "psychasthenic tic" or "compulsive tic" deserves our special attention. We do not consider a repetitive movement to be *hysterical* unless it is an isolated behavior fragment which is out of keeping with the shared environmental context, and develops as a reaction to need or anxiety. The hysterical tic is a recurrent symptom, it is true, but it does not develop as the end-point in repeated episodes of mounting anxiety; and the patient does not report that he is alternately resisting and giving in to it. As far as the term "compulsive tic" and its older synonym "psychasthenic tic" are concerned, it seems best to avoid their use entirely in the interest of clarity, reserving the term *tic* for hysterical autonomy.

We have said earlier, in discussing obsessions, that we do not call a repetitive movement *compulsive* unless it is a direct reaction to recurrent phases of mounting anxiety which brings the patient immediate though transient relief. In other words, it is wisest to be sparing in the use of *hysterical* and *compulsive* as applied to repetitive movement. Repetition is, after all, a common normal phenomenon, and repetitions that are strictly neither hysterical nor compulsive occur in other behavior disorders, particularly in schizophrenia.

In clear-cut cases, the distinction between hysterical and *schizoprenic disorders* is seldom a serious problem. Hysterical inactivation and autonomy are adjustive techniques which operate by overexclusion. The hysterical patient, through the process of eliminating the reactions with which he cannot cope, succeeds in preserving his behavior organization otherwise. The schizophrenic patient shows overinclusion and, as one consequence of this, he is unable to preserve a workable organization of his biosocial behavior. As we shall see in Chapter 15, reactions which are incongruous, inappropriate and contradictory develop in response to so many shared situations that the schizophrenic patient characteristically becomes unable to get along in any but a restricted, protective environment. The hysterical patient, even when he is suffering from diurnal somnambulism, fugue or multiple personality, exhibits a remarkable ability to make use of his environment in an organized fashion. The schizophrenic patient with comparable involvement is virtually helpless in a normally complete biosocial environment.

In spite of what has just been said, the task of differentiating between hysterical and schizophrenic disorders is often an exceedingly difficult one, because they are often by no means clear-cut, and sometimes it cannot be achieved to everyone's satisfaction. We do not, for example, have adequate criteria of early disorganization; people are vague and dreamy in beginning schizophrenia, we say, but so are a great many hysterical patients. The gesture and posture language of hysterical inactivation and autonomy, as we have pointed out, has its counterpart in schizophrenic symbolism; hysterical tic and schizophrenic stereotypy are undoubtedly related phenomena. Except for its marked phasic character, even the hysterical seizure and its aftermath remind one of the peculiar role-taking, preoccupation and passivity often found in schizophrenia. In schizophrenia we shall also meet aphonia and mutism, anorexia, and anesthesias as complete as in hysterical inactivation. What we do not find in typical schizophrenia is the amnesia so characteristic of hysterical disorders and upon which, along with other forms of overexclusion, the continued ability of hysterical patients to maintain adequate relationships with their environment may depend.

Hysterical symptoms are not uncommon in *depressive* and *manic disorders,* but the sadness or agitation in one and the elation in the other determine the diagnosis. Hysterical symptoms also appear in behavior disorders developing on the basis of *cerebral incompetence,* but if the signs of impaired cerebral function are prominent, the hysterical symptoms are regarded as incidental modifications, the outcome of the patient's reactions to his reduced effectiveness, status and security. Finally, hysterical disorders differ from *paranoid disorders* in two important respects. The symptoms of inactivation and autonomy are not a part of the paranoid disorder, and although disowning tendencies are usually dominant in both, they do not lead to projection in typical hysteria. The hysterical patient may deny, in effect, that he has a certain characteristic or is guilty of a certain attitude, by excluding from his behavior repertory something which is symbolic of it. But he does not ascribe the characteristic or attitude which he represses to other persons, or to members of a *pseudocommunity,* and then organize his reactions around that ascription, as paranoid patients do.

13 *Delusions and Hallucinations*

in Behavior Disorders

DELUSIONS AND HALLUCINATIONS are of such widespread occurrence among the behavior disorders, and in some of them have such important effects, that they deserve special consideration before we go any farther. Together they form another of our many bridges that link normal to abnormal behavior. For everyone occasionally develops a firm conviction that is based upon misinterpretation, unwarranted inference or unjustified conclusion, and then proceeds to act upon this conviction as though it were established fact. Such behavior constitutes *delusion*. And there are few persons who have never responded to stimulation from their own fantasy behavior which they mistakenly attribute to sources outside of fantasy. This response with its characteristic misreference is what we term *hallucination*.

In normal as well as in abnormal persons there are certain conditions which favor delusional and hallucinatory developments, such as tense expectation, emotional arousal and urgent need. We see illustrations of this among persons witnessing well-staged magical tricks or attending a fervid revival meeting,[1] and among the members of an angry or a frightened mob. Individuals also develop delusions and hallucinations when they are personally insecure, anxious, suspicious or jealous, and when they are emotionally attached to or hostile toward some person, group or symbol.

The individual who is expectant and in need, or who is insecure, emotionally aroused or emotionally attached, is of course selectively reaction-sensitive in relation to certain kinds of stimulation. Anticipant attitudes are dominant in his behavior which facilitate certain

[1] H. Cantril and M. Sherif, "The kingdom of Father Divine," *Jour. Abnorm. Soc. Psychol.*, 1938, vol. 33, pp. 147-167.

interpretations and inhibit others. The emotional reinforcement, and the disequilibrium which defines need, reduce his ability to suspend final action — to wait, maintain a skeptical, analytic attitude and weigh the evidence. In short, we find once more the conditions which we described in the preceding chapter as *hypersuggestibility*. We may now proceed to a discussion of delusional reactions and of the closely allied hallucinatory responses.

DELUSIONAL REACTIONS IN BEHAVIOR DISORDERS

Delusional reactions may play an important part in the development of any of the behavior disorders. In hypochondriacal overconcern and in fatigue syndromes the delusional reactions with respect to illness and weakness are as a rule limited in scope. However, as we have seen in our case material, the convictions which some patients develop in these disorders may introduce considerable distortion into their way of living. As we might expect, delusions often figure prominently in acute anxiety disorders, particularly in phobias and in panic reactions where progressive misinterpretation may culminate in precipitate flight, suicide or homicidal assault.

The compulsive disorders, as we have seen, are characterized by unwarranted inferences regarding sin, contamination, impending danger and the like in the patient's relationships with his environment; and the patient places unjustified credence in rituals and charms as preventives. Delusional misinterpretations also enter into hysterical disorders, although in most cases they are limited to the presenting symptom. In seizure, however, the patient acts as though his fantasy context were the shared social context, as do normal dreamers, even though the biosocial environment contradicts the assumptions basic to his behavior in the attack. When we come to paranoid disorders, we find that they are essentially delusional disorders; indeed, it might simplify our classification if the term "paranoid" were discarded entirely. Delusions are also of first-rate importance in schizophrenic disorders, as we shall see in Chapter 15, and they are seldom absent from mania or the depressions.

Delusions are common in persons who for any reason suffer a serious reduction in the physiological competence of the brain. We see this in systemic disease or intoxication, in metabolic disorders, high body temperature, exhaustion, starvation or dehydration; we see it also in cases of brain damage as a result of the direct effect of infection, tumor, trauma or deterioration. The patient, because of relative cerebral incompetence, cannot handle complex interpersonal relationships adequately, and his misinterpretations are an expression of his inadequacy. The mere fact that florid delusions are a part of the typical delirium is further evidence of the widespread character of delusional behavior. For, since anyone can deliberately be made delirious by intoxication, it follows that the delusional reaction is within the range of everyone's behavior and is not confined to certain peculiar kinds of people. We shall return to this point in Chapter 17 when we take up the subject of brain damage.

Delusions may be defined as *convictions based upon misinterpretations, unwarranted inferences or unjustified conclusions, which are the result of unusual anticipant attitudes, emotional arousal, personal need or physiological incompetence, and usually lead to behavior that is socially detrimental, inappropriate or inept.* The decision as to whether a delusional reaction shall be considered pathological or not can best be made on the basis of its effects in the biosocial behavior of the individual. We would call delusion definitely pathological if it proved responsible for introducing behavior impoverishment or distortion, if it rendered a person ineffectual in his social relationships, if it prevented his attaining important satisfactions or made their attainment disproportionately effortful and time-consuming.

The heterogeneous character of our culture makes it difficult to place limits on what we shall consider normal delusion. There are among us, for example, social groups whose members consider it a sign of strength and virtue to reject without examination all evidence that contradicts certain group beliefs. The clearer and more cogent the contradictory evidence, the more highly is blind rejection esteemed as proof of superior courage and integrity. This prescientific negativism, which in earlier eras seems to have been almost universal, can be accepted as an instance of normal delusion, provided its effects upon the individual are not those outlined in the preceding paragraphs. In the discussion that follows we shall confine our attention to delusional reactions as pathological behavior.

Temporal variations in delusion

The significance of delusional behavior in an individual's life is to some degree a function of its duration. A *single transient delusion* may develop in anyone's reactions as the incidental result of some temporary disturbance, but unless it leads at once to undesirable action, or is remembered and used against a person by others or by himself, it is unlikely to create special difficulties. The *recurrent transient delusion* may have more serious implications. It is true that some individuals go through recurrent pathological delusional episodes, under emotional stress or when ill, exhausted or intoxicated, and succeed in returning to normal after the precipitating situation has cleared up. However, delusional reactions that recur stand the same chance of becoming habitual as do nondelusional reactions that recur. The person who repeats his delusional behavior is likely to grow reaction-sensitive to stimulation in the environment and in his own thinking which tends to arouse his particular unwarranted inferences. The recurrent delusion, like other learned behavior, may also generalize and acquire new excitants until it becomes no longer merely intermittent but progressive.[2]

The *progressive* or *expanding delusion* is one in which both the variety of excitants and the scope of the delusional organization are on the increase. Delusions tend to expand in many conditions of acute or growing tension, in emotional disorders such as mania and depression, in progressive disorganization of biosocial behavior as in schizophrenia, and in the disorientation and deterioration of behavior which appear when there is serious reduction in the competence of the brain as an organ. However, it is important for us to realize that delusions also tend to grow progressive, once they have become established, without any change in the conditions to which they owe their origin. As we shall see in paranoid disorders, when a delusional reaction appears in anyone's behavior, the question of its progress or recession will be settled largely by the relative skill and competence of the individual in using the common techniques of social inquiry. Other things being equal, the more skilled a person is in role-taking and in shifting his perspectives, the more readily he will arrive at a correction of his unwarranted inferences and the misinterpretation to which they have led him.[3]

[2] W. Jahrreiss, "Delusional episodes," *Dis. Nerv. System,* 1943, vol. 4, pp. 207-215.

[3] N. Cameron, "The development of paranoic thinking," *Psychol. Rev.,* 1943, vol. 50, pp. 219-233.

The *chronic delusion* is one which, even though there may be fluctuations in scope and changes in detail, remains fairly constant and predictable. Sometimes a delusional reaction appears suddenly in a person's behavior and persists without change as a chronic delusion; but as a rule the chronic delusion represents an end-stage of a previously expanding or progressive one. It was once naïvely assumed that to become chronic a delusion must please or satisfy the patient; but pleasure and satisfaction are no longer accepted as exclusive principles of explanation in behavior pathology, any more than they are in normal behavior. Anyone who has worked long among chronically deluded patients knows that delusional reactions are commonly the outcome of an unhappy compromise, and often lead to confusion or social disarticulation from which the patient can no longer be rescued, either by his own efforts or by the efforts of anyone else. The fact is that early in delusional development a person may have opportunities for genuine choice; but after a certain stage in the development has been reached, further expansion and ultimate chronicity become almost as inevitable as the progress of an irreversible chemical reaction toward its end-point. We shall analyze the development and persistence of delusion further when we discuss paranoid disorders.

Isolated delusional reactions, even though in themselves quite absurd to others, sometimes persist indefinitely in a person's behavior repertory. Among chronic but partially recovered schizophrenics, for example, one can often find the residue of a simple stereotyped delusion which the patient may express with little show of interest. It survives — much as the hysterical tic survives — as the fragment of a once more meaningful reaction whose attitudes have largely disappeared. Stereotyped and more or less isolated delusions occasionally persist as chronic reactions after a manic or depressive illness. Thus, for example, a depressed man who developed the conviction that the townspeople were going to lynch him remained suspicious and apprehensive in public afterwards, although this had never been his prevailing attitude prior to his depression. Likewise a delusional misinterpretation, developed during a delirium of toxic, infectious or febrile origin, may persist unchanged for months — or even permanently — after illness and convalescence are over. In such instances we can assume that the delusional reaction, arrived at through serious emotional disorder or cerebral incompetence, is prevented from disappearing afterwards because of its relation to the rest of the patient's biosocial behavior organization which supports it.

Degrees of delusional systematization

Delusional behavior varies in organization from the fleeting, more or less unrelated fragments characteristic of dreams and delirium, to the internally consistent systematization of paranoia. Indeed, so high may be the degree of internal consistency in the latter that the ordinary person, once he accepts the patient's major premise, may be unable to resist the patient's argument or come to a contrary conclusion. Paranoic persons frequently convince lay juries of their sanity and sometimes win favorable decisions in lawsuits whose circumstantial evidence is held together only by the patient's own systematized delusions. The logical leaps made by the intelligent paranoic patient are, after all, no more remarkable than those one hears in everyday political arguments, and the patient's obvious faith and sincerity in what he says give him strong allies in his quest for personal justice or vindication. If the archaic and unstandardized test of knowing right from wrong is given to the person with well-systematized delusions, he may make a better impression in open court than the normal citizen who recognizes its ambiguities.

The vast majority of pathological delusions, however, are not well systematized. In the case of transient delusional reactions occurring at infrequent intervals, this is not difficult to understand. Frequent repetition without too great spacing is essential to the acquisition of most new behavior organization, and delusional organization is no exception. Moreover, the single or the rare delusional reaction occurs under unique or exceptional circumstances, such as in unusual emotional disturbance or intoxication, when a person is not in his customary relationship with his social environment. Thus the emotionally disturbed or intoxicated individual, like the person who is asleep and dreaming, gives his delusional reaction under conditions that are least favorable to biosocial systematization. The reaction tends to remain disconnected and in terms of the biosocial person meaningless or unaccountable to anyone but a behavior pathologist.

Patients who acquire progressive and chronic delusions do not, of course, lack practice. Nevertheless, they rarely succeed in developing a well-systematized result because they carry on their practice in private fantasy where operations are not under the same pressure to appear consistent and plausible to others as are operations carried on in public. As we shall see in paranoid disorders, the techniques of solitary imagining, unless their products are checked repeatedly with the results of shared behavior, are almost sure to follow lines established by the lone thinker's habitual private fantasy. Personal need, wish, fear, anxiety, frustration and conflict can, under these circumstances, produce misinterpretations which reflect the ambiguities and ambivalences of the patient's unshared private thought.

In extreme cases, unchecked and unvalidated fantasy grows irresistible and plays a dominant and continuous part in the patient's life. Behavior in the field of social operations then becomes subordinated to the fantasy life and often merely a part of it. Under these conditions, even though the delusions may become more numerous and elaborate, they do not lead toward coherent systematization. They incline rather to grow dreamlike in character, vague, fragmentary and disjointed, until eventually they may be unintelligible to the most patient listener and inexplicable even to the patient himself. The most remarkable delusional developments of this sort are encountered in the odd, fantastic and grotesque delusions of schizophrenia.

Between these two extremes — the plausible, systematized paranoic delusions and the fantastic disorganized delusions of schizophrenia — belong those of mania and the depressions. In these disorders the delusional reactions are nearly always in keeping with the prevailing mood, being optimistic and expansive in mania, self-depreciatory, fearful and pessimistic in depressions. Manic and depressed patients as a rule are persons who have not in their pre-morbid lives relied as much upon the techniques of solitary brooding and puzzling as have most schizophrenics, and therefore while they are ill they characteristically maintain better contact with their social environment. Consequently their delusional developments show relatively little tendency toward bizarre elaborations unless anxiety, agitation or elation grows so extreme as to disorganize behavior. This is undoubtedly one explanation of the much better prognosis in these disorders than in schizophrenia, regardless of the form of therapy.

There are, as one might expect, many exceptions to these general rules. For example, adolescents and socially immature adults who become manic or depressed may develop queer delusions, which at the time seem to presage disorganization, but which clear up completely when the elation or depression clears. The delusional organization in cerebral incompetence is to a large degree dependent upon the premorbid biosocial organization of the patient, as we shall see in Chapter 17.

VARIETIES OF DELUSIONAL REACTION

There are as many possible varieties of delusional reaction as there are kinds of belief. We shall restrict ourselves in what follows to those varieties which are of the greatest significance for behavior pathology — *delusions of persecution, of influence, of grandeur, of self-depreciation, of body change* and *of environmental change.* The particular character of a delusional reaction is determined by many factors, among which we may mention the character of the precipitating situation, a person's habitual modes of response to increased stress and strain, and his dominant habitual attitudes and fantasy themes.

We see the influence of the precipitating situation the moment we compare typical delusional reactions in acute anxiety, frustrating humiliation and irretrievable loss. For in the first fearful delusions predominate, in the second we are more apt to find vengeful or compensatory delusions, while in the third the patient is likely to become self-depreciatory, or to generalize from destruction of his loved object to destruction of the world. A person's individual preferred adjustive techniques may also be reflected in the delusion he develops, some patients showing predominantly aggression and disowning projection, for example, and others reacting with submission and identification. Individual differences in habitual premorbid attitudes and favorite fantasies contribute to differences both in the prevailing background and in the thematic form of delusional reactions. Thus even in recurrent bromide intoxication certain persons show persecutory trends each time, while others become suspicious, aggressive, expansive or self-depreciatory.

Delusions of persecution

In delusions of persecution the patient believes that he is being deliberately interfered with, discriminated against or threatened, when actually he is not. The most prevalent persecutory themes one hears are obviously products of our everyday culture, taken over from newspaper accounts, gossip and rumor, stories, movies, radio, and regional folklore. This in part explains the striking similarity one finds in the structure of delusions from person to person. Patients complain, for example, that they are being unfairly treated, plotted against, pursued or persecuted by organizations of political, racial and religious haters, by gangsters, dope rings or spy rings, by the police and the FBI, by white-slave and other sex racketeers, or by a malicious clique of fellow-workers, competitors, employers or neighbors. The inferred hostile agency may include whole communities — local, national or even international in scope — or it may be restricted to one neighbor and his family, to a business associate, a friend, one's mate or one's child.

In telling his story, the patient may speak of being duped, framed or exposed, of plots and schemes, of traps ready to be sprung upon him, or of pursuers tracking him down and closing in for the kill. His reaction-sensitivity in such directions leads to persistent *self-reference*.[4] At work, at home, in restaurants, on the street or on the bus he overhears remarks, laughter or threats that seem aimed at him; even the newspapers, magazines, radio, movies and sermons seem full of personal references to him. His special reaction-sensitivity makes him read personal significance into the way objects are left around or arranged by others. A magazine lying open at a certain page means to the patient that someone wants him to look at an article or advertisement; and of course when he does so, he tends to read into what he sees the meanings to which he has been sensitized. A book replaced upside down on his desk means to the patient that someone is testing his alertness, implying that he is illiterate or signifying contempt for his belongings. Some patients find in every look, smile or gesture a reference that fits their delusions. Clothes piled in a certain way, the character of vehicles parked in the block, the theme of window displays, shop signs and billboards, the arrangement of milk-bottles left at the door — all of these appear to the reaction-sensitive patient as if intended as signals to him, or as signals to others concerning him.

To the person with progressive persecutory delusions even the most casual question asked by an acquaintance may seem to have some special significance, although the patient is often unable to

[4] R. Sears, "Experimental studies of projection. II. Ideas of reference," *Jour. Soc. Psychol.*, 1937, vol. 8, pp. 389-400.

discover its apparent meaning. He finds that his personal effects seem to have been searched, or that they have apparently been deliberately disarranged to exasperate him and make him seem disorderly and incompetent. People seem to be spying on the patient and spreading rumors about him. He notices strangers lounging about the neighborhood, or standing on street corners, evidently planted there to watch his movements and signal to unseen confederates; if they disappear, it must be to report on what they have seen.

If the patient fears some specific fate, it also will usually be one that he derives from the background of what he hears, sees and reads about. Some patients expect to be kidnapped, beaten, exposed, tortured, poisoned, enslaved, mutilated, imprisoned or lynched. Most victims of persecutory delusions are frightened and openly resent their predicament; a minority, usually among depressed persons, feel they deserve severe punishment but try to escape it, while a few welcome it or even seek and ask for it.

Often the patient with delusions of persecution is vague and uncertain as to who or what is persecuting him and why he should be singled out for special attention. He is sure only that he is in danger, that something is wrong, that things are happening which he cannot seem to grasp and which he may frankly say he cannot understand. Like any other perplexed or anxious person, the deluded patient needs an explanation and goes after one — usually by watching for significant incidents and by pondering a great deal over his mystifying situation. It is under these circumstances that the important phenomenon of *sudden clarification* occurs, and the patient says with conviction, "I suddenly realized what it was all about," or "Suddenly it all became clear to me."

Sudden clarification in delusional thinking is frequently treated as though it were a peculiar, abnormal process, foreign to ordinary thinking. As a matter of fact it is not anything of the kind. The expectant, needful patient developing his delusions hits upon his explanation by the same general method as that by which the expectant, needful scientist hits upon his hypothesis — and one may be just as mistaken as the other. Moreover, the sudden insight is not confined to any one form of delusion, nor to any one behavior disorder. What the patient reports as sudden clarification seems to belong to the group of terminal reactions which in normal behavior we call *closure*. In delusion the closure consists of the patient's sudden discovery of a formulation which justifies all of his suspicions and premonitions by uniting them all under one plausible hypothesis. The hypothesis is mistaken for fact either because of the patient's defective social techniques, which we shall discuss under paranoid disorders and schizophrenia, because of the emotional distortion in his disorder, as we shall see in depressions and mania, or because of the physiological inadequacy of the patient's brain, as in cases of cerebral incompetence.

Of course, not every delusion of persecution develops sudden clarification or progresses to any kind of a dramatic climax. In depressions and schizophrenia, for example, one often finds vague delusions of persecution which seem to consist of little more than discrete fragments of suspicion or resentment. In chronic schizophrenia some of these are the remnants of reactions that were once related in an inclusive but poorly systematized delusional organization. But a great many schizophrenic patients never succeed in developing anything approaching a coherent plot or plan out of their misinterpretations. Their vague delusions from the very start sound like the chaotic fears and suspicions in normal dreaming.

We shall consider the origin and development of persecutory delusions in more detail when we discuss paranoid disorders, schizophrenia and depressions, in each of which the delusion may play a different part. Here it will suffice to say that many delusions of persecution, regardless of the specific behavior disorder setting, seem to arise as denials or justifications, or as elaborations of imagined punishment in relation to a person's unsanctioned trends, to forbidden things fantasied, feared or done. We see persecutory delusions in the following case developing in response to guilt and to fear of retaliation, but at the same time perpetuating the forbidden relationship.

A socially ambitious but unattractive young woman, married to a man who failed to come up to her expectations, became infatuated with her dentist who was both distinguished looking and financially successful. In an unguarded moment she revealed her infatuation to her husband who became greatly incensed, upbraided her for her disloyalty and then wept. The patient herself expressed guilt and deep remorse, and promised never to see the dentist again. Two weeks later, to her husband's astonishment, she reported that she had seen a man who looked exactly like the dentist talking with the janitor and evidently arranging something with him. The husband thought the patient might be mistaken, but he was sufficiently insecure and jealous to be unable to shake off the suspicions which her report aroused. When, however, on a trip they took together she began pointing out strangers at a distance as the same dentist, and when she became fearful of sexual assault each time she was left alone, the husband realized that she was ill and sought medical aid. The patient was unwilling to submit to prolonged or drastic therapy, and as the husband was accustomed to her domination and felt guilty over his part in precipitating the illness, he confined her treatment to his own protection and reassurance. Two years later, although the couple had moved to another city, the patient was still convinced that the dentist kept appearing in the neighborhood and that he planned ultimately to disgrace her.

Delusions of persecution are the commonest of all varieties. Transient persecutory delusions appear in pronounced excitements of all kinds, in acute anxiety and panic, and in anxious depressions. They are of especially frequent occurrence in deliria and are therefore a problem of grave concern to all who care for the sick, for surgeons as well as internists, for ophthalmologists, obstetricians, pediatricians and neurologists. Indeed, the post-operative, posttraumatic, febrile, toxic or infectious disease patient whose delirium gives rise to delusions of persecution, no matter how transient and absurd these may be, is one of the most serious risks on a general hospital ward. For at any unguarded moment, while the nurses are busy with a new emergency, for example, the patient may attempt to escape his imaginary pursuers even if this means jumping out of the window or down a stair-well. And one must not lose sight of the fact that delusions do not always disappear after general recovery, and that, however absurd and inappropriate they may seem, they come out of the patient's own behavior repertory, and sometimes represent the distorted overt expression of a chronic covert fear. Therefore the delusion of persecution occurring under these conditions may open up opportunities for biosocial therapy, when the crisis is past, that goes beyond the specific illness and into the patient's personal life.

Delusions of influence

In delusions of influence the patient usually complains that he is affected at a distance, controlled, interfered with or owned by some person, group, force or spirit. Often he is unable to designate the agent responsible; it remains for him something vague, mystical and undiscovered. Delusions of influence are obviously related to the age-old belief in demon-possession. They are closely allied to delusions of persecution and might, indeed, have been included with them in the preceding section, except for the fact that they are sometimes conceived by the patient as something beneficial and even exalting. In schizophrenia it is often the case that the patient believes himself destined to perform some mission in accordance with the direction given by a supposed influence, but cannot find out what it is that he is expected to do. Sudden clarification is not uncommon in delusions of influence and may lead to immediate action, either against the influence or in accordance with what seems to be required of the patient.

Delusions of influence most commonly arise in relation to delusions of persecution. The patient, already convinced that something harmful is being done to him, begins to suspect that he is somehow being controlled and manipulated — perhaps by means of a powerful instrument, the so-called influence machine which patients sometimes draw on paper. Hypnotism, electricity, magnetism, radio, x-rays, atomic energy and cosmic rays are frequently invoked as the probable means by which the patient's body or mind is being kept under the control of another person's will. In some cases there may be a basis for such delusions in an ordinary local paresthesia which is misinterpreted by the anxious confused patient as an electric current, or as radiant energy, being sent through his body. Sometimes the delusion seems to involve incompletely repressed erotic arousal, toward which the patient has ambivalent attitudes, as in the following case.

A young unmarried woman, in an acute schizophrenic episode whose dominant trends were all sexual in character, for several weeks accused one of the staff physicians of controlling her mind electrically by means of a keyboard upstairs. She complained that every now and then she could "feel electrical currents" flow through her body, and sometimes she burst from her room and ran screaming down the corridor to escape their influence. Often the electricity seemed to her to come out of the bedsprings when she was trying to sleep. The patient insisted that a certain staff physician was experimenting on her sexually, and whenever she saw him she demanded that he stop his "electrical experiments." On two occasions during rounds she furiously attacked him.

Some of the specific sources for the unwarranted inferences of this delusion were known. The patient had previously seen someone (actually a male patient) manipulating the keyboard belonging to the clinic pipe-organ in a dimly lit control room upstairs. As the organ was not playing at the time, the patient expressed disbelief when told that the man was practicing. She was by no means the only insecure patient who had focused suspicion upon the organ keyboard. As for the accused physician, he had once tested the patient in front of the interns for the presence of abnormal postural reflexes, turning her head from side to side manually and talking of forced automatic movements. It is probable that inadequately repressed erotic interests also contributed to her selection of him as the sexual experimenter. This patient, once her acute episode had subsided, was able under planned aggressive therapy and brief motivational analysis to make a complete recovery.

It is not uncommon for patients to suspect and then become convinced that they are being influenced by drugs administered to them in food or drink, by injection or inunction, or in the air they breathe. The agents most frequently cited are gases, anesthetics, opiates, aphrodisiacs, anaphrodisiacs and slow poisons. As a rule the patient, who is usually schizophrenic, paranoid, depressed or delirious, conceives of the supposed drug effects as detrimental. He believes, for example, that through drug action he is being made ready to come under the influence of a person, gang or force so that his will and his power to resist may be destroyed, that he is being made to think more slowly and less clearly, or made sexually excited or impotent, for the same general purpose, or that drugs are changing him into a different and more compliant being.

There is a particularly interesting group of delusions of influence concerning thinking and communication which are most often encountered among schizophrenic patients, although by no means absent from other behavior disorders. Many of these delusions show clearly the effects of incomplete repression and disowning projection. The patient complains that his thinking is being influenced by some outside agency, which he usually cannot identify, that his mind is being controlled, his thoughts forced into some undesired, violent or disgraceful pattern, or put under pressure and made automatic. He may say that something is interfering with his thoughts, suddenly interrupting them (*blocking*) or taking them away entirely (*thought-deprivation*). Sometimes a patient will complain that some influence is putting thoughts into his brain or words directly into his mouth, that his tongue is being moved by an outside agency and made to say words that do not come from him. Patients state and believe that they are somehow made to assume certain postures and perform acts which they can neither prevent nor control, nor even predict, and for which they cannot in any way be held accountable. Their attitude toward these influences is usually one of protest and resentment. Influenced, forced or "manufactured" thoughts, words and acts are found usually in schizophrenia, but one sees them also in paranoid disorders, mania, depressions and in behavior disorders arising in a setting of cerebral incompetence.

Delusions of grandeur

The thematic material in delusions of grandeur, like that in delusions of persecution, is taken from one's surrounding culture, including its current folklore and its literature. The delusions vary all the way from mere exaggerations of ordinary self-assertive pride, optimism, boastfulness and self-esteem to the most extravagant and impossible claims. Patients state and believe that they are millionaires, magnates, nobles, kings, queens, dictators or great generals; they tell of owning valuable lands and properties, of having extraordinary special abilities and privileges, and of possessing important secret political or scientific knowledge.

The *Mignon delusion,* found most commonly among adolescent and young adult schizophrenic patients, is of special importance to behavior pathology because of its obvious relationship to the difficulties in parent identification exhibited by normal children, which we discussed in Chapter 2. The patient asserts that the persons claiming to be his parents are frauds or dupes, and that he is actually the child of a noble, wealthy or powerful family. If he elaborates upon this basic theme he is likely to say that he was kidnapped as an infant by gypsies, gangsters or a vengeful domestic, or that his real parents lost him. One of our patients, born of humble parents out of wedlock, maintained a pleasant but haughty and restrained pose. He sat, stood and walked very erect, his right hand usually held in the breast of his jacket. As he believed himself to be the son of an English lord, he spoke always with an imitation English accent, used stereotyped English phrases in place of conversation (*Quite all right! Cheerio! Oh, I say! Oh, really?*), and gave his home town an elegant name in place of its ugly official one.

Among delusions of grandeur those based on Messianic claims are most familiar to the average layman. Many patients believe that they have a great mission to perform, that they are creators or destroyers of life, saviors of the world and mankind — religious, moral, political or military leaders chosen to bring man into a new era. Some call themselves God, Christ, the Virgin Mary or another sainted character, Joan of Arc, the Pope or Mahatma Gandhi. Amatory themes are also prominent among delusions of grandeur. Patients boast of their irresistible sexual attractiveness, of great conquests, of the important persons in love with them, of their own potency or fruitfulness, and of the extraordinary number or quality of their offspring. The observed fact that delusions of grandeur frequently include claims of sexual power with those of religious greatness may be attributed to the reactions of exaltation and of creation or dedication which are common to both.

Delusions of grandeur are most frequently encountered in mania, schizophrenia and paranoid disorders. Indeed, delusions of grandeur are as characteristic of manic excitements as delusions of self-depreciation, poverty and persecution are of depressive illnesses. In schizophrenia the delusions are typically bizarre, poorly systematized and supported by hallucinations, while in mania and paranoid disorders they are relatively well systematized. Most of us have witnessed the transient exuberant delusions of alcoholic intoxication which makes many individuals temporarily boastful, aggressive and erotic.

Nearly all delusions of grandeur, unfortunately, tend to stimulate the inexpert person who witnesses them to become facetious and jocund also. Or, if an onlooker is himself inclined to be proud and proper, the patient's behavior is likely to offend him and to arouse attitudes of contempt and dislike that no other serious illness would arouse. Delusions of grandeur remind the average person at once of some acquaintance or public character whose conduct they seem to caricature. Patients make absurd statements, behave in a vulgar or clownish fashion, take on pompous, erotic or sanctimonious airs, and indulge in such uninhibited boasting and self-assertion that they seem to the untrained observer or custodian to forfeit all right to consideration and respect. Indeed, delusions of grandeur perhaps more than anything else have alienated the common man's sympathy for the whole field of behavior pathology and kept this vast area of human suffering in disrepute. It is only when

one is made to understand what may be happening to the personal
life of the deluded patient, and to the lives of those close to him,
that the delusion of grandeur is recognized for what it is — the
symptom of a serious illness — and for what it may become — a
bleak human tragedy for everyone concerned.

Delusions of self-depreciation

Under delusions of self-depreciation we include the conviction
that one is hopelessly inadequate, unworthy, guilty, sinful or a
despicable sham. These delusions differ from delusions of persecution in this important respect, that the patient anticipates punishment on the basis, not of others' malignity, but of his own supposed
shortcomings which he may or may not regard as fact. If he regards these shortcomings as fact, he usually shows little or no open
resentment toward others, does not attempt to escape the retribution he fears, and frequently invites retaliation or inflicts it upon
himself. If the patient attributes his self-accusations to the mistaken judgment of others (*disowning projection*), his behavior may
vary from that of a hurt and misunderstood person to that of an
unresisting stoic awaiting martyrdom. But whatever the patient's
attitude toward the judgment of others, his faith in the verity of
impending harm is unshakable.

Some patients, whether claiming or disclaiming fault, are never
clear as to just what punishment they anticipate or from what quarter they believe it will come. Others are quite definite as to what
they expect and from whom it will come. For example, a depressed
married man in his thirties spent most of his leisure time during
six months in watching the ward door. No explanation of his behavior was obtained until he had almost recovered, when he stated
that he had been hourly expecting a mob of his townspeople to
break in and lynch him for failing in certain public duties. It was
a fact that he had neglected to provide funds for a town celebration the day before he had quit work because of his illness; the
oversight had, however, been corrected by someone else. His guilt
over this shortcoming became the focus of his whole apprehension
even though it had nothing to do with precipitating his depression.

In extreme cases patients ask to be beaten, starved, degraded,
imprisoned, pilloried, mutilated or killed. Some do so because of
an intolerable torturing sense of guilt, some because they believe
that otherwise an innocent person will be made to suffer for their

transgressions, and some because they cannot endure the tension of waiting for the punishment they are sure will some day come to them. For example, a depressed unmarried woman in her late twenties begged her physician every evening not to delay her fate any longer. She expected to be thrown naked into the street at night to be beaten by a crowd. Her illness had begun with the development of excessive guilt over an unconventional act of minor importance for which she had actually received vigorous but unjustified censure. After her recovery she could not account for her expectation of specific punishment; it seems to have been a dramatic reification of her own self-attitudes.

Delusions of self-depreciation, we have said, are as characteristic of depression as delusions of grandeur are of mania. We shall return to a discussion of self-depreciatory convictions and their origin when we come to the depressive disorders. However, the belief that one is miserably inadequate, unworthy, guilty, sinful or an unpardonable hypocrite may be found in any of the behavior disorders — just as the corresponding suspicion that one has these qualities is common in normal behavior. In anxiety disorders, for example, an unjustified conviction of specific guilt sometimes reaches delusional proportions. Thus, a married woman of thirty-four years, suffering from a typical chronic anxiety reaction punctuated by acute episodes, developed the belief during therapy that the acute attacks were punishment for a murder of which she was innocent. The origin of this delusion was two-pronged: a friend had been questioned by the police in connection with her husband's sudden death, and the patient had fantasied the death of her own husband and her children not long afterwards.

We have already discussed the important part played by the conviction of guilt, sin and uncleanliness in the development and perpetuation of compulsive disorders. In schizophrenia self-depreciatory delusions are by no means unusual and, because of the patient's biosocial disorganization, the delusions may give rise to unpredictable action. A schizophrenic young woman, for example, known to have been preoccupied for months with the sinfulness of her thoughts, one night wrapped paper around her head and face, set it afire and burned herself so severely that she died. A schizophrenic young man, having concluded on the basis of protracted solitary brooding that he was a sinful hypocrite, decided to show himself to the world as he really was. This decision he carried out literally by appearing naked in public.

Delusions of body change

The conviction — based upon misinterpretations, unwarranted inferences or unjustified conclusions — that one's body has in some important respect undergone a change, is a common and potentially most serious delusion. It is not surprising that delusions of body change frequently develop out of hypochondriacal and fatigue complaints which, after all, are themselves delusional in character. Hypochondriacal disorders, as we have seen, are based upon a conviction that one's organs or systems are incompetent, deteriorating or diseased, when actually they are functioning reasonably well. In fatigue syndromes the patient is convinced, similarly, that his body is physiologically delicate or inferior, a conviction which is based upon misinterpretations of the patient's own self-reactions of unreadiness and aversion in relation to new or continued activity.

If, in either of these behavior disorders, a patient believes that he is growing progressively worse, he almost inevitably develops delusions of body change. The viscera that he has focused upon in body overconcern may seem to him to be going into a final deteriorative phase. Thus, we find a depressed person, whose gastrointestinal system had been the target of his hypochondria, insisting that his bowels have actually petrified; he could feel them, he said, and they had turned to stone. A schizophrenic young man concluded early in his illness that his brain must be diseased, since he could no longer think clearly; later on he became convinced that it was rotting away and that he was blowing it out through his nose. Some patients, with a start in hypochondria or fatigue, develop delusions of body change which are compensatory in character. These may then lead to a new delusional behavior organization based upon the substitute conviction that one is powerful, beautiful, or changed in some other direction consonant with the derived need.

Delusions of body change are likely to have grave consequences if the patient grows preoccupied with his apparently progressive symptoms or with his compensatory developments. For if, by so doing, he further insulates himself from the social reactions of other people, and elaborates upon his supposed body changes in private fantasy, the outcome may well be a schizophrenic disorganization, a chronic paranoid disorder or a serious depressive illness. Thus we have in body overconcern and preoccupation with fatigue symptoms the possible beginnings of another chain reaction which goes from need or anxiety to conviction, from conviction to delusional elaboration, and from this finally to behavior that is incompatible with social demands and necessitates removal of the patient to a restricted, protective environment for treatment.

Of course this progression, from hypochondriacal overconcern or fatigue symptom to expanding delusions of body change, is only one of several routes by which the same end-result may be reached. We must not forget that body change is a normal occurrence in everyone's life and, particularly in relation to growth and maturing, involution, accident and disease, that body change normally leads to self-reactions of considerable personal significance. Persons who for any reason have been made reaction-sensitive concerning body appearance and performance, in relation to their social status, integrity or personal worth, are apt to respond to frustration, anxiety or rejection by pondering over and examining their anatomical and physiological characteristics. Under these circumstances they overreact to normal and expected variations, tend to make perfectionistic demands upon themselves, to exaggerate in their self-reactions what they see and imagine regarding their looks, body conformation and general bearing.

The face, because of the prevalent mirror habits in our society, comes in for a great deal of self-examination on the part of patients. Most of them accept as fact the mischievous untruths that goodness makes the countenance clear and beautiful, that wickedness puts lines and shadows in the face, and that the eyes are windows of the soul. So the depressed person, weighed down by hopelessness and conflict, looks at his sad unrested face and sees worthlessness, ugliness and sin where there is only illness and pain. The adolescent, struggling alone with guilty fantasies, eroticism or social failure, looks fearfully in the mirror for the visible signs of his depravity or inferiority. To look fearfully is often to see what one fears even though no one else can see it, and to stare at one's face is to provide a tense, staring model for further misinterpretation. Likewise, to look in the mirror in a mood of exaltation or ecstasy may lead the manic or schizophrenic patient to decide that his face looks powerful, beautiful, unearthly or transfigured. Thus, one patient insisted that his eyes had grown so powerful that he could sterilize things by looking at them, shrivel plants or make the wax on the hospital floor melt and run.

Delusions of change in the size and general appearance of the body, limbs and head may be found in many of the behavior disorders, but particularly in deliria, schizophrenia and depressions. In the *enormity delusion*, for example, which occurs most often in deliria, the patient complains that his body has become enormous. One of our patients became agitated every evening because he was convinced that he could not fit into his bed, his room or even the whole ward; he would burst the walls, he said. In the daytime the complaint subsided.

The hands, being socially important instruments and easily accessible to self-reactions, are common foci of delusion. Patients complain that their hands have grown strange-looking, swollen, claw-like or misshapen. The head and its contents come in for delusional convictions that reflect patients' attitudes. Thus, a freshman medical student, suffering a schizophrenic disorganization, insisted that when he pressed on his temples his brain whirled around; he said that he could even feel and hear the membranes tear. A well-educated business executive in his forties complained that his head had cracked wide open during an anxiety attack and had snapped shut again. He showed no curiosity about the alleged incident, could offer no explanation of it, but believed it completely even after he had made a complete recovery from his anxiety disorder and returned to work.

Sexual maladaptation is a common source of delusions of body change which center about sex functions and the acquisition or loss of primary and secondary sex characteristics.[5] Drugs, radiant energy, magic and hypnotism are frequently accused as the indirect agents of change by the patient, and thus we see delusions of influence in effect supporting delusions of body change. Sometimes direct sexual manipulation or surgery during sleep or under general anesthesia is alleged to have been the source of sexual alteration. Among women the chief complaints are of sexual arousal, defloration, pregnancy — not infrequently by an animal — abortion and masculation (development of male characteristics). Men tend to focus upon increased emissions, decreased potency and femination. Two brief examples will illustrate this point.

A rather gentle, soft-spoken young man of slight stature came to the clinic with the complaint that his voice was growing progres-

[5] G. Bychowski, "Disorders in the body-image in the clinical pictures of psychoses," *Jour. Nerv. Ment. Dis.*, 1943, vol. 97, pp. 310-335.

sively higher and weaker, his skin and hair softer and more delicate-looking, his musculature weak, his genitals shrunken and his body contour more and more womanlike. Physical examination, how-ever, revealed normal male physique throughout. The patient had been brought up by a domineering overprotective mother and had all his life been teased by boys and girls because of his gentle, sub-missive behavior. A young adolescent girl with an unattractive face, large hands and feet and a poor figure, came to the conclusion under the influence of advertisements that her unpopularity came from her skin blemishes and from body odor.[6] She developed severe guilt reactions over autoerotism, which had increased with increasing loneliness and neglect, and she began secondarily blam-ing the erotism for her acne and the body odor. On the basis of some folklore she believed as to the effects of autoerotism on geni-talia, and on the basis of her failing to attract men, she came to the conclusion that she was developing male genitals and a man's body. Both of these patients showed distress and resentment over their supposed metamorphoses, and neither recovered.

The viscera are often the target of delusions of body change. The gastrointestinal system is most commonly accused since, as we pointed out in the hypochondriacal disorders, it is relatively easy of access, much discussed, important in social ritual and not difficult to affect through manipulation of the diet and by direct interfer-ence. The middle-aged or elderly depressed person, for example, is apt to complain that his stomach has shriveled up to almost nothing or turned to stone, that his bowels are "locked" or lying motionless, or that he actually has no stomach or intestines at all (nihilism). These complaints, which may be related initially to retarded motility, persist long after adequate emptying has been established, and they disappear as the depression clears. The schiz-ophrenic patient complains that his stomach and intestines have gone, but his interpretations usually include bizarre elaboration;[7] the viscera have rotted away or been eaten up by a snake. More-over, the schizophrenic patient with such a complaint, unlike the depressed person, may eat well and with good appetite. Complaints of changes in the liver, kidneys, bladder, heart and lungs are not infrequent among delusions of body change. In depressions the

[6] This is not an uncommon conclusion among maladjusted adolescents. See for example, H. Stolz and L. Stolz, "Adolescent problems related to somatic variations," *Yearbook Nat. Soc. Studies Educ.*, 1944, vol. 43, pp. 80-99.

[7] R. Hemphill, "Some considerations of the physical factor in delusional states," *Jour. Ment. Science*, 1939, vol. 85, pp. 119-125.

delusions tend to be of fatal disease or nihilistic; in schizophrenia they are usually bizarre and inconsistent with the rest of behavior.

Delusions of unreality, environmental change and nihilism

This important but imperfectly understood group includes complaints to the effect that objects, people and happenings are unnatural or unreal, or that everything is disintegrating or has disappeared. The conviction that things are unnatural or unreal (*delusion of unreality*) is particularly characteristic of severe anxiety disorders, of agitated depressions, schizophrenia and deliria, but it is often present also in other behavior disorders. The linguistic difficulty in fixing and formulating in words so queer and unfamiliar a reaction is attested by the variety of statements that patients make in delusions of unreality. It is difficult for the patient, who may be made more anxious and confused by the change, to communicate the nature of his difficulty to the clinician who may never have reacted similarly himself or who may have formulated unreality differently to himself. For this reason the acute distress that delusions of unreality occasion is frequently not realized by the clinician, and their potentialities for secondarily disorganizing the patient's behavior and isolating him from his community are often overlooked. The few illustrations that follow can give little more than a hint of the rich variety of symptoms.

In anxiety disorders, as we have seen, the complaint is common that things and people seem changed, different, far away or unreal, and that the patient seems unreal to himself. This complaint usually follows an acute anxiety attack, but it may persist indefinitely afterwards, the patient saying that "things have never seemed the same since." Similar complaints are often heard from depressed patients.

A fifty-one-year-old married woman, in an agitated depression, insisted that the clinic ward was not real, the patients were not actually patients, that the nurses were different every day but made up to look the same. Everything outside, she said, had changed too. "It will all be chaos when I get out of here. They've changed all the automobiles in the street, all the houses and buildings." She said the clocks were all going backwards and the newspapers were all changed somehow. Another patient, a fifty-two-year-old woman in a retarded depression, complained that the birds singing in the trees were artificial birds and their songs unrealistic imitations.

A thirty-three-year-old married woman, diagnosed "schizophrenic with depressive features," complained persistently for a year that everything was unreal. Patients, nurses and doctors were not really what they seemed or not persons at all. Letters sent her were faked or things were written into them, which she would identify and read aloud to the nurse; they looked queer and the postmarks were crooked or upside down. Outside, the houses seemed queer, "like picture houses," and she often insisted that she was walking in the wrong direction because everything was strange and different. When she went to church the prayer book was all changed, the sermon and the music were different, and it couldn't really be a church in a city, anyway, because roosters were crowing outside [they were]. The trees outside the clinic were not real and they were changed overnight to test her. The flowers were artificial and painted in unreal colors; she plucked and chewed a tulip, but it was not a real tulip to her. An automobile in the street was not real, "You know perfectly well a car couldn't twist and turn like that one." The sun was a fake and the sunsets were "made up." She said that she must be "terribly ill" if people felt they had to use artificial things like that to make her well. The patient recovered, but thirteen years later had a severe recurrence.

Another schizophrenic woman, twenty-three years old and single, complained of "that feeling of unreal, as if everything is nothing and yet we're living. . . . Nothing is real. I'm talking and I'm nothing." At times it was she that seemed unreal, at others the world was unreal and she was the only real thing in it. A thirty-six-year-old married woman, in a restless, confused, post-operative disorder of uncertain diagnosis, had similar complaints for several months. She refused to window-shop because everything was changed and "crazy" in the windows. She was unable to weave, sew, knit or embroider because the tools, the materials and the occupational therapists seemed strange and unreal to her. She could find "no sense" to the books, magazines and newspapers around her, so she concluded that they also were "changed" and "not normal."

In some of these illustrations complaints have been included that things are disintegrating or becoming nothing (*nihilistic delusions*), which we also encountered in delusions of body change as the conviction that organs had rotted away or simply disappeared. Delusions of disintegration and nihilism are most frequently found in schizophrenia and in depressions of middle and late life. Depressed patients, for example, become convinced that they have no food, no clothing, no shelter and no money, that their dear ones are starving or freezing to death and the world is disappearing, or that all their friends and relatives have ceased to exist and they are left alone.

> An elderly woman went about the house at the height of her agitated depression — from which she later recovered — heaping blankets and woolens on her sleeping relatives because the world was coming to an end and they would all perish that night of the cold. In the daytime she would point to the empty parked automobiles in the street and say their presence proved that everyone was disappearing from the world; she was certain that during the night they were all removed to make room for the next day's crop of disaster. A depressed elderly married man, of considerable wealth, declared over a period of more than a year that he was penniless and would starve to death. The certified statements that his financial agents prepared were angrily tossed aside as obvious frauds, and visits from his legal advisers apparently contributed nothing in the way of reassurance.

It has been evident in what we have been saying that delusional behavior is frequently complicated by hallucination. Indeed, as we shall see particularly in the schizophrenic disorders, hallucinatory responses commonly arise in a setting of delusional attitudes and often contribute significantly to the further development and persistence of delusions. Before proceeding, therefore, with our presentation of the behavior disorders, we shall discuss some of the more common varieties of hallucinatory behavior.

HALLUCINATION IN BEHAVIOR DISORDERS

We may define *hallucination* in behavior disorders as *a response whose stimulus is within a person's fantasy behavior, but is mistakenly attributed by the responding individual to sources outside of it*. Hallucination so defined is not essentially different from responses that occur under special circumstances in normal behavior. A great many individuals can be found who report hearing and seeing things, under conditions of intense excitement, expectation or ecstasy, which they would ordinarily recognize as their own fantasy. The tense, expectant members of a religious cult, for example, can be led to hallucinate with comparative ease; and if their anticipant attitudes have been made uniform by careful preparation, there may be a considerable degree of uniformity in their testimony. The hallucinations they report, however, will usually fit into the convictions of their own cult and not into those of a despised or rival cult. In other words, even normal hallucinatory responses depend upon antecedent and supporting delusional attitudes for their occurrence, and in general correspond to the bio-social organization of those attitudes.

Hallucinatory responses are facilitated by great anxiety and need. Fearful persons and threatened communities are usually reaction-sensitive to signs of both calamity and reassurance, since they dread the one and want the other.[8] If the suspense is prolonged and grows intolerable, closure may ultimately be achieved through hallucination, the individual or the members of a frightened group hearing and seeing things that, at least for the moment, seem to bring them certainty. Shipwrecked persons on a raft may see a barracuda fin where there is none, hear a comforting voice at night or sight rescue ships approaching in the daytime. In some instances several shipwrecked individuals have agreed in hallucinating a rescue ship when the horizon seemed clear to their other companions.[9]

The commonest hallucination reported by normal persons is that of a dead relative or friend, appearing usually but not always at night. The dead individual is often described as looking natural and lifelike, and he seems to the hallucinating person to be talking to him. The talk may be commonplace, enigmatical, reproachful or comforting. The person's general reaction to his hallucination will vary in accordance with his habitual attitudes toward death, the occult, and the deceased. Undoubtedly most of these incidents occur during half-sleep, but the same can be said of many hallucinations reported in the behavior disorders. Indeed, as we might expect, the differences between the normal hallucinations which we have been discussing and the pathological hallucinations, to which we shall next turn, are largely differences in the extent of their influence upon biosocial behavior and their significance as part of delusional development.

[8] H. Good, "Fifteen days adrift on a raft: a clinical evaluation of five survivors," *Naval Med. Bull.*, 1943, vol. 41, pp. 367-373.

[9] E. Anderson, "Abnormal mental states in survivors, with special reference to collective hallucinations," *Jour. Res. Naval Med. Serv.*, 1942, vol. 28, pp. 361-377.

Temporal variations in hallucination

The temporal variations in hallucination have the same implications for the behavior disorders as do the temporal variations in delusion. To become significant factors in behavior disorder, hallucinatory responses must develop against a background of delusional attitudes which can support them and give them continuity. In other words, it is the hallucinatory misreference leading to delusional conviction, or appearing in an already established delusional setting, that is most likely to become an integral part of a pseudo-community,[10] and even its dominant characteristic.

The single transient hallucination is not apt to have personally important consequences unless it represents or induces dramatic closure. The recurrent transient hallucination, however, is potentially a more serious threat. Its mere repetition carries with it the greater likelihood of permanence and usually indicates that delusional behavior which supports the hallucinatory response is also recurring. In general, hallucinatory responses tend to increase in duration and in scope when they are components of a progressive or expanding delusional organization; and they likewise tend to become chronic, or chronically intermittent, if the delusional behavior to which they belong grows chronic. For our purposes, the persistent hallucinations which occur in chronic, progressive or expanding delusional developments are by far the most significant variety; and it is to these that we shall devote the greater part of the discussion which follows.

VARIETIES OF HALLUCINATION

In the behavior disorders, as in ordinary dreaming and daydreaming, the hallucinatory responses that occur may include several varieties at once. An hallucinated individual can be seen, heard and felt; flowers are seen and smelled at the same time that music is heard and a voice speaks to the patient; an hallucinating person, who believes she is being projected into space, reports that she feels herself rock and sway while planets and jewels appear, and a voice tells her what she must and must not do. However, for the sake of simplicity in exposition, we shall draw most of our illustrations from hallucination in which the patient reports that one or another variety is dominant.

[10] For a definition and discussion of the pseudocommunity, see Chapter 14.

Auditory hallucination

The auditory hallucination is the commonest persistent hallucinatory response in the behavior disorders,[11] and its function is usually communicative. The clarity reported for hallucination shows wide variations. Some individuals speak of hearing confused sounds, mutterings, whispers or indistinct mumblings, while others say they hear voices as natural and loud as that of the examiner when he is actually speaking. The sounds, mutterings, whispers, mumblings or clear voices may seem to the patient to be coming from a distance, from a point close by, or even from within his own body.[12] Sometimes the patient reports responses which resemble hallucination, but which neither he nor the behavior pathologist studying him can with certainty distinguish from ordinary thinking and recall.

Hallucinating persons vary greatly in the definiteness with which they localize the stimulus. At one extreme the patient may say that voices seem to come out of the air, out of his thoughts or mind, that the voices are all around him, or that they "just happen" and apparently give no clue whatever of their possible source. At the other extreme the localization is made with assurance. The voice comes from a certain corner of the room, from the roof or the basement, or through a particular window. One patient in the clinic heard his father "and a woman up there" getting in touch with him from an upper floor through the radiator. Another could hear talking coming from the water faucet when it was not running. Overhead lights are frequently accused by the hallucinating individual of transmitting the sound of voices. A patient who was greatly frightened by voices that shouted at him in his room said, when he was out on the ward, "The voices don't yell at me out here; they're in that room back there."

The hallucinated voices may be attributed to specific individuals, with or without the simultaneous occurrence of visual hallucination. Thus, patients report hearing the voice of God or the devil,[13] of a prominent living or historical personage, of a parent, grandparent, sibling, offspring or other relative, of some specific friend or lover,

[11] J. Hill, "Hallucinations in psychosis," *Jour. Nerv. Ment. Dis.*, 1936, vol. 83, pp. 405-421.

[12] E. Semrad, "A study of the auditory apparatus in patients experiencing auditory hallucinations," *Amer. Jour. Psychiat.*, 1938, vol. 95, pp. 53-63.

[13] A. Childers, "A study of some schizoid children," *Ment. Hyg.*, 1931, vol. 15, pp. 106-134.

or of an enemy. Sometimes they complain that the voices are strange and unfamiliar, of persons they have never seen or heard before and do not know. One of our patients wrote her family: "I've been getting encouragement from unknown voices and have been hearing daddy calling me and voices I've heard before. They're the only things that have kept a ray of hope in me alive that I might see my relatives some day. . . . I've heard George Jasper's voice ever since I came." Another heard a famous actor calling to her and saying, "You'd better be true! You'd better be true!" God's voice said to another patient that he was doing wrong: "I hear him all the time. . . . I believe I have a religious complex. He says he is going to kill me dead tonight if I don't get some will power." To another the voice of God said, "Tears, no supper, Christ and blood."

The auditory hallucination may be of voices speaking to the patient, conversing with him or only talking about him. As in some of the examples just given, the hallucinating person often reports the words said to him whether he is able to attribute them to a specific source or not. When the voices speak to the patient, they may threaten, reproach or revile him, give him orders and instructions, warn and advise him, supply him with information or news, and sometimes comfort or entertain him. Not infrequently an hallucinating patient cannot repeat what he hallucinates, but can at most render the general sense of it. In some cases this is undoubtedly an expression of unwillingness to confide, and in others the hallucinated words are very likely repressed. However, there are many patients whose hallucination seems not to be formulated in readily communicable speech, but probably represents unverbalized attitudes which they attempt to share with others in speech equivalents.

The importance of what is said varies from the most dramatic command ("They say to kill myself!"), accusation ("I hear someone in the air telling me I've committed a great sin and there's no forgiveness"), or announcement ("Collins is king!") down to the most trivial small talk. Sometimes the anxiety or anger which gives rise to hallucination, or results from it, precipitates sudden aggression, assaults on persons or things, headlong flight or suicide. Hallucinating patients also commit assaults upon others and themselves without acute anxiety or anger. This is particularly true of schizophrenics who hear voices directing them to mutilate or kill and who, if they survive, can give no reason for the act other than that a voice commanded it.

Some patients hallucinate scraps of talk that seem to mean nothing to the patient at the time. For example, one patient asked in great perplexity, "Why do voices say, 'Two days old'? They keep saying that and it doesn't make sense." In certain instances hallucinated words simply echo the person's own self-reactions, even to the point of using the pronoun *I*, instead of *he* or *she*.

The following verbatim account illustrates several of the characteristics of auditory hallucination to which we have referred. There are variations in relative clarity and in the definiteness of the patient's ascription of her responses to particular persons. Toward the end of the paragraph an interesting transition occurs from self-reaction echoes, to a woman's voice, a man talking to the woman, a family fight, identification of the man's voice as a member of the family, and finally small talk and information. This sample was recorded while the patient, a schizophrenic young woman in the fourth month of her illness, was actively hallucinating.

"... They were sure plentiful when I first got here. Voices all the time saying I'm dying or something. 'If you like criminal colleges, stay there!'" The patient could not say whether these voices, which she still sometimes heard, were men's or women's or what their source might be. She continued: "When I came I'd hear voices telling me not to go to bed and, believe me, I didn't go! I was so scared. I'd hear voices in the morning telling me to get up. I thought it was someone I knew that was up here giving me instructions. I hear it now. It said, 'I'm hit.' You'll hear it! You wait a minute (listens). There! 'You dern fool!' I can't imagine what they mean. Listen! Listen carefully. Don't you hear a kind of sobbing voice? You can hear it distinctly, 'I'm sick.' See if you can't hear it. It's a kind of mumbling voice. Once or twice I've heard my name mentioned. 'I'm through,' 'I'm a fool.' I hear it just as plain as day, in both ears, a sobbing voice above the (running) water. I hear a woman's voice now. Sounds like he's talking to her, sounds like a family fight. It sounds exactly like daddy's voice. You listen. Says something about Mrs. Jones, says somebody's going to Yale."

Conversations between the patient and the voices that he hallucinates are not uncommon. These discussions, like conversation between two normal persons and like the role-taking of ordinary soliloquy, may be pleasant and earnest; or they may be exceedingly unpleasant and even amount to an open brawl.

Thus, one of our patients argued endlessly with voices which she said came out of the steampipe mains. Every now and then she would begin shouting and cursing at them. She included in her rebuttals some of the accusations she had been hallucinating, so that a listener could get many clues as to what the voices were calling her. When her physician spoke to her during one of these episodes, she struck him "for taking sides" against her.

Another patient spent the greater part of her time over a period of more than three months in conversation with imaginary persons. Some of these she evidently hated, while others seemed to please and entertain her. One of the latter was a man with whom she was in love. Scraps of the conversations, or rather of her side of the conversations, could often be overheard. For example, when she was alone in her room one day, the patient said aloud, "It's nice to be *friends*," and, "Yes, you *did* say it, but you didn't understand my implication!" She could be seen smiling at the invisible speaker and arching her eyebrows coquettishly as she answered him. When someone entered her room, she sometimes continued the conversation without spoken words, by means of smiles and frowns, facial grimaces, noddings and shakings of her head and little gestures.

Some patients hallucinate voices which do not speak directly to them or converse with them, but only talk about them, criticizing, deriding, defending or praising them, commenting on everything they do, predicting what they will do next, or discussing them with other hallucinated voices. Thus, one of our patients believed that he could hear a man and a woman perpetually discussing him, his activities, his past and his intentions. The man usually accused him and the woman defended him. On the other hand, a female patient of ours, who also heard herself discussed by a man and a woman, had the impression that the man approved her doing things that were good for her, while the woman was "just judging, not interested one way or the other." These voices were so continuously present that she thought, "It may possibly be two women and two men, for they must relieve each other."

As some of our illustrations have already shown, patients differ greatly in their general reaction to the voices they hallucinate as well as to the mere fact of hallucinating at all. Some are terrified by the situation, some appear only mystified and perplexed, while others are obviously pleased and comforted by what they hear. Moreover, the reaction varies in many patients from time to time, as the character of what they hallucinate varies.

The woman whom we cited above as conversing coquettishly at times with hallucinated voices, showed at other times a very different reaction to her hallucination. The appearance of interest and entertainment would often change to one of indignation, anger and outrage. Sometimes she wept and screamed because, she said, she had to listen to such disgusting things. Occasionally she appealed to physicians and nurses for help against hallucinated persons. One day, for example, she suddenly burst into sobs and cried out loudly, "They don't understand! I am *not* crazy. . . . No one believes me, but that man keeps talking to me all the time. He is right up there in the corner of the wall. He must be mentally deficient, and when he keeps talking to me he makes me feel that I'm mentally deficient. Please find out if you can where he is. Get someone who planned this building to let you see the plans. . . . He's been here ever since I have. No one believes me. Doctor Thompson says I don't hear him, but I *do*. Please believe me. I can't stand it much longer. Don't leave me alone, because he'll start talking to me again."

Patients with behavior disorders, like normal persons, usually try to account for the voices they hallucinate. Many of the hypotheses they advance are the same as those advanced by normal individuals to explain dreams, hypnagogic hallucinations and coincident thinking. Thus, patients commonly attribute what they hear to spirit communication, inspiration, possession, thought waves and telepathy. Some hallucinating persons crystallize their misinterpretation early and never change it; these have their normal counterparts in the many persons who are forever firm in the conviction that they have heard a dead relative speak to them. Other patients remain uncertain for a time, but eventually fix upon an interpretation which as a rule is woven into the delusions they develop, and shares the general drift and organization of the delusions. It may therefore be plausible or absurd, well systematized or weird and bizarre, communicable or incommunicable. The explanation offered to the inquirer, especially if the hallucinating individual has already been much questioned, is frequently one which has been found empirically to bring a quick release from the clinical inquisition.

Some patients do not fix upon a finalistic interpretation of their hallucination for a long time, even for years. Among persons who are accustomed to self-inquiry and verbal formulation, one often meets a patient whose explanations range from the most superstitious to the most sophisticated hypotheses.[14] Thus the same individual says she hears "spirit voices" telling her to do and not to do things, but adds that they are "probably just thoughts in my brain." Sometimes they seem like the voices of people around her and sometimes they are voices in herself. Another patient talks to a voice she hears from outside her window, but she "knows" it must be her imagination. An almost recovered patient spoke freely of her delusions in retrospect as absurd and imaginary, but said that she "could not see how" the hallucinating could be in her own mind. There was some evidence that hallucination, although denied, was still sometimes present. Occasionally one finds a patient who is puzzled and inquisitive about the voices he hears, but remains completely at a loss to account for them.

The behavior pathologist who studies auditory hallucination quickly discovers that the voices reported to him are as a rule projected self-reactions. That is to say, the hallucinated attitudes and responses are the patient's evaluative reactions to his own behavior. These he has previously acquired from the evaluative reactions of other persons to him or to individuals with whom he now identifies himself.[15] In his hallucinations he commands himself with God's voice or his father's, he reproaches himself with his mother's voice, reassures himself and speaks compassionately with the voice of Jesus, a saint or a beloved person who has died.[16] He curses and sneers at himself with the voice of detractors; he praises and exalts himself with the voice of a worshiper or a lover. The models for these self-reactions are all around him. He has been reared on expressions of social evaluation in the form of direct comment, of transmitted commandments, of promised reward and punishment, and of discussions and characterizations of others' behavior. He has practiced self-evaluation and the evaluation of other persons in his talk and his fantasy, both when awake and when asleep.

[14] An important contribution to the phenomenology of hallucinations comes from the hand of a patient whom A. Rosanoff has diagnosed as schizophrenic. See J. Lang (pseudonym), "The other side of hallucinations," Amer. Jour. Psychiat., 1938, vol. 94, pp. 1089-1097 and 1939, vol. 96, pp. 423-430; "The other side of the affective side of schizophrenia," Psychiatry, 1939, vol. 2, pp. 195-202; "The other side of the ideological side of schizophrenia," Psychiatry, 1940, vol. 3, pp. 389-394.

[15] F. Curran reports that some alcoholic women hallucinate the voice of a parent or grandparent telling them not to drink. "Personality studies in alcoholic women," Jour. Nerv. Ment. Dis., 1937, vol. 86, pp. 645-667.

[16] See self-reactions in Chapter 4, disowning projection in Chapter 6, self-control, self-criticism and conscience in Chapter 10.

A remarkably naïve use of the hallucinated commands of God is obvious in the reports given by an intelligent but negativistic schizophrenic patient. "God tells me to take the water, but he says I do not want the pill." "His voice tells me not to eat that supper." "God tells me not to dress but to lie still in my kimono" — and the patient became combative, saying she would not oppose God's will, when the nurses insisted that she dress. Another patient, who expressed hatred toward the hospital personnel, reported hearing the voice of God telling her she must leave at once and go to her distant home; she then attempted to run away, even though she had neither money nor traveling clothes. A depressed young man, who was failing hopelessly in his college studies, heard the voice of Jesus comforting and reassuring him as he walked about the campus. After he was dropped from college, he no longer heard the voice, even though he remained depressed for several months. A lonely young woman, whom we shall cite later on, saw and heard her mother who, in effect, asked the patient to die and join her in heaven. Bender and Lipkowitz,[17] in a study of hallucinating children, whom they found to be lonely and unhappy, report similar self-reactions with disowning projection.

Fantasy becomes hallucination, we have said, only when the fantasying person attributes what he imagines to some source outside of his own thinking. In most of the cases we have used as illustrations the patient has disowned his self-reactions and attributed the words, and the attitudes appropriate to the words, to persons or agents other than himself. This is exactly what the normal individual does in dreams and daydreams, and to a limited degree also in social communication, as we have pointed out in Chapter 6. The variations that patients exhibit in their ability to assign voices to specific persons or spirits represent, of course, variations in the completeness of their disowning projection. Thus, we would call disowning projection *maximal* when an hallucinating individual insisted that he could hear his dead father's voice counseling him, *incomplete* when he rejected the voice as his own but was unable to attribute it to a specific source, and *minimal* when he believed the voice to be in his thoughts, his brain or his mind.

Although, as we have indicated, most of the auditory hallucination in behavior disorders refers to speech, not all of it does.

[17] L. Bender and H. Lipkowitz, "Hallucinations in children," *Amer. Jour. Orthopsychiatry*, 1940, vol. 10, pp. 471-490.

Patients also report hearing laughter, groans, screams and animal cries. Some complain of the sound of bells, horns and music, or of shots and the noise of fighting. A schizophrenic girl said, "Different factions are fighting against each other and revolutions are going on. Last night I heard two shots and I thought my father and my brother had been killed." A depressed woman could hear people whistling, church bells ringing and drums beating, and she added, "There are no noises in my head." Auditory hallucination, like auditory recall, is frequently accompanied by visual imagining which is also mistakenly attributed to the stimulation of a receptor by something other than the patient's own behavior. Visual hallucination also appears without auditory accompaniment.

Visual hallucination

Visual hallucination in the behavior disorders is next in order of frequency to auditory. According to hallucinating patients, what they see may vary in clarity from something shadowy and indistinct, of which they themselves remain uncertain, to objects as realistic as anything in the shared environment. Hallucinated things may appear as integral parts of the social context, or seem independent of it and even contradict it. Sometimes they appear in their own hallucinated context which more or less obliterates the social one. A patient may assign what he hallucinates to a specific place in the shared environment; he may locate it in another world or just in space, in his own eyes, his head, brain or mind. And he may be uncertain as to whether he has seen, hallucinated, dreamed, recalled or imagined what he reports.

The person or object which a patient hallucinates may seem to him familiar or unfamiliar, trivial, commonplace, extraordinary, monstrous or indescribable. If, as in many acute behavior disorders, the patient is confused and exceedingly anxious, the occurrence of a visual hallucination may initiate aggression, assault, flight or suicide, just as in the auditory variety. Also, as in the case of auditory hallucination, a patient who is not acutely anxious or angry may be directed by a vision to mutilate or kill another person or himself. However, even in acute episodes visual hallucination sometimes provides comfort and entertainment, while in subacute and chronic behavior disorders the patient may derive his greatest satisfaction from it.

Visual hallucinations vary in theme and development as richly

as do dreams and daydreams to which, of course, they are intimately related. Their variety and their relationship to dreams and
daydreams will again be taken up when we discuss schizophrenic
disorders and acute cerebral incompetence. At this point, however,
we shall introduce by way of illustration a few characteristic examples that cut across the classifications in the chapters that follow.

A schizophrenic girl complained that when she closed her eyes
she saw all kinds of figures, flowers and plants floating through the
air, large rooms and many colors, a stairway and banisters, a mop
and somebody feeling for the handle, the hem of a skirt and someone reaching for her shoestring. She saw bright lights when she
pressed her eyeball, but one day when she did this she saw a restaurant and was frightened. Sometimes when she put her hand on
a doorknob the door began swinging back and forth. A hand
reached out at her from a bookcase. She saw pictures "of almost
anything,"and believed that this was the result of "imagining so
hard that things seemed real."

In contrast to these fragmentary but relatively commonplace
visions are the weird, inexplicable "pictures" of which a patient in
an averse retarded depression complained.

"I'm not a bit better, and the pictures I can't describe. The pictures are far away, and everything makes pictures. I'm begging so,
and I can't reach them. I say this all the time, so don't write it
down. I feel every *minute* I breathe. The top of my head is like
the sky, and these things are on it, everything, hospitals and the
world. When I close my eyes, I go into these pictures. My body
makes a jump, and I don't know the difference between yesterday
and today. I have to close my eyes. Each layer is like layers. It's
like a body left on earth. . . . And there is more, of my mother —
she tries to reach me. Not so much of my father. . . . They aren't
dreams. Everything makes pictures — streets, people, electricity,
streetcars. They all make pictures in my head, and there won't be
anything to prove it. Your reports are past reports and I'm in the
present — that sounds crazy."

A patient in an acute schizophrenic excitement, who was exceedingly frightened at the time, shouted at a man she was hallucinating:

"Come on in here and fight like a man! Come on! Come on in!
You'll be caught and killed. You are killing me. Here he comes.
He's going to kill me. Kill him! Kill him with a mallet!" She
screamed and began to cough. "Now he's cutting my windpipe —

are you going to let him kill me?" And on another occasion, "I see
him around that light — he is looking at me. I can't see him like
that!" Pointing at her pillow, she said in a frightened voice, "There
are two eyes over there; they are burning right into me." Another
schizophrenic patient complained of visions that took fantastic forms
derived from Greek mythology which she had studied. At one time,
for example, she saw her dead grandfather and grandmother who
had apparently been brought up by Neptune from the bottom of
the sea to sleep with her.

A depressed woman gave the following retrospective account of
visual and auditory hallucinatory behavior which, she said, took
place in broad daylight.

> She had been thinking of her dead mother and wishing she
> could join her in death. She began crying and then saw her mother,
> who spoke to her. "I thought she was trying to get me out of my
> suffering. She said it was very lovely where she was and she'd
> like to have me with her. She looked like herself — I thought it was
> real. I wasn't particularly frightened then. I wanted to go to her.
> . . . I told her I'd like to come. I could hear her voice. There was
> nothing unusual about her."

The behavior pathologist finds important *similarities* between
visual and auditory hallucination. The responses in both are derived
from fantasy, both show a close relationship to the delusional attitudes of the patient, and both represent disowning projection similar to that of normal dreaming and daydreaming. Visual hallucination exhibits maximal, incomplete and minimal disowning projection according to the same criteria advanced for auditory: that is,
according to the degree to which the patient identifies and locates
what he hallucinates outside of himself. Visual self-reactions,
like auditory, are the result of years of self-observation, of learning
to behave toward oneself as a social object in some of the ways that
others behave toward one. Visual hallucinations are to some extent
derived from visual self-reactions and from the reactions a person
sees others give to his appearance.

The most important *difference* between visual and auditory
hallucination derives from the relatively incidental character of
visual participation in ordinary normal communication, as contrasted with the leading part played by auditory participation.
Human biosocial behavior is organized chiefly in terms of talking
and thinking; and as we pointed out in Chapter 4, thinking is itself

moulded by verbal communication as language behavior is acquired during childhood. Talking and thinking, we have said, provide everyone with an almost continuous flow of behavior sequence which serve as well in intraindividual communication as in inter-individual. Visual participation in communication and in the recall of communication may at times be an important or even a crucial auxiliary, but as a rule the continuity, the sequential character of communication and recall, is not provided by visual activity alone.

We must not forget that in the behavior disorders the most significant factors are always biosocial in origin or implication. The individual develops need and meets delay, thwarting and conflict which interfere with satisfaction or with his after-reaction of gratification. In this situation the behavior of any individual, his adaptive and maladaptive techniques, his pondering and his self-reacting, consist largely of role-taking carried on in symbolic form. For many persons visualization may be indispensable in rounding out recall, speculation and imagined satisfaction. But it is the participation of language behavior in some form, or of fantasy originally organized in communicative terms, that forms the matrix of this role-taking and gives it continuity.

What applies to the visual components of fantasy applies also to visual hallucination which is fantasy's product. The typical visual hallucination in normal and abnormal persons is something that comes and goes; if it remains long or develops a sequential organization, the probability is that communicative techniques are also being hallucinated. Otherwise, what is hallucinated tends to be successive rather than sequential, a shifting panorama or a series of relatively discrete scenes. Even the "pictures" of which our depressed patient complained seemed from her account to consist of a succession of objects and places without continuity; moreover, she reported that there was no talking mingled with them.

Visual hallucination usually occurs in a setting of deep preoccupation with personal need, anxiety or frustration, and its recurrence suggests that the situation giving rise to it has recurred. It may impress the patient because it suddenly increases his need, anxiety or frustration, even though these are responsible for its occurrence in the first place. It may also impress him because it represents closure, whether the closure be comforting, frightening or awe-inspiring. But in any case the visual hallucination in behavior disorders always arises from antecedent or coactive fantasy, and it is usually preceded, accompanied or followed immediately by auditory and other varieties of hallucination.

Other varieties of hallucination

Next to auditory and visual hallucination the most important varieties in the behavior disorders are the olfactory and the gustatory. Both the latter appear as a rule in persons already made selectively reaction-sensitive to danger by their delusional development. Thus, persons who believe themselves persecuted, or under a malign influence, often insist they can smell or taste poisons by means of which they expect to be rendered helpless or killed. Others maintain that they are being deliberately annoyed by foul smells and tastes which someone is introducing into the air and the food. It is not uncommon for patients to complain of body odors. These complaints, as we said in discussing delusions of body change, may arise as the result of conflict over autoerotism and are sometimes accepted by a patient as evidence of disease or decay. Occasionally, a person who is convinced that he is dead, at a funeral or in heaven, reports smelling fragrant flowers when no fragrance can be detected by an impartial observer. An example of this will be given in our presentation of schizophrenic disorders.

Hallucinations of movement and of changes in equilibrium — such as rocking, swaying, floating, swimming and flying — are less common than the other varieties in behavior disorders. Their significance can usually be derived from the delusional context. Thus, a depressed person, who believed that she was condemned to wander through the universe forever, could feel her bed rock and pitch at night as though it were a ship at sea. A schizophrenic patient, who believed that her hope of salvation lay in her reaching the moon, hallucinated objects whizzing past her and could feel herself flying through interplanetary space.

Cutaneous hallucination and visceral hallucination are common and frequently important responses in the behavior disorders. Like the other varieties, they derive their significance from the delusional attitudes which support them and to which they in turn contribute. We have already encountered both cutaneous and visceral hallucination in relation to delusions of influence and delusions of body change; and we shall meet them again in the depressions, in schizophrenia, and in the paranoid disorders to which we shall now turn.

14   *Paranoid Disorders*

THE TERM *paranoia* was current in ancient Greece and Rome up to about the second century A.D., but it seems to have been used more or less indiscriminately in a sense equivalent to that of our modern catch-all, *insanity*. It was revived for a brief period in the eighteenth century and again in the nineteenth, since when it has remained permanently in the literature but with widely varying meanings. Paranoia received its present rather precise formulation under the influence of Kraepelin, who reserved the name for cases of chronic, highly systematized delusions without personality deterioration.

The Kraepelinian conception of paranoia, however, has turned out to be so restricted in scope that only the rare case of systematized delusion can qualify under it. On the other hand, paranoia-like cases are not at all uncommon in office, clinic and hospital practice. These do not quite correspond to Kraepelin's formulation of paranoia, being less often chronic and having delusions that are less systematized, but they still show neither serious disorganization nor serious deterioration. Such cases have for many years been called paranoia-like or *paranoid*. A growing recognition of the relatively greater importance of these paranoid disorders has finally led to the inclusion of paranoia under them as merely a rare variant.[1] It should be noted that in contemporary usage the word *paranoid* is equivalent to *delusional*, and the once prevalent term *paranoid delusion* has thus been reduced to tautology.

By *paranoid disorders* we mean *behavior which is dominated by*

---

[1] *United States Army Technical Medical Bulletin No. 203* (Washington, D.C.: United States Government Printing Office, October 19, 1945), Section 18. Also reprinted in *Jour. Ment. Science,* 1946, vol. 92, pp. 425-441, and in *Ment. Hyg.,* 1946, vol. 30, pp. 456-476.

more or less systematized delusional reactions, but which shows little or no tendency toward disorganization or deterioration, is not incidental to mania or depression, and lacks an adequate basis in organ or tissue pathology. Of the delusions already discussed, only two kinds appear prominently in paranoid disorders, those of persecution and those of grandeur, and delusions of persecution are by far the commoner of these two. The greater prevalence of persecutory paranoid disorders is undoubtedly related to the fact that our culture provides an abundance of fear, hatred, guilt and insecurity excitants for everyone, while it offers comparatively little support to persistent self-reactions of personal grandeur. Because the persecutory variety is the prevalent form of paranoid disorder, we shall use it in what follows as our principal example.

DEVELOPMENT OF PARANOID DISORDERS

Delusional behavior, we have said, is common among normal individuals and most common under conditions of special need or anxiety. Thus, in everyday life we find that expectant or emotional attitudes and reactions of personal insecurity tend to favor delusional development by making one reaction-sensitive to whatever arouses them, while detached or relatively unemotional attitudes and reactions of personal security tend to avert delusional development.[2] Delusional incidents are of frequent occurrence also, because everyone must be continually acting on the basis of incomplete and uncertain data. Indeed, to proceed only on the basis of completeness and certainty would be to accomplish virtually nothing, since almost nothing is finished and sure. Those exceptional individuals whose need or anxiety compels them to seek absolute certainty, as we saw, for example, in the compulsive disorders, are by that very fact rendered susceptible to the development of serious behavior pathology.

The normal person has neither the opportunity nor the time, nor for that matter even the inclination, to check rigorously on everything he does, sees, hears or thinks. It is therefore inevitable that he should make frequent mistakes in his everyday interpretations, inferences and conclusions. Many of these mistakes are never cor-

---

[2] See, for example, the study of reactions to a radio broadcast of the fictitious account of a Martian invasion of the United States. H. Cantril, *The Invasion from Mars.* Princeton, N.J.: Princeton University Press, 1940.

rected, and in the great majority of instances no harm results. But every now and then a misunderstanding has important personal consequences that call for a reconsideration, if trouble is to be averted.

To be successful in correcting the important mistakes in interpretation, inference and conclusion, and thus to eliminate the possibility of a paranoid disorder, a person must have adequate skill in taking roles and shifting his perspectives under stress, and his need or anxiety must be neither excessive nor everlasting. For we know that ease in shifting perspective in a crisis — from that of participant, for example, to that of disinterested observer — is the basis upon which the average person is enabled to correct in one role what he may have misunderstood in another. If, instead, an individual must depend upon rumination, solitary observation and unshared surmise in personally vital matters, there is little to prevent his delusional convictions from growing into paranoid disorders.

Contrary to popular belief, paranoid disorders end as a rule in recovery and rarely develop the elaborate, logically systematized organization of classical paranoia. The rarity of rigid logical systematization in paranoid disorders should not surprise anyone, since it is exceptional, even among highly intelligent and well-trained normal persons, for matters of deep personal and emotional significance to be settled by operations of strict verbal logic.[3] Moreover, as we have already pointed out, different kinds of human behavior show different degrees of social maturity in the same individual; and it is the unshared, personally important emotional behavior which in all of us is most likely to include ambiguities, self-contradictions, ambivalences and other logical violations in its organization. Thus, we find, in intelligent or highly trained persons as well as in the unintelligent or untrained, that delusional convictions often develop into paranoid disorders on grounds which seem almost incredibly absurd to a dispassionate observer. We shall see most of these fundamental facts illustrated in the two following cases.

A thirty-nine-year-old successful lawyer consulted an internist, complaining of sleeplessness, tension, headaches and loss of appetite. The internist, finding no adequate basis for the complaints in

[3] J. Morgan and J. Morton, "The distortion of syllogistic reasoning produced by personal convictions," *Jour. Soc. Psychol.*, 1944, vol. 20, pp. 39-59.

organ or tissue pathology, referred him to a psychiatrist. In the course of several consultations with the psychiatrist, the patient gave no important evidence of personal difficulties excepting his repeated, unsolicited insistence that his sex life had nothing to do with his symptoms. "I know what you doctors think," he kept saying. Eventually, however, it came out that for several months he had been tormented day and night by the conviction that he was the victim of a conspiracy between his wife and her physician, and that her family knew of the conspiracy and condoned it.

According to the patient, he had become suspicious when his wife, who was of Italian extraction, had insisted upon going to an Italian obstetrician, the friend of her parents. This was her second pregnancy, and in her first she had been content with the care of a general practitioner whom none of them had previously known. The patient's distrust was heightened by the fact that his wife seemed pleased with the frequency and regularity of her visits to the obstetrician and praised the kindness and consideration with which he treated her. Finally, suspicion of her conduct was transformed into certainty that she had been unfaithful to him when, following his wife's delivery, the patient received a bill far smaller than he had expected. He was convinced that the child was not his but the obstetrician's, and that this explained his wife's choice of physician, her failure to complain of the tedium of repeated examinations, the small amount charged for professional services, and even his wife's delight in her baby and her decreased attention to her first child.

The novice, hearing this succession of unwarranted inferences and their outcome in delusional conviction, may easily be himself misled into concluding unjustifiably that the patient must be incapable of reasoning or must have a "diseased mind." He can avoid committing such an error if, instead of being preoccupied with questions of mere verbal logic, he attempts to understand the biosocial background of the delusional development. Our patient, first of all, was a proud man, proud partly because he was chronically insecure, but both proud and insecure also because his parents had consistently overcompensated for their own humble origins by stressing always the importance of status and the high virtue of conformity. He was trained to look out continually for the approval of his neighbors, and to consider appearances before everything else.

The patient left home for good when he was twenty-four, and at the age of thirty-one moved to a metropolis where he was thrown in with persons of widely different backgrounds. It was under these circumstances that he met and fell in love with a girl of Italian parentage. In spite of secret misgivings and the warnings he received from his own parents, he allowed himself finally to marry into a family for which he had neither liking nor respect. When he entered marriage, the patient did so also with the realization that his premarital sex pace had always been considerably below the level claimed by his companions. He feared that he might be unable to come up to the sexual expectations which, with no basis other than his own prejudices, he attributed to his wife because of the nationality of her parents.

Because of his social prejudices and his doubts concerning his sexual adequacy, the patient found that his marriage meant a reduction in personal security and status, whereas what he needed was an increase in both. His wife's first pregnancy raised no major problems for him, but during the second one he involved himself in an extramarital sex adventure which was in part a spite reaction to his wife's supposed attachment to the obstetrician, and in part an attempt at reassuring himself as to his own adequacy. This adventure unexpectedly aroused in him considerable guilt, self-condemnation and fear of discovery, which was augmented by the unwillingness of his partner in it to terminate the affair.

From this brief sketch of the patient's background, it is clear that his paranoid disorder arose, not because of some primary defect in reasoning, as behavior pathologists would have assumed fifty years ago, but because of selective reaction-sensitivity which was in turn determined by the patient's life history. This insecure, conventionally reared man married into a cultural in-group from which his own prejudices excluded him in his self-reactions. He could not accept his wife's relatives and friends because he felt different in kind from them as well as superior. The sexual characteristics which he attributed to his wife, at first solely on the basis of prejudice and insecurity, became reinforced in his thinking as one result of his own sex misbehavior (*assimilative projection*).

Out of an actual in-group of Italian-Americans, and the interactions of its members, the patient organized in his own thinking a *pseudocommunity* made up of the interrelationships he believed to exist between his wife, her physician and her family. They all differed from him and agreed among themselves in cultural background, national derivation, childhood tongue and anatomical appearance. The second baby when it came looked, he said, like a little foreigner. It seemed to belong to this in-group from which he had by his own reactions excluded himself, and he could therefore not accept it as his child. Thus, the baby's advent, instead of bringing pride and increased confidence to the patient, had only confirmed his conviction and increased his isolation. Under prolonged motivational analysis this man succeeded in working out the origins and implications of his emotional attitudes sufficiently to overcome his paranoid disorder.

We have said that it is exceptional for the uncomplicated paranoid disorder to persist indefinitely. Nevertheless, the accumulated total of those cases that do become chronic constitutes a grave social problem, for the community at large as well as for institutional psychiatry. It is therefore of importance to the average citizen, as it is also to the behavior pathologist, to understand the background of persistent and cumulative delusional convictions.

For delusions of persecution to develop into a chronic paranoid disorder several conditions must be present. There must be something of importance to which the patient is strongly reaction-sensitive, something that arouses insecurity, guilt, fear, humiliation, resentment or a sense of isolation and inadequacy. The patient must be one who builds up cumulative or persistent tensions easily, so that he tends to be habitually anxious, but at the same time intolerant of suspense. He must have well-established habits of dealing with personal problems in solitude, by brooding, puzzling and ruminating, and poorly developed habits of shifting perspectives and taking successively different roles under stress. As a result of this one-sided development, such an individual lacks skill in the techniques of analyzing or retesting situations that make him uneasy; and because he cannot adequately share his attitudes in personal matters with others, he has no way of objectively validating his conclusions in these areas.

Cumulative and persistent paranoid disorders develop chiefly in persons who for some reason have failed to acquire adequate role-taking skills and have not learned habits of free discussion and interchange of attitude with others, excepting in impersonal matters and at a relatively superficial level. When such an individual arrives at a conclusion, he cannot shift to another point of view, and therefore this conclusion remains the only possible one. Starting afresh with his conclusion, he proceeds with the same inadequate techniques and the same single perspective to make further inferences and arrive at similar conclusions, until finally he builds up a more or less consistent delusional organization. The patient's progressive reaction-sensitivity determines his selection and interpretation of new incidents which fit into his growing paranoid system. In his ruminations the patient reshapes what he recalls — a procedure that is common also in normal remembering [4] — and includes this distorted product as confirmatory and supporting evidence for his delusional convictions (*retrospective falsification*).

Once an insecure, socially unskilled person becomes suspicious, it is never difficult for him to find apparent grounds for his distrust. His long-established habits of ruminating over personal difficulties without sharing them, and his relative ineffectuality in testing social interrelationships, make it easy for him to build up elaborate structures of interpretation out of flimsy evidence. At every choice point such a person, because of his selective reaction-sensitivity, goes in the direction of prevailing fear, suspicion, resentment or guilt. He looks about him for confirmatory signs and finds them. Like a man who is actually wanted by the police, he watches everything and suspects everyone. The little movements, gestures, looks and signs that are always going on around us become to the reaction-sensitive, suspicious patient indications of a concerted plot of which he seems to be the object. Out of these selected fragments of behavior he organizes the paranoid *pseudocommunity* whose members seem united against him. In the following case we shall see how childhood determinants, vocational peculiarities, unfortunate incidents and lifelong habits of social isolation are interwoven in the development of a paranoid disorder.[5]

> The patient, an unmarried man of forty-nine, was brought to the hospital by relatives with the complaint that he believed himself pursued by gangsters who intended to capture, torture and then kill him. According to the patient, his difficulties had arisen suddenly the day after a quarrel over a small racing bet which he had placed with bookies. It is of some importance to note that the patient, who had a steady income from previous business ventures, had not been working at all for several years prior to the onset of

[4] See for example F. Bartlett, *Remembering, a Study in Experimental and Social Psychology*. Cambridge, England: Cambridge University Press, 1932.
[5] N. Cameron, "The development of paranoic thinking," *Psychol. Rev.*, 1943, vol. 50, pp. 219-233.

his paranoid disorder. He lived alone in a cheap hotel and spent his entire time in sitting around idly, reading the papers, thinking, conversing, playing cards, placing around a dozen small bets daily on the ponies, and occasionally looking into business prospects without finding anything he wanted. It was in this setting of idleness, fantasy and small talk that his illness developed. There was, as we shall see, also a background of guilt, suspicion and resentment to help account for the patient's reaction-sensitivity to signs of punishment and persecution.

The quarrel which seems to have precipitated the disorder grew out of the patient's attempt to collect on a winning horse when the bookies insisted that he had put his money on a different horse. The patient, after fortifying himself with a few drinks, returned and noisily demanded the pay-off, shouting insults at the bookies, threatening them with prosecution and inviting them out on the street to fight. Eventually he cooled off and returned to his hotel, where he began thinking over what he had done. He remembered hearing stories of national gangster protection given to bookies. The more he thought about it, the more dangerous his threatening and insulting them seemed to him.

Next day the patient noticed some strangers in the lobby, "rough-looking characters," and they seemed to him to be looking at him intently and to be signaling to each other. During the morning an automobile full of men stopped in front of the hotel door and the patient was convinced that he was about to be kidnapped, tortured and killed for the trouble he had been making. He began to notice strangers and loiterers everywhere he went, and they all seemed to be watching or shadowing him. He felt that he was a marked man, and barricaded himself in his room. From there he communicated by telephone with a relative, who was thoroughly convinced at the time that the patient was in deadly peril. They arranged to leave town next morning on a long automobile trip. However, the patient decided during the night that his telephone message must have been tapped by the gangsters, so he skipped town before morning, alone in his car, and headed for the home of another relative a thousand miles away.

As the patient drove on, it became apparent to him that he was being trailed. In one city, for example, he saw a policeman examining his auto license; this meant to him that the police were in league with the gangsters and were tipping them off. Once, in a shoeshining parlor, the attendant eyed him narrowly; this was a sign that "the grapevine system was catching up." He was determined not to be caught alive, so he concealed razor blades about his person, carried a bottle of lysol in his pocket and sealed a lethal

dose of sedatives in a chewing-gum package. When he reached his
relatives, it was evident to them that the patient was ill, they got
wind of his suicidal intent, and, on the advice of a general practitioner, took the patient by air to the hospital.

In the hospital the patient felt for some time contented and
secure. He was well-oriented, his talk was circumstantial but clear
and sequential, there were no signs of behavior disorganization and,
while he obviously preferred his own company, he was pleasant
and courteous to others. In conferences with his psychiatrist he
made frequent allusions to things in his past that he would like to
get cleared up; but although given many opportunities to go into
them, he could bring himself only to recount some unethical business dealings. When a shift in the medical staff was made, the
patient persuaded the new physician to let him telephone a local
pastor to come and visit him in the clinic. To the pastor he told
the story of his recent difficulties and, without consulting the
physician, the two arranged for another visit at which, the patient
intimated, he would go into other matters.

After the pastor had gone, the patient began pondering over the
visit in his usual way, and the more he thought about it, the more
he suspected that he had been unwise to confide so much to a
stranger. He recalled that the pastor was somewhat dark-skinned
and foreign-looking, and he suddenly realized that his telephone
call had probably been intercepted by the gangsters, who had sent
around a confederate to pose as a minister of the gospel. He suffered a violent resurgence of fear and, although under expert sur-
veillance, made a serious but unsuccessful suicidal attempt. Following this incident, the patient no longer felt safe in the hospital. He
was unable to entertain any interpretation of the pastor's visit other
than the one which fitted into his delusional system. He wished, he
said, that he could be in a hospital that was in the middle of an
army encampment. Failing this, he insisted upon being transferred to a government hospital.

Because of the patient's inability to establish an adequate communicative relationship with his psychiatrists, there remain serious
gaps in what is known of his personal history, particularly in relation to his sex behavior and interests. Nevertheless, even his relatively superficial account gives us important clues to the origins of
his selective reaction-sensitivity and of his lack of the social skills
he needed to protect him from paranoid developments. The
patient's childhood was motherless and he was shifted about among
various relatives, "from farm to farm and from state to state," now

with siblings and now separated from them. He never had the feeling that he had a settled place to live in. He grew up a lonely, insecure, brooding child who got along well in casual contacts, but lacked close friends with whom he could share confidences and exchange perspectives. He had always felt the need to confide and confess, he said, but he had never been able to do either.

Early in adulthood the patient drifted into vocations that permitted him to continue in the pattern of living he had acquired during childhood. As a salesman he worked alone and on his own schedule, leading a restless, unsatisfying, roving life, moving his headquarters innumerable times and changing from one job to another. In spite of these shifts, and in spite of never liking his work, the patient achieved substantial financial success. By the time he had reached his middle forties, he was able to live on a modest scale without working. He never gained personal security and he never succeeded in identifying himself emotionally with the firms that employed him. The patient felt that his employers underrated him and discriminated against him; they seemed always suspicious of him as he was of them. In view of the fact that spotters were regularly employed to check up on salesmen, it is difficult to decide how much of this was projection on the patient's part and how much was justified by what he knew. For a time he was himself employed as a spotter, checking secretly on the activities of other field representatives. This work, he said, heightened his distrust, but it made him better able to recognize "what was going on."

After his return to selling, the patient believed that the operatives of his employers and competitors were continually watching and trailing him, a belief that may not have been wholly unfounded. His habitual insecurity at this time was increased by guilt over some business dealings outside of his agreements. Whenever he became convinced, on the basis of rumination and circumstantial evidence, that he was being persistently trailed, his reaction was to make a sudden change in his headquarters without consulting anyone. He had never seriously doubted the validity of these convictions. It is obvious that the socially inadequate techniques by means of which the patient, under the stress of fearful fantasy, built up a *pseudocommunity* of homicidal gangsters were the same techniques which had kept him perpetually insecure in his work. It is also clear that the patient's lack of skill in role-taking and in shifting perspectives stood in the way of his recovery.

The paranoid pseudocommunity [6]

Both of the cases cited above illustrate well the development and operation of the paranoid pseudocommunity, which is a product of reaction-sensitivity and projection as we have defined them in Chapters 3 and 6. The patient, like the normal person, reacts selectively to his environment on the basis of dominant attitudes which facilitate certain responses and inhibit others. When he thinks he is under suspicion or scrutiny, he may proceed to watch and listen, as indeed anyone else might, and to ponder over what he sees and hears. However, as we know, skill in interpreting the attitudes and intents of another person depends chiefly upon skill in role-taking, since it is only by taking a person's role that we can gain his perspective and see things approximately as he sees them. The person who is relatively incompetent in this maneuver lacks one of the most important social techniques for the prevention and correction of delusional developments. In the extreme case, as we have pointed out, the patient has but one perspective in personally important matters, and he can therefore arrive at only one kind of conclusion which, for him, is inescapable fact.

The average person, when his observations, hypotheses and role-taking maneuvers only increase his insecurity or perplexity, usually turns to someone he trusts and shares his difficulties. This procedure objectifies the situation by making it something discussed in terms of social communication, instead of something only brooded over in private fantasy. It gives the frightened or perplexed individual the comfort of sharing his anxiety, and it brings the role-taking resources of another person to bear upon the now mutual problem. The patient who, like our salesman, has never succeeded in developing habits of confiding and sharing, lives in a world of strangers with whom he cannot communicate in personal matters and from whom he can get neither comfort nor support when he feels discriminated against or threatened.

The frightened solitary patient who seriously lacks the requisite skills with which to carry out shared social operations is like an unskilled and inexperienced man who finds himself lost at night in a jungle, and seems suddenly to become the focus of a hostile, living environment which is at first obscure and unintelligible. Every shadow, every sound and movement seems to threaten him

[6] N. Cameron, "The paranoid pseudocommunity," *Amer. Jour. Soc.*, 1943, vol. 49, pp. 32-38.

personally. His fear binds together trivial and unrelated incidents around him into a great net from which he can see no escape. Likewise, the anxious patient, inept in social skills, attributes harmful intent to the trivial and unrelated responses of persons in his environment and of other persons whose existence he imagines or infers. He unintentionally organizes these individuals through his own reactions of fear and projection into an apparent community; in his interpretations their responses, attitudes and plans seem unified and all directed toward him. The organization of this pseudo-community does not, of course, comfort and reassure the paranoid patient, but it does satisfy his immediate pressing need for an explanation of what is going on. It brings the kind of relief from doubt and suspense that expected bad news brings when it finally comes.

The community which paranoid patients thus build up fails to correspond, of course, to any shared organization of interpersonal behavior. Moreover, the attitudes and intentions ascribed by the patient to those individuals whom he identifies as members of the community are not actually maintained by them, and they are not united in any common undertaking against him. In other words, what he takes to be a functionally integrated social group is only a pseudocommunity, an organization of his own reactions into a structure without social validity. We may define this *pseudocommunity as an organization of a patient's reactions to the observed or inferred behavior of actual and imagined persons, on the basis of delusional conviction, which makes the patient seem to himself a focus or a significant part of some concerted action, malignant or benign.* The patient's conviction often comes suddenly, as closure or *sudden clarification*, with the familiar statement, "It has all become clear to me."

Unfortunately, the organization of a pseudocommunity in a patient's reactions usually adds impetus to the whole delusional development, much as a new integrating scientific hypothesis may suddenly speed up research. The pseudocommunity, once organized and formulated, tends to expand through progressive reaction-sensitization to include new activities and new personnel until the patient finally considers it a grave threat to his security. It is at this point that the paranoid patient bursts into defensive or vengeful activity in the field of social operations against his pseudocommunity. The social community, which usually cannot share in his

attitudes any more than he shares in the community's, meets his
aggression with counteraggression, and this seems to the patient
final evidence that his fears and suspicions have been fully justified.

The best organized pseudocommunities are to be found among
the paranoid disorders, but they are by no means restricted to this
group. For example, in the delusional behavior of schizophrenic
patients we find disorganized but often richly fantastic pseudocommunities. Manic and depressed persons also frequently develop
this kind of delusional organization, although with them it is usually
a by-product of the mood disorder which tends to disappear without special attention as the illness subsides.

DETERMINANTS OF PARANOID DISORDERS

It has been obvious throughout the preceding discussion that
paranoid disorders are most likely to develop in those individuals
who cannot readily seek counsel, who habitually work out their
difficulties in solitary brooding, and who lack skill in the techniques
of role-taking and in shifting their perspectives under conditions of
personal stress. Many such individuals, by the time adolescence is
reached, already have well-established attitudes of suspicion, criticism and resentment toward others, expect and demand special
consideration of everyone, or show marked concern over the opinions others have of them, while lacking the necessary skills for
sampling those opinions. We shall turn briefly to a discussion of
some of the childhood influences that help to develop these predisposing behavior trends.

Childhood influences

Any child, in adopting the prevailing attitudes of his early environment, is likely to develop habitual suspicion, resentment, pride
and overconcern regarding his neighbors' opinions of him, if these
are the habitual attitudes of his elders. For example, in an isolated
mountaineer community where strangers are always treated as suspect and unwelcome, the average child will exhibit an attitude of
suspicion and hostility toward strangers that would be considered
pathological in the child of an ordinary rural or urban community.
However, there are always individual families within the ordinary
rural and urban community whose elders, for personal rather than
general cultural reasons, are habitually dominated by attitudes

favoring delusional developments and tend to train their offspring in similar attitudes.[7]

Children reared in a domestic or general cultural atmosphere where such attitudes prevail must be regarded as more susceptible than the average to paranoid disorders in middle life. Their dominant attitude organization tends to make them chronically insecure in personal interrelationships, interferes with their acquisition of social techniques and serviceable self-reactions, and so leaves them in a crisis with fewer behavior resources than they need to deal successfully with later biosocial problems. Of course, by no means all individuals with this childhood background become paranoid. As we pointed out in Chapter 2, adult personality organization is not usually determined by the characteristics of one parent or the effects of one personal trauma. There are two parents interacting with each other to help determine a child's attitudes, there are siblings, a neighborhood with other children and other influential elders, and, sometimes most important of all, the peer culture at every age level from childhood through adolescence and adulthood.

The social inadequacies that favor paranoid disorders may be the result, not of adopting a prevailing pattern, but of failure to find opportunities for developing social skills. As we pointed out in Chapters 2 and 4, the prime requisites for the development of adequate role-taking in childhood are parental acceptance, a secure home, freedom to explore the neighborhood at an early age and to engage in associative and cooperative play with other children. The child who, through neglect, denial, rejection or inhibitory supervision, is denied the security or opportunity he needs for the practice of social skills may be unable in later adult life to avoid paranoid disorder under personal stress. The same is true of the child whose elders lead him to develop self-attitudes of inferiority or guilt through their habitual reactions to what he says and does, or through the implications of what they do for him (*indulgent overprotection*) or to him (*domineering overprotection*).

Parental attitudes such as these sometimes lay the ground in a child's self-reactions for the development in later life of paranoid

---

[7] If a child or an adult is directly indoctrinated in some specific delusional behavior by a dominant paranoid person, it is customary to speak of *induced paranoid disorder* or *folie à deux*. See the article and bibliography by A. Gralnick, "Folie à deux: the psychosis of association; a review of 103 cases and the entire English literature with case presentations," *Psychiat. Quart.*, 1942, vol. 16, pp. 230-263 and 491-520.

grandiosity. The grandiose paranoid disorder may be a direct reaction against parentally induced self-reactions of inferiority or guilt. It may also be an outgrowth of fantasied achievements with which the adult has learned to console himself for his failure to accomplish what parental overevaluation in childhood had led him to expect.

Age and paranoid disorders

It is undoubtedly significant that the great majority of paranoid disorders develop between the thirty-fifth and fifty-fifth years.[8] Two plausible explanations for this age-range present themselves. In the first place, the paranoid disorder is arbitrarily limited by definition to delusional developments which are more or less systematized and show no serious tendencies toward behavior disorganization. These specifications eliminate the delusions characteristic of the schizophrenic disorders which usually begin fifteen or twenty years earlier. From this it can be inferred that the socially inept person who undergoes maximal stress during adolescence or early adulthood suffers behavior disorganization because he is at the time relatively immature. His social techniques are not yet well established at the level of adolescent or adult life and, like any other complex behavior that is still imperfectly learned, are more easily disintegrated by emotional disturbance, failure or conflict. To such a result we give the name *schizophrenic disorder.*

The socially inept individual who manages to get through adolescence and early adult life without developing severe behavior disorder, but who undergoes maximal stress after a decade or two of adult life, does not as easily develop disorganization as a reaction to severe emotional disturbance, conflict or failure. His social techniques, although still relatively inadequate, are sufficiently established as habitual operations to preserve the patient's general personality organization in spite of delusional distortion. To such an outcome we give the name *paranoid disorder.* We shall return to this hypothesis when we consider the schizophrenic disorders.

[8] N. Dayton, *New Facts on Mental Disorders; Study of 89,190 Cases* (Springfield, Ill.: Thomas, 1940), pp. 308-318; *United States Army Technical Medical Bulletin No. 203* (Washington, D.C.: United States Government Printing Office, October 19, 1945), Section 18. In a study confined to a university population, T. Raphael and L. Himler found that the mean age of persons developing paranoid disorders was 11.6 years older and the median age 13.0 years older than that of persons developing schizophrenic disorders. "Schizophrenia and paranoid psychoses among college students," *Amer. Jour. Psychiat.,* 1944, vol. 100, pp. 443-451.

Another possible explanation for the age-range in paranoid disorders may supplement the one suggested above. We know that between the thirty-fifth and fifty-fifth years there are many occasions for new and increased personal insecurity. Each adult, as his youth recedes, must one day recognize what growing older means for him. For some the most impressive thing seems to be a sudden realization that one's life-span is limited, for others it is the growing certainty that lifelong goals will never be attained. Waning or lost youth means to many the loss of abilities, attractiveness and status.

Among the varied reactions to the increased need or anxiety which ageing fosters are those of attempting to preserve one's self-respect by blaming others for one's difficulties, and of seeking aggressively to overcome obstacles and frustration by greater effort. Either technique in the hands of the socially inept may lead to paranoid disorder. The first is, of course, one of the commonest precursors of delusional organization. The second, the aggressive increase in effort, will only hasten a showdown if the individual is unsuccessful, thus adding to the conditions responsible for the original aggression. Moreover, the aggressive use of unskillful social techniques is likely to stimulate counteraggressions in other persons and thus open the way for the patient to develop in his own reactions an organized paranoid pseudocommunity.

The importance of sex need, frustration and conflict in paranoid disorders, which Freud was the first to recognize, is now a generally accepted fact. However, the original formulation, which ascribed all persecutory delusions to narcism and latent homosexuality, has turned out to be unnecessarily restrictive.[9] It has been found, for example, that paranoid disorders appear in women with well-established heterosexual interests, either because marital opportunities have dwindled or because forbidden heterosexual attachments have developed which arouse anxiety and guilt.[10] Men whose sex code has been unusually rigid sometimes develop para-

[9] J. Page and J. Warkentin, "Masculinity and paranoia," *Jour. Abnorm. Soc. Psychol.*, 1938, vol. 33, pp. 527-531; R. Knight, "The relationship of homosexuality to the mechanism of paranoid delusions," *Bull. Menninger Clinic*, 1940, vol. 4, pp. 149-159.

[10] F. Curran, in a study of acute alcoholism, found that women patients commonly hallucinated voices accusing them of sexual inferiority and prostitution, but were less troubled by hallucinated homosexual self-accusations than were similar male patients. "Personality studies in alcoholic women," *Jour. Nerv. Ment. Dis.*, 1937, vol. 86, pp. 645-667.

noid disorder under comparable circumstances. It is always possible, of course, to argue that these are all cases of latent homosexuality with a heterosexual façade, but this claim needs more than
logical plausibility to support it. Moreover, as we pointed out in
Chapter 5, no matter how important sex factors may be in behavior
pathology, they are always part of a more inclusive personality
organization and can be understood only within their biosocial
framework.[11]

Paranoid disorders as adjustive techniques

Persecutory paranoid disorders, since usually they increase anxiety by amplifying and crystallizing the apparent threats to a person's security, are of relatively little use as adjustive techniques.
However, we sometimes find the paranoid patient utilizing delusional accusations, in which he himself, of course, believes, as
aggressive weapons for the control and manipulation of situations
for his own benefit. Paranoid disorders, whether persecutory or
grandiose, may sometimes function as *identification.* The patient, in
organizing his pseudocommunity, may develop the conviction that
he is being persecuted or honored because he is thought to belong
to an actual or fantasied group — religious, societal, national or
racial — which arouses these reactions in others. Sometimes a paranoid person concludes, from the attitudes he seems to find in others,
that he must really belong to such a group, or that he must be the
reincarnation or representative of a persecuted or honored personage.

Paranoid disorders are frequently *compensatory.* Compensation
is obvious, for example, when a woman substitutes the conviction
that she is being pursued by a would-be lover or assailant for her
previously unsatisfied need to be desired and overcome. Both persecutory and grandiose paranoid disorders are known to originate
often as attempts to gain status — for example, as an important
victim, leader or criminal — as a substitute for satisfactions which
the patient has failed to gain for his other needs, including the
sexual. Sometimes the delusional system, after it has been developed, is used as *insulation* or *negativism* which enables the patient
to escape participation in unwelcome duties or hazardous competition. The interrelation of *rationalization, projection* and *repression*

[11] Compare C. Miller, "The paranoid syndrome," *Arch. Neurol. Psychiat.*,
1941, vol. 45, pp. 953-963.

in paranoid developments has already been discussed in Chapter 6, and it will be further illustrated in the disorganized delusions of the schizophrenic disorders.

PARANOID DISORDERS IN RELATION TO OTHER BEHAVIOR DISORDERS

The wide distribution of delusions throughout the behavior disorders is responsible for the exclusive character of the definition of paranoid disorders. We bar those cases in which the delusions are a by-product of mood disorder, and we specify that neither serious disorganization nor serious deterioration must be present. In spite of these exclusions, however, the task of differentiating paranoid from other behavior disorders is often an exceedingly difficult one.

Hypochondriacal overconcern is a common complication of paranoid disorders. Indeed, chronic body complaints frequently dominate the clinical picture before paranoid developments are evident, and sometimes a fixed hypochondriacal preoccupation becomes the foundation for an organized delusional system. This close relationship between paranoid and hypochondriacal disorders is not surprising in view of the fact that both are so often outgrowths of compensatory and rationalizing techniques, and the incidence of both is high in the same period of life.[12] A similar close relationship can be demonstrated between fatigue syndromes and paranoid disorders. The differentiation between paranoid disorders, on the one hand, and hypochondriacal disorders and fatigue syndromes, on the other, is made chiefly on the basis of whether or not the patient has developed organized delusions.

Anxiety is almost always present in paranoid disorders at some stage of development or recession, while fleeting delusions are characteristic of many cases of anxiety disorder. The distinction is made on the basis of the degree to which delusions are systematized and dominate the clinical picture. Acute anxiety and panic reactions are by no means uncommon in cases of paranoid disorder, and occasionally what begins as panic reaction may terminate in paranoid disorder. There is seldom serious difficulty in distinguishing paranoid from *hysterical disorders* on the basis of dominant symptomatology. Both frequently involve disowning reactions, but whereas in hysteria this results in autonomy or inactivation, in

---

[12] E. Billings, *Elementary Handbook of Psychobiology and Psychiatry* (New York: Macmillan, 1939), p. 126.

paranoid disorders it leads characteristically to the organization in the patient's reactions of the paranoid pseudocommunity. Hysterical symptoms may appear in what is predominantly a paranoid disorder, while a certain degree of delusional organization is sometimes incidental to hysterical inactivation and autonomy.

The distinction between paranoid disorders and *mania* or *depression* is made on the basis of whether or not the delusions are incidental to a mood disorder; if the delusions are not incidental, we speak of paranoid disorder. In practice this differentiation is frequently difficult and occasionally impossible to make. The same difficulties arise in relation to *brain damage*. A patient with unquestionable brain damage may nevertheless develop a delusional system on the basis, not of his deficit, but of his reaction to the fact that he has suffered injury or has been made to feel inferior and underrated. We shall return to this problem in Chapter 17.

The most difficult distinction of all is that between paranoid disorders and *schizophrenia* to which we next turn. Indeed, there is a considerable area of overlap between the definitions of paranoid disorder and paranoid schizophrenia, since perfect organization is exceedingly rare in the former and severe disorganization frequently absent from the latter. The most helpful attitude to take in relation to these syndromes is that paranoia lies at one extreme of the scale of an organization continuum, while at the other extreme lies the severely disorganized schizophrenic. The less completely systematized paranoid disorders extend from paranoia toward paranoid schizophrenia with which they overlap; while paranoid schizophrenia extends from this area of overlap down toward the more disorganized varieties of schizophrenic disorder.

15   *Schizophrenic Disorders*

SCHIZOPHRENIA today enjoys a greater degree of public and professional interest than any of the other behavior disorders whose care and treatment usually require institutionalization. The reason for this attention is fourfold. Schizophrenic disorders are of common occurrence, particularly in adolescence and early adulthood. The prognosis, unless competent therapy is available early, is grave so far as social recovery is concerned, and even with early and competent treatment the prognosis is not good. Thus, although schizophrenia accounts for about 19 per cent of first admissions to psychiatric hospitals, schizophrenic patients make up approximately 50 per cent of the hospital population.

Interest in schizophrenic disorders has also been stimulated by the introduction of various forms of shock therapy during the past decade and a half. The hypotheses advanced to account for improvement in many shock-treated cases are still vague and contradictory. There is general agreement, however, that an important contribution to this improvement is the widespread substitution of an aggressive, hopeful attitude on the part of therapists in place of the old stagnant pessimism. This interpretation has received substantial support from the published data on the results of competently planned psychiatric treatment in adequately staffed and equipped hospitals.

Cheney and Drewry,[1] for example, in a follow-up study of five hundred cases two to twelve years after discharge, found that 47 per cent were well or improved sufficiently to get along without hospitalization. Rennie, in another series treated in a different hospital, found that of 222 cases with a follow-up period of approxi-

---

[1] C. Cheney and P. Drewry, "Results of non-specific treatment in dementia praecox," *Amer. Jour. Psychiat.*, 1938, vol. 95, pp. 203-217.

mately twenty years after first admission, 27 per cent had recovered and remained at their previous level of biosocial adequacy. Nine per cent more had recovered, but at a level of reduced adequacy, another 16 per cent were able to work in spite of symptoms or relapses, while 9 per cent lived as family invalids, doing little or no productive work.[2] None of the patients in Rennie's series, or in the series of Cheney and Drewry, had been treated by shock, prolonged narcosis or cerebral insult.

A fourth source of lay and professional interest in schizophrenia is not new. Schizophrenic disorders exhibit a richness and variegation of behavior pathology unequaled by any of the other behavior disorders. In consequence, they provide an inexhaustible source of wonder and mystification to the layman and a perpetual challenge to the behavior pathologist.

It was Kraepelin who, toward the close of the nineteenth century, recognized that certain syndromes, previously described as independent dementing diseases of youth, could be brought together as related subtypes of a single disorder.[3] For this disorder Kraepelin appropriated the already current term *dementia praecox*, and under it he placed four subgroups which corresponded roughly to four of the supposedly dementing diseases. *Dementia simplex* became the simple type of dementia praecox. Patients assigned to this type have usually been described as undergoing a progressive decrease in effectiveness in meeting environmental demands during adolescence and early adulthood. They seem to drift gradually into apathy and indifference, without developing emotional outbursts or conspicuous delusional and hallucinatory episodes.

Hebephrenia was renamed the *hebephrenic type* of dementia praecox and its description was somewhat modified from that given by Hecker, who coined the original term. In this subgroup have been traditionally placed those patients in whose behavior incongruous and inappropriate smiling, giggling and laughing are prominent, delusions are bizarre and fragmentary, and grimacing, odd mannerisms and hallucinatory activities are common. The name of this type is intended to cover both the early onset, which as in the

[2] T. Rennie, "Follow-up study of five hundred patients with schizophrenia admitted to the hospital from 1913 to 1923," *Arch. Neurol. Psychiat.*, 1939, vol. 42, pp. 877-891.

[3] For a summary of this development, see N. Cameron, "The functional psychoses," in J. Hunt (editor), *Personality and the Behavior Disorders* (New York: Ronald Press, 1944), pp. 861-921.

simple type is described as insidious, and the silly, childish behavior which is often interpreted as an indication of regression. The
same interpretation has led to the arbitrary inclusion within this
type of those schizophrenic patients who develop incontinence or a
strong interest in urine and feces.

Catatonia, first described by Kahlbaum, who called it also *tension
insanity,* was changed into the *catatonic type* of dementia praecox.
In line with nineteenth-century thinking, Kahlbaum unhesitatingly
ascribed catatonia to a degenerative disease of the central nervous
system, and referred the symptomatology to specific localized neurological lesions, which, however, have proved to be fictitious. The
catatonic patient is the patient whose clinical picture is dominated
by motility disorders — excitement or stupor, overtalkativeness or
mutism, resistive behavior or catalepsy ("waxy flexibility"), symbolic
gesturing, posturing, grimacing, and stereotyped repetitive activities. The onset, unlike that of the preceding two types, is described
as frequently sudden and stormy.

A fourth syndrome, *dementia paranoides,* was transformed by
Kraepelin into the *paranoid type* of dementia praecox. To this subgroup have been traditionally assigned those patients whose behavior is dominated by delusions, is usually hostile, aggressive and
unpredictable, and includes hallucinations. The delusions are as a
rule persecutory in character, but may also be grandiose, ecstatic,
mystical or hypochondriacal; they are never as well-organized and
systematized as are the delusions of classical paranoia. The paranoid type is distinguished from the others also on the basis of a
later average age of onset. It differs from the simple and hebephrenic types, but not from the catatonic, in being often characterized by episodic excitement and retardation.

Neither the term *dementia praecox* nor the subdivision into four
types has proved satisfactory in practice. The term is a misnomer
and the types actually overlap in almost every detail of their symptomatology.[4] Indeed, Kraepelin's synthesis had hardly been accepted before objections were raised to the use of *dementia* for a
disorder in which disorganization was common but genuine de-

[4] A radical but welcome departure from this tradition is encouraged by the
wording in *United States Army Technical Medical Bulletin,* No. 203 (Washington, D.C.: United States Government Printing Office, October 19, 1945),
Section 18. It provides that schizophrenic patients need no longer be "forcibly
. . . classified into a Kraepelinian type."

mentia unusual,[5] and to the use of *praecox* when the onset of disorganization was by no means confined to youth. This critical trend was crystallized by the appearance of Bleuler's now classical monograph in which the disorder was renamed schizophrenia and the defects in Kraepelin's types were clearly pointed out.[6] "A case which begins as hebephrenia," Bleuler wrote by way of illustration, "can a few years later be a paranoid." He retained the Kraepelinian subdivisions for his schizophrenia on the grounds that he could find no convenient substitute.

Bleuler's great contribution in this field, however, was not his terminological reform, but his reinterpretation of the psychopathology of schizophrenia under the direct influence of Freud, Jung, Riklin and Abraham. By bringing the fructifying concepts of the then youthful system of psychoanalysis into contact with his own vast clinical knowledge of schizophrenia, Bleuler was able to produce a new structure for the psychiatric world. Through the monograph and a textbook,[7] which soon became an international standard, he succeeded in directing the interest of behavior pathologists in Europe and the Americas toward the origins of schizophrenic symptoms in personal need, frustration and conflict.

This reformulation, while it led to many important advances in the understanding of schizophrenia, also suffered from a serious defect. Bleuler could never bring himself to abandon the faith, almost universal in his early years, that schizophrenia would one day turn out to be a brain disease. As a result of this predilection, he always fell back upon some hypothetical tissue pathology as the ultimate explanation of schizophrenic symptoms. It was Adolf Meyer, in this country, who first set up the hypothesis that dementia praecox could be derived from normal behavior on the basis of adjustive insufficiency and habit deterioration. This he did in a series of three papers [8] which appeared shortly before Bleuler's monograph. It is of particular interest that Meyer was at the time not a

---

[5] A study of sixty-year-old chronic schizophrenics, for example, revealed no deterioration, in Kraepelin's sense, even though the patients had been schizophrenic for several decades. See S. Lehrman, "Schizophrenic deterioration," *Psychiat. Quart.*, 1940, vol. 14, pp. 140-156.

[6] E. Bleuler, *Dementia Praecox oder Gruppe der Schizophrenien*. Leipzig: Deuticke, 1911.

[7] E. Bleuler, *Lehrbuch der Psychiatrie*. Berlin: Springer, 1917 (translated by A. Brill as *Textbook of Psychiatry*. New York: Macmillan, 1924).

[8] A. Meyer, "Fundamental conceptions of dementia praecox," *Jour. Nerv. Ment. Dis.*, 1906, vol. 34, pp. 331-336; "The dynamic interpretation of dementia praecox," *Amer. Jour. Psychol.*, 1910, vol. 21, pp. 385-403; "The nature and conception of dementia praecox," *Jour. Abnorm. Psychol.*, 1910, vol. 5, pp. 274-285.

clinical psychiatrist, but brain pathologist for the Worcester State Hospital. Indeed, he cited the fact that indications of cerebral histopathology in schizophrenic cases were slight and inconsistent as evidence in support of his thesis.

It is obviously a short step from Bleuler's Freudian interpretations and Meyer's formulation in terms of adjustive insufficiency and habit deterioration to the conclusion that schizophrenia is a disorganization of the biosocial reaction systems that define personality. Personality, we said in Chapter 2, is the organization of interlocking behavior systems that each of us develops through learning processes, as he grows from a biological newborn to a biosocial adult, in an environment of other individuals and cultural products. Almost everyone who studies schizophrenic persons, regardless of his theoretical prejudice, seems to be struck by the same thing: the patient's behavior, especially in matters of personal importance, tends to become unintelligible and unpredictable in terms of the organized social perspectives dominant in his culture. In short, his behavior has undergone a biosocial disorganization.

In schizophrenic disorganization, as our clinical cases will illustrate, the patient's role-taking becomes desocialized. It moves away from its social derivation in directions that are determined by private fantasy, and includes responses in shared social situations which have validity only in a fantasy context (*overinclusion*), until eventually it no longer corresponds to the socially determined role-taking of other persons in the same culture.[9] The schizophrenic person, in other words, loses some of the social skills, the techniques and the perspectives which he has laboriously, and as a rule not too effectively, acquired through years of social interaction and cooperative work with other individuals in a shared environment. The loss of social skills — the "adjustive insufficiency" that Meyer emphasized — is most evident in the complex interpersonal relationships upon which adult and adolescent status depends. Thus, we find schizophrenic disorders beginning most commonly in a series of unsuccessful attempts to cope with situations peculiar to early and approaching biosocial maturity.

[9] N. Cameron, "Reasoning, regression and communication in schizophrenics," *Psychol. Monog.*, 1938, vol. 50, No. 221; "A study of thinking in senile deterioration and schizophrenic disorganization," *Amer. Jour. Psychol.*, 1938, vol. 51, pp. 650-665; "Deterioration and regression in schizophrenic thinking," *Jour. Abnorm. Soc. Psychol.*, 1939, vol. 34, pp. 265-270; "Schizophrenic thinking in a problem-solving situation," *Jour. Ment. Science*, 1939, vol. 85, pp. 1012-1035.

With this as our background, we may now define the *schizophrenic disorders* as *disorganization and desocialization of the acquired behavior systems constituting personality, and their replacement by behavior dominated or determined by private fantasy, in the absence of organ or tissue pathology adequate to account for the disorder.* Behavior that is dominated and determined by private fantasy, whether in schizophrenia or in normal daydreaming, cannot at the time be completely articulated with, or even adequately influenced by, the organization of the shared social environment. The normal daydreamer, in returning to socially shared operations, abandons the role-taking that belongs to his private fantasy. The schizophrenic patient, because of his lost social skills, is a daydreamer who cannot completely return.

SCHIZOPHRENIC SYMPTOMS

One important result of schizophrenic disorganization is the production of an overwhelming multiplicity of symptoms whose interrelationships are far from obvious. It is as bewildering to come unprepared and untrained into the presence of a disturbed schizophrenic patient as it would be suddenly to happen on a disturbed, disorganized community whose history one does not know or cannot understand. This is why so many students who have been highly trained in the physics and chemistry of man's interior, but relatively little trained in the study of personal interrelationships, are certain within themselves that marked behavioral confusion can arise only from some chemical or cellular catastrophe. But many years of intensive investigation confined to biochemistry and biophysics [10] have yielded little of significance for our understanding of the genesis, development or outcome of schizophrenia.[11]

[10] See the summaries in R. McFarland and H. Goldstein, "The biochemistry of dementia praecox," *Amer. Jour. Psychiat.*, 1938, vol. 95, pp. 509-552; N. Cameron, "Physiological psychology. I. The functional psychoses," *Annual Rev. Physiol.*, 1943, vol. 5, pp. 453-464; N. Cameron, "The functional psychoses," in J. Hunt (editor) *Personality and the Behavior Disorders* (New York: Ronald Press, 1944), pp. 861-921.

[11] For a contrary view and prediction, see the able presentation by R. Hoskins, *The Biology of Schizophrenia.* New York: Norton, 1946. Hoskins marshals the arguments for restricting effort in schizophrenia research to biophysics and biochemistry; he condemns the Hippocratic view of man as "that will-o'-the-wisp, that semiprojective synthetic artefact, 'the patient as a whole.'" (See especially the section entitled *Research Approaches,* pp. 167-170.)

If, however, instead of turning away immediately from a patient's behavioral confusion to concentrate upon his colloids, we begin by investigating the antecedents of his disorganization and the conditions of its development, we shall have something more substantial than a future hope on which to build our understanding. Indeed, the progression from order to disorder is no less intelligible for the behavior of biosocial persons than it is for communities and individual cells. But let us not make the common pedantic mistake of starting our discussion of schizophrenia by describing a sideshow of distorted behavior such as one can find on any large chronic service. For the end-products of behavior pathology, like the ruins of a strange civilization and the stained slide from a biopsy, can have little or no meaning to the person who does not understand their pathogenesis.

In the case presented below we can follow the patient's progression, from her aggressive but unskillful attempts to deal overtly with a complex social situation in a little domestic community, through her organization of a pseudocommunity including fantasied as well as social persons and acts, to her final withdrawal into an autistic community whose acts and persons existed only in her private fantasy behavior. As the patient's role-taking is practiced more and more in terms of her private fantasy, and comes less and less under the influence of events in the shared social field of operations, we see it growing increasingly desocialized until it reaches a point where we can no longer share it.

> The patient, a Kansas City high-school girl of seventeen, was brought to the hospital after a suicidal attempt, complaining of uncontrollable nervousness and terrible dreams. Both she and her father independently placed the onset of her illness in her fourteenth year, following in time the death of a paternal aunt who had reared her from infancy and who had given her both domineering and indulgent overprotection. Her father noticed with surprise that, in spite of her overdependence and apparent devotion to her aunt, the patient seemed to grieve little over her loss. Instead, she became suddenly arrogant, self-assertive and demanding, insisting that the home was now hers and that her aunt's daughter, a young woman of twenty who had been brought up with the patient, must hereafter take orders from her.
>
> Toward her father, on the other hand, the girl continued to display an affectionate attitude as she always had. However, she began exercising certain additional prerogatives usually claimed by

the adult matron, such as criticizing her father's deportment and characteristics, even in front of visitors, nagging him, and demanding that he spend more money on her, particularly for clothes. At the same time the patient expressed increasing anxiety and insecurity. She reminded the others that her aunt had always been afraid of the house and had said more than once that it had a curse on it. She protested against her father's leaving the house key under the door mat when he went out for an evening, saying that a stranger might find it and come in. She kept the light burning in her bedroom all night long and complained of horrible dreams. One night her father found her thrashing about the room with a cane — killing snakes, she said.

Meanwhile, at school the patient grew poorer and poorer in her studies; she seemed bored, inattentive and irritable. By the time she was fifteen and a half, she required the help of a private tutor to keep her from being dropped altogether. Eventually, even tutorial aid was not enough. The principal asked the girl to leave school and advised the father to consult a psychiatrist. The psychiatrist recommended immediate hospitalization, but his recommendation was not followed.

The patient showed a parallel decline in her social relationships to her contemporaries. She had, however, in this respect never attained an adequate level of social skill because of her restrictive overdependence upon her aunt. As one so often finds in the over-protected child, she had frightened and repelled the neighborhood children by her temper tantrums and her uncompromising demands. As an adolescent she had become, as we shall see, too involved in her own preoccupations to make adequate social contacts among her peers. The climax came about a year before admission to the clinic. She bought a new dress for a high-school dance, but when her escort arrived she refused to see him. After considerable persuasion she finally consented to go, but half an hour later she returned home without her escort. That was her last social engagement. Following her withdrawal from school, her father arranged little parties for her to help her get well, but she would not leave her room as long as the guests remained.

The girl's attitude toward her cousin had remained hostile and resentful throughout, in spite of her father's attempts to act as peacemaker. Once in an altercation over playing the radio the patient gave her cousin a bite that took two weeks to heal. Another time, while she was playing the piano for her cousin's guests, she suddenly banged her hands on the keys, ran out of the room and would neither explain her act nor return. The three-cornered feud that grew up between the two girls and the father finally ended when the cousin married and left home just before the patient turned sixteen.

It was somewhere around this time that the father noticed a change in his daughter's attitude toward him. Her usual expressions of affection disappeared, she declined to kiss him any more, she spoke insolently to him and began accusing him publicly of mistreating her. Nevertheless, on several occasions when dreams had frightened her, the patient insisted that he get in bed and comfort her, as her aunt had comforted her; and then she later upbraided him for having done so.

During the months between her leaving school and entering the hospital, the girl spent her time lying around the home; occasionally she went on a shopping trip alone. Her purchases were sometimes odd. Once, for example, she spent about forty dollars on history books, although the money had been given her for clothes. She spent twelve dollars on cosmetics on one trip, and a few days later burned them because, she said, she ought not to have bought them. She got up early one day and after collecting all the playing cards in the house she burned them, saying they were sinful. Although the patient had never been particularly religious, she began to express great concern over religion, church, sin, charity and the hereafter. She gave the housekeeper a five-dollar bill because she had to be charitable "in order to get to heaven."

The patient dated the onset of her illness from her fourteenth year, not because she recognized any change then in her own behavior, but because that was when she began autoerotism. On the basis of the same folklore that misleads so many adults, she came to the conclusion when she was fifteen that autoerotism was driving her crazy. This conclusion increased her already intolerable guilt and anxiety and undoubtedly contributed to her belief that she would burn in hell for her sins and that her hands were diseased. "I have leprosy," she said at the hospital; "look at my hands. But that's not punishment enough for all my evil. Faust — yes, he gave himself to the devil. That's what I've done. Don't touch me! You'll be sorry, you'll get leprosy too."

The patient's fantasies, which ultimately overwhelmed her and replaced all of her social role-taking, seem to have troubled her first as anxiety dreams — of snakes, murder, people in the house and assault. "I used to read stories and things, and then go to bed and lie awake and think about them. I'd be scared silly to be in the room by myself. That house is so spooky." When she closed her eyes and tried to sleep, she would have horrible visions and see faces that seemed to grow enormous. She thought men were climbing in the window and walking on the roof; she could not be sure whether it started with dreaming, but it seemed real when she knew she was awake. A man across the street seemed to control the house and he had people walking back and forth on the roofs. She began hearing voices at night and finally one voice, a man's, told her that she was to do whatever she was told.

The patient became convinced that her home was the headquarters of an opium gang which had murdered her father and put an impostor in his place. "My father wouldn't treat me the way this man has treated me," she said. "My father and I were friends. I've been love-starved and forsaken, and I thought someone was bringing in opium." People hit her and beat her and tied her up. They seemed able to read her mind and to control her by hearing her thoughts; she tried to keep back her thoughts, but the effort hurt the back of her head. She had horrible dreams and fantasies of killing her father and other people, of cutting them up and chewing their flesh, of being God and of being murdered as a sacrifice. She felt that she was someone else, her body was changing, she might be going to have a baby, she had a brain tumor and was going crazy.

The suicidal attempt was an act of self-punishment; she was going to hell for her sins, she said, and the quicker she got there the better. "I thought it would make me suffer; if I hadn't become so hardened it would have hurt terribly." In the hospital she was sure she would be executed or given a life-sentence for her awful thoughts; she wished she would "get black smallpox or something." She said, "I got hipped on the subject of Christianity. I thought I should torture myself. . . . I try to figure out ways of torturing people. It seems I have been in so much pain — well, no, not exactly pain, but trouble — and I want other people to have the same thing."

One night the patient called the nurse, who found her trembling and wringing her hands. "I think I'm pushing people's eyes in. I'm dreadfully wicked. (Were you dreaming?) No. It's those awful thoughts that go through my head." Once in the daytime she cried to a group of patients, "If I had the strength of Christ I would kill every one of you! Yes, I would kill you all because a more horrid doom awaits you than death!" She had to be taken away by nurses. Another day when angry she struck a depressed patient on the elbow with a chair. "That's nothing in comparison with what I'm going to do; I'm going to chop off your heads, every one of you! You'd better go home and chop off your families' heads. . . . You're not going to keep me here and make me bear children."

The patient told the psychiatrist that she felt she had a powerful influence over people and was responsible for everything that happened. She thought she might get superhuman ideas — "such as how Christ turned water into wine, I had to find out how it was done." As God she must suffer to help others and because of her sins she ought to kill herself. But the attempt had failed. "So," she said, "I came to the conclusion that I would have to forget. As time goes on, I'll forget all my troubles, my experiences and so forth." This was just what the patient seemed to be accomplishing. Years before, she had begun a struggle at home with a tangled personal situation involving social persons. This struggle in the shared social community was gradually replaced by the even greater complexities of her pseudocommunity, which included a mixture of real and imagined persons, and from this she was withdrawing finally into an autistic community consisting of fantasied persons and acts appearing only in her own private fantasy context.

In spite of active therapy, the patient grew increasingly uncommunicative. One day, while saying to the psychiatrist that she liked "dreamy states," she slipped into an apparent stupor, with her eyes closed and the eyeballs rolled upward, her arms and legs limp. The eyelids resisted opening, the limbs and the jaw became stiffer with passive movement. Another day when the patient was lying on her side on the bed, just before lunch, a sudden clap of thunder made her go so rigid that she could be picked up and placed in a chair by the nurses with no more change in her posture than if she had been a statue. Then the lunch trays arrived and an experienced nurse was given the task of coaxing and spoon-feeding her in an attempt to re-establish her reactions to her surroundings. After about ten minutes of this, the girl suddenly got up, rubbed her eyes and then ate her lunch with the others as though nothing had happened.

The patient seemed to sleep well at night without medication and in spite of occasional disturbing dreams. In the daytime she spent most of her time in apparent daydreaming. Her talk began to develop marked disorganization until it became a poor instrument of communication. She was frequently observed talking excitedly to herself, and sometimes she smiled and laughed as though she were hallucinating. Often she stood straight against the wall with her hands high above her head, but she would give no explanation of this posturing. Finally, her father decided to place the patient in a state hospital near her home. Her prognosis on transfer was poor for social recovery.

In this case we see, first, the adolescent struggle of a girl whose lifelong overprotection by a foster-mother had given little opportunity for the development of adequate role-taking skills in any but a dependent relationship.[12] The affectional situation was suddenly complicated by the death of the foster-mother, who was not only the mother-substitute and the dominant female in the household, but also the father's sister and mother to the foster-sister rival. The girl's unskillful attempts to usurp her foster-mother's role are obvious in the history. Her growing confusion can in part be attributed to the conflicts and contradictions which these attempts precipitated. For the jealous overprotected young adolescent could hardly take the role of domineering mother to her adult cousin. She was even less well prepared than the average fourteen-year-old motherless girl for the not uncommon attempt to transform a dependent daughter role into that of woman of the house in relation to a widowed father. She had been reared an anxious, socially immature child; and it was as such that her foster-mother's death left her to work out alone her multiple conflicts, including her clearly expressed guilt over sex and hostility, in a household with a man in whom she had never learned to confide and a woman whom she hated.

The other important factor in this girl's disorganization and desocialization was the progressive intrusion of fantasy techniques and fantasy productions into the field of shared social operations. In her own account, the patient gave many indications that long before her aunt's death she had found difficulty in distinguishing between dream and daydream, that she had utilized fantasy freely in satisfying need, and that she had also suffered from terrifying dreams and hypnagogic visions which drove her to seek the protection of her aunt's bed. In her unsuccessful attempts to cope with the involved domestic situation after her aunt's death, she carried her conflicts into her waking and sleeping fantasy life. This procedure did not provide an escape from the conflict situation; indeed, her fantasying seemed actually to increase her anxiety and complicate her problems. She simply went on doing something she had always done. But now the problems were adult and there was no one to whom she could flee for comforting in the night.

The patient said that, for more than two years before admission to the clinic, she had spent most of her nights half-awake because

12 Compare the characteristics cited by J. Kasanin, E. Knight and P. Sage, "The parent-child relationship in schizophrenia. I. Over-protection-rejection," *Jour. Nerv. Ment. Dis.*, 1934, vol. 79, pp. 249-263.

of her anxiety, and much of her days half-asleep because of her fatigue. She continued the struggle, which she had been waging for status in the family constellation, on into her day and night fantasy context, imagining aggressions and counter aggressions — torturing, murdering and eating people in hate and being herself tortured and murdered as expiation of her guilt, becoming omnipotent and being sacrificed to save others. Emotional conflicts such as this girl had might have at least temporarily disorganized the behavior of any adolescent who had no way of escaping from them. But this girl was well below average in her ability to form new affectional attachments and to handle personal interrelationships skillfully, and she was well above average in her reliance upon fantasy.

We have seen that the patient as a child was unable to distinguish between what she had done in a fantasy context and what in a shared social context. This overinclusion [13] in one setting of what belonged to the other was relatively unimportant in the life of a dependent, overprotected child. But it quickly became a major factor in developing disorganization when there was no longer anyone to protect and comfort the young adolescent, and no one to depend on.

The confusion resulting from her overinclusion helps to explain why the patient's reactions of hostility, resentment, guilt and grandiosity generalized indiscriminately to fantasied persons and to strangers in the social community — to patients, for example — and eventually to everybody ("people" and "they"). When these reactions brought the girl no security, but only more restraint and counteraggression from the social community, she finally carried out her threat to "forget everything" — all her past troubles — by confining her behavior completely to an autistic community. Here, as in normal dreaming, what one does need not be shackled by the stricter antecedent-consequent relations of shared behavior, sin can be enjoyed, crime go unpunished, and power be unlimited and unchallenged.

The indefinite, insidious *onset* of the illness just described and the sudden overt act which frightens relatives into accepting expert help — in this case a suicidal attempt — are typical features in the histories of a majority of hospitalized schizophrenic patients. There are still, however, a great many cases which follow the classical

[13] See the discussion of exclusion and inclusion in behavior organization, in Chapter 3.

descriptions of so-called "dementia simplex." The patient, instead of showing in adolescence and adulthood an increasing effectiveness in dealing with adult environmental situations, progressively declines in his effectiveness until he cannot meet the ordinary demands of everyday routines. He may drift gradually into attitudes of apathy and indifference toward his social environment, eventually reaching a behavior level below that requisite for life unprotected in the community.

The absence of an aggressive outburst or an episode of overt submission in these cases can often be ascribed to the lack of sufficient stimulation from the social environment and to non-interference by other persons with the patient's withdrawal, or with his socially inappropriate behavior.[14] One of our patients, for example, had parents who for two years refused to consider the boy's schizophrenic disorganization as anything more than an amusing affectation. It was only when he became unable to find his way around town, attracted the notice of people in the street and was finally brought home by the police, who recognized what was wrong, that the family took the situation seriously. Shock therapy brought a mild improvement which, however, soon disappeared.

Sudden onset is more often apparent than real in severe schizophrenic disorders, the overt act to which we have referred being mistaken for the beginning of the illness. However, as we saw in Chapter 9, acute anxiety can lead to acute disorganization with marked hallucinatory and delusional behavior which then persists as schizophrenia. We shall present a case later which developed suddenly on a surgical ward and terminated ten days later in complete recovery under psychiatric care and treatment. Improvement and recovery in schizophrenia are also as a rule gradual and slow. They are so often incomplete and temporary that the more pessimistic therapists prefer to speak only of remissions and to consider every recurrence a relapse, just as was the custom in relation to pulmonary tuberculosis forty years ago. The outcome, unfortunately, to some extent justifies a gloomy therapeutic attitude. But recoveries from early mild schizophrenic illnesses are common, and even in cases with severe delusional and hallucinatory involvement the

14 In a series of five hundred cases of schizophrenia, definite precipitating events were reported in over 72 per cent. T. Rennie, "Follow-up study of five hundred patients with schizophrenia admitted to the hospital from 1913 to 1923," *Arch. Neurol. Psychiat.*, 1939, vol. 42, pp. 877-891.

outcome depends at least in part upon the therapist's skill and enterprise.[15]

Delusional reactions seem to characterize all schizophrenic disorders, although in some cases their presence can only be inferred from other behavior because of defects in social communication. All of the varieties discussed in Chapter 13 are to be found among schizophrenic patients — *delusions of persecution, influence, grandeur, self-depreciation, body change* and *environmental change.* It is usually the case that early in the disorganization the delusions are more logical than later, more restricted in scope and supported by more congruent emotional participation. Thus, one finds anxiety, resentment, suspicion, self-assertion and self-beatification developing in some recognizable relationship to the patient's fear, guilt, frustration, threats, need and compensatory self-attitudes.

As disorganization progresses, however, the delusions conform less and less to roles which normal persons in their imagination can take and understand. Under the conditions of overinclusion the delusional reactions generalize indiscriminately, as we have seen, to excitants in the social environment and in the patient's private fantasy; thus their character grows fantastic, vague, grotesque, bizarre and mystical. In many chronic patients this may be the final picture. However, if the disorganization progresses still farther, a level may be reached at which delusional reactions are stabilized as stereotyped recitals without congruent emotional participation, like the complaints of chronic hypochondriacs. Frequently, all that remains of a delusional eruption are a few fragmentary responses which, like some hysterical autonomous fragments, have a history but no contemporary meaning. Or the specific delusions are lost and the attitudes that once supported them remain; the patient shows merely suspicion and aloofness, like a released prisoner, or has an air of haughty condescension, like the retired head of an industrial empire or an eclipsed society leader.

A great deal has been made of the so-called "emotional incongruity," "emotional insufficiency" or "affective flattening," some writers going so far as to maintain that a schism between faculties of intellect and emotion is the fundamental event in schizophrenia

[15] According to Appel, studies of the results of therapy in schizophrenia indicate that the use of therapy in *some* form seems more important than the type of therapy employed. K. Appel, "Psychiatric therapy," in J. Hunt (editor), *Personality and the Behavior Disorders* (New York: Ronald Press, 1944), pp. 1107-1163.

that justifies its name.[16] It is indeed common for a patient to tell of something terrible that is happening to him, or of some frightful thing he has fantasied, planned or done, without anything approaching the emotional participation a normal person expects of him. A man says that a snake has devoured his intestines and he can feel his food drop out of his stomach; but he smiles pleasantly as he tells it, he eats and sleeps well and he has normal evacuation. Another, in a matter-of-fact voice, describes horrible treatment to which he or someone close to him is being subjected. A third mutilates himself or kills his own child without showing a fraction of the emotional disturbance the ordinary person would.

We do not have a complete explanation for what is called "emotional incongruity" in schizophrenia. Contrary to popular belief, it is a comparatively rare phenomenon in early schizophrenic disorganization. The fact that it is so often found in first admissions to psychiatric hospitals means only that first admissions in schizophrenia occur usually late in the disorder because of public ignorance and neglect. One finds in carefully observed cases that many patients, after months of anguish, become secondarily dull and indifferent as an apparent escape technique in which they render themselves inaccessible, not to the behavior of others, but to the stimulation of their own reactions. That is what our high-school girl did, and that is what apparently happened to concentration camp victims in Europe.[17] This evolution of emotional apathy does not make it normal, but only intelligible. Sometimes the ridicule to which patients are exposed makes them conceal and minimize anxiety or fervor, just as normal people do when ridiculed.

In many other cases of schizophrenic disorder the normal observer gets an impression of emotional incongruity in the patient's behavior because he and the patient are unable to take each other's roles adequately. They consequently cannot see things from each other's perspective. In other words, what appears to be emotional incongruity is actually a by-product of desocialization which involves a breakdown in communication. For example, what a patient

---

[16] This, however, was not actually Bleuler's justification. He launched his new term with these words, "I name dementia praecox *schizophrenia* because, as I hope to show, the disintegration of the most varied mental functions is one of its most important characteristics." E. Bleuler, *Dementia Praecox oder Gruppe der Schizophrenien* (Leipzig: Deuticke, 1911), p. 5 (my translation).

[17] B. Bettelheim, "Individual and mass behavior in extreme situations," *Jour. Abnorm. Soc. Psychol.*, 1943, vol. 38, pp. 417-452.

says, does or thinks may be justified by his delusional reactions; if the observer could share these delusional reactions, his emotional behavior might be like that of the patient. However, as we know, schizophrenic delusional reactions are often so individualistically organized or so disorganized that they can neither be formulated in equivalent conventional language behavior, nor in any other way adequately shared by the socially organized normal man.

In some schizophrenic patients, especially those suffering from severe desocialization, the social attitudes which had once been acquired through social role-taking have been lost, along with the specific techniques of interpersonal behavior they once supported.[18] Thus, the emotional component of a reaction may be missing because the attitude of which it was a part is missing; the result is a response without its behavioral context or, as we ordinarily say it, a response without meaning. In still others, for example our case of the man with the snake in him, the complaints have meanings for the patient which they do not have for the listener. In terms of these unshared meanings the emotional participation, or its absence, is congruent for the patient but disconcerts the normal observer because he lacks the patient's supporting attitudes.

The *general behavior* of schizophrenic patients is highly variable — from excited to stuporous, from resistive to cataleptic, from over-talkative to mute, from hostile and hateful to dependent and erotic, from indifferent to ecstatic, from extremely aggressive to extremely submissive. We shall not attempt to list the countless individual responses that belong with these variations; to a large extent they can be anticipated by an observer who grasps the patient's dominant attitude at the time and understands the effects of disorganization upon behavior. Sudden shifts in attitude are, however, of relatively common occurrence in schizophrenic patients and these are often impossible to predict. They are sometimes the product of ambivalence in a confused person; [19] sometimes they seem to be related to the abrupt shifts in attitude that normal people make under emotional stress as, for example, in lovers' quarrels. But one of the commonest sources of unpredictable change in schizophrenic

[18] Compare the study of schizophrenic behavior in a free-play social situation by J. Slotkin, "The nature and effects of social interaction in schizophrenia," *Jour. Abnorm. Soc. Psychol.*, 1941, vol. 37, pp. 345-368.

[19] See, for example, the case in Chapter 3 of the girl who suddenly struck her mother without warning a few moments after they had apparently been on affectionate terms.

patients appears to be the sudden intervention of an auditory or a visual hallucination.

Hallucinatory behavior is nowhere more common among the behavior disorders than in schizophrenia. One of the most surprising things about the hallucinating, deluded schizophrenic is that, in contrast to the delirious patient, he can usually give his bearings correctly — where he is, the approximate date and time of day, and who the persons around him are — and his recall is far superior, as a rule, to that of persons in delirium. Schizophrenic hallucinations are most often auditory, less often visual and least often olfactory, gustatory, tactual and visceral. Hallucinatory behavior early in the illness corresponds in mood and topic with the delusional reactions it accompanies, but as disorganization progresses it may be reduced, as the delusions also are, to stereotyped grotesque and disconnected response fragments. The patient who has already been much questioned and prodded will generally deny that he is hallucinating when he is preoccupied, and the behavior pathologist is often obliged to base his interpretations upon inferences warranted by his study of known hallucinators.[20]

A great many common schizophrenic symptoms are only exaggerations of the behavior of a normal person engrossed in his own preoccupations. To this category belong the motionless sitting, standing and staring, the giggling, smiling, laughing and talking to oneself, for which there may be an explanation in private fantasy but none in the shared environment. To it belongs also behavior which we call merely incongruous or inappropriate, but which consists actually of overt responses in the social field to events in a fantasied context. In other words, something unseen, unheard and unshared by an observer may nevertheless provide attitudes which, although they remain private, still give congruity and appropriateness to the responses from the patient's point of view. For the lay observer the patient's responses are senseless and often annoying, like recurrent laughter next door or one side of a telephone conversation. However, schizophrenic symptoms may seem as strange and fragmentary to the patient as they do to the normal observer. That is, as a product of his progressive disorganization and desocialization, the patient has developed highly individualistic and incom-

[20] Compare the autobiographical account by a patient diagnosed as schizophrenic. J. Lang (pseudonym), "The other side of hallucinations," *Amer. Jour. Psychiat.*, 1938, vol. 94, pp. 1089-1097 and 1939, vol. 96, pp. 423-430.

municable behavior patterns which he no longer controls through self-reactions based upon the social attitudes of social persons.

Most of the symptomatology which Kahlbaum mistook for signs of neural degeneration, when he developed his concept of *catatonia*,[21] has turned out to be behavior that is, or once was, symbolic in function. Gestures, grimaces, postures and mannerisms are either the overt, public part of an otherwise covert, private activity, or else they are residual fragments of a personally important role that once belonged in a person's behavior. They appear to others strange and meaningless because their context cannot be shared, and often because their context and origin have been lost even by the patient.[22] The maintenance or stereotyped repetition of symbolic and residual responses in schizophrenia reminds one immediately of the autonomous tremors, cramps and tics in hysteria and the rituals in compulsive disorders. All of these symptoms are similar in that they represent at some time in the patient's history a personally significant attitude or response; and all remain unintelligible, even to the patient, until their lost context has been reconstructed in behavior.

The peculiarities of *language* and *thought* in schizophrenia have attracted a great deal of the attention of behavior pathologists during the past forty years.[23] As we pointed out in Chapter 4, it is impossible to separate talking and thinking. As the acquisition of language habits proceeds in the shared social activities of a person's childhood, thinking is gradually modified into less individualistic and more conventional patterns. The two varieties of symbolic behavior thus develop together, inextricably intermingled in some reactions and in others supplementing or to some extent opposing each other. Because schizophrenia is a disorganizing and desocializing disorder, it could be predicted that the chief biosocial instrument of interpersonal communication, talking, would suffer from and contribute to the disorganization and desocialization of the individual. And because thinking and talking as behavior are so

[21] We have discontinued the use of the term *catatonic* because its contemporary meaning is fully rendered by *schizophrenic*. Thus, "catatonic" excitement, stupor or posture is the same thing as schizophrenic excitement, stupor or posture.

[22] O. Kant, " 'Inappropriate laughter' and 'silliness' in schizophrenia," *Jour. Abnorm. Soc. Psychol.*, 1942, vol. 37, pp. 398-402.

[23] For a statement of contemporary views see J. Kasanin (editor), *Language and Thought in Schizophrenia*. Berkeley: University of California Press, 1944.

closely interwoven, it could also be predicted that his thinking would show the same changes and have the same effects upon the patient as his talking. Moreover, if we recall the origin and the mode of operation of self-reactions in talking and thinking, we can make a third prediction: that self-reactions will follow the same general pattern of disorganization and desocialization as do symbolic reactions to other persons and to shared situations.

The patient's talking and thinking may show no greater change than an indefinable vagueness of communication and reports by the patient of unclearness in his thinking. A school-teacher, for example, complained as follows: "I just exactly can't talk as clearly. I'd give a pretty dime to talk like I like or place my words in talking with people noticing." Of her thinking this young woman says, "It slips because you go on and talk and have imaginations and try for others and seems just to come back to you." A high-school boy of sixteen, in an experimental test situation, completed the phrase, *My hair is fair because,* with the statement, "Because of something else, it's on my head, it comes from my mother." After partial recovery he completed the same phrase with, "Because I inherited it from my parents." To the stimulus phrase *The wind blows because,* he replied while ill, "Just cosmic dust," but after partial recovery his answer became, "Because of atmospheric air-currents changing."[24] It is hardly necessary to reiterate that these symbol distortions involve the patient's thinking along with his talking.

In severe language disorganization the schizophrenic patient may reach a level of verbal discontinuity (*scatter*) at which his talk is useless as an instrument of communication. The conventional sequence of words and the use of appropriate connectives partially disappear, giving the flow of talk a disjointed character that is not the same as aphasic *agrammatism,* but can be just as disabling socially to the patient.[25] In early cases, scatter may be evident only in relation to personal conflicts, but eventually it often includes

[24] N. Cameron, "Reasoning, regression and communication in schizophrenics," *Psychol. Monog.,* 1938, vol. 50, No. 221.

[25] For comparisons between the language behavior of schizophrenic and of senile persons, the latter with cerebral incompetence, see N. Cameron, "A study of thinking in senile deterioration and schizophrenic disorganization," *Amer. Jour. Psychol.,* 1938, vol. 51, pp. 650-665. For a comparison of the test performance of schizophrenic and of normal presenile persons, see A. Magaret, "Parallels in the behavior of schizophrenics, paretics, and presenile non-psychotics," *Jour. Abnorm. Soc. Psychol.,* 1942, vol. 37, pp. 511-528.

everything but a few stereotyped replies to stereotyped questions. New words (*neologisms*) also appear in the talk of some patients. These may be simply the further development of personal idioms in a seriously desocialized individual, or they may result from the condensation of two or more ordinary words. In the latter instance they are similar to the condensations that appear in normal dreams, and in the daytime talk of the normal person who is hurried, excited, anxious, ambivalent or preoccupied.

A development of particular importance in schizophrenic language behavior is the use of words and phrases in ways that approximate their usual meaning but are sufficiently lacking in precision and definition to confuse and fatigue the average listener. Some patients develop their own idiom, which becomes intelligible to a listener if he studies it in relation to each patient's personal difficulties, his delusions and his history. Thus, a patient states that he is alive, "Because you really live physically because you have menu three times a day; that's the physical." (*What else is there besides the physical?*) "Then you're alive mostly to serve a work from the standpoint of methodical business." A knowledge of the patient's habitual idiom and his preoccupation with serving the world makes this translation possible: "You live physically because you have three meals a day and you live to perform a service in your daily routines." The effect upon the listener of this use of personal idiom in schizophrenic talk, which is otherwise not disorganized, can be judged from the following verbatim example.

To the question, *Why are you in the hospital?* the patient replied:

"I'm a cut donator, donated by double sacrifice. I get two days for every one. That's known as double sacrifice; in other words, standard cut donator. You know, we considered it. He couldn't have anything for the cut, or for these patients. All of them are double sacrifice because it's unlawful for it to be donated any more. (*Well, what do you do here?*) I do what is known as the double criminal treatment. Something that he badly wanted, he gets that, and seven days' criminal protection. That's all he gets, and the rest I do for my friend. (*Who is the other person that gets all this?*) That's the way the asylum cut is donated. (*But who is the other person?*) He's a criminal. He gets so much. He gets twenty years' criminal treatment, would make forty years; and he gets seven days' criminal protection and that makes fourteen days. That's all he gets.

(*And what are you?*) What is known as cut donator Christ. None of them couldn't be able to have anything; so it has to be true works or prove true to have anything, too. He gets two days, and that twenty years makes forty years. He loses by causing. He's what is known as a murder. He causes that. He's a murder by cause because he causes that. He can't *get* anything else. A double sacrifice is what is known as where murder turns, turns the friend into a cut donator and that's what makes a daughter-son. (*A daughter-son?*) Effeminate. A turned Christ. The criminal is a birth murder because he makes him a double. He gets two days' work for every day's work. . . . (*What is 'a birth murder'?*) A birth murder is a murder that turns a cut donator Christ into a double daughter-son. He's turned effeminate and weak. He makes him a double by making him weak. He gets two days' work for every one day's work because after he's made a double, he gets twice as much as it is. He's considered worth twice that much more. He has to be sacrificed to be a double."

Mutism is not uncommon in schizophrenia. Its most distinctive characteristics are the abruptness with which it may begin and cease, and the frequently obvious relationship it bears to the rest of a patient's biosocial behavior. For example, one of our patients, after too much confession under pressure said, "I've talked too much," and remained mute thereafter for almost a year. Another, after several months of mutism without stupor awakened one night and asked to see her physician. When he came, she conversed with him for over an hour, her manner somewhat dreamy and her sentences sometimes trailing off without a finish, but the general form of her talk normally relevant and coherent. She spoke as one who had been in another world and had just returned, asking questions about the hospital, the nurses and attendants, the patients and her family. Finally she said she wanted to go back to bed. The next morning she was as uncommunicative as ever; a month later she began to speak in the daytime and eventually she made a social recovery.

A third patient, who had become mute before admission, was one day visited unexpectedly by her relatives who were conducted straight to the ward by a nurse. She jumped up from a chair at once to greet them and conversed freely and naturally. When her psychiatrist, who had been doing a physical examination on a new patient behind bed screens, suddenly appeared, the talking patient became silent again, resumed speaking as soon as the psychiatrist left, and finally relapsed into mutism when her visitors departed. She also recovered some months later under psychiatric therapy.

We have already discussed the important complaints of *thought-deprivation, unnatural interference* and *blocking* of *words* and *thoughts* under delusions of influence in Chapter 13. We said there that the schizophrenic patient sometimes claims that words are put into his mouth and thoughts into his mind by persons or machines in control of him, or that someone or something forces his tongue to move and to say things he does not himself think. These complaints arise obviously from disowning projection in a disorganized person.[26]

VARIETIES OF SCHIZOPHRENIC DISORDER

We have seen that the Kraepelinian division of schizophrenia into four types originated, not from a preliminary planned study of patients, but from a recognition that the descriptions of four apparently different diseases included many identical or similar symptoms. What Kraepelin attempted to do in his synthesis was to give each of the formerly independent entities a semi-autonomous status, like four political states brought into a single confederation. The chief reason that these subdivisions are now in the process of being discarded is that each of them has been found to have characteristics supposed to identify one or more of the others. For example, all schizophrenic disorders involve important delusional developments and so may be classified as paranoid, in the modern sense. Most, if not all, schizophrenic patients at some time show excitement, stupor, mutism or one of the other motility features formerly called "catatonic." And almost any schizophrenic person, if he is sick long enough, may develop progressive apathy, indifference and habit-deterioration, hallucinate and exhibit "silly" behavior — characteristics that were once supposed to be peculiar to the simple and hebephrenic types.

But the moment we discard the Kraepelinian types, on the grounds that they are not valid, we discover that we need some other system of subdivision because schizophrenia undivided is too

---

[26] See the interpretation of some of these phenomena in the autobiographical account of J. Lang (pseudonym), "The other side of the affective side of schizophrenia," *Psychiatry*, 1939, vol. 2, pp. 195-202; "The other side of the ideological side of schizophrenia," *Psychiatry*, 1940, vol. 3, pp. 389-394.

cumbersome to handle. The limitless variety of the symptomatology makes such an ordering necessary and the large numbers of schizophrenic patients make it feasible. Since one of the most striking and important characteristics of schizophrenic disorganization is the disturbance in the patient's relationship to the social community, we shall begin by grouping schizophrenic patients in accordance with this relationship, whether it is predominantly *aggressive, submissive* or *detached*. Under the *aggressive schizophrenic reactions* we shall for convenience distinguish between *persecuted, grandiose* and *self-punitive* patients; under the *submissive schizophrenic reactions* we shall similarly distinguish between *compliant, dedicated* and *transformed* patients; and under the *detached schizophrenic reactions* we shall distinguish between the primarily *avoidant* patient and the primarily *adient* patient.

In setting up and using such a scheme of subdivision we must avoid above all the mistake of acting as if these groups and subgroups were mutually exclusive types. On the contrary, a submissive patient may become predominantly aggressive and then, if his aggression is sharply countered by other persons, he may grow unreactive to the social community and show progressive desocialization. Indeed, it is the changeability of the schizophrenic syndrome that constitutes one of its most important challenges to the therapist and the behavior pathologist. In all three major subdivisions the onset may be gradual or sudden, the progress may be slow or rapid, steady or episodic, and the outcome may be in recovery, partial recovery or no recovery.

Aggressive schizophrenic reactions

Persecuted patients. The persecuted aggressive schizophrenic patient is one whose attitude is predominantly hostile and resentful toward the social community. He attempts actively to outwit, elude or counteract the supposed attacks upon him, to obtain vindication from his detractors or to pay his persecutors back in kind. The delusions most characteristic of the subgroup are those of persecution and of influence. Patients frequently complain at first that there is "something wrong in the atmosphere," or something going on that they cannot quite understand. If sudden clarification develops, there may be an abrupt unexpected assault, a panic reaction, headlong flight, suicide or insistent demands upon authority by the patient for protection and for the punishment of those who persecute him.

An ex-college student, for example, after years of unshared pondering, fantasying, watching and cautious questioning, came to the wholly unfounded conclusion that acquaintances of his had been involved in crimes of rape and incest. On the basis of bizarre misinterpretations of ordinary city street scenes, such as the exchange of greetings between pedestrians and shouts or laughter from people in passing automobiles, he organized an extravagant pseudocommunity of plotters and counterplotters. This pseudocommunity he peopled with the acquaintances whom he suspected, and with imagined persons who talked to him at night. In his preoccupations — which were deep enough to make him lose one job after another for inattention to duty — the patient fixed upon first one and then another person as the ringleader of the criminals. Finally he "realized the truth," heard the same night that his discovery would cost him his life, sought out the man who he "knew" was the mastermind, and assaulted him with almost fatal results.

Grandiose patients. The grandiose aggressive schizophrenic patient is typically a disorganized self-assertive person whose dominant delusions are those of grandeur. The claims he makes to special distinction or power from the beginning lack the systematization that characterizes paranoid disorders. As the patient grows more and more desocialized, his formulation of his claims becomes increasingly difficult for other persons to share or comprehend. The grandiose subgroup includes patients who in their self-reactions attempt to play the role of political, religious or military leader, of scientist or inventor, of author, poet or painter, of industrialist, labor leader, landowner or aristocrat.

Some patients describe themselves as president or king, as God or as the emissary of a powerful agency or person, and seek to compel acknowledgment and acceptance of their status from other persons. Others assert that there is something important which they have been entrusted to perform, hear voices and have visions which confirm their delusional beliefs, but are unable clearly to formulate the mission or to put their convictions into organized action.

A patient of ours, a college graduate, tried for a year to explain and to initiate a master program of industrial reform in his father's factory. He was given a good salary, a small staff of his own selection and complete freedom. But at the end of this period no one was able to understand what the program was, not even the staff, and nothing had been achieved beyond the accumulation of a shed full of junk and parts for some obscure enterprise. The father, who was a self-made man, at first interpreted his son's vagueness and strange techniques as the effects of four years in college which he hoped would be overcome by the realities of business. When, however, the patient threatened him with a loaded revolver for defeating the master program, the father realized that his growing concern over the boy's health was only too well founded.

Schizophrenic grandiosity seems often to follow upon unsuccessful attempts to meet new challenges of the social environment. Thus, our schizophrenic boy with the *Mignon delusion* developed his first public sign of grandeur after an adolescent sex adventure in which he was frustrated and humiliated by the effects of his own anxiety. Another patient began developing a fantastic scheme of cosmic reform, in which visions of extraordinary wealth, power and sexual potency were intermingled, after he failed repeatedly in business. He had been successful in his brief military career during the war of 1917-18, and he had expected to rise quickly, and to gain the security and approval he needed, when he returned to civilian life. Such grandiose reactions as these are obvious compensatory need-satisfaction substitutes in fantasy for other need-satisfactions which the patient has failed to attain in the shared social environment.

The interrelations between schizophrenic delusions of grandeur and of persecution often result in a complex clinical picture which includes characteristics of more than one subgroup of schizophrenia. The grandiose person may conclude that, as a great person, he must have enemies who hate, fear and envy him. This makes him reaction-sensitive to signs of danger and favors his finding evidence which seems to justify his fears. Grandiose patients also explain away their failures and their confinement in a hospital by attributing them to the work of jealous and frightened detractors. Religious, moral and sexual delusions of grandeur often arouse anxiety and guilt, with fear of punishment, which in turn lead to the growth of a persecuting pseudocommunity or to self-punitive reactions. The evolution of delusions of grandeur from those of persecution follows similar lines; for example, patients seeking to account for their imagined persecution often conclude that to merit so much attention they must be great. Delusions of grandeur and persecution side by side in the same person's behavior are common among schizophrenic patients.

Self-punitive patients. The self-punitive aggressive schizophrenic patient directs his hostility toward himself in ways that resemble closely the coercion and self-punishment in compulsive disorders and the self-punitive behavior of depressed persons. We have already discussed, in Chapter 5, the common confusions of sadism and masochism, of righteousness, cruelty, sex and religion in relation to need-satisfaction sequences and self-reactions. The dangers of such confusions in the disorganized and desocialized schizophrenic are many and grave. The need for severe, disabling and even fatal punishment, for example, is not always confined to self-punitive reactions that harm the patient. It may spread to involve other persons, who are helpless or unsuspecting, and since the spread usually develops in accordance with the patient's unshared fantasy context, it can seldom be completely anticipated.

The young woman mentioned in Chapter 13, who burned herself fatally about the head and face, belongs in the group of self-punitive aggressive schizophrenics. So does a young man who deliberately dropped the leg of an iron cot on his finger because, he said, it might help him. A schizophrenic woman burned her hand with a pressing iron, explaining afterwards, "I felt I should be punished." She repeatedly extinguished cigarettes with her finger-tips, burning them so that they required bandaging. Another succeeded in stealthily cutting through a good part of her biceps muscle with manicure scissors while she lay in a hospital bed under observation. This self-mutilation was followed soon after by her statement to her physician that she had been troubled by monstrous hallucinations of vampire-like creatures which experimented on human beings and sucked their blood. There was no clear evidence that the act was carried out with suicidal intent. In schizophrenia, cases are not unknown in which a patient amputates his own hand or an ear, or blinds himself in one eye. The clinical reports of these cases make it seem probable that during mutilation the part is selectively reaction-insensitive, to the same degree as the insensitivity found in hysterical inactivation.

Submissive schizophrenic reactions

Compliant patients. The compliant submissive schizophrenic patient is one who believes that he is being somehow used, controlled, compelled or scapegoated. Instead of aggressively resisting, seeking protection or trying to escape, however, he maintains a relatively passive attitude toward the predicament of which he complains. He may even attempt to cooperate with dominant personalities and influences in his pseudocommunity and actually invite, or at least do nothing to avert, the climax which he sees approaching. The compliant schizophrenic patient nearly always exhibits delusions of influence and usually those of self-depreciation also. Persecutory delusions, when they are present, arouse in the submissive patient at most some complaining and objecting, but they do not lead to hostile attack, active flight or vigorous defense.

One woman was convinced, for example, that her physicians and nurses were all converging on her with magnetism, radium and electricity to make her lose her mind and so bring her will under their control. At the same time she said she knew it was for her own good, to make her well, and that she must have a "scientific baby" before she could recover. A schizophrenic man felt compelled to go abroad and join the foreign legion so that he would be killed. Sometimes he said that he had been ordered to do this as expiation for the unpardonable sin; sometimes he said he was being sacrificed so that his family might escape the death. Another patient believed that her behavior was controlled by a machine and that the nurses checked on what she was thinking by snapping switches on and off in the ward kitchen. Messages appeared in the newspapers or over the radio that told her what to do and where to go. She was part of someone's plan, but she did not know what the plan was about. Her one great duty was to please and obey those who controlled her.

Dedicated patients. The dedicated submissive schizophrenic patient is one who considers himself a passive instrument through which something of unusual significance is to be accomplished — a mission is to be performed or a great evil to others is to be implemented. The patient does not actively perform the mission or implement the evil, but through his living or dying, or through his transfiguration, the goal set by someone else is realized. Often he seems to have nothing more to go on than a conviction that in some obscure way, which he himself cannot understand but must not resist, something strange or momentous is about to happen because of him. This reaction is one of grandeur and often of ecstasy and possession, but the dominant attitudes, instead of being aggressively self-assertive, are those of humility, self-effacement and surrender. The patient's symbolism is usually permeated by mysticism in which there may be a confusion of ambivalent trends, religious exaltation, guilt, anxiety and sexual need.

An adolescent girl, after several months of aloof secretiveness in the home, announced to her mother that she was going to give birth to a baby. She said that she had never believed in immaculate conception before, but now she knew it was true. She knelt down in front of her mother and wept, saying that she had been worried about being sinful and was so glad not to be frightened any more. In the hospital she postured in the crucified position, made signs of reverence and submission to God, said that she had something which it was her duty to protect, and spoke of the Christ child and of being sinful. She heard voices, especially at night, and was obviously frightened by them, but she could not tell what they had said. After three weeks she became stuporous.

Another patient, a medical student, developed acute anxiety following a visit home where a physician friend told him it would take him half a lifetime to establish a secure practice. Before making this visit, he had been falling behind in his work and worrying over his intellectual and moral fitness for the career he had chosen. Back at school the patient noticed the cross of light that the street lamp made on his window screen and mistook it for a crucifix in the sky. During the night he heard God telling him to submit to His will, to go home and be dependent on his mother. In the clinic he said that he understood he was a link in a chain of helpers who would "bring good influences to the people and change them." After seven months of active therapy in a hospital he recovered, recognized his episode as an illness and went to work as a store clerk, living under the parental roof again, with apparent satisfaction.

Transformed patients. The transformed submissive schizophrenic patient is one whose body seems to him to have undergone important changes. These sometimes develop out of hypochondriacal preoccupations as delusions of body change in a person whose behavior is for any reason disorganized. Body transformations seem to be most often reported, however, by schizophrenic patients who have serious doubts concerning their own personal adequacy, who are suffering from the effects of severe guilt reactions or who, because of their anxieties and ambivalences, have become confused over the culturally determined roles they feel called upon to play. The conviction of important body change may thus be an outgrowth of attempts to account for failure, just as in the hypochondriacal disorders, or an expression of the acceptance of a subordinate or a dual role. In the following case we see a bizarre delusional development that illustrates most of these points.

The patient, an unmarried electrical engineer of thirty, appeared one day alone in an out-patient clinic, complaining that a snake was in his belly and that he was three persons in one — a man, a woman and a child. He was admitted the next day as an in-patient, and the following account of his illness and its background was obtained. His mother had died a few days after his birth, and he was almost at once legally adopted by a childless couple and separated from his siblings. His foster-parents were unusually indulgent, his foster-mother was domineering and possessive toward him, and he had no children to play with until he went to school at the age of eight. He recalled that he was always happy in playing imaginative, solitary games; and he always regarded his foster-mother as perfect, an opinion which was not shared by his other relatives who described her as demanding, nagging and short-tempered.

When he was fourteen the patient began practicing autoerotism, and developed great concern and guilt over it, which by the time he was fifteen reached the proportions of an adolescent anxiety disorder. He imagined terrible things happening to him because of his sin, among them the feeling that his blood had been turned into a snake which whirled about in his body. This illness lasted six months, but never kept him from school for more than a few days at a time. At engineering college he had two similar episodes of shorter duration, each developing in a setting of stress, fatigue and failure in examinations. He was graduated from college at twenty-two, obtained employment as a draftsman whose task it was to devise and test electrical signaling circuits, and returned to live with his foster-mother, who had meantime been widowed.

Although the patient speaks of this phase of his life as "the happy days," it must also have been difficult for him. For his foster-mother was soon paralyzed by a stroke and became, according to relatives, a terrible old lady, a cantankerous, "impossible" invalid. The patient had to run the house and the finances, and look after his foster-mother while holding down an exacting job. In spite of all this he managed to devise and patent a new kind of wheel chair in his spare time. He fell in love with a girl during this period and asked her to marry him. She accepted his proposal on the condition that he give up his mother, but he decided instead to stay with his mother and gave up the girl. When he was twenty-eight, the patient lost his job because of the depression and, failing to get another, began making and selling his patented wheel chairs. This brought him in only about two hundred dollars in a year's time. Then he came down with influenza and gave it to his foster-mother who died quite suddenly. He had to get out of a sick bed to make the funeral arrangements and attend the burial.

When it was all over, and he had sold the home and gone to live with acquaintances, he still felt ill and sad. He had been able to make few close friends while his foster-mother lived, and now he found life empty and lonely. He tried hard to establish himself in the affections of his siblings, behaving as if he had been brought up with them, but they were cool and their failure to accept him hurt and bewildered him. His only consolation was the friendship of a girl whose acquaintance he made at this time. He did not propose marriage to her until later, but he took it for granted that when he did the girl would accept him.

A year after his foster-mother's death, and eight months prior to his admission to the clinic, the patient succeeded in getting a job as mechanic's assistant in another city, where he worked with a gang of good-natured but earthy men. As an awkward, socially inexperienced person, he quickly became the butt of his fellow-workers' witticisms. He made the mistake one day of admitting that he had never had sexual intercourse, and from then on he was called a virgin. His virginity, with its possible implications, was repeatedly discussed and commented on in his presence. Since teasing of this kind usually includes deliberately ambiguous references to the sex of the person being discussed, it is highly probable that this banter gave the patient a great deal of material for his subsequent confusion over his own sex.

For recreation the patient spent week-ends in his home city visiting acquaintances and his girl friend. During the week, as he had no friends in the city where he worked, he went occasionally to public dance halls where dancing partners were provided by the management. One night, about five months before admission to the clinic, he found an abrasion on his genitals after he had indulged in considerable sex play with a girl at the dance hall. When a rash appeared on his body a few days later, he was not unnaturally alarmed at the possibility of syphilis; he apparently feared it as punishment for his sexual play, but he did nothing about it excepting to worry. Two months before admission, after changing to harder work, the patient developed back pains; and at about the same time his girl friend told him that she was in love with someone else and not interested in him. The pains became worse and spread to his abdomen and groin. His fears about syphilis finally drove him to seek medical help and, in the course of diagnostic investigation, cystoscopy was performed which was painful, resulted in genital paresthesias and heightened the patient's anxiety.

The physician reported to the patient that urine specimens obtained in cystoscopy showed kidney infection and gave him two bottles with the instruction, "If you feel anything unusual down there take some medicine." He said there was nothing to worry about because he had "washed out the kidneys." Unfortunately the patient was acquainted with the popular superstition that tampering with the kidneys changed a man's sexual powers. He said later, "It all started after I had my kidneys cleaned out. . . . The medicines cleaned me out front and back and I was practically hollow there." He returned to work, but "everything seemed like a dream," his eyesight was dim and he saw spots before his eyes. He visited his physician twice "to see what it was all about," but the medicines prescribed made him feel more upset than ever.

The patient said that his two sides were no longer working together and the right was stronger than the left. One night he awakened to find that he seemed to have grown a female breast on the left and to have acquired boy's genitals which were not a part of himself. He believed he could choose through his mind which of these three persons he might become — the man, the woman or the child. But the medicines he took moved all the fluid from his testes to his rectum, causing the boy to "win out." Now, it seemed to him, his voice grew boyish, his hands lost their squareness and became soft, he felt weak and his heart felt weak, only one side of his intestines was working, and a hernia which had been corrected in boyhood seemed to come back. At one time he was sure that he had three hearts, one on the right, one on the left and one in his genitals; and the blood rushed back and forth between the two sides. He thought that his father's blood was in the right side of him and his mother's in the left. He heard a voice telling him to drink much more milk and he would be well; he was not sure whether it was God's voice or the devil's. At night he had horrifying dreams and in the daytime he began walking the streets alone, feeling that terrible things were happening to him.

He dreamed, for example, that he was giving birth through his chest to a litter of kittens, all chewing and scratching. After an anxiety dream, another night, he turned on the light to find that his body had turned white. One night he dreamed that his body had shriveled up and awoke expecting death. In his fright he made a will and sat down in a chair to die; his body became stiff and then he knew he was dead. But he felt better after a while and went out for some food. In the morning he was so weak he could hardly walk, his food fell through him like a stone and the snake was in him. Of this episode he said, "I've been bothered by seeing myself all kinds of shapes after I'd taken that medicine a couple of weeks. . . . One was iron. My body was shrinking up, and I felt death creeping up on me and I ate sour fruit. Next morning the snake was in my belly and then in my back, and it's been traveling around in me ever since. . . . When I walk, I walk like a snake." His blood rushed around his body "like a wriggling snake," as it had in his adolescent illness.

In desperation the patient returned to his home city for help. His old family physician advised him to go to a psychiatric clinic and his friends told him he was getting on their nerves. He telephoned his former girl friend, but she only said, "You must paddle your own canoe." He said to himself, "There's no one in the world to help me now." Back in the city where he worked, he at first wandered about indecisively, then went to one psychiatric clinic asking for a blood test, made an appointment at another clinic, and finally, after seeing another physician in town, returned to the first one, where he was examined and the next day, as we have seen, admitted as an in-patient. After a few days of confusion the patient seemed to improve rapidly. He dismissed his former interpretations as "crazy stuff" and said he "must have been nuts." At the end of four weeks he was discharged to return to work and report to the out-patient clinic for continued psychiatric treatment. Eleven days later he was readmitted, dirty, disheveled, agitated, suspicious and confused, saying that he was "falling to pieces." After five months of only superficial improvement, the patient was removed to a private sanitarium near home. A year later he was reported to be mute and withdrawn, apparently sitting most of the time by himself, hallucinating, smirking and giggling.

This case describes a man who, throughout most of his childhood and young adulthood, was denied opportunities which the average person has of acquiring adequate techniques of social role-taking, particularly those he needs for affectional attachments outside of the family group. As a result of his limitations in these respects, the patient, once his foster-parents died, was unsuccessful in his attempts to establish himself in the cultural pattern of his contemporaries as an independent adult among adults. Each time he met failure he tended to develop self-reactions of a socially immature character in which hypochondriacal preoccupations were prominent. He seemed never to have reached a socially mature adult level in his sexual adjustments. His inadequacies in this direction are obvious in the ineffectuality of his attachments to women of his own age, and in the acute anxiety he developed over the possibility that he was being punished by syphilis for his sex play. Indeed, even his hallucinations gave a hint of childlike dependence when, in desperate need of relief from his mounting anxiety, the best he could do was to hear a voice tell him to drink more milk.

The loss of his foster-mother, who received her fatal infection from him, left the patient alone in the world for the first time in his thirty years. He suffered the humiliation of being reduced in social status from the rank of an electrical engineer to an assistant mechanic. His siblings and his girl friend rejected him, and his fellow-workers made a clown of him and taunted him because of his sexual inexperience. He developed pains on the basis of an unimportant urinary tract infection and acute anxiety on the basis of its treatment. Finally, in a whirlwind of hypochondriacal misinterpretations, horrible dreams, delusions of body change, and frightening distortions in his self-reactions, the patient became severely disorganized and ultimately desocialized, with almost complete detachment from the social community.

Detached schizophrenic reactions

Avoidant patients. The avoidant detached schizophrenic patient is one whose reactions are directed primarily away from situations of need-frustration, anxiety and guilt, with a resulting restriction of behavior chiefly in terms of an autistic fantasy community. The detachment or insulation from the shared social community may be transient, recurrent or chronic, it may be stationary or progressive, and it may vary in degree from mere vagueness and apparent inattention to an almost wholly unreactive schizophrenic stupor. Detaching avoidance occurs most often toward the end of a succession of other attempts at solution, all of which have failed. In these prior attempts there may be little evidence of behavior disorganization or, as in our Kansas City high-school girl, disorganization may be obvious long before avoidant detachment reaches serious proportions.

Sometimes avoidant detachment seems to develop gradually through adolescence without clear-cut evidence that serious, consistent attempts have been made to meet recurrent frustration, anxiety and guilt by the utilizing of other adjustive techniques. This approximates the classical description of *dementia simplex*. However, a great many of these cases turn out on closer study to have been lacking, not so much in overt incidents as in competent observation and reporting on the part of relatives and friends. In other words, the more carefully and completely the development of a schizophrenic disorder is studied, the less likely it is to resemble the classical *dementia simplex*. Detaching avoidance may also develop with dramatic abruptness, usually in response to sudden anxiety, as the following case will illustrate.

The patient, a single woman of thirty who owned and operated a small shop, developed recurrent attacks of abdominal pain and vomiting, on the basis of which her family physician made a diagnosis of appendicitis and advised surgery. For two weeks this advice was persistently rejected. The patient had always been exceedingly afraid of hospitals, even to the extent of crossing the street to avoid passing near one; she could never be persuaded to visit a hospitalized relative or friend, but instead would send flowers and an apologetic note. However, one night she became so frightened by an attack that she allowed herself to be taken to a hospital where she was immediately operated on for acute appendicitis. The appendix when removed was found not to be acutely inflamed and recovery was surgically uneventful, except for a low-grade fever which disappeared after adequate hydration and elimination had been established on the psychiatric service.

Psychiatric consultation was requested after the patient became increasingly difficult to arouse and spoke vaguely of having cancer, of dying, of giving birth to a baby, and of seeing angels and flowers. When visited by the psychiatrist, the patient was lying almost motionless in bed, her eyes were closed and the eyeballs rolled upward, her limbs were moderately flaccid, her lips occasionally moved, and a serene smile appeared every now and then on her face. She submitted to neurological examination with neither resistance nor cooperation. It was difficult to rouse her sufficiently from this semi-stuporous condition to answer questions, and when she spoke her answers were fragmentary and often seemed irrelevant. She said, "All the beautiful flowers" several times, and spoke slowly and disconnectedly of angels and music, the garden, cancer and dying. She said she might have been baptized a Baptist or gone to a Methodist kindergarten; actually she had been brought up as a Catholic in a Catholic family. When she stopped speaking, and before closing her eyes again, she would stare at the ceiling with a tranquil look and a fixed faint smile. It is especially noteworthy that the patient was quite well oriented, missing the date by two days, getting month and year correct, naming the hospital and city, and recognizing that the persons around her were nurses, doctors and patients.

On the psychiatric service, after physical examinations and blood studies had again revealed no organ or tissue pathology, the patient was gotten up and placed upon a full regime of planned psychiatric therapy, under the close supervision of the psychiatric resident and the head nurse. She required constant therapeutic pressure during the day to keep her from lapsing into deep preoccupation and complete inactivity. When left alone for a few minutes, she would slump in her chair, sometimes almost falling out of it onto the floor. Because of her fright over medical instruments the patient was hydrated and fed entirely by mouth, at the cost of great effort and patience on the part of the nurses. Enemas were discontinued after an exacerbation of acute anxiety in which she said that snakes were being put in her body and would gnaw her vitals; this fear did not recur. Within a week of her transfer to psychiatry, she was able without ill effect to give a retrospective account of the development of her illness, which was checked against the observations made by the medical and nursing staffs and the family.

According to her statement, as she went under the anesthetic the patient was dominated by two fears: one that she would die, and the other that she would advertise, to everyone around the hospital, a misdeed of her adolescence to which she attached great importance. When she came out of the anesthetic, she was frightened at being on a surgical ward, thought she was dying and said, "Take care of father and mother." The day after her operation a doctor brought nurses to her bedside and discussed her case; she gathered from what was said that something terrible was the matter with her. She asked about the appendix and was told that it had not been found acutely inflamed. Then another surgical patient came to her bed and heightened her anxiety by telling her not to trust the doctors and nurses. This patient had also been told, she explained, that she had appendicitis, but she really had cancer and they had been lying to her to fool her. "Now look what they've done to me," she said, and she showed our patient her colostomy wound under the surgical dressings.

In her anxiety the patient came to the following conclusions: there was a conspiracy to keep the truth from her; things more terrible would happen to her in the hospital; she was dying; the nurses and doctors were against her; she had made her secret public and everyone would reject and disown her; she had cancer or "a disease"; she had given birth to a child; something crooked was going on around her; she was being killed by a "dry gas" — the kind she had always smelled when she went past a hospital; her blood was gone or was bad. Her family was upset next day to hear her say that they must get her out of the place, that the nurses would give her no attention and were trying to get rid of her and that she must see the supervisor. She asked her sister to pray for her soul and said she had cancer or "a disease." These complaints were all the more surprising as the patient had never confided her troubles, personal or business, to anyone, and rarely criticized or commented unfavorably upon others. That night the patient heard her mother's voice saying, "Do the best you can with her. No use taking her home now." Another voice spoke of killing her sister and throwing a rock through the window. The next day she seemed suspicious of everyone and refused all food and fluids.

It was around this time that the patient began seeing and hearing the angels. They were in the air above her and they kept saying, "Come up into the garden," which meant to die. There were beautiful flowers and music. She said to the nurses: "I feel like I'm going up and away." A little later she explained, "I would just start to wander up in the air, rise up and leap, then find I was on the bed. . . . I was dreamy all the time, from morning to night, just dreamy. I couldn't wake myself up. I've been dreaming for two days. (*Are you coming out of it?*) I hope so. (*Did you enjoy it?*) Oh, no! I had everybody in my dreams. Angels, flowers all around. They thought I ought to come up there; I thought I was. I thought I had cancer. (*Before the operation?*) No, after that." At this point the patient was asked when she had had her operation. She replied correctly, "Monday," but then closed her eyes and went limp; her eyeballs rolled upward and she became cataleptic when manipulated. On being roused she asked, "Why did my blood go out? I'm waiting for the gas to go through and touch my heart. When it fills up it'll put me to sleep. They'll put me in the morgue. I'm not afraid to die now."

Two days after the patient had become practically symptom-free, a fellow-patient, assuming that she was married, unfortunately asked her how many children she had at home. She was greatly disturbed and said soon after that she believed all her fears about exposing her misdeed were well-founded. That evening she heard the radio broadcasting about her and insisted that an "extra" had been gotten out to tell her life story. She interpreted crying on the ward as a sign that others knew she was doomed. She seemed fearful, suspicious and bewildered. She said: "I'm drawing my last breath. I beg you to send me home so they can put me in the graveyard. . . . It's too late now to think anything." Later in the day she said, "I guess I'm only a spirit and these are angels around me. (*Who?*) The nurses. It's all too good to be true. I know they are real. I'll be dead and you can throw me in a furnace." The next day she seemed much improved and said, "I don't know if it was all a nightmare or what." There were no further episodes of fear and confusion. She was finally discharged, clinically well, three weeks after her operation. Because of her continued dread of hospitals and hospital personnel, she was followed up for two years through a relative who reported that the patient appeared to have recovered completely.

Adient patients. The adient detached schizophrenic patient is one whose reactions are directed primarily toward fantasied situations in an autistic fantasy community, through fascination or preference, and without evidence of the dominance of antecedent anxiety and guilt. Detaching adience may also be transient, recurrent or chronic, it may be stationary or progressive, and it may vary in degree from mere vagueness and apparent inattention to an almost wholly unreactive schizophrenic stupor. In many cases, detaching adience seems to be one of the first serious attempts made to achieve satisfactions which the social community does not provide. Our case of the dishwasher-duchess, cited and discussed in Chapter 4, illustrates this variety. The girl found her imagined activity in a fantasy context so fascinating and so satisfying that she confined her behavior almost completely to reactions in terms of an autistic community. In this community she played in imagination the role of a beautiful, envied aristocrat to whom other persons were subordinated.

In many cases, detaching adience follows upon other less successful attempts at meeting adult or adolescent problems. Usually, however, the patient's history gives evidence that he had become exceptionally well-practiced in fantasy techniques before the onset of schizophrenic symptoms.

A young engineer, who had graduated creditably from an engineering school and landed a good job for himself, showed a gradual decline in his ability to do his work until he finally lost his job. At home he spent his days lying around the house; he had no complaints. After admission to a psychiatric clinic he said frankly that there was nothing anyone in the world could offer him as valuable as his daydreams.

This patient said that as a child he had always had an imaginary boy playmate who meant a great deal to him. In adolescence the imaginary playmate became a girl with whom he fell in love. He made strong attempts in college to get away from this autistic affair and managed to fall in love with a married woman who appears, from all the evidence available, to have considered him as no more than a good friend. He did well in his studies and went aggressively and successfully after a job, as we have said. But here the difficulties involved in getting started in a competitive field, where rewards were only in a vague and distant future, proved too much for him.

It was the imaginary playmate of his daydreams who rescued

him from this situation.[27] In his fantasy he courted and married
her; and they lived a complete life together as man and wife in the
autistic community of his own imagining. Thus, the satisfactions he
had learned to find by this technique, throughout childhood and
adolescence, now culminated fittingly in the perfect autistic union.
To leave this fantasied world for the drab loneliness of the shared
social community was to give up everything he valued in return for
nothing. He said, "I know where this is leading me, but it doesn't
matter."

Schizophrenic disorders in relation to organ and tissue pathology

In the introduction to this chapter, we referred to the difficulty
that Bleuler had in abandoning his neurologizing predilection when
he developed his new formulation of schizophrenia under the influence of Freud. We said that it was Adolf Meyer, at the time a
brain pathologist, who seems first to have recognized the greater
promise held out by a consistently behavioral interpretation. Students of schizophrenia, however, are still sharply divided on this
issue, one group maintaining that schizophrenic disorganization
and desocialization can be accounted for in terms of biosocial development and environmental stress, the other group insisting that
such a formulation is inconceivable.[28]

Those on one side of the controversy point to the meager and
contradictory character of evidence for brain pathology or biochemical change as the fundamental fact in schizophrenic development.
They contrast the cases of reversibility and complete recovery —
with and without shock treatment — in schizophrenia with the practical irreversibility of the clinical picture in cases of brain damage
sufficient to produce a symptomatology of comparable severity and
complexity. Those on the other side deny that recovery from schizophrenia is possible, call freedom from complaints and symptoms a
remission — no matter how long it lasts — and look to better histo-
logical techniques and more refined biochemical analysis of the
future to provide the data they need. This difference of opinion is
currently an important stimulus to further work on schizophrenia.

It should be said at this point that the anxieties and needs pre-

---

[27] Compare the report of L. Bender and F. Vogel that normal children use
the imaginary companion when they need him and give him up when the
need is over. "Imaginary companions of children," *Amer. Jour. Orthopsychiatry,* 1941, vol. 11, pp. 56-66.

[28] For a discussion of this problem, in relation to both normal and abnormal
behavior, see Chapter 3.

cipitated by some other illness or an accident may become factors in the development or the ingravescence of a schizophrenic disorder. In one of our cases, for example, we saw that the manipulations and the cautions incident to cystoscopic examination certainly accelerated the process of schizophrenic disorganization; while in another case cited, acute anxiety over sin and the threat of death turned an otherwise uneventful surgical recovery from appendectomy into schizophrenic detachment. Indeed, the growing recognition today that the implications to the patient of illness, injury or surgical operation may be of the greatest importance in determining his improvement has led in some quarters to the inclusion of biosocial studies of the patient-as-a-person in the examination procedures of general hospitals.

BIOSOCIAL BASES AND DETERMINANTS OF SCHIZOPHRENIA

In our case material and the analysis of symptoms we have already answered the question, *What are the characteristics of normal behavior from which schizophrenic disorganization and desocialization are derived?* When the schizophrenic disorder develops under the eyes of observant and articulate persons, so that adequate data are available, there is usually little difficulty in tracing its evolution from antecedent anxiety, frustration, conflict, guilt, confusion and ambivalence.[29] It will be recalled that even in our early discussions of behavior organization, exclusion and inclusion, emotional and symbolic reactions, role-taking, need and the basic adjustive techniques, we took some of our clearest examples of transition from normal to abnormal from the behavior of persons who became schizophrenic. The disorganization and desocialization that characterize schizophrenic disorders, as we have repeatedly pointed out, are closely related to and derived from the less serious confusion and asocial withdrawal which any normal adolescent or adult may show under strong and persistent personal stress.

If at this point we ask our second question, *What are the determinants which seem to favor the development of schizophrenic disorders in some persons and not in others?* we shall find that it, too,

[29] See for example G. Terry and T. Rennie, *Analysis of Parergasia*, Nerv. Ment. Dis. Monog. Series, 1938, No. 64; T. Rennie, "Follow-up study of five hundred patients with schizophrenia admitted to the hospital from 1913 to 1923," *Arch. Neurol. Psychiat.*, 1939, vol. 42, pp. 877-891.

has been already answered. Schizophrenic disorganization and desocialization appear to develop most readily in anxious solitary individuals who are socially immature as well as socially inept. In fact, as we have seen, the illness may first become obvious after some awkward and ineffectual attempt has been made to meet one of the many challenges of adolescence or young adulthood. In other instances the precipitating situation has its effect because the patient had previously been shielded in some way from the full impact of adult competition, or what is worse for many overprotected persons, from adult indifference. Practically all persons developing schizophrenic disorders have for one reason or another relied heavily upon fantasy as a technique for overcoming frustration, gaining rewards, resolving conflicts and taking revenge.

The schizophrenic patient is usually a person who has never acquired the degree of social skill he needs for shifting his perspectives through taking successive culturally determined roles when he is under stress. In other words, he has not succeeded in establishing himself firmly in his culture.[30] He does not share his anxieties, conflicts, suspicions or loneliness with others because he lacks the techniques for doing so. He may be overtrained in dependence and made reaction-sensitive in the process to the approval and censure of other persons; but he has been kept so consistently on the receiving end of this relationship that he is incapable of checking on the validity of his own interpretations by taking the roles of persons whose conduct frightens or puzzles him.

Such an individual is left in a personal crisis with only the relatively inept techniques of private fantasy, furtive observation and unwarrantable inference at his disposal. The initial disorganization which develops — as it might in any normal person under critical conditions — renders the socially unskilled and immature person still more inadequate and isolated, while his increasing isolation tends in its turn to reduce yet further his opportunities for the effective personal interaction upon which social adequacy must depend. Thus the patient's behavior may describe a descending spiral from comparative inadequacy to complete ineffectuality, and sometimes to complete inaction.

The pseudocommunity and the autistic community

In cases of clear-cut uninterrupted progression, like those of our

[30] N. Cameron, "Experimental analysis of schizophrenic thinking," in J. Kasanin (editor), *Language and Thought in Schizophrenia*, 1944, pp. 50-64.

Kansas City high-school girl and the electrical engineer, it is possible to distinguish three successive phases in the development of schizophrenic desocialization. In the first phase, the patient attempts to meet a personally challenging situation primarily in terms of the social community, that is, with reactions oriented in relation to a functionally integrated social group of which he is a member. The high-school girl, for example, began with aggressive attempts to establish herself as the dominant female in a complex domestic situation. The electrical engineer, after he had lost through death the one person he loved, tried actively to form new affectional attachments with his siblings and a girl he knew. These patients were both unsuccessful, as we have seen, because they had not acquired in childhood a degree of skill in social techniques that would enable them to deal adequately with a major personal crisis.

The same want of adequate social techniques is responsible for the relatively rapid development of the second phase, in which a pseudocommunity partially supplants the social community as the focus of a schizophrenic individual's behavior. We have already discussed, in Chapter 14, the evolution of this pseudocommunity as an organization of the patient's reactions to the observed and inferred behavior of actual and imagined persons on the basis of delusional conviction. A third phase is especially characteristic of schizophrenic desocialization but is not confined to it. In this phase the dominant reactions in the patient's behavior are made up of the imagined activities of imagined persons in a fastasied context. This organization of behavior is what we have earlier referred to as the autistic community. The high-school girl, the electrical engineer and the surgical patient each eventually restricted behavior almost wholly to an autistic community, two of them permanently and the other temporarily.

We may now define the *autistic community* as *the organization of an individual's reactions to the imagined activities of imagined persons in a fantasied context*. It is obvious that autistic communities are characteristic, not only of behavior in schizophrenic disorders, but also of normal dreaming and daydreaming and of behavior in the autonomous hysterical seizure. However, in dreaming the person who fantasies is asleep. When he awakens, his behavior is restructured by his social environment and the autistic community of his dream organization disappears from his behavior.

In daydreaming, as in schizophrenic desocialization, the daydreamer's reactions are organized as an autistic community despite his being awake and surrounded by cultural objects and social persons. But, as we pointed out earlier, there is a fundamental difference between the normal and the schizophrenic daydreamer — the one can readily break the thread of his fantasy and react adequately in terms of the shared social community, whereas the other cannot. This comparison at once reminds us also of the situation in autonomous hysterical seizures which we discussed in Chapter 12. The patient who suffers from episodic hysterical seizures is protected from serious general behavior disorganization by the very fact of his *overexclusion*. For we saw that his behavior in the seizure radically excludes reactions belonging to the social context, while his behavior at other times radically excludes reactions belonging to the seizure context. Thus, in each of these alternating phases the behavior organization is kept relatively intact.

Schizophrenic disorganization, in contrast to daydreaming and hysterical autonomy, is characteristically overinclusive. The three phases we have mentioned always overlap at some stage of desocialization, resulting in a confused mixture of behavior organized simultaneously in relation to the social community, a pseudocommunity and an autistic community. As we saw in our cases, even though a patient may ultimately restrict his behavior almost wholly to an autistic community, he reaches that point by way of a prior confusion of contexts from which, indeed, ultimate restriction seems often to be his mode of escape. Thus, we see the disorganized schizophrenic person meeting problems in the shared social situation with techniques and attitudes which have validity only in a fantasied context. We see him attempting reactions, toward imagined persons and events, which are appropriate to the shared social context. And we find him reacting simultaneously and by the same techniques to persons, objects and events belonging to both contexts without any clear indication that he is able to discriminate between them.

Chronic institutionalized patients often become secondarily stabilized on a basis which permits them to react consistently in terms of each type of community, depending upon the relationships involved in a given activity. Thus, for example, a hospitalized patient may perform with reasonable adequacy in terms of the shared social community when he eats with others at a table, plays cooperative and competitive games, or works in the hospital shops. In his relationships with relatives, nurses and physicians, on the other hand, he may complain constantly of being the victim of a plot, and cite the observed and inferred behavior of actual or imagined persons in support of his contentions. And whenever he is left entirely to his own resources, the same person may restrict his behavior wholly to fantasied reactions in a fantasied context. It is sometimes possible to demonstrate in such patients that the degree of disorganization and desocialization varies roughly in accordance with the degree to which environmental stimulation arouses personal problems to which the individual is pathologically reaction-sensitive.[31]

Age and schizophrenic disorders

While it is true that schizophrenic disorganization may begin at almost any age, the majority of cases develop before the age of thirty. Paranoid disorders, on the other hand, develop as a rule between the ages of thirty-five and fifty-five. In other words, schizophrenia is characteristically a product of adolescence and young adulthood, whereas paranoid disorders belong to later adulthood and middle life.[32] In the preceding chapter we put forward the hypothesis that this difference in the age of onset explains the much greater tendency toward disorganization and desocialization shown by schizophrenic patients than by paranoid patients. Such an hypothesis receives further support from the fact that those cases of schizophrenia which are the most difficult to distinguish from paranoid disorders — the *aggressive schizophrenic reactions* or Kraepelin's "paranoid type" — are also the ones which develop on the average later than other cases and show least disorganization.

This age differential assumes particular importance when one considers the strong similarity in the childhood influences reported for paranoid and schizophrenic disorders. In both we find a background of chronic insecurity in personal interrelationships. In both there is typically a history either of parental neglect, denial, censure and rejection, or else of parental overprotection that trains a person

---

[31] Compare the verbalization obtained through sodium amytal narcosis by O. Kant, "Clinical analysis of schizophrenic deterioration," *Psychiat. Quart.,* 1943, vol. 17, pp. 426-445.

[32] N. Dayton, *New Facts on Mental Disorders: Study of 89,190 Cases,* 1940, pp. 308-318; *United States Army Technical Medical Bulletin No. 203,* Section 18, dated October 19, 1945; T. Raphael and L. Himler, "Schizophrenia and paranoid psychoses among college students," *Amer. Jour. Psychiat.,* 1944, vol. 100, pp. 443-451.

in needs and expectations which social communities cannot or will not meet. In the childhood of both paranoid and schizophrenic patients, also, there have been developed self-attitudes which leave the individual unusually reaction-sensitive to signs that he may be guilty, inferior or unworthy in the eyes of others. Indeed, excepting for the relatively greater dependence and more striking social immaturity among those who become schizophrenic patients, the description of childhood determinants for the one behavior disorder parallels that for the other.

It is probable, then, that the greater tendency toward disorganization and desocialization in the schizophrenic patient is in part a function of his age.[33] Let us assume that of two persons, equally lacking in social skills, one develops symptoms of disorganization at the age of twenty and the other at forty. It is at once obvious that the older patient will have had twenty years longer in which to establish himself in his culture than the younger one. To make the contrast still clearer, let us suppose that in both cases the period of stress began five years before the onset of unmistakable symptoms. The man of twenty would thus have been subjected to disruptive emotional conflicts during a period when even the average adolescent finds difficulty in adapting his behavior to what his environment and his own self-reactions demand of him. The man of forty will have long before passed through this period of adolescent adaptation and, however unskillful he may still be, he has at least had fifteen years of living as an adult among adults before his disruptive emotional conflicts disorganize him.

Of course this hypothesis would not make age the only determinant of schizophrenic in contrast to paranoid disorders. The very fact that one person, and not the other, succumbs to the stresses of adolescence and young adulthood may speak for a relatively less mature and more dependent personality organization in the one who goes under. And it may indicate a greater selective reaction-sensitivity to the problems peculiar to that phase of development. In our culture, it is during the period of adolescence and young adulthood that emancipation from parental ties and their replace-

[33] Compare Miller's finding that the delusional organization in his younger patients tended to be relatively illogical and therefore more labile than in the older patients. C. Miller, "Factors affecting the prognosis of paranoid disorders," *Jour. Nerv. Ment. Dis.*, 1942, vol. 95, pp. 580-588. It is to be noted that Miller uses the term *paranoid disorders* to cover all behavior disorders in which delusions are prominent.

ment with heterosexual attachments must be effected. It is the period during which some philosophy of living must be adopted 'or evolved. And it is characteristically a period of rapid body change, of emotional upheavals, particularly in relation to sex and religion, and of strong interest in the techniques of interpersonal influence. This is the general framework within which the development of schizophrenic disorganization and desocialization must be comprehended.

Schizophrenic disorders as adjustive techniques

Schizophrenic disorganization and desocialization involve principally the withdrawal or escape techniques, but to a certain extent they usually serve also as aggression and defense. The schizophrenic patient, for example, may make the same *aggressive* use of delusions that paranoid patients do in controlling and manipulating situations; sometimes he also frightens his relatives more or less deliberately by giving them dramatic reports of the hallucinations he is having. Either the aggressive or the submissive schizophrenic may show *identification* in organizing his pseudocommunity. This he does by reacting to the persons, groups and symbols which he fantasies as though their achievements, their status or possessions, were also his own. The Mignon delusion, with its effects upon the patient's bearing and his speech, is an example of schizophrenic identification.

Compensation, rationalization and *projection,* as we have formulated them in Chapter 6, may all enter into the delusional developments of schizophrenic disorders. This was obvious, for example, in our high-school girl. In her pseudocommunity she found omnipotence and satisfying revenge which were denied her in the domestic social community. She excused her murderous aggression toward other patients with a melodramatic statement that she was saving them from something worse than death. She ascribed to her father motives that were actually her own, and then disowned the father along with the motives.

When it comes to *insulation, negativism* and *fantasy,* there is no need to repeat here what has already been presented in considerable detail, both in Chapter 6 and in the present chapter. These techniques to a certain extent define schizophrenic disorders. The disorganization and desocialization of schizophrenia are frequently referred to as constituting *regression.* In the sense of our definition of regression — as a reversion to ways or objects which during earlier phases of one's development were accepted as adequate and appropriate — it is obvious that schizophrenic techniques frequently deserve to be called regressive. However, the older designation of schizophrenia as a "regression psychosis," which implied sometimes a return to childhood and sometimes an atavistic reversion to primitive man, is not justified by the clinical facts.[34] The breakdown of organized *repression* in schizophrenic disorders is an important contributing factor in disorganization, but can hardly be classed as an adjustive technique.

SCHIZOPHRENIC DISORDERS IN RELATION TO OTHER BEHAVIOR DISORDERS

We have designated behavior disorganization and desocialization as the distinguishing characteristics of schizophrenic disorders. However, as we have seen, a certain degree of disorganization is common in many emotional reactions, whether these be fearful, aggressive, erotic or ecstatic. Moreover, desocialization occurs frequently in illnesses other than schizophrenia, notably in the chronic invalidism of hypochondria, fatigue syndromes and hysteria, and in severe depressions. The differentiation of schizophrenic from other behavior disorders will therefore depend upon the extent to which disorganization and desocialization dominate the clinical picture and overshadow the other features.

Hypochondriacal overconcern is found in a high percentage of schizophrenic disorders, sometimes in the form of ordinary body complaints such as anyone might make, sometimes as body delusions which, as we have seen, are frequently bizarre. *Fatigue reactions* are common precursors or accompaniments of schizophrenic disorders, and, as we pointed out in Chapter 8, frequently represent in both an unreadiness or aversion in relation to new or continued activity. *Anxiety reactions,* as we have said, are characteristic of a considerable proportion of schizophrenic disorders, particularly in acute phases; while extremely acute anxiety, as in panic reactions, may end in schizophrenic behavior disorganization. On the other hand, *hypochondria, fatigue syndromes* and *anxiety disorders* can be distinguished from schizophrenic disorders by the

[34] N. Cameron, "Deterioration and regression in schizophrenic thinking," *Jour. Abnorm. Soc. Psychol.*, 1939, vol. 34, pp. 265-270.

absence in the former of dominant delusions, hallucinations and severe disorganization. In *panic reactions,* as we observed in Chapter 9, a differentiation from schizophrenia can often not be made.

Compulsive symptoms are sometimes present in the behavior of a person, who later becomes schizophrenic, perhaps antedating disorganization by several years. They frequently form a part of an early schizophrenic development, and sometimes they appear after disorganization is obvious. However, as we pointed out in Chapter 10, a great many symptoms that are loosely referred to as "compulsive" are merely repetitive, stereotyped fragments of earlier symbolic behavior. We reserve the term *compulsive* for activities which arise periodically in response to mounting anxiety and by their performance bring temporary relief from it. We have already discussed the important question of the relationship between schizophrenic and *hysterical disorders* in Chapter 12, and of that between *paranoid disorders* and schizophrenia in the present and the preceding chapters.

A distinction between the *deliria* of toxic, infectious or febrile origin and schizophrenic disorders can usually be made on the basis of orientation, recall and the presence or absence of cerebral disorder. The typical delirious patient is disoriented, shows fragmentary, grossly inadequate recall and recognizable signs of cerebral incompetence, which we shall discuss in Chapter 17. Schizophrenic disorganization and desocialization may, of course, develop in a person who is suffering from *brain damage,* just as it may in a person with kidney damage, diabetes mellitus or a cardiac lesion. But unless the clinical picture is dominated by symptoms characteristic of brain damage, we consider disorganization and desocialization in such a person as the presumptive signs of a schizophrenic reaction to the consequences of injury or illness.

The distinction between schizophrenic disorders and the group of *manic* and *depressive disorders,* to which we shall turn next, is not a difficult one to make in typical cases. Manic and depressive disorders usually lack the impressive disorganization of schizophrenia and seldom include prominent hallucinatory behavior or the posturing, gesturing and mannerisms so characteristic of schizophrenic disorders. However, schizophrenic patients are often excited, aggressive and elated, while manic patients frequently do or say bizarre things, and may assume postures and describe gestures that are extremely odd. Similarly, schizophrenic patients are often retarded in behavior, apathetic and sad or hopeless, while depressed patients frequently hallucinate, take absurd roles and express queer delusions of persecution and body change. Indeed, a considerable number of patients will always fail to conform strictly to the pattern of either group of disorders, and for these cases a differential diagnosis necessarily does violence to one major aspect or the other of the actual clinical syndrome.

16 *Manic and Depressive*

Disorders

ALTHOUGH it has been customary to call all manic and most depressive disorders "manic-depressive," one finds in actual practice that the great majority of patients who have the one kind of attack never have the other. Rennie,[1] for example, has reported that in his series of 208 carefully studied cases less than one-fourth suffered from both manic and depressive illnesses, even though in almost 80 per cent of the cases there was at least one recurrence. The histories and follow-up studies of these patients covered twenty or more years. There is, however, ample evidence to show that mania and depression are closely related syndromes which may advantageously be considered together.

Neither the recognition of this relationship nor the coining of a single term to cover both syndromes is a recent achievement.[2] Statements that mania and melancholia, as depression is still called, are parts of a single disease appear in medical writings of the first century A.D. A prominent physician of the sixth century described the two as occurring in the same persons "periodically and in a cycle," thus anticipating Falret's *folie circulaire* by thirteen hundred years. In the sixteenth century we find this interesting comment, "Most physicians associate mania and melancholia as one disorder, because they consider that they both have the same origin and cause, and differ only in degree and manifestation; others consider them to be quite distinct."[3] Of course there is no denying that many syndromes called mania and melancholia by ancient and

[1] T. Rennie, "Prognosis in manic-depressive psychoses," *Amer. Jour. Psychiat.*, 1942, vol. 98, pp. 801-814.
[2] For an historical review with bibliography see N. Cameron, "The functional psychoses," in J. Hunt (editor), *Personality and the Behavior Disorders* (New York: Ronald Press, 1944), pp. 861-921.
[3] J. Whitwell, *Historical Notes on Psychiatry.* London: Lewis, 1936, p. 212.

renaissance physicians would be differently designated today. The fact remains, however, that our contemporary custom of regarding manic and depressive attacks as phases or cycles of a single disease entity is but the continuation of an old, established medical tradition.

The modern name embracing the two disorders seems first to have appeared in the seventeenth century, when Bonet wrote a medical essay on *La folie maniaco-mélancolique,* after which variants of the term occur frequently in the literature. Toward the close of the nineteenth century, first Kahlbaum and then Kraepelin adopted the extreme position that all severe depressions, and all elated excitements not due to paresis or intoxication, were only manifestations of a phasic endogenous disease-process. The depression, they maintained, represents one pole of metabolic activity while the excitement represents the opposite metabolic pole, with the normal level occupying an intermediate position. They gave no place to the influence of life situations and personal conflict in the etiology of their hypothetical bipolar disease. This general hypothesis, even though there is little evidence to support it, is still widely accepted today.[4]

We owe the rebirth of interest in the origins, characteristics and significance of manic and depressive disorders to Karl Abraham, one of a group of Bleuler's assistants who became distinguished disciples of Freud. In a series of papers on the metapsychology of the ego, id and superego, Abraham called attention to the marked ambivalence in affectional attitudes shown by depressed persons.[5] He maintained, in effect, that the depressed patient turned upon himself the hostility he felt toward the love object, and the hostility which had earlier in his life been turned against him by a parent or parent substitute. Freud himself concurred in and elaborated upon these contributions.[6] Abraham and Freud, while accepting

[4] For a critical summary of this problem see N. Cameron, "The place of mania among the depressions from a biological standpoint," *Jour. Psychol.,* 1942, vol. 14, pp. 181-195; N. Cameron, "Physiological psychology. I. The functional psychoses," *Annual Rev. Physiol.,* 1943, vol. 5, pp. 453-464.

[5] K. Abraham, "Notes on the psychoanalytical investigation and treatment of manic-depressive insanity and allied conditions," in *Selected Papers* (London: Hogarth, 1927), pp. 137-156; "The first pregenital stage of the libido," in *Selected Papers* (London: Hogarth, 1927), pp. 248-279; "A short history of the development of the libido," in *Selected Papers* (London: Hogarth, 1927), pp. 418-501.

[6] S. Freud, "Mourning and melancholia," in *Collected Papers* (London: Hogarth, 1924), vol. 4, pp. 152-170.

the Kahlbaum-Kraepelin bipolar hypothesis as fact, were still able
to present the manic attack as a reaction against the anxiety of
depression.

Today we recognize that manic and depressive disorders always
begin in tension and anxiety. Sometimes the development is that
of a steady increase from the initial tension and anxiety to exaggerated apprehension in which delusions of unreality, nihilism and
environmental change dominate the clinical picture. Often one
finds that the tense, anxious patient has started with hostile aggression aimed at a loved person toward whom, as Abraham pointed
out, he has strongly ambivalent attitudes. As we shall see in the
case material, if the patient includes hostile self-reactions in his
anxiety behavior, he may go on to develop delusions of self-depreciation with intense guilt and the need or expectation of severe
punishment. Sometimes patients react to their tension and anxiety
with excessive compensatory overactivity, grandiose delusions and
aggressive self-assertion, which may easily be mistaken by the
inexpert as unmixed joy, but is actually more like a noisy celebration at a wake.

VARIETIES OF MANIC AND DEPRESSIVE DISORDERS

Kraepelin in the last edition of his encyclopedic *Lehrbuch* [7] distinguished twenty varieties of mania and depression, most of them
mixed or intermediate forms which shaded over into one another
and into paranoid, schizophrenic and anxiety disorders. The classification Kraepelin proposed has not proved to be a practicable one
and has largely been abandoned. However, it points up the important fact that agitation, sadness, slowing, despair and compensatory elation are not peculiar to one specific group of behavior disorders, but may be found in any or all of them. Indeed, this is
exactly what we should expect if we considered how common these
reactions are in normal everyday behavior.

In the discussion that follows we shall limit ourselves to the
three major syndromes belonging to this group — the *agitated depression*, the *retarded depression*, and the *manic excitement*. But
before proceeding to consider each syndrome separately, we may at
this point describe certain characteristics common to all three. In

---

[7] E. Kraepelin, *Psychiatrie: ein Lehrbuch für Studierende und Aertzte.*
Leipzig: Barth, 1909-1913, 4 volumes.

the first place, they occur as a rule in circumscribed attacks with a fairly definite beginning and ending. In Rennie's series, the usual period elapsing between the occurrence of the prodromal tension and anxiety symptoms, and their development to a stage at which they were recognized as signs of illness, varied from one to six months.[8]

It is particularly significant that in almost 80 per cent of these carefully studied cases there were definite disturbing life situations immediately preceding the onset, and that the relationship was most obvious in recurrent depressions. This finding contrasts strikingly with the old contention that manic and depressive disorders are unrelated to personal and situational factors. Recovery from a first attack in these disorders is almost invariable, regardless of the specific kind of therapy employed. In Rennie's cases, none of which received shock treatment, prolonged narcosis or brain damage, 93 per cent recovered completely under a regime of competently planned and carried-out psychiatric therapy. The average duration of first attacks in this series was six and one-half months, of which only two and one-half months on the average were spent in hospitals.

Recurrences proved to be extremely common, more common than in any previous reports. Seventy-nine per cent suffered a second attack, 63.5 per cent had a third, and 45 per cent had a fourth attack. Later attacks showed some tendency to last longer than the earlier ones, but in only 7 per cent of the cases did the illness become chronic. It is most likely that the higher incidence of recurrence in Rennie's group, as compared with the figures usually given, is to be accounted for on the basis of the greater completeness of the data. For each case, it will be recalled, there was a history covering a span of at least twenty years of adolescent and adult life.

The remarkably high rate of recovery in these disorders, the relative unimportance of specific therapy, and the high probability of recurrence suggest a serious flaw in our contemporary attack upon the problem of mania and depression. For a great deal of effort is being currently expended upon the devising of new modes of treatment and upon the collecting of evidence to show the superiority

[8] T. Rennie, "Prognosis in manic-depressive psychoses," *Amer. Jour. Psychiat.*, 1942, vol. 98, pp. 801-814. The data in this and the succeeding three paragraphs are drawn principally from Rennie's study.

of one mode over the others. This aspect of the problem seems actually to be the least important of all and to be least in need of improvement. The evidence suggests that a concerted effort might better be directed toward a planned study of the conditions under which attacks are precipitated, so as to be able to devise methods for heading them off or aborting them. In view of the high incidence of recurrence, a beginning could most easily be made by instituting long-term detailed studies of persons who have already recovered from a first attack.

Agitated depression

The agitated depression is characterized by restless overactivity, sustained tension, despair, and apprehensive or self-condemnatory delusions, but without serious behavior disorganization and without an adequate basis in organ or tissue pathology.[9] Agitated depressions always begin in a setting of unrelieved personal stress and strain. They are usually the direct outgrowth of prolonged anxiety reactions which have become complicated by cumulative and self-perpetuating delusional developments. In some cases the dominant delusional themes are of self-reproach, of personal guilt and worthlessness, of hopelessness for which the patient considers himself to blame, and of the dread of deserved punishment. In others one finds an overwhelming personal insecurity which generalizes to include impending disaster for loved ones also, and sometimes includes catastrophic destruction of the world and everyone in it.

The onset of agitated depression may follow closely upon a single precipitating incident, such as the death of someone, a sudden disillusionment, an unexpected personal conflict or the loss of one's home or business by fire. Usually, however, there is a prodromal period lasting weeks or months in which anxiety, tension, conflict, hostility or guilt reactions are more or less obvious. For a long time the picture may be one of worry, inability to relax or sleep properly, and a tendency to harp on personal problems or on topics of body overconcern. Gradually, however, the patient loses not only sleep but appetite and weight as well. One or more of the

[9] The so-called "psychoneurotic depression" is a subacute agitated or retarded depression. The term *reactive depression* is meaningless, since all depressions are reactive to something. Compare A. Lewis, "States of depression: their clinical and aetiological differentiation," *Brit. Med. Jour.*, 1938, part 2, pp. 875-878.

other anxiety components is usually added to the complaints — spastic constipation or diarrhea, urinary frequency, precordial discomfort, dyspnea, muscular aches and pains, impotence or menstrual irregularities and dyspareunia, and disturbances in coordination, thinking or dreaming. As a direct result of the increased tension, there is sometimes an increase in sex need which usually does not lead to adequate satisfaction. Augmented food intake is also occasionally seen, as in other disorders with marked anxiety.

The patient grows more and more tense and restless until he may be unable to sit on a chair or lie on a bed for more than a few minutes at a time. Sleep is commonly reduced to two or three hours a night, and sometimes less. Activity is almost continual, but its range is limited to pacing back and forth, rubbing and picking at the body, moaning and crying, wringing the hands, talking incessantly about one's preoccupations or simply ejaculating phrases of apprehension, despair and self-reproach. One elderly woman, for example, paced about the wards of a state hospital for three months saying virtually nothing but "Oh my!" in a monotone that never lost its note of despair. She made a complete recovery. A middle-aged woman, who also recovered, sat for months picking her hair out by the roots and repeating that she was lost and would wander over the face of the earth forever.

The delusional developments are typically in keeping with the patient's self-reproach and guilt, or his fear and insecurity.[10] As we pointed out in Chapter 13, delusions of unreality, environmental change and nihilism are especially characteristic of agitated depressions; indeed, most of the illustrations given there came from this one group. We find delusions of body change also in the agitated depressed patient, often growing out of prior body overconcern, but sometimes resulting from the visceral contributions to anxiety reactions mentioned above. Delusions of self-depreciation are nearly always present in agitated depressions, and the behavior of some persons becomes completely overshadowed by them. This is particularly so when serious personal conflicts arise in a hostile, aggressive reaction such as the following case illustrates.

The patient, an unmarried private secretary of forty-eight, was admitted to the hospital complaining that she was terribly worried

[10] See, for example, the account by A. Lewis, "Melancholia: a clinical survey of depressive states," *Jour. Ment. Science,* 1934, vol. 80, pp. 277-378.

and could not sleep. Her relatives added that she was greatly depressed and wanted to commit suicide. Her illness had apparently been precipitated by the occurrence of two family crises in quick succession. Three and a half months before her admission to the clinic the patient heard indirectly that a brother, whom she had helped financially through a "cure" for alcoholism the year before, was drinking again. That night she could not sleep and was worried, but otherwise seemed to herself all right. A week later the brother was found drunk in a tavern, and she realized that her hopes had been in vain, her investment wasted and the prospects for her brother's financial future gloomy.

As the most stable and responsible member of her family, the patient had for thirty years played a steadying, parental role in relation to her siblings and even to her own parents. Of late she had been doing this, however, with increasing reluctance and resentment as the demands made upon her grew more and more burdensome. Next the news came, soon after the one brother's lapse, that another brother was failing in business. The patient at once foresaw renewed demands for financial assistance, which she had been giving this brother intermittently for many years, more family conferences, and in the end a further depletion of her savings.

She began lying awake night after night, going over and over the situation in anticipation of her brother's financial collapse, trying to see a way out of it for herself but finding none. She thought with bitterness that, no matter how prosperous the times, no one in the family ever repaid the loans she made them or even let her have the interest they had always promised. About ten weeks before the patient's admission to the hospital, she began noticing that she could not seem to concentrate on her work and that she was becoming irritable and inefficient. About eight weeks before admission, the patient quarreled sharply with her niece over the latter's decision to go off on a vacation which, under the circumstances, looked like sheer extravagance. She reflected on the inconsiderate, heartless, irresponsible attitudes of all members of the family toward her. She began upbraiding herself for not being brave enough to kill herself and leaving them to shift for themselves.

Six weeks before her admission, the visitation which the patient had been anticipating with anxious dread became an actuality. The second brother appeared with insistent, "persecuting" demands for financial help, the family conferences began and they ended just as she had expected. She found herself almost a thousand dollars poorer and with no faith left in the ability of either brother to make a go of his own life without continual aid from her. By this time she was averaging not more than two hours' sleep in twenty-four. Sometimes, as she lay awake, her heart would thump so hard that she would have to spend a good part of the night sitting up in a chair. "It was like being terribly scared," she said. She discovered that although she continued eating as before she was steadily losing weight; she began to be troubled by persistent constipation.

Four weeks before her admission, the time for her own vacation arrived and she went to the home of a friend in the country to keep expenses down. Here the patient found she could not relax in the day or sleep at night. She could not retain so much as one paragraph of what she read in newspapers and light magazines, even though she read it over a second time. Nothing seemed to stir her emotionally as it had, not even the movies. She had always cried easily, but now she seemed to be in a "stony" condition. Things seemed unreal to her and horrible. She felt that she was losing her mind. Three times she went to a bridge to throw herself into the river, but each time she could not summon the courage to do it. She said afterwards that she began then to realize that she would never be able to go back to her former work.

At this stage the patient returned to her own home and consulted the family physician. To him she poured out her complaints against the family, her own disgust and misery over everything and her suicidal ruminations. He advised immediate hospitalization, and, according to the patient's account, told her that in her own way she was just as bad as her brothers. Her relatives stated that, from this point on, there was a marked increase in self-depreciatory and self-accusatory comments in her talk. One night she confessed to relatives that she was planning to turn on the gas and die before morning. She was brought to the hospital and admitted at once.

On admission the patient looked sad, dejected and tense; she had a fixed, pained frown on her face. She rubbed her forehead, stared ahead and wrung her hands. Tears filled her eyes, but they did not brim over; she made no crying movements. Her speech was terse and measured, but neither vague nor irrelevant. She said, "I can't make myself feel that I can get over this. . . . Nothing seems to affect me, because I have no hope." She freely reported suicidal plans when asked, but she added, "I was too spineless to carry them out. Not spine enough left for anything. I've never seen such an awful mess." There was no disorientation present. Recall of recent and remote events in the patient's history was reasonably good. She showed poor retention of digits and of a simple test story. In doing the routine serial subtraction, of seven from one hundred and seven from each subtrahend, she kept losing the continuity of her performance and starting over again; but she ultimately completed the operation with only one error. She said she knew this was the end of her mentally, and she asked to be put in a public institution where she would be less expensive to keep.

During four months in the hospital this patient showed no improvement, and in some respects grew worse. She required sedatives for sleep; she ate, she said, from "an animal desire to live"; her weight fluctuated, showing neither important gain nor loss. When not occupied in supervised activities or asleep, she spent her time pacing to and fro, wringing her hands, picking and rubbing, and going from physician to nurse to attendant demanding insistently, "Tell me the truth! Tell me the truth! Let me go out and do the only decent thing!" Three interrelated themes of preoccupation were dominant: one her financial worry, another her conviction that she was sinful — a liar, a coward, a cheap-skate, a hypocrite — and a third her belief that the hospital was conspiring to expose her to the world.

Early in her stay the patient complained that an ophthalmological examination would ruin her financially. But when assured that consultations were not charged for, she said, "If I'm paying anything here I should — as a pay patient — pay him something. I can see you and everyone around here begin to know what I am and despise me as you should." She deplored the fact that she could no longer help the family, but sent her resignation to her employer and then, when it was not accepted, demanded that he be told the truth about her. Of her illness she said: "Things get too much for you, you can't face them, you get sleepless, you try to evade things. Yet morally you're obligated to do it; there's a conflict that way — try to persuade yourself you're not responsible — I've always paid everything; I've always been conscientious." Of her brothers she said, "I'm just like them. I just have to lie down and take everything from them." She complained that her mind ran around "like a pig in a poke," or that she felt like a statue, a vegetable, had no thoughts and feared everything would go away.

As the patient's anxiety and her preoccupation with her own unworthiness and sin increased, her suspicions concerning the hospital also grew and her delusional misinterpretations became more self-centered and involved. Her aggression and hostility were no longer turned upon her family but upon herself and the hospital staff. She showed a constant need to tell her story, to convince everyone that she was too degraded a person to remain, but the telling brought her no satisfaction. On the contrary, the more she talked the more agitated she became and the more she demanded punishment, exposure, jail, the penitentiary, public disgrace, to be thrown into the street. She followed the nurses and the physicians about, insisting she be sent away. She accused the staff of giving her false letters with the forged signatures of relatives and friends, and of rewriting her letters and suppressing the truth in them.

She gradually built up a delusional system, a pseudocommunity united in a grand plot to show her up and prove to her as well as to everyone else that she was no good. The nurses, she said, switched her letters from one envelope to another at night to test her recognition, they gave her other patients' dresses — she marked a dress secretly to prove this — they hid her hairpins. The extension of her vacation to a leave of absence from her firm was obtained, she said, under false pretenses. The hospital was collecting data on her and would publish all the facts in a few days — about her "fake," her "farce." Other patients who wept did so because her relatives did not remove her. Everything was planned to give her the third degree. "They dress people up to look like people I know. . . . Why, even a coat that someone has on is like one of mine. The faucets in the kitchen are like mine. They've been put there since I came here, and I don't know who's doing all this unless it's the Rockefeller Endowment."

The patient was sure she heard attendants and patients discussing a love affair about which she had told the psychiatrist. She said, "I demand, I *demand* that I be given a criminal trial!" and "End it, end it, end it! Send me to jail where I belong!" She felt she could never return to her job or her people. "It's got to be. I could never face people. You don't know what awful things I've done. . . . I can never pay back the thousands of dollars they've spent on me here, trying to make me see what I am. They run buses up and down Hamilton Street all day and all night. Think of those trucks out there. And you know what they've done across the street — painted a door red to show I'm a prostitute — and I'm not that." The patient refused to shake hands with a physician on rounds. "Don't shake hands with me. I'm a rotten yellow dog. No one can help me. I've been rotten all along." She afterwards said that cars in the street were painted yellow to show her up. She wished to issue a statement of her guilt and have it certified by the hospital staff. She insisted upon doing the cleaning on the ward, but complained that even this was a sham and she should be made to do "really menial work." She was finally removed to a midwestern state hospital where she soon began improving and was discharged practically well after a few months without special treatment.

Our patient began with marked anxiety over serious threats to her financial security; the threats became actualities and the anxiety was further augmented by her reactions of hostility toward the only loved persons left to her. The sleeplessness, tension and pre-occupation, which arose in response to these threats, continued afterwards because of the hopelessness of the situation, and because there was an upsurge of other conflicts and hostilities in relation to the patient's own concealed and partially repressed love life. She became frightened by the decline in her work efficiency and by her inability, on vacation, to retain the lightest reading material available. Her suicidal ruminations aroused further guilt, and her failure to make the fatal jump gave her something in the immediate present on which to base active self-disparagement. Finally, her interpretation of a physician's comment to mean that she was as worthless as the siblings she had recently hated, coming at a time when she was desperately in need of comforting and understanding affection, helped turn all her hostile aggression toward her guilty self. Although we know that nearly all such cases ultimately recover, it is possible that recovery in this case was hastened by transfer to an environment which many patients consider drab, humiliating and deliberately punitive.

This case presents us with an almost straight-line progression from the patient's original anxiety, resentment and hostility in relation to her loved siblings to her extreme agitation and marked self-reactions of hostility and condemnation. The accusations which the patient made against her siblings in her ruminations were all based upon fact, and her self-accusations were not without foundation. What she showed in her emotional upheaval of guilty conflict was the kind of exaggeration one frequently sees in public confessions of sin and unworthiness, as for example at revivalist meetings. Taken in this context of sustained excessive anxiety attitudes, the statements of remorse, self-hate and self-condemnation seem in either case neither absurd nor unintelligible to the trained impartial observer.

In agitated depressions the greatest danger, of course, is that of suicide.[11] Unfortunately it is also one of the most difficult hazards to evaluate. There is no simple relationship between the duration of a depressive attack, or its estimated severity, and the probability of a suicidal attempt. Little or no reliance can be placed upon the patient's assurance that he would never consider such a thing. If

[11] For a discussion of the problem of suicide in relation to mania and the depressions see H. Fox, "Dynamic factors in the affective psychoses," *Amer. Jour. Psychiat.*, 1942, vol. 98, pp. 684-689.

he is desperate enough to kill himself, he can hardly be expected to let an untruth stand in his way. Besides, the patient often can no more predict his outlook tomorrow than can his relatives or the physician.

Neither his philosophy of life nor his religious convictions can be depended upon to keep the depressed patient from suicide. For in his deep pessimism and self-depreciation, the arguments that once seemed most cogent to him are likely to appear trivial or meaningless. In his religious preoccupations a patient may at any time reach the conclusion that his sinfulness has already damned him beyond hope of redemption; he might as well begin his eternal punishment with self-execution. There is additional danger to the depressed patient in a widespread popular fallacy that repeated threats of suicide need not be taken seriously.[12] No responsible person can afford to hold this view and no experienced person does. Depressed individuals are not infrequently convinced that dependents and loved ones also face misery, suffering or disaster; when they attempt suicide they are likely to include these other persons in their plans.

Suicide and protective homicide are not the only serious hazards in the agitated depression. There is also the failure of depressed persons to eat and sleep adequately, and to keep up a minimal interest in routine body care. Since a majority of depressive attacks occur after the fortieth year of life, one must think not alone of increased vulnerability to intercurrent infection, but also of organ or tissue pathology which may arise because of dietary neglect, continued overactivity and lack of rest. In addition there is the danger that relative incompetence at work, and judgment warped by pessimism and self-accusation, may lead to severe economic loss and reduction in social status.

Retarded depression

The retarded depression is characterized by a general slowing up and restriction of activity, with sadness, dejection and self-depreciatory delusions, but without serious behavior disorganization and without an adequate basis in organ or tissue pathology. Retarded

---

[12] Suicidal talk is listed as an important warning sign by J. Wall, "Psychiatric problems of suicide," *Amer. Jour. Psychiat.*, 1944, vol. 101, pp. 404-406. Twenty-three of the thirty-three suicides in his series were manic-depressive cases.

depressions, like agitated depressions, begin in a setting of unrelieved personal stress and strain. There is always also an initial period of increased tension and anxiety which, however, may easily be overlooked by relatives and friends, particularly if the patient is taciturn in personal matters.

The retarded depressed patient, like the agitated, reacts to this initial increase of tension and anxiety at first with increased effort. But sooner or later he slows down, loses all interest in work and recreation, and becomes gloomy, sad, withdrawn and preoccupied. He develops striking loss of initiative. He shows the aversion to and unreadiness for new or continued activity which, as we saw in Chapter 8, define the fatigue reaction. His movements grow heavy and effortful, his talk is slow and monotonous, he may have crying spells, and he complains of difficulty in thinking, in concentrating and in remembering. This is the retarded depression.

Superficially, the patient in a retarded depression gives the appearance of being overrelaxed. Whether he sits, stands or walks, his posture is a drooped one, his head is bowed, his arms seem to hang limply and his face looks careworn, lined and haggard. Moreover, gastrointestinal motility is greatly slowed up,[13] persistent anorexia and constipation are the rule, salivary and sebaceous secretions are often diminished, and there is nearly always a reduction in potency or cessation of the menses.

But this appearance of relaxation is deceptive. Closer study of the retarded depressed patient usually reveals that he, like the agitated one, is actually tense and unrelaxed. He reminds us of the patient with a tense fatigue syndrome who complains of being tired out but cannot seem to rest.[14] He is troubled constantly by hopeless, fearful ruminations and when he manages finally to fall asleep for two or three hours, he is often disturbed by anxious dreams. He talks like a man who is doomed; he sits with his head in his hands as one who believes all is lost. He can no more interest himself in the ordinary activities of daily life than a person can who is soon to be hanged.

We cannot possibly understand the retarded depression, of course, until we find out what the patient is thinking. When we do, we may discover that he is indeed convinced that he is doomed,

---

13 G. Henry, "Gastrointestinal motor functions in manic-depressive psychoses," *Amer. Jour. Psychiat.*, 1931, vol. 88, pp. 19-28.

14 See the account in Chapter 8.

that all is lost or that his execution is not far off. He may even hallucinate to the same effect, in support of his delusions. If he does not go as far as this in his convictions, he will at least believe that he is worthless, a failure, degraded, a sinner unfit for decent company, a sorrow to others, or a malefactor deserving punishment and disgrace. In short, the patient in a retarded depression is characteristically involved in delusional convictions, in a pseudocommunity which is relatively well-organized and centers about his actual or imagined shortcomings. The following case represents a common clinical development.

> The patient, a post office employee of thirty-seven, was brought to the hospital by his wife, on the recommendation of the family physician. For three weeks he had been absent from work on sick leave, complaining of fatigue, insomnia, loss of appetite, and inability to understand what he read or remember what he was supposed to do. He had become convinced that he was losing his mind and would never be able to work again. The day before bringing him to the hospital, his wife had come home unexpectedly to find him in the garage preparing to commit suicide by running the automobile engine with the garage doors sealed.
>
> On admission to the hospital, the patient sat slumped in a chair, frowning deeply, staring at the floor, his face looking sad and drawn. When questioned, he answered without looking up, slowly and in a monotone. Sometimes there was such a long pause between question and reply that the patient seemed not to have heard. Every now and then he shifted his position a little, sighed heavily and shook his head from side to side. His first verbal response was, "It's no use. I'm through. All I can think is I won't be any good again." In response to further inquiries he made the following comments, relapsing into silence after each short statement until again asked a question. "I feel like I'm dead inside, like a piece of wood. . . . I don't have any feeling about anything; it's not like living any more. . . . I'm past hope. . . . There's nothing to tell. I've lied to everybody. My family is ashamed of me. I've messed up my life. I'm no good to anybody. . . . My memory is gone. I forget everything. . . . I can't look people in the eye any more. I've done everything wrong. You're wasting your time on me."
>
> This illness had its beginning in economic success. About four months before admission to the hospital, the patient had been promoted in grade and transferred from a suburban to a central office. He had sought and welcomed the promotion both for the increased salary it brought and as a sign of personal worth. However, the

change proved much more difficult for him than he had anticipated. The suburban office was a fairly quiet place, there was one superior, a steady-handed fatherly man, and the patient worked among old friends. In the central office he was a stranger in a strange place. He found that he now had many superiors, and all of them seemed brusque or indifferent. There was a constant hurry and rush about the place which made him feel always on the point of losing his grip and falling behind in his work.

Three months before admission the patient, who had generally kept his troubles to himself, commenced complaining of fatigue, headache, eyestrain and aching legs. His wife persuaded him to try resting more at home, but he found relaxation and sleep difficult to achieve. As time went on, he grew increasingly preoccupied with the topic of his work, said it was too complicated and detailed, that things went too fast for him and everybody seemed to be under strain. He could not understand how the others took it day after day. On his time off he revisited the branch office, but although he felt better while there, he felt out of it afterwards and seemed to his wife more downhearted than ever.

His wife first began to worry about him when the patient showed that he could no longer hold his own in playing bridge. He could not remember what had been played, made gross errors in bidding, grew confused and irritable, and finally gave up. This was around two and one-half months before admission. The patient seemed to lose interest in his family and his friends, in recreation and in food. He often awakened early in the morning, got up before dawn and roamed around the house or sat on the porch doing nothing. Self-disparagement appeared more and more in his talk. He compared himself with his fellow-workers and with friends his own age, saying that he "couldn't take it," and was getting old and worn out. His wife, who was herself now growing tense and anxious over the situation, seems to have alternated between reassuring the patient and expostulating with him, telling him that he could "snap out of it" if he tried.

One evening while his wife was arguing with the patient and trying to make him see how groundless his self-disparagement was, the patient surprised her by impulsively confessing an infidelity he had committed several years before. He followed this confession up immediately with another concerning his adolescent autoerotism which, he said, was responsible for his present lack of stamina. He told of having once before become ill "like this" during his adolescence, and of having pulled himself out of it. But now, he said, it was entirely different — he would never get well again.

Following this episode the patient was more reticent than ever.

He seemed to be brooding most of the time, answered questions slowly or curtly, and if goaded would often speak angrily and then seclude himself or leave the house. It was in this general setting that he went on sick leave, because he could no longer keep up with his work. And his sick leave, as we have seen, was the prelude to suicidal arrangements and his admission to the hospital.

During the first few months after hospitalization, the patient showed no sign of improvement whatever. There was a convincing finality about his statements of hopelessness. He slept little. His eating at times fell to a point where expert coaxing and spoon feeding were necessary, and constipation was a continual problem. When the patient finally began sleeping and eating better, gaining weight, looking more alive and talking spontaneously, he still insisted gloomily for some time that he would never recover. However, ten months after admission he was discharged improved, had a brief period of tension and overactivity two months later, and finally returned to work at another branch office, with apparently complete recovery.

This case illustrates the prodromal period of tension and anxiety, the initial attempt to meet stress, aversion, loneliness and dissatisfaction with increased effort. It also gives us an example of the so-called "promotion depression." [15] A gain in prestige and income should make a person glad, and it did in this case at first. But upgrading and a pay raise are not the only factors to be considered in a change of work and of place. This patient had been reared by an energetic, overprotective mother who trained him in dependence upon approval and affectionate domination. His wife had been able to give him some degree of the same protection, but, from her own account, not as much as he would have accepted. He had evidently succeeded also in establishing a filial relationship with his superior which gave him further security at his place of work.

It was the disruption of this dependent relationship in the work situation that seems to have precipitated anxiety, dissatisfaction and fatigue. The patient found himself suddenly in a whirlpool of confusing activity, where there was neither time nor organizational opportunity for personal contact with superiors, and everyone seemed indifferent or threateningly competitive. His reaction of

[15] W. Titley, "Prepsychotic personality of patients with agitated depression," Arch. Neurol. Psychiat., 1938, vol. 39, pp. 333-342; N. Flanagan, "The promotion depression," Jour. Amer. Med. Assn., 1942, vol. 120, p. 1383.

increased effort, of course, had no effect upon the factors responsible for his difficulties; and his next move was to complain of personal inadequacy — a technique which had probably been overlearned in childhood. This brought him sympathy for a time at home, but no relief at work, and eventually even this sympathy turned into remonstrance. The double-barreled confession that followed might have been in part a spite reaction to his wife's reproaches, but it revived the patient's old, partially repressed conflicts and added them to his burden. Thus, by a succession of cumulative and self-perpetuating reactions an anxiety disorder became a retarded depression which nearly ended in the patient's death.

What has already been said of suicide in relation to agitated depressions applies equally well to retarded depressions. In some ways the hazard in retarded cases is greater, because the fatigued, sagging patient, whose initiative is so conspicuously impaired, does not impress the average person as much of a risk when it comes to planned acts of desperation. But by far the greatest menace to recovery from retarded depression is that of suicide. Indeed, it often requires the utmost in vigilance and trained imagination to ward off a fatal outcome, and even expert vigilance and imagination sometimes fail. The ill effects of dietary neglect, continued tension, lack of rest or sleep, and the threats to economic, social and personal security have the same serious implications that they have in agitated depressions and, for that matter, in manic excitements as well.

Manic excitement

The manic excitement is characterized by elation or aggressive self-assertion, which may reach delusional proportions, and by energetic overactivity without serious disorganization and without an adequate basis in organ or tissue pathology. Manic excitement, like depression, always begins in a setting of unrelieved personal stress and strain. There is a prodromal period of increased tension and anxiety, which may be as brief as a few hours or as long as several weeks. The excitement seems to represent a compensatory reaction to a situation in which the patient is markedly ambivalent. The dominant delusional themes are usually those of grandeur, and the frustrated or unsuccessful grandiose patient may also develop secondary delusions of persecution and influence.

Manic excitements are sometimes precipitated by a single incident, occasionally with startling abruptness. One of our patients developed a full-fledged manic attack within a few hours of the sudden death of her husband, to whom she had been unhappily married for twenty years. Another patient, an unmarried farmer of twenty-five who had been greatly overworked for two weeks, burst into tears when harshly criticized by his father, tried to get a gun to kill himself, and was found later in the day excited, sobbing and distressed over his unfinished work. The next day he was overactive, elated and full of grandiose plans which led to his hospitalization in an acute manic attack a week later. Of particular interest to the behavior pathologist is the fact that, whether the onset be gradual or abrupt, there seems to be no difference between the character of situations giving rise to manic excitements and those giving rise to agitated or retarded depressions.[16]

In the more usual cases of relatively gradual onset, the patient, after a preliminary phase of tension or anxiety, becomes overactive, restless, excited and aggressive. He usually shows a striking increase in initiative with an equally impressive impairment in judgment. Our farmer, for example, tried to hire a fleet of trucks for a grandiose business enterprise, and actually did engage a dance hall with orchestra to give a party for his friends, although he had no money. The manic patient is characteristically self-assertive, domineering, impatient and critical, but intolerant of criticism or restraint from others. If he is actively interfered with, he is apt to become irritable, resentful, angry and combative. His inability to take consequences into account sometimes results in his becoming dangerously destructive to property and, less commonly, to persons.

The manic patient usually shows an inability to remain long at any one thing. Everything seems to distract him, even his own acts, words and thoughts; he shifts without so much as a pause from one activity, object or topic to another. Nowhere is this more evident than in the usually continuous flow of manic talk which, without becoming disjointed or bizarre, goes rapidly on from one topic to another (*topical flight*).[17] If exuberant elation dominates the clinical picture, the talk is interspersed with quips, puns, rhymes, wit-

---

[16] C. Bonner, "Psychogenic factors as causative agents in manic-depressive psychoses," *Jour. Nerv. Ment. Dis.*, 1931, vol. 11, pp. 121-131.

[17] An example of *topical flight* will be found in the case of the midwestern housewife which follows.

ticisms and personal references, some of which may be vulgar and obscene.

The patient may sing, shout himself hoarse, whistle, adorn himself or strip naked, dance and prance, go through calisthenics, walk in circles, tease others, play pranks and act the clown. He may give neither time nor attention to food, rest or elimination. Sleep is sometimes limited to less than an hour a night, patients are frequently starved, dehydrated and lose a great deal of weight. An interesting finding is the slowing of gastrointestinal motility in acute manic disorders.[18] Throughout manic excitement, unless it becomes hyperacute, the patient's behavior remains fairly well-organized and his level of communication, for all the overactivity, is a relatively adequate one. To the normal observer the excitement seems intelligible as exaggerated elation or, as in the following case, exaggerated self-assertion.

> The patient, a married man of fifty-eight, had been employed as a minor race-track official before his illness. Three years before his admission to the hospital, his income, which depended upon the prosperity of the race-track, began steadily to diminish. Within a year he was obliged to move into a poor neighborhood, which caused him great concern, particularly as he had a fourteen-year-old daughter for whom he wanted the best. Twelve weeks before his admission, the patient finally came to the end of his resources and appealed to his aged father for financial help. His appeals, however, were repeatedly rejected, and he was harshly criticized, and called stupid, a poor thing and no good.
>
> This treatment humiliated and angered the patient, particularly as he was an only child and his father had inherited an income of ten thousand a year which he occupied most of his time in spending on horses and betting. For a month the patient slept poorly and seemed tense, discouraged and upset. Then, eight weeks before his admission, he attended an important racing event and struck his acquaintances as garrulous, excitable, argumentative and sometimes belligerent, whereas he had been ordinarily a cheerful, even-tempered man, although often tense and somewhat overconscientious. He became extremely hard to please at home, continually criticizing his wife and everything about the household.
>
> Four weeks before his admission to the hospital, the patient entered two horses, which he owned, in an important racing event. Following this it was noticed that he was overactive, overtalkative,

<hr>

[18] G. Henry, "Gastrointestinal motor functions in manic-depressive psychoses," *Amer. Jour. Psychiat.*, 1931, vol. 88, pp. 19-28.

excited, expansive and jovial, and more sleepless than ever. He wrote a great many letters, telephoned friends over and over in the middle of the night to tell them about horses and horse-racing, and began sending radiograms to Chicago about purchasing horses. A few days before admission, he bought several hundred dollars' worth of blankets and trunks for his horses unnecessarily, and spoke of organizing huge rallies for the coming presidential election. He was at first hospitalized on a general service where he promised his nurse fifty thousand dollars and said he would like to marry her.

After a few days the patient was transferred to the psychiatric service. He said: "I never felt better in my life. I want my day nurse; she reminds me of my mother. I began to feel despondent July 15 when I ran out of money and my daddy was damned hard on me. I never felt better in my life, doc. I like it here, but I want my nurse with me." His neurological examination, blood and cerebrospinal fluid studies were all negative. His behavior on the ward showed marked restless overactivity which was more self-assertive and expansive than elated.

The patient was extremely talkative, but gave no evidence of topical flight, no rhyming and virtually no punning. He said repeatedly that he felt fine and "like a two-year-old." He talked about horse-racing, family affairs, politics and nurses, said he would make so much money on the horses that the patients would all get radios, the nurses mink coats and the hospital a hundred thousand dollars. Against Jewish patients he directed disturbing anti-Semitic tirades, and he frightened a depressed clergyman by assuring him that the doctors were going to castrate him.

A sample of the patient's talk at the height of his illness follows: "If I don't send these letters it will cost me at least fifty thousand dollars. I can make a hundred thousand dollars if I can get my letter in the hands of the right man. This is worse than jail — you get out of jail sometimes. But I like it here. I like you. I could do with that one nurse now. Yes, by golly, I'd pay twenty dollars a day to have her. If I were younger I'd marry her. . . . I think 'Miss Ohio' [another nurse] should marry that rich farmer. She will have half a million. Just think! To be a young rich widow — and he won't live more than a year."

This patient was treated at first by restricting but not eliminating his contacts with other persons, and by continuous warm tubs and occupational therapy on the ward. As he began to quiet down, he was led to participate more and more in the life of the ward, to go with other patients to the various forms of group work and recreation, and to go into his personal problems with his psychiatrist. He left the hospital much improved. In his illness he showed clearly an initial phase of anxiety, worry, discouragement and resentment, followed by a compensatory push of activity, aggression toward others and an outburst of self-assertion and grandiose plans. At no period of his hospital stay did he seem genuinely happy or carefree.

The situation leading up to this manic attack included a grave threat to the patient's security, a severe blow to his pride in having to move his family into a poor neighborhood, and finally the humiliation of being railed at and rejected by his affluent father. The compensatory character of the patient's reaction is obvious. The only unusual feature of this attack is the almost complete absence of even an appearance of gaiety. In the case that follows, we shall see a manic excitement arising, similarly, in a setting of anxiety and tension; but the reaction includes more prankish behavior behind which, however, spite and bitterness can be clearly detected.

The patient, a married woman of thirty-four who lived in a small midwestern town, was brought to a psychiatric hospital in a near-by city by her husband. She said: "I didn't think I really needed to come. I came voluntarily because my husband asked me to. It was against my wish, but I came just the same." The patient's husband stated that she had shown a "nervous disposition" during the preceding week. She had been at first angry, aloof and preoccupied, but had then become excited, talkative and sleepless, spending her days and nights in restless activity, singing, rhyming, punning and laughing.

A week before her coming to the hospital, the patient had returned from three months alone at a summer resort on the Michigan upper peninsula, where she had been working as a cook. Her object in going there had been chiefly that of getting away from her unhappy home life in a house full of her husband's relatives. Before returning, she had given her husband an ultimatum to the effect that she would leave him if he persisted in his mode of living and did not provide her with a home of her own.

The background of her ultimatum was briefly this. The patient and her husband had spent the ten years of their married life in the home of her husband's family, where lived his parents, an invalid aunt, and a married sister with her own husband. Here the patient had little housekeeping to do and nothing whatever to say in the management of the home which was ruled over by her sister-in-law. She felt always an outsider, whose activities were frowned upon and critically discussed, and whose friends were treated with deliberate coolness by the family. The patient belonged to lodges and bridge clubs; and she enjoyed bowling, dancing and movies. To get away from the in-laws she frequently took odd jobs and spent the money she earned on clothes, which she loved, even though this use of her earnings brought continual criticism from her sister-in-law, who enjoyed saving.

The patient's failure to bear children had for years been a source of continual disappointment and frustration to her, especially as repeated gynecological examinations had disclosed no basis for her sterility. The in-laws expressed openly their opposition to her becoming pregnant, and had said that if she had a child she would have to leave the house. This, of course, gave the patient further reason to want a family. According to her and to one of her kinsfolk, the husband had been drinking excessively for five years and had had at least one affair which was the talk of the town. He spent most of his evenings out, and when he did stay home, he sat around without speaking and often with his eyes shut as if asleep.

The husband noticed nothing unusual about his wife's behavior when he visited her during the summer before the onset of her illness. Three weeks before she returned home, the patient wrote her sister that she believed she was pregnant, but a week later when visited by her sister she seemed downcast and irritable, wept at the mere mention of her husband and said she would get a divorce unless he agreed to move out of the family home. On the Sunday of her departure, she was hurt and humiliated by her husband's failure to show up, as she was sure he had promised to do. She found herself wondering if he was spending the day with another woman. The next day she arrived in her home town and went directly to her husband's place of business where, after kissing him, she gave him a dressing-down for his neglect. This was one week before her admission to the psychiatric hospital.

During the ensuing five days the patient's behavior toward her husband and his family was uncommunicative and unfriendly. Once she visited her husband's place of business and stood staring intently out of the window. When the husband came up and asked her what was the matter, she turned abruptly on her heel and left the place without answering him. The patient was at home less than usual at this period because she was spending a great deal of time at her lodge, helping with preparations for a forthcoming town celebration. Even when she stayed in the house she was engrossed in memorizing some material for the part she was to have played in the festivities.

Two days before her admission to the hospital, the patient appeared suddenly at an evening meeting of a men's lodge, because she suspected that her husband was lying when he told her that he intended going to it. Finding him actually present, she merely smiled and went quickly away. It turned out later that from the lodge she went to the local hotel, where she made the proprietor play cards with her until midnight. Then she insisted that he and a guest drive her around town looking for her husband. She laughed and sang as they went through the streets.

Around one in the morning the patient arrived home and found her husband already in bed. She undressed, but could not settle down. She was overactive and overtalkative, jumping from topic to topic, reciting the piece she had been memorizing, singing, laughing and making rhymes. At two-fifteen the fire-whistle blew and the patient dashed out of the house in pajamas, bedroom slippers and a coat. Her husband found her back at the hotel, hiding behind a door. It took him an hour to get her home, and then in a few minutes she was out again. She insisted on walking up and down the streets, laughing and singing; she stole a banana from a truck; she sat on the hotel steps with her husband for two hours. The family physician was sent for and came, but he could not get her off the streets. She finally went home and to bed at six o'clock and fell asleep, but only for half an hour.

All the next day the patient talked, laughed and sang. She made a scene in her father-in-law's presence, was rude to him, swore at him and became combative. Once she struck her husband in the face. To everyone around her she kept saying, "I told you this would happen!" On the day following, she was taken to the city where she and her husband stayed at a relative's home. When they were out driving, she threatened playfully to jump out of the automobile. After they had gotten out to get frankfurters at a stand, it took an hour to coax the patient back into the car. All night long she stayed up, working around the house with a dust mop, talking, singing and praying. She was admitted to the hospital the next morning.

In the hospital the patient's behavior continued in the same general direction. There was no disorientation, and no evidence of disorganization. Neurological examination, blood and cerebrospinal fluid studies yielded negative results. A gynecological consultation revealed no evidence of pelvic disorder and it was the consultant's opinion that the patient was not sterile. When the next day her husband left for home, the patient was agitated and wept for a short period, but then brightened up and resumed her previous overactive and overtalkative conduct.

The following sample of talk shows definite flights of topics, rhyming, punning and distractibility, even though no evidence of happy elation was observed in the patient's behavior: "You go out and stand pat — pat, you hear! Who was Pat? What does he wear when he's in Ireland? This hair won't stay out of my eyes [brushes it aside and touches pillow]. See this pillow [raising it behind head]? Now is it even, even or odd? Even or odd, by God; I take it even, by God. By God we live, by God we die, and that's my allegiance to these United States. See. my little eagle [bedsheet wrapped around feet and stretched taut]? These are my wings. No, I have wings of a girl." Patient sings *Prisoner's Song*, making flying movements with her arms to accompany the lines, "Over these prison walls I would fly." Then sings, "One little Indian, two little Indians," and suddenly shouts, "Heap big Indian chief! I'm not afraid. I got a heart right there, I've got a key to my heart. I don't want instant death. No, not one little teensy, eensy, weensy, not one little teensy, eensy, wittsy, wonsy bit. Right is right, wrong is wrong, two rights don't make a wrong. So they are, all over the world. God made the world, but this isn't Adam speaking, it's me. Mr. Adam, you can't just walk out of here. It's O.K. by me, I've said my say. Out you go! Take me if you want to or leave me. Shoot if you want to. I have just one heart, a right heart. I'm so tired. So shoot, shoot, but only once. Point the gun at the right breast. I'll know him wherever I see him, dead or alive. Shoo-oot, 'Oh, Columbia the gem of the ocean' [sung]. Shoot, I'm ready, 1-2-3, shoo-oot! [hand over heart, eyes closed]. My husband, my sweetheart. Oh, how my heart aches, oh, it aches, I'm tired, I'm tired, I'm tired."

In her outpouring of talk, the patient revealed clearly her chief topics of concern, her ambivalent attitudes toward her husband, her ambivalent self-attitudes and her underlying anxiety and unhappiness. She said that she was going to have a baby, would conduct an orchestra, and boasted of her bridge playing and her evening dresses. In the tubs she frequently pretended she was swimming, laughed and sang, skipping from one song to another without finishing any. Within a week after admission, she had quieted down to an almost normal level of general activity and talk. There was easy irritability, however, and occasional temper outbursts over ward routine.

Five weeks after admission, the patient was sent with her husband to spend the night at her mother's home. There she quarreled with him over his having stopped a charge account, because of her illness, and she returned to the hospital tense, overtalkative and overactive. At first she showed no elation but only irritability, sleeplessness and anxiety. She spoke of fearing that she would die and her husband also. Within four days she was again excited and elated. She rhymed, punned, swore, laughed and sang, spoke aggressively of divorcing her husband and told everyone of her desire for children. Her recovery after this was slow, with some fluctuations of irritability, resentment and angry crying, but without episodes of sadness or mourning. She was discharged as recovered four months after admission, and a follow-up ten months later found her apparently well.

The background of this manic attack is one that would have seriously disturbed almost any woman in some way. From all the available evidence, it seems clear that the husband was a socially immature man who could neither emancipate himself from his own home nor face the responsibilities of starting his own family. His alcoholism, philandering and neglect, coupled with his ten years of delay in setting up a home for his wife, led the patient to issue an ultimatum to him. However, it is clear that, long before her manic attack, she was markedly ambivalent toward her husband. She threatened him with divorce, and she was pleased when she thought herself pregnant. She looked forward to his coming to get her at the resort and talked about it to her sister, and when he disappointed her, she reacted with an angry outburst followed by deliberate coldness toward him. When she reached home, the patient had to plunge at once into the task of memorizing and preparing for a public pageant. This placed her under additional pressure, and must have increased the ambivalence toward her return home, which, as we have seen, had for some time been evident in her behavior.

In going to the hotel proprietor for company, the patient seems simply to have picked on the nearest available man and to have celebrated her sorrow with him in public. The noisy drive about town in search of her husband was evidently an ostentatious demonstration of spite and distrust. From the moment of her arrival home, she indulged in unrepressed aggression, first by pranks that humiliated and exasperated her husband and his family, and then by profane and combative behavior directed against the in-laws. Notwithstanding, when her husband left the patient alone at the hospital, she grew agitated and wept, but reacted to this loss with compensatory elation. Five weeks later, following a quarrel with her husband in her mother's home, she became suddenly sleepless, irritable and anxious, expressing fear that both she and her husband might die. Then she reacted once again with compensatory elation and said publicly that she intended to divorce her husband.

Recovery after this was slow, but at the end of ten months of hospitalization apparently complete.

The sudden changes from self-assertion and elation to fear, anxiety and bitter unhappiness in this patient's behavior are representative of a great many manic excitements. So also are the unmistakable signs of ambivalence. This evidence, the practical identity of the immediately antecedent conditions, and the common prodromal period of tension and anxiety, together bring out the close relationship of manic and depressive attacks. The manic excitement is apparently not an automatic swing from one pole of metabolic activity to the other, but rather a coordinate substitute for a depressive attack, a compensatory defensive reaction against depression.[19] Indeed, in the care of manic patients, one must pay the same close attention to suicidal hazards and to the dangers of personal neglect, insomnia, exhaustion, and even of gastrointestinal stasis and starvation, that one does in agitated depressions. The additional threats to the patient's and family's safety, socio-economic status and reputation must be obvious from the two case histories we have cited.

Manic-depressive cycles

Patients only occasionally pass from an attack of manic excitement immediately into a depressive attack; still less frequently they pass from depression into mania.[20] The widow, whom we mentioned earlier as developing a manic attack immediately after her husband's death, followed her partial recovery with a depression that lasted more than a year. She then had two more manic attacks separated by a period of apparently good health. In all of these episodes the patient complained of loneliness and need for close affection. Even as an adolescent she had been known as a person who concealed her shyness, timidity and dependence by a mask of witty, happy-go-lucky sociability. She exchanged a stern, irritable, domineering father for a husband similarly inclined. Thus, she continued well into middle life as a habitually dependent, dissatisfied person. Her husband's death gave her personal freedom, but it

[19] N. Cameron, "The place of mania among the depressions from a biological standpoint," *Jour. Psychol.*, 1942, vol. 14, pp. 181-195.

[20] In Rennie's series, cited early in the chapter, the 24 per cent listed as "cyclothymics" were made up chiefly of cases whose manic and depressive attacks were separated by years of good health or by recurrent attacks of the same kind. These cannot justifiably be regarded as cyclic.

brought her neither a mature independence nor the second marriage she had always hoped for. In reacting with manic and depressive attacks she seems to have followed, in an exaggerated way, her lifelong patterns of defensive and dependent behavior.

In addition to the brief episodes of sadness and anxiety which occur during the course of most manic attacks, clinicians find that the recovering manic patient often expresses concern over what he remembers of his talk and general conduct during his excitement. His concern is seldom unfounded, although, if the excitement has been worked off in a sympathetic hospital environment, the danger of social disgrace is greatly lessened. The characteristic upheaval of conflict material, however, is frequently well remembered by the recovering patient.

Unless adequate individual therapy is available in the phase of convalescence from a manic attack, the patient may develop severe anxiety and self-disparagement as a reaction to what he remembers of his earlier behavior. Such a reaction is very likely the source of depression immediately following mania in the relatively few instances where this succession occurs. The rarer cases of immediate manic reaction to convalescence from depression seem to have the same origin as manic attacks that are not preceded by depression at all. They are, in other words, compensatory reactions to threatening anxiety which arises in these cases during recovery from the depression. Further detailed study is needed, not so much to explain why mania occasionally follows immediately upon depression, or vice versa, as to account for the fact that this occurrence is relatively infrequent.

Involutional melancholia

The official American classification [21] defines involutional melancholia as a depression of middle and later life characterized chiefly by agitation, uneasiness and insomnia, and often by self-condemnatory trends. This description does not in itself differentiate involutional melancholia from any other agitated depression. However, it is officially listed under the heading of "psychoses due to disturbances of metabolism, growth, nutrition or endocrine functions." This listing is the subject of considerable controversy and

---

[21] C. Cheney, *Outlines for Psychiatric Examinations.* Utica, N.Y.: State Hospitals Press, 1934. Also reprinted in full in A. Rosanoff, *Manual of Psychiatry and Mental Hygiene,* 7th edition (New York: Wiley, 1938), pp. 967-985.

the source of widespread confusion. The confusion is reflected, for example, in the fact that neither the official British classification, derived like the American directly from Kraepelin's system, nor the recent United States Army classification, indicates that involutional melancholia is due to such disturbances. Psychiatric textbook authority is similarly divided. Thus, Henderson and Gillespie devote a full chapter to this syndrome while Billings, who is both internist and psychiatrist, dismisses it as simply an agitated depression occurring in middle or later life.[22] The published reports of clinical experimentation show equally sharp contradictions; and even the definitions offered by clinical writers who accept involutional melancholia as a differentiable syndrome do not agree one with another as to the discriminating characteristics.[23]

One important source of the contradiction and confusion, which should be relatively easy to eliminate, is the old mistake of treating involutional melancholia as though it were purely a biochemical disturbance of the internal environment. This is the same mistake that was responsible for the now discarded groups of *gestation*, *postpartum* and *lactation psychoses* which have for several decades been recognized as reactions of a biosocial person to the fact and the implications of pregnancy, childbirth, breast-feeding and child care. But the recognition has been slower in coming that involution also has serious implications for the senescent woman in our society. Her social status and personal security are often directly dependent upon sex behavior, fertility, child care and the preservation of a youthful appearance. When these activities and characteristics are threatened, the woman's status and security are likely to be threatened.

The woman who has found compensatory satisfaction in motherhood, which helps her to disregard her disillusionment in wifehood, faces irretrievable loss in middle life when her children one by one grow up and leave the home. The senescent man whose active career has been everything to him, or who has made his youth and

22 For example, see the contrast between D. Henderson and R. Gillespie, *Textbook of Psychiatry for Students and Practitioners*, 6th edition (London: Oxford University Press, 1944), pp. 265-287, and E. Billings, *Elementary Handbook of Psychobiology and Psychiatry* (New York: Macmillan, 1939), pp. 159-161.

23 For a discussion of this controversy, with bibliography, see N. Cameron, "The functional psychoses," in J. Hunt (editor), *Personality and the Behavior Disorders* (New York: Ronald Press, 1944), pp. 883-885.

vigor his chief bulwarks against anxiety, must inevitably suffer a disturbing reduction in personal security as his opportunities dwindle or he loses youth and strength. The senescent person finds that sickness and death seem suddenly to invade his circle of friends and associates, and this discovery becomes also a source of anxiety and insecurity for many men and women in middle life.[24] We shall have occasion to return to this important problem of human reactions to biosocial ageing in the next chapter where pathological senility is discussed.

Manic and depressive disorders in relation to organ and tissue pathology

Mania and depressions, we have seen, are essentially anxiety disorders which have been complicated by cumulative and self-perpetuating delusional developments, and in the case of mania, also by compensatory reactions. Therefore what has been said, in Chapter 9, about the relationship of anxiety disorders to organ and tissue pathology applies here also. Patients who are for any reason made anxious by illness, accident, surgery or convalescence may react with a depressive disorder, and sometimes with a manic attack. Post-influenzal convalescence, for example, with its characteristically profound apathy, is a notorious precipitant of mild depression which usually clears as the apathy disappears. However, it is frequently the case in illness and convalescence that what is loosely called depression is actually only weakness, anxiety and fatigue. That is to say, the persistent hopelessness and the delusional self-depreciation which define the retarded depression are both absent.

Great difficulty is often encountered in evaluating depressive and manic disorders. For example, one of our patients was referred to a psychiatric hospital because of complaints of sadness, crying spells, suicidal ruminations, sleeplessness, anorexia and loss of weight. It was soon found, however, that she was also suffering from carcinoma of the uterus. The carcinoma was cleared up by radiation therapy and surgery, while the depressive disorder ran a longer but typical course, ending also in recovery. In the next chapter, on cerebral incompetence, we shall present cases in which mania or depression develops in persons suffering from central nervous system intoxication, infection, injury and degeneration.

[24] A more detailed discussion of the factors precipitating behavior disorders in middle life will be found in N. Cameron, "Neuroses of later maturity," in O. Kaplan, *Mental Disorders in Later Life* (Stanford University, Calif.: Stanford University Press, 1945), pp. 143-186.

BIOSOCIAL BASES OF MANIC AND DEPRESSIVE DISORDERS

We come now to the question, *What are the characteristics of normal behavior from which manic and depressive disorders are derived?* One answer to this question has already been given and we may summarize it at this point. Mania and depression are themselves direct products of increased tension and anxiety; their origins in normal behavior to a considerable degree coincide with the origins of other anxiety disorders which we have earlier discussed.[25] The *agitated depression* is best understood as an anxiety disorder complicated by cumulative and self-perpetuating delusions. The *retarded depression* is basically a tense fatigue reaction to anxiety, similarly complicated by delusions; it duplicates in many respects the characteristics of the tense fatigue syndrome described in Chapter 8. The *manic excitement* is also a reaction to anxiety, but a compensatory reaction whose cumulative and self-perpetuating delusions are grandiose and self-assertive.

Normal agitation, retardation and excitement

Agitation, retardation and excitement in response to increased tension and anxiety are common everyday reactions that occur in normal persons who never become manic or depressed, as well as in those who do. Almost every adult occasionally develops a circular reaction in which worry begets worry, and the resulting increase in tension and anxiety revives doubts or conflicts over his own personal adequacy and integrity. Business worries, for example, whether justified or not, may lead to anxiety regarding home and family; anxiety over home and family is likely to raise the issue of personal health and vigor — since upon these a man's ability to work well depends — and this pondering is almost sure to make a person question his own competence and dependability. The new anxieties thus stimulated and the new doubts raised add to the worried man's insecurity and further heighten his tension.

The average housewife is in a situation that makes her especially vulnerable in certain respects to the development of such circular reactions. She is without diverting adult company a good part of each working day. She cannot greatly improve her socio-economic

[25] D. Cameron suggests that mania, anxiety disorders and depression constitute a behavior continuum. "Some relationships between excitement, depression and anxiety," *Amer. Jour. Psychiat.*, 1945, vol. 102, pp. 385-394.

status and security directly through her own efforts; instead, she must depend upon her husband's competence, which she is seldom in a position to evaluate objectively, or materially to influence. The man or woman who is not only habitually insecure, but also selectively reaction-sensitive to doubts cast upon his social responsibility, is likely to react to increased tension and anxiety with mild agitation, and an upheaval of concern over his ability to measure up to his duties and his ideals. In most persons mild agitation soon subsides, in many it persists for some time as chronic anxiety, and in a few it goes on to self-indictment and the agitated depression.[26]

Increased anxiety or tension, and the development of circular reactions such as we have mentioned, do not lead to mild agitation in all persons. In some, there is a noticeable reduction in overt activity, a temporary loss of initiative, an unreadiness for new or continued activity, and even an aversion to it. The anxious person, instead of growing mildly agitated, sits alone and worries, he is hard to interest in doing anything else, he complains of being tired, of not wanting to go out, to meet people or play games. He may go farther, and cast doubts upon his general ability or integrity. If examined, he shows no sign or symptom of anything but tension, anxiety and fatigue. In a few days, when things seem different to him, the previously worried man returns to his usual level of biosocial behavior. We could, of course, call such episodes as this mild depressions; but to do so would be to make almost everyone recurrently depressed. It is more useful to look upon them as episodes of mild and transitory fatigue reactions to increased tension and anxiety, the normal counterparts and sometimes the precursors of retarded depression.

Circles of augmenting tension and anxiety also lead to overactivity with self-assertion and increased initiative. Employers and employees, parents and children, teachers and pupils, learn in their interrelationships to recognize aggressive, insistent self-assertion as a symptom of tension or anxiety in the aggressor, however inexpertly they may formulate their recognition. They often are able to interpret boastful exaggerations as signs of insecurity and a need for reassurance. Sometimes a worried, harassed or frightened person is able himself to recognize the source and meaning of his self-assertive, boastful behavior; more often he is not.

[26] Compare the report by H. Myers and S. Von Koch, "Reactive depressions: a study of one hundred consecutive cases," *War Med.*, 1945, vol. 8, pp. 358-364.

Tense, anxious individuals frequently react with apparent gaiety and irresponsibility instead of self-assertion. Thus, for example, some normal men and women who are habitually the life of the party at social affairs originally developed this pattern as a compensatory reaction when they were insecure and uneasy. Their unrelaxed overactivity and superficial lightheartedness are compensatory techniques which neutralize the tension and anxiety aroused by their own self-reactions of inadequacy in the company of their peers. It is customary in our culture, and perhaps necessary, to get away periodically from the effects of worry, conflict, fear, confining work, failure and personal loss, through an episode of excitement or hilarity. This may be planned and deliberate, or a spontaneous act of spite, resentment or rebellion; but in either case it must be recognized as a close relative of the compensatory excitement, elation and self-assertion one sees in the less transient and less moderate episodes of manic excitement.

Indeed, many normal individuals intentionally induce or prolong a transient outburst of elation, under stress, by means of the stimulation and support of an exciting, permissive environment, convivial company, erotic activities and alcoholic release. There is a tendency, on the part of persons who wish to control and prevent this kind of behavior without first trying to understand it, to ascribe it wholly to alcohol and evil companionship. But this thoughtless ascription ignores the most significant, the central factor in the situation — the reacting biosocial individual. For he is responding not alone in terms of his immediate environment and the solace or diversion it provides, but in terms also of his own prior anxiety and tension. His compensatory techniques may be personally unwise or socially undesirable, but their origins go deeper than a thirst for conviviality, alcohol and sex. In manic excitement, likewise, the exaggerated, unwise and frequently offensive behavior of the patient can be understood only as the product of an earlier phase of unhappy conflict and intolerable strain.

Cumulative and self-perpetuating reactions

The most impressive thing about manic and depressive disorders is that they can be so intense and prolonged, and be dominated by frankly delusional self-reactions, without serious impairment of behavior organization throughout the illness. To a certain extent we have already accounted for the rise and persistence of the attacks by pointing out their origin in increased tension and anxiety. Mania and depressions share with anxiety disorders the cumulative and self-perpetuating effects of sustained ambivalent conflict, selective reaction-sensitivity, language behavior and thinking, role-taking and self-reactions, as we have indicated in Chapter 9. They differ from the typical anxiety disorder, however, in the fact that in them delusional self-reactions sooner or later become and remain dominant. We may begin our discussion, therefore, by taking for granted the rise and persistence of the anxiety behavior, and the fatigue or the compensatory reactions to it, and turn our attention to the part played by the delusions.

Since *agitated depressions* are more directly in the line of development from excessive anxiety than either the retarded depression or the manic excitement, we may simplify our exposition at this point by limiting it chiefly to them.[27] The delusional self-reactions of the agitated depression have their beginnings in a phase of emotional upheaval that results from acute tension and anxiety. The crucial event in this emotional upheaval is the appearance in the immediate conflict situation of self-reproachful or self-condemnatory attitudes. These attitudes support and facilitate the resurgence of old, partially repressed conflicts which lead to delusional self-accusations, further confessions, and the demand or expectation of punishment and degradation.

This crucial shift, however characteristic of agitated depression it may be, is not without its parallels in normal conduct. When, for example, crops fail, the bottom drops out of one's business, grave illness develops in one's family, or a near relative or a revered public person dies, a common reaction in the emotional upheaval precipitated is the statement of human inadequacy and unworthiness, and the revival of personal conflicts long since repressed. This we see in the familiar rush of sinners to church, the public lamentations and the declaration of personal unimportance that follow a communal crisis, and on the part of individuals whose attitudes may not ordinarily be religious, sorrowful or self-abnegatory. Moreover, in quasi-religious groups that encourage confession and self-accusation in public, an atmosphere of acute tension and anxiety is deliberately fostered at revival meetings to bring out these reac-

[27] Compare C. Rogerson, "The differentiation of neuroses and psychoses, with special reference to states of depression and anxiety," *Jour. Ment. Science,* 1940, vol. 86, pp. 632-644.

tions. Some of these groups also capitalize on the facilitating effects of self-accusation upon further and more severe self-accusation by urging the sinner to go on and on, once he has begun. What comes out of such emotional upheavals need have no relationship to what produced them other than the common background of intense anxiety.

The emotional upheaval in agitated depressions, we have said, is frequently the result of prolonged conflict and stress in which the patient develops marked ambivalence. It may arise, for example, when a person under conditions of intense anxiety reacts with overt or fantasied hostility toward someone for whom he has attitudes of love, reverence or awe. This was the situation, it will be recalled, out of which our private secretary developed her sequence of hostility, ambivalent conflict, emotional upheaval and delusional self-hate. We see similar developments when, during a phase of generally heightened anxiety, a person becomes involved in activities or relationships — actual, imagined or remembered — which threaten his personal integrity, violate an important ideal or break a commandment.

The self-accusatory reactions that arise in the agitated depressed patient, during his emotional upheaval, grow cumulative and self-perpetuating because he is unusually reaction-sensitive to his own guilt and has been overtrained in remorse and penitence. He has acquired earlier in life habitual unforgiving attitudes toward the smallest lapse in ethical responsibility. When, therefore, under conditions of unusual stress he develops marked tension, anxiety and an emotional upheaval, it is almost inevitable that his reactions will include self-reproachful and self-condemnatory attitudes. These attitudes then facilitate the revival and intensification of old personal conflicts in a new setting, and the *crucial shift* has been accomplished. The patient now becomes preoccupied with playing the familiar role of an indignant, outraged, vengeful parent which alternates with its complementary role of the intimidated, guilty penitent child.[28] In the one he accuses, threatens, condemns and execrates the culprit; in the other he cringes apprehensively, dreading the retribution he has earned, but also inviting it.

---

[28] This dual role is reminiscent of that which characterizes many compulsive disorders. Indeed, it will be remembered that, in our case of the government clerk, the onset of handwashing compulsions marked the disappearance of a depressive reaction.

The terrible crime or the unspeakable degradation, of which the agitated patient may accuse himself, is a reflection of his overwhelming anxiety. He might as a child have developed comparable anxiety in consequence of his parents' frightening threats of retaliation for his childhood guilt or hostility. But as an acutely apprehensive adult, he must find a rationalization on an adult level that will justify his overdetermined, exaggerated agitation. Therefore he accuses himself of multiple, unpardonable sins like the anxious, excited penitent at a revival meeting, and declares himself deserving of horrible punishment. Most depressed persons sooner or later begin to ascribe their own condemnatory self-reactions to the attitudes and intentions of society, the law and God. By the familiar technique of projection they proceed to organize their delusional convictions into a vengeful, threatening pseudocommunity.

We have said that anticipation of punishment is fundamental to the development of guilt reactions. But there is a corollary of this principle which for depressive disorders is equally important: the appearance of an acquired guilt reaction results in anticipation of punishment, and the severity of the punishment anticipated is related to the intensity of the patient's guilt. This helps to account for the expectation of extravagant torture and cruel death which preoccupies some patients. To some agitated depressed persons the consequences of their sinfulness seem to threaten everyone and to grow into an impending world catastrophe. The demand a patient makes, that he be made to pay for his crimes or his worthlessness, comes in part from need-satisfaction sequences which most persons acquire in relation to guilt during early childhood. The child's misdeed is met by parental condemnation and rejection, but punishment cancels out the crime and brings the child acceptance. The demand also has its source in the need to end intolerable suspense — the same need which leads often to suicide.

Retarded depressions, as we have seen, become cumulative and self-perpetuating through the interplay of similar factors in similar ways. But the delusional self-reactions that develop are directed primarily at the patient's inadequacies and his failures, rather than at his crimes as in agitated depressions. Aversion and unreadiness replace aggression in the clinical syndrome, and the dominant techniques are those of withdrawal, insulation and a tense but passive anticipation of punishment for shortcomings. In his self-reactions the retarded depressed patient usually takes the role of a sad,

chagrined and disappointed parent, and matches it with the reciprocal role of a disgraced, unworthy child. His guilt reactions and
the punishment he awaits may be as overwhelming to him as are
those of the worst agitated patient; but his overt behavior does not
reveal this to the casual observer.

Manic excitements, like depressions, arise out of a prodromal
phase of increased tension and anxiety; and an undercurrent of
anxiety must be reckoned among the important cumulative and
self-perpetuating factors in the attack. The excitement, in other
words, originates as the reaction to a threatened increase in anxiety,
and the same threat sustains the excitement. Of course there are
excited patients who, in spite of tension and anxiety, apparently
enjoy the things they do. But most persons in a manic attack take
the role of an insecure braggart or an unhappy clown. By their
exaggerated delusional compensations, they defend themselves from
the threat of overwhelming anxiety, just as normal persons often
defend themselves with boasts and hearty songs against their milder
fears. The relationship between anxiety and manic behavior was
clearly shown in our case of the woman among critical in-laws, for
each serious increase in tension and anxiety was followed by intensified aggression and elation. Under the protection and support of
a planned hospital routine both anxiety and excitement were given
the opportunity to subside.

Behavior organization in mania and depressions

We have said that manic and depressive disorders, in spite of
their intensity, duration and delusional developments, are characterized by the preservation of relatively good behavior organization. This fact at once invites a comparison with the quite different situation in schizophrenia. The manic or depressed patient, like
the schizophrenic, usually goes through an initial phase in which
he attempts to meet some challenge in terms primarily of the *social
community* — that is, with reactions oriented in relation to the functionally integrated group of which he is a member. With the delusional development his behavior becomes organized also in terms
of a *pseudocommunity,* and, at least in the case of retarded depression, his behavior may even be restricted to an *autistic community.*[29] However, neither in the patient's pseudocommunity nor

[29] The *pseudocommunity* is defined and discussed in Chapter 14, and the
autistic community in Chapter 15.

in his autistic community do we find disorganization comparable to that which is characteristic of schizophrenia.

To begin with, there is little in the *overactivity* or *underactivity* of manic and depressed patients that the normally imaginative clinician cannot understand. It is far less difficult, for example, to teach an intern to observe and record accurately the behavior of a manic patient than that of an excited schizophrenic. If the intern is as alert and intelligent as the manic, he will soon discover that his slower pace is his chief handicap. He will learn that with practice he can predict a great many of the manic patient's shifts of focus, and follow close behind most of the others, whereas the excited schizophrenic is apt to make the intern as confused as he is. A similar distinction can be made between the overactive agitated depressed and the overactive frightened schizophrenic patient, and between the underactive depressed patient and the underactive schizophrenic — unless, of course, both of the latter become stuporous and, for the time being, indistinguishable.

This relative superiority of behavior organization in manic and depressive disorders is especially evident in *communication.* In what we have called *topical flight,* for example, the manic makes rapid shifts from topic to topic, but the alert, attentive listener can keep up with the changes because they do not differ fundamentally from the changes in subject a normal elated person might make. The shifts in schizophrenic talk, as our verbatim examples in Chapters 3 and 15 clearly show, are confused by the indiscriminate overinclusion of material belonging to both shared social and private fantasy contexts. The manic in his talk keeps to social trails of communication, even though he may change his direction on them at every moment; the schizophrenic does not keep to social paths, but makes his own trail as he goes.

The character of the *delusions* also indicates relatively good preservation of behavior organization in mania and depressions. They are typically delusions which the normal observer can comprehend if he takes the role of a manic or a depressed patient and shares his perspective. But the normal person cannot seem to put himself in the place of the typical schizophrenic patient, take his role and share his perspective. Schizophrenic delusions are therefore difficult and sometimes impossible for the normal observer to comprehend. They represent a more individualistic and less socialized development which others cannot readily share with fidelity and success.

It is perhaps most striking of all that the retarded depressed person, when he withdraws and grows desocialized, still does not become seriously disorganized. He becomes deeply preoccupied, broods, is silent most of the time and refuses to participate in activities with other persons. He restricts his reactions almost entirely to his pseudocommunity and his autistic community. But even these behavior organizations in the retarded depressed patient do not deviate remarkably from the pseudocommunities which normal people develop when they are tense and anxious, or from the autistic communities of normal unhappy daydreams.

In contrasting the manic or depressed with the schizophrenic patient, we are distinguishing neither between different disease entities nor between so-called constitutional types, but between groups of individuals showing different degrees of social skill in meeting or succumbing to personal stress. The crux of the differentiation seems to be that the manic or depressed person shows the effects of a lifetime of adequate interpersonal give-and-take. He may fail to meet his challenge, as the schizophrenic fails, but when he is overwhelmed by anxiety, or reacts to it with excited overcompensation, his behavior does not disintegrate. In his ambivalence, his conflicts and his emotional upheaval he gives evidence that both his hostility and his love, his evil and his good, his reactions to others and his self-reactions, are organized into roles which correspond fairly well to normal social roles.

This difference suggests that manic and depressed patients have been generally more successful than schizophrenics in establishing themselves in their culture. They have evidently acquired a higher degree of social skill in taking culturally determined roles, in shifting perspectives and in sharing them with other persons. They have relied less upon the comparatively inept techniques of private unshared fantasy, furtive observation and unwarranted inference when under stress. It is apparently this background of relative social adequacy that protects them from behavior disorganization, whether they take the more aggressive roles of agitated depression and mania, or the more passive, tense desocializing role of the retarded depression.

BIOSOCIAL DETERMINANTS OF MANIC AND DEPRESSIVE DISORDERS

We have seen that agitation, retardation, elation and aggressive self-assertion are all to be found among normal reactions to increased tension and anxiety, and that emotional upheavals also occur in persons who never develop mania or depression. This brings us at once to our second fundamental question, *What are the determinants which seem to favor the development of tension, anxiety and emotional upheaval into a manic or depressive disorder?* In other words, why is it that some individuals and not others react in a personal crisis with extreme self-depreciation or self-condemnation that reaches delusional proportions, or with equally exaggerated compensatory elation and self-assertion?

Childhood influences

We have already indicated that manic and depressive attacks arise during an emotional upheaval which typically follows a phase of increased tension and anxiety. The attacks show the cumulative and self-perpetuating effects of sustained ambivalent conflict, selective reaction-sensitivity, language behavior, thinking, role-taking and self-reactions. In these respects, of course, manic and depressive illnesses do not differ fundamentally from other behavior disorders. But they are most closely related to the anxiety disorders, a relationship which is evident, not only at the adult level, but also in the similar background of both groups of patients. Indeed, what we have said in Chapter 9 about childhood training in anxiety, in chronic insecurity, in guilt and the expectation of punishment, applies with equal force to the manic and the depressed patient.

Thus, the person who develops a manic or depressive disorder as an adult is one who has been rendered in childhood reaction-sensitive to signs that he is considered inadequate, inferior, unworthy and guilty. As a child he learned that these signs heralded frightening threats to his personal security and frequently ended in rejection, condemnation and punishment by his elders. It is this sequence of selective reaction-sensitivity, threat, anxiety and hostility toward his own behavior and himself that he carries over into his adult reactions and self-reactions. For although, like the schizophrenic, he may be schooled in overdependence upon the censure and approval of others, unlike the schizophrenic he is overtrained in taking the role of the hypercritical, unforgiving parent toward his own behavior. In this respect he is, of course, closely related to the compulsive patient, whose childhood background we discussed in Chapter 10.

There are certain similarities and certain differences in the childhood of the compulsive and the manic or depressed patient which should be pointed out here. The sustained ambivalent conflict, which is a prominent characteristic of the prodromal phase of manic and depressive attacks, undoubtedly owes its intensity to the overdevelopment of a strict, vindictive parental role similar to that found in compulsive disorders. However, the chasm between the conflicting parental and filial roles, which we described in compulsives, is certainly far less evident in most manic and depressed patients. This difference suggests that the adult who develops clearcut mania or depression has succeeded in establishing somewhat more adequate emotional relationships in childhood with his parents, or parent surrogates, than has the typical compulsive patient.[30]

We may characterize the self-reactions of manic and depressed patients in terms of the interaction of filial and parental roles as follows. In the *agitated depression* the patient does not usually resist, in his filial role, the harsh condemnation of his parental role; he rather seeks to reinforce and amplify it by more and more confession. He encourages others or himself to implement the punishment, which in the parental role he insists, and in the filial role he admits, that he deserves. Some agitated depressed patients disown their guilt and ascribe their delusional parental self-reactions to punitive agents in a pseudocommunity (disowning projection), thus giving their syndrome some of the characteristics of paranoid disorders.

The *retarded depressed* patient as a rule acknowledges more passively his guilt and unworthiness; in the delusional self-reactions of his filial role he maintains the attitudes of one who is helpless and hopeless. The parental role is not a prominent component of his behavior, but it is implied, of course, in his delusions. In *manic attacks,* also, the parental role is present only by implication, and not as an immediately controlling or threatening delusional self-reaction. The manic patient is typically in rebellion against the implied parental role, and often gives a convincing and unequivocal performance of uninhibited filial revolt. Parent identification, however, is sometimes a conspicuous part of the manic reaction. Our race-track official, for example, certainly gave the distinct impression of taking his father's role in relation to the social community when he raced two horses, and then began ordering expensive equipment for them in a financially irresponsible fashion.

[30] Compare the section on parent-child relationships in Chapter 10.

Adult antecedents of manic and depressive disorders

Of course, not everyone made vulnerable in childhood to adult manic and depressive disorders will develop them when he grows up. There is always some antecedent precipitating situation, in overt or covert behavior, which brings on an attack. The most common preconditions, as we have seen, are those which stimulate reactions of severe, protracted anxiety and tension. The attitudes thus aroused favor the evolution of the characteristic delusional self-reactions to which the patient's childhood training has made him particularly vulnerable. As we pointed out in our case analyses, the most effective precipitants are those exciting marked ambivalent conflict, hostility and guilt in relation to a loved person. However, a great many manic and depressive attacks appear in response to relatively simpler threatened or actual losses in possessions, socio-economic status, personal prestige, health, reputation or future prospects.

What has already been said of the special problems of middle-aged and elderly persons in connection with anxiety disorders and paranoid disorders is true of them also in relation to mania and depression. Tension and anxiety are exceedingly common reactions to the signs of biological ageing and to the almost inevitable indications of reduced personal significance and socio-economic security that go with ageing.[31] The individual whose acquired personality organization leaves him vulnerable to depressive self-reactions, and their compensatory manic equivalents, is likely to develop a manic or depressive attack as a result of his changing biosocial status.[32] If earlier in his life he has already reacted under severe personal stress with an attack, the likelihood of his reacting again in the same or a compensatory way is increased. His earlier attack has given him practice that favors a recurrence.

Manic and depressive disorders as adjustive techniques

The successful and unsuccessful use of manic and depressive disorders as adjustive techniques has been emphasized throughout our discussion and needs only a brief recapitulation here. The agitated

[31] N. Cameron, "Neuroses of later maturity," in O. Kaplan (editor), *Mental Disorders in Later Life* (Stanford University, Calif.: Stanford University Press, 1945), pp. 143-186.

[32] E. Doty, "A study of manic-depressive psychoses occurring during the later life period," *Amer. Jour. Psychiat.*, 1942, vol. 98, pp. 645-649.

depression is characteristically an *aggressive* reaction, on the part of the patient, with respect both to himself and to others in his environment. *Identification* is evident in the patient's assumption of the dominant parental role, and *projection* when that role is secondarily disowned and ascribed to others. The manic excitement is primarily *aggressive* and *compensatory;* manic patients frequently show *identification* as well as *projection,* which may be *assimilative* or *disowning.* The retarded depression is predominantly a reaction of *withdrawal, insulation* and unaggressive *projection.* All three major syndromes clearly involve *rationalization, negativism* and *regression* in varying degrees.

MANIA AND DEPRESSION IN RELATION TO OTHER BEHAVIOR DISORDERS

There is no single sign or symptom of manic and depressive disorders which cannot be found in some other behavior disorder, or for that matter as at least a temporary feature of normal behavior. What, for instance, is a more common everyday reaction to tension and anxiety than a transient change in pace — either overactivity with self-assertion and increased initiative, or a slowing-up with aversion and unreadiness to participate? Call these mild excitements or depressions if you like, but the fact is that they are to be found at some time in the reactions of almost every normal person. Sadness, apprehension, dejection and despair are likewise common normal reactions to failure and loss, whether personal or communal, and whether kept to oneself or made public.

Of course, not everyone who falls short of his goal or watches the failure of others, in whom he has put his faith, develops reactions of self-condemnation or self-depreciation. And not everyone who suffers an emotional upheaval undergoes the *crucial shift* — from the original excitants of increased tension and anxiety to self-attitudes which facilitate the revival and intensification of old conflicts in a new setting. But even the condemnatory or depreciatory self-reactions and the rearoused personal conflicts, if they are not universally present, are still familiar incidents in the lives of great numbers of normal men and women. Moreover, we also find them cropping up continually in the case studies of individuals whose dominant complaints lead us to diagnose some behavior disorder other than manic or depressive. Thus, we differentiate mania or depression from other behavior disorders on the basis of the relative prominence and importance of the particular behavior pathology that we have described as characteristic of it.

Hypochondriacal overconcern is one of the commonest symptoms of the prodromal phase of tension and anxiety in manic and depressive developments. In agitated and retarded depressions it can to a large extent be attributed to the profound changes in visceral and skeletal performance which are a part of the anxiety and fatigue reactions. In manic excitements hypochondriacal complaints, if they appear, do so as a rule sporadically in the form of energetic demonstration, facetious reference or momentary frank worry. *Fatigue reactions* are also frequent in the prodromal period of tension and anxiety; in the retarded depression, as we have seen, they dominate the clinical picture. Both hypochondriacal overconcern and fatigue reactions may reach delusional proportions to produce some of the behavior we have described in Chapter 13. *Anxiety reactions* are, as we have said earlier, components of all manic and depressive disorders.

Compulsive behavior is frequently present in manic and depressive disorders, but particularly in agitated depressions. This we might anticipate in view of the fact that compulsive behavior is a reaction to mounting anxiety which occurs in ambivalent persons faced by serious conflict. Indeed, compulsive reactions are sometimes so prominent and persistent in agitated depressed patients that one hardly knows which is worse for them, the anxiety or the technique they use to relieve it. Minor *hysterical* complaints are often encountered in manic and depressive disorders. However, in agitated and retarded depression, what looks like indifference at first glance usually turns out to be satisfaction with the self-punishment or the personal worthlessness implied by defect, or may be simply an expression of hopelessness and doom. These latter reactions are, of course, not consonant with our conception of hysterical disorder.

Delusional behavior is so characteristic of mania and depressions that a differentiation from *paranoid disorders* is often extremely difficult to make, and sometimes impossible. The paranoid patient, like every other human being, has his moments or his days of slowing down and of speeding up, of decreased and increased initiative, of sadness, dejection, despair and apprehension. He may conclude at times that he is of little worth, sinful, inadequate and deservedly unloved. These are not his usual conclusions; but behavior pathologists and clinicians must be prepared to meet the paranoid patient on a day when he is unsuccessful in compensating, rationalizing and projecting. They must expect also to find the manic or depressed patient with delusions of persecution, influence, grandeur, body change and environmental change that sound like part of a paranoid disorder. If it is important to make a differentiation in these cases, it must be made on the basis of the relative significance the diagnostician attaches to one or another symptom group.

In this and the preceding chapter we have given in some detail the differential characteristics that distinguish mania and depressions from *schizophrenic disorders,* when a distinction can be made. Disorganization, as we have defined and illustrated it, is not a prominent feature in the typical manic or depressive illness. Extreme agitation and extreme elation or self-assertion, like extreme anxiety or excitement in normal persons, frequently result in temporary disorganization. If this disorganization persists after the agitation, elation or self-assertion have subsided, we say that a schizophrenic disorder has developed as the outcome of a disorganizing episode. If, after the subsidence of the acute disorganization, the person is again agitated, elated or self-assertive, but no longer seriously disorganized, we call his illness what it then is, depression or mania.

Similar diagnostic criteria may be applied in those cases of retarded depression in which unreactivity reaches a stuporous level. Usually depressive unreactivity is followed by ordinary depressive retardation and we speak of the entire illness as depression. If, however, depressive unreactivity leads to persistent disorganization, after the stuporous phase is over, we say that a schizophrenic syndrome has developed. In other words, as we have pointed out before, we are dealing neither with rigid disease entities nor with rigidly defined constitutional types, but with individuals who, because of differences in acquired biosocial behavior organization, react differently to equivalent stress. We should therefore not be mystified and ourselves grow confused when the occasional patient begins in a manic or depressive attack, and later disorganizes and becomes schizophrenic.

The syndromes of *cerebral incompetence,* to which we next turn, include certain signs and symptoms peculiar to them and absent from the behavior disorders. However, as we shall see, mania and depression frequently arise in a setting of acute or progressive cerebral incompetence, and when they do, their significance may be missed. On the other hand, manic or depressive attacks may overshadow the signs and symptoms of developing cerebral incompetence so that the fact of brain damage is not at first recognized. And finally, relative cerebral incompetence may coexist with manic or depressive disorder, but apparently without influencing its course in any significant way. Thus, one of our patients, admitted in his eighties because of a manic attack, showed the same cerebral deficit reactions upon discharge which were found upon admission; but his manic disorder followed a typical course, and cleared up quickly with no manic or depressive residuals.

17 Behavior Disorders and Cerebral Incompetence

THE BRAIN, like other organs, is dependent for its efficient operation upon the maintenance of physiological equilibrium within a relatively narrow range that provides optimal conditions for its metabolic activities. Anything which seriously disturbs this equilibrium may reduce cerebral competence to the point of impairing biosocial behavior. Among the common sources of such disturbance are marked changes in temperature, water balance and the concentration of electrolytes in the brain, interference with the supply of oxygen and food materials or with the removal of waste products, dysfunction of the cardiovascular system, head injury, intoxication, brain disease and brain deterioration.

If the cerebral disequilibration is sudden or extreme, as in acute febrile illnesses, overwhelming intoxication or severe brain injury, an immediate result may be one of the major clinical syndromes of acute cerebral incompetence — delirium, stupor or coma. If, however, the disturbance of physiological equilibrium in the brain develops slowly, there is a greater likelihood that some degree of compensatory adaptation will also develop, biosocial as well as biochemical. The progressive compensatory adaptation to increasing cerebral incompetence may abruptly terminate at some phase in this development, and the sudden decompensation usually precipitates acute cerebral incompetence.

The effectiveness of compensatory adaptation shows considerable variation from individual to individual under comparable circumstances, and in the same person under different physiological and biosocial stresses. For example, if the dosage of alcohol is held constant, a given individual will react differently when such conditions as food and water intake, work, rest, incentive and social stimulation are varied. Even if all of these factors are controlled, it is still possible to demonstrate marked individual differences in susceptibility to alcoholic intoxication. As we shall see later, there is also wide diversity among different individuals, and in the same individual under different conditions, with respect to compensatory adaptation to cerebral injury, disease and deterioration.

Cerebral incompetence often develops gradually and becomes progressive without being either preceded or interrupted by an acute episode. Thus, a patient whose brain infection has been arrested after some cortical damage may adjust satisfactorily at a level of reduced biosocial complexity in his home or in an institution. Senile persons with progressive cerebral incompetence usually show a gradual decline in biosocial adequacy. Some of them decline even to the point of an almost vegetative existence without developing an acute disturbance of any consequence. Ultimately they may require institutionalization, but only because the home environment does not provide the degree of protection and care which their incompetence demands.

A most significant advance in modern behavior pathology has been the general recognition that behavior disorders are by no means inevitable in progressive cerebral incompetence. Indeed, when they do occur, it is nowadays considered imperative to examine every case for their biosocial antecedents. For, as we shall see, an injury, infection or intoxication of the brain may help precipitate a behavior disorder which then becomes chronic, or grows progressively worse, even though meanwhile complete recovery from the cellular effects of cerebral damage has apparently been effected. Moreover, we know today that anxiety disorder, a manic attack, disorganization or an agitated depression may develop, during senile deterioration, for example, and clear up under adequate therapy without a corresponding improvement in the senile picture.

Equally significant is the realization that many behavior disorders which used to be ascribed unhesitatingly to cerebral histopathology have no such basis. They represent the reactions of sick or injured persons to the fact or the consequences of being sick or injured, and differ in no fundamental way from reactions to illness or accident involving other parts of the body. A person may develop hypochondriacal overconcern or a fatigue syndrome on the basis of a broken head or a broken leg. He may react with anxiety or agitation to an attack of dizziness and syncope regardless of whether this is incident to cardiac disease or to cerebral arteriosclerosis. He can develop hysterical inactivation of an arm following head injury or following back injury, and the influence of financial payments may be similar in both. With these facts as our general background, we can now turn to the consideration of cerebral incompetence, its relationship to personal and situational stress, and its misidentification by the patient who is reacting with a behavior disorder to an illness or an accident.

BIOSOCIAL SYNDROMES OF CEREBRAL INCOMPETENCE

Cerebral incompetence, as one might expect, yields an almost infinite diversity of signs and symptoms, whose relative importance varies according to the attitudes and needs of the person studying them. For the sake of brevity and clarity, we shall restrict the discussion that follows to those signs and symptoms which are of common occurrence and of special interest to the behavior pathologist. These we shall group into the biosocial syndromes of *acute cerebral incompetence* and *progressive cerebral incompetence.*

Acute cerebral incompetence

Syndromes of acute cerebral incompetence are characterized by gross disorientation, defective retentivity and signs of central nervous system pathology. The major syndromes of acute cerebral incompetence are *acute delirium, stupor* and *coma,* which not infrequently follow one another in that order. Of these, by far the most important from the standpoint of the behavior disorders is the acute delirium.

To an observer the delirious patient appears at first restless, irritable and confused. His attention is difficult to get and hold; he seems uncertain as to his whereabouts and the identity of persons and objects around him; his talk becomes rambling or groping, and he misspeaks, slurs and mispronounces words. At night he sleeps fitfully and awakens often with a start. He complains of weird and terrifying dreams, and of dreamlike hypnagogic hallucinations when he shuts his eyes. He begins to show obvious defects in recent memory and immediate recall, but his remote memory may be relatively little affected.

As the delirium progresses, the patient appears increasingly confused and disoriented, misidentifying persons and objects and grossly misinterpreting what goes on in his environment. He may develop tremors, particularly noticeable in the fingers, tongue and facial muscles, and he may become ataxic, show marked reflex changes and sweat profusely. He grows more and more restless and sleepless, hallucinating now with his eyes open, and in the daytime as well as at night. Sometimes the patient speaks to those around him as if they were other persons with different functions; sometimes he seems to be listening to and talking to hallucinated individuals in hallucinated settings. Every now and then he may attempt to get up and go out in response to imagined demands made upon him, or imagined threats directed against him and his relatives or his friends. Often he engages in confused, fragmentary activities resembling his usual occupation or an habitual mode of entertainment. When interfered with or restrained, he may respond with angry or frightened combative behavior which is sometimes dangerous to himself and others.

The acute delirious syndrome may last a few hours, or persist for days or weeks, and in exceptional cases for many months. It is not uncommon for a person in the midst of a delirium to clear up quite suddenly for a brief period and then relapse into as great confusion as ever. This transient clearing-up is the so-called *lucid interval*. Thus, a patient of ours, in a restless, disoriented, paraphasic disorder, showed great improvement one afternoon and began asking for information as to where he was and what had happened to him. He conversed connectedly with the nurse and the physician, discussed persons and places of mutual interest, described accurately a previous visit to another division of the hospital, and appeared to understand his present situation. There was some groping for words, and there were occasional long silences, but otherwise nothing unusual in his behavior. By evening, however, the patient's talk was becoming less adequate, and by night he was again acutely delirious. His illness had followed an arteriosclerotic cerebral accident. It ended in partial recovery after four months of delirium; but less than a year later death came as the result of a second cerebral accident.

Recovery from acute delirium may be a gradual affair with progressive improvement in cerebral competence, or it may occur rapidly following a deep sleep, as in many cases of febrile disease. If, on the other hand, the acutely incompetent cerebrum grows still more incompetent, the patient typically shows a general reduction in his reactivity. His restlessness and noisy insomnia give place to drowsiness and torpor, with occasional tossing about; his movements are slower, more aimless and disjunctive; and his speech is fragmentary, incoherent and muttering. He becomes at first difficult to arouse and to keep aroused (*stupor*), and later he may become impossible to arouse (*coma*). In the moribund patient deepening stupor and coma are the usual preludes to death. The patient who recovers from a comatose state returns to normal as a rule by way of stupor. The stuporous patient, as he improves, sometimes passes through a delirious phase on the road to recovery.

When cerebral incompetence occurs with great suddenness, as in cases of head injury, cerebral hemorrhage, blood-loss, massive infection or overwhelming intoxication, the comatose state may be almost instantaneously induced. Coma occurring under such circumstances is popularly called "unconsciousness"; it is, of course, a condition of maximal unreactivity short of death. Persons recovering from abruptly induced coma also may develop a delirious syndrome after first passing through a stuporous phase. For example, one of our patients, who had sustained a severe head injury in an explosion, spent several days in profound coma. Then, as he improved, he became reactive enough to be called stuporous, and followed this with a typical delirium lasting several weeks. Marked defects in orientation and recall persisted throughout most of the delirious period; but the ultimate recovery was complete, with no residual deficits that could be detected on clinical examination.

We may now define *acute delirium* as *a syndrome of acute cerebral incompetence which is characterized by gross disorientation, defective recent memory, hallucinations and delusions*.[1] Because of their greater reactivity, delirious patients have always aroused the interest of behavior pathologists far more than have the stuporous and comatose. The most striking and distinctive feature in delirium is the disorientation. It usually appears early in developing cerebral incompetence as a disturbance primarily in the continuity of behavior. To the patient, the environment seems unaccountably shifting and changeable, objects come and go unexpectedly, and people do things that appear inappropriate to other preceding or

---

[1] The so-called "acute hallucinoses," which show neither disorientation nor serious memory defects, are not included among deliria. Many of them seem to be schizophrenic reactions appearing during and after intoxication, injury or febrile illness. See, for example, K. Bowman and E. Jellinek, "Alcoholic mental disorders," in E. Jellinek (editor), *Alcohol Addiction and Chronic Alcoholism* (New Haven: Yale University Press, 1942), pp. 141-143.

simultaneous activity. To an observer, the patient's behavior seems fragmentary and uncoordinated, it is no longer as predictable as it was, and the patient seems unable to keep up with the ordinary sequence of events in his surroundings.

What has happened in delirium, of course, is that the patient through cerebral incompetence has become incapable of maintaining his habitual anticipant and supporting attitudes in the face of trivial and distracting stimulation. Consequently, his responses, which lack their usual behavior matrix of interlocking attitude, begin to lose relatedness and temporal continuity. They grow discrete, incoherent, and therefore unpredictable to the patient as well as to others.

As we saw in Chapter 3, the exclusion of competing, contradictory and irrelevant responses is essential, not only to the acquisition of manual and social skills, but also to the preservation of effective biosocial behavior organization. The delirious patient, when he loses the ability to exclude, suffers behavior disorganization of the kind we have called *overinclusion*. Delirious disorganization, however, differs from schizophrenic disorganization, which is also overinclusive, chiefly in the presence of gross disorientation and defective recent memory, to which we shall again refer later in this discussion. Indeed, delirious behavior obviously bears a much stronger resemblance to the normal vivid action-dream than it does to schizophrenia, in the disorientation, the fragmentary recall and the early hallucinatory and delusional developments.

Normal dreaming, with its disorientation and fragmentary recall, its hallucinations and its delusions, is the behavior of a person suffering from the cerebral incompetence of normal sleep. The same holds for well-known occurrences during the hypnagogic phase of falling asleep and the hypnopompic phase of awakening. Indeed, the normal man who is only half-awakened from a heavy sleep may draw the same mistaken conclusions regarding his environment as he does when partially intoxicated. He may speak and move in a similarly ataxic and disjunctive manner, confuse what he imagines with what he sees and hears, and show the same defects in orientation and recall. We are dealing in both instances with an individual whose relative cerebral incompetence has rendered him incapable of sustained, adequately organized biosocial behavior.

The hallucinations and delusions of acute delirium develop at first under conditions similar to those of normal dreaming. The patient may complain early of terrifying dreams which are dominated by disturbing hallucinatory and delusional behavior, such as that encountered in any nightmare. However, with increasing cerebral incompetence these disturbing reactions begin to trouble him when he is between waking and sleeping, so that he is often afraid to close his eyes. Eventually, what the patient imagines while he is awake becomes intermingled with the effects of environmental stimulation, and his behavior grows increasingly confused and discontinuous.

It is well known that the hallucinatory and delusional behavior in acute cerebral incompetence is in general of an apprehensive, insecure and fearful character. This is, of course, only another instance of the prevalence of anxiety in human reactions to which we have already alluded. In normal as well as delirious persons anxiety develops and easily grows acute when the surroundings begin to seem strange, undependable or unpredictable. The exceptional delirious patient is comforted or entertained by what he seems to hear and see. Thus, a Negro patient in a toxic delirium was amused and pleased by "all the little white babies" which appeared to her to be sitting around her on the floor.

The specific fears, suspicions, needs, satisfactions and adjustive techniques occurring in delirious hallucinations and delusions belong, naturally, to the specific biosocial personality of the individual patient. Sometimes a person in acute delirium is preoccupied chiefly with his habitual business or domestic routine ("occupational delirium"). Usually the patient's partially repressed anxieties, the conflicts and ambitendencies of his recent and remote past, appear in disconnected, dreamlike behavior episodes. Occasionally, as we shall see, these episodes lead to the development of frank behavior disorders which may outlast by weeks, months and even years the symptoms of cerebral incompetence. The fact that a patient's habitual occupation and his personal anxieties, conflicts and ambitendencies are prominently represented in his delirious behavior is, of course, no more surprising than the fact that while delirious he speaks his own language and not the unfamiliar tongue of someone else.

The memory deficits characteristic of acute delirium are of complex origin. There is better recall, as a rule, for remote events than for recent ones, a fact that may in part be ascribed to the advantages of greater practice which lifelong habits usually enjoy. In this respect the situation does not differ from that in progressive cerebral incompetence, as we shall see. The poor recall of recent events is sometimes also a consequence of the fact that these events occurred during the early prodromal phase of the delirium.

The discontinuity of behavior in deliria, which we have already discussed, is also a factor in the memory deficits. Even in a person who is not delirious, but only emotionally disturbed, the lack of sustained anticipant and supporting attitudes hardly provides optimal conditions for acquisition, retention and subsequent recall. The delirious patient, because of his cerebral incompetence, is distractible and disoriented, his attention-span is greatly reduced, and he has in addition the confusing and usually frightening effects of his delusional and hallucinatory reactions. While he is delirious, his behavior is thus too disjunctive and disorganized to permit normal acquisition and immediate recall. After he has recovered, his recall of events belonging to the delirium does not fit readily into his normal behavior organization; it seems weird and unnatural to him, like many of his normal dreams.

When the recovered patient tries to remember what occurred during his delirium, his recall is always fragmentary or, as it is usually called, "patchy." He can describe parts of delirious episodes, separated in time by unequal intervals, and usually bearing no discernible logical relationship to one another. This "patchy" recall, of course, also links delirium with normal dreaming which shows the same characteristic. The most probable explanation in both conditions is that fluctuations in brain physiology are mainly responsible; the islands of relatively good recall represent periods of relatively high cerebral competence which favor acquisition and retention.

Progressive cerebral incompetence

Syndromes of progressive cerebral incompetence are characterized by decreasing retentivity, diminishing biosocial adaptiveness, and increasing signs of cerebral pathology. Progressive cerebral incompetence may develop slowly and insidiously, running a course of gradual decline over a period of years and sometimes of decades. Many cases that begin with a slow and insidious development are interrupted by an apoplectiform or epileptiform convulsion, after which the symptoms of incompetence are generally more pronounced and the decline more rapid. Other cases have an abrupt onset with transient confusion, acute delirium or a convulsion, followed by progressive incompetence and usually punctuated by convulsive episodes. Temporary remissions of brief duration are not unusual; occasionally a remission lasts a few months and rarely a few years.

However, regardless of the character of onset and the occurrence of remissions, the course of progressive cerebral incompetence is steadily or intermittently downhill. Some patients, before they die, reach an almost purely vegetative level of existence, their biosocial behavior having been reduced to a few stereotyped responses and perhaps a phrase or two, which they may utter entirely out of context. One of our patients, for example, did nothing but sit and rock all day, wetting and soiling herself, and having to be fed, washed, dressed and undressed as though she were a baby. No matter what was said to her, whether a kind greeting, a threat or an oath, she always replied, "Yes, darling," "Why, of course, darling," or "Certainly, darling."

In progressive cerebral incompetence there is considerable variability in the order of appearance and the prominence of different symptoms, as well as in what changes are first noticed and reported by the patient or his associates. We have already seen, in acute delirium, that one of the most important indications of cerebral incompetence is a reduction in retentivity, as measured by immediate recall and by recall of recent events. In the insidiously developing progressive cerebral incompetence, the first observed change frequently is increasing forgetfulness. The patient cannot remember where he has left or hidden personal belongings, he does not recall having met recent acquaintances before, and he forgets engagements whether these are recreational or in the line of duty. He tends to repeat himself, often telling the same thing over and over with the same detail to the same person. He fails to retain new things that others tell him, he cannot learn new procedures, and he becomes easily confused in a new environment. One of our patients, for example, was first recognized as incompetent by his family when he could not find his way to the hotel at an unfamiliar summer resort. A check-up with his business associates, however, revealed that he had been showing poor judgment and inadequate recall for at least a year before this vacation incident.

The loss in recent memory is often equaled or exceeded by a progressive loss of those acquired biosocial attitudes which have been characteristic of the patient, and upon which his interpersonal relationships have in the past depended. Thus, an individual with an infected, senile or arteriosclerotic cerebrum may seem a changed man, at first to his close relatives and intimate friends but eventually to everyone. He becomes careless of his dress, appearance and deportment, reacts with indifference, anger, joviality or tears to situations that would not have elicited these reactions before, and shows a degree of instability and unpredictability quite foreign to his habitual behavior.

A previously adequate person may begin to exhibit striking ineptitude in business, social or domestic affairs. He squanders or gives away his own property and that of others, or dissipates his earnings by glaringly injudicious spending. One of our patients, following a cerebral accident which left him with hemiparesis, attempted to force his industrial competitor to sell out to him at a price far above the market. Only the ethical restraint of the competitor saved this patient and his whole family from poverty. Some persons lose the respect and affection of their friends and relatives by becoming entangled in a sexual liaison of an inexplicable character, or by committing sex offenses in relation to minors, before their cerebral incompetence is realized.[2]

The emphasis usually placed upon the inferior, the unethical and the anti-social reactions which may appear in progressive cerebral incompetence is certainly justified by the possible seriousness of their consequences. But the interpretation of these reactions often given, that they are signs of moral degeneracy and social atavism, has no greater validity in behavior pathology than it has in modern criminology. Indeed, an inability to include the probable consequences and implications of an act as controlling factors in a patient's own behavior is one of the most striking defects in cerebral incompetence, whether of toxic, traumatic, infective, arteriosclerotic or senile origin. A person's behavior, in other words, may still be relatively well-organized with respect to the immediately present, but grossly defective with respect to past training and future probability.[3]

[2] J. Henninger, "The senile sex offender," *Ment. Hyg.*, 1939, vol. 23, pp. 436-444.

[3] W. Freeman and J. Watts have pointed this out in the post-operative behavior of patients whose brains have been made relatively incompetent as a therapeutic measure. See their *Psychosurgery: Intelligence, Emotion and Social Behavior Following Prefrontal Lobotomy for Mental Disorders* (Springfield, Ill.: Thomas, 1942), pp. 284-294.

There can be no doubt that the decline in biosocial adaptiveness, characteristic of progressive cerebral incompetence, is in part a product of the decreasing retentivity. The effect of progressively impaired recall is to render the patient less and less able to participate in the life around him, his interest flags with his decreasing attention-span and his increasing fatigue, and he may fall back on reminiscences because he can no longer keep up with the immediate sequence of events. However, contrary to popular belief, there is no compensatory improvement of remote memory as recent memory dwindles. For whenever in progressive cerebral incompetence the recall of remote events can be checked against verified facts, gross inaccuracies and generous confabulation are always found. Remote memory may at first suffer far less than recent, but eventually it also becomes hopelessly inadequate.

The gradually diminishing effectiveness of recall at first isolates the cerebrally incompetent person by disarticulating him from his immediate social environment. As long as his recall of remote events is sufficiently preserved, the patient is likely to locate present happenings in the remembered daily routine of his younger years. If he recognizes that he is not at home or in a familiar place, he may seek to account for this by a more or less reasonable confabulation. The confabulation, as might be expected, is quite characteristic of a given individual and refers to actual happenings in his own past. The details often vary considerably from recital to recital, but the theme usually remains quite consistent.[4]

One of our patients, for example, a woman of eighty-three, always gave her age as eighteen or nineteen, and when questioned as to her whereabouts would say that she was resting awhile before going on home. Almost every evening she asked the physician on rounds if she could "stay in this hotel tonight," often adding that she had started out too late to reach home before dark. She usually lamented her inability to help her father with the milking that evening. However, when asked her father's age, she frequently replied, "Oh, he's been dead many years," forgetting what she had just said about helping him.

---

[4] The disarticulation in progressive cerebral incompetence contrasts sharply in origin and development with the disarticulation of schizophrenia. In the latter, disorientation and an inability to recall recent events are not determinants of withdrawal, and the schizophrenic patient shows tendencies neither to confabulate nor to fall back on reminiscences. See N. Cameron, "A study of thinking in senile deterioration and schizophrenic disorganization," Amer. Jour. Psychol., 1938, vol. 51, pp. 650-665.

When a patient's recall of remote as well as recent events grows fragmentary, and verbal confabulations no longer fill in the gaps, the continuity of his biosocial behavior virtually disappears. Certain relatively simple automatized sequences remain, such as walking, getting up and down from a chair or a bed, chewing and sucking. Otherwise the organized continuity of behavior depends upon the organized continuity of immediate environmental stimulation. If the environment is simplified enough, and the sequence of stimulation is planned to initiate and direct the sequence of a patient's responses, it is possible to maintain an appearance of behavior organization as long as visceral activities continue adequate. Of course, such provisions, like those which supply artificial breathing, are expensive in terms of the behavior of other persons.

It would be difficult to exaggerate the importance of language organization in the preservation of biosocial behavior adequacy and continuity. As we pointed out in Chapter 4, language and thinking together provide everyone who acquires them with a flow of almost continuous behavior sequences which are capable of influencing any human activity. Language behavior and thinking are sooner or later involved in progressive cerebral incompetence. In the more fortunate case their loss coincides with the general decline or even lags behind it. In the less fortunate, particularly in cases of cerebral arteriosclerosis and general paresis, the machinery upon which language behavior depends may be irreparably damaged at an early stage. The patient is thus severely handicapped at the onset by impairment of his symbolic skills. This not only interferes with interindividual communication, but it also deprives the patient himself of the language and thought organization which has always been at least in the background of all his biosocial behavior, in private fantasy as well as in public, shared reactions.

There are many indications of progressive cerebral incompetence other than those we have discussed. Some of them are important chiefly as clinical signs of brain damage and do not in themselves contribute significantly to biosocial behavior pathology. Examples of this group are numerous intraocular and extraocular changes, the increase, decrease or inequality of tendon reflexes, postural and visceral changes and serological reactions.

Certain other consequences of cerebral incompetence are likely to complicate the behavior pathology. Among these may be mentioned the tremors, which frequently interfere with manipulation and speech, numerous forms of incoordination, paralysis and receptive disturbances, and increased emotional lability. The last-mentioned defect, commonly called *emotional incontinence*, varies from mere exaggeration and perseveration of the normal emotional component of behavior to inappropriate as well as uncontrollable laughing or crying, which to the patient may seem unaccountable. Emotional incontinence often resembles superficially the symptoms of such behavior disorders as mania, depression or schizophrenia.

BEHAVIOR DISORDERS IN THE CEREBRALLY INCOMPETENT

No one needs to be reminded that behavior disorders develop in persons who at the time show signs and symptoms of cerebral incompetence, as well as in persons who do not. What does merit re-emphasis, however, is that the mere presence of relative cerebral incompetence never justifies the clinician in discussing a behavior disorder as sufficiently explained in its terms alone. It is just as essential to look for the antecedents of behavior pathology in the one case as in the other. Indeed, one not infrequently finds that cerebral incompetence, although indubitably present, plays an insignificant part in the behavior disorder. Neither in the pattern of his reaction, nor in the ease with which he reacts, does the patient differ significantly from other patients, who are subjected to equivalent stresses and strains, but give no evidence of cerebral incompetence.

When the consequences of cerebral incompetence contribute significantly to the precipitation of behavior disorders, they may do so in one of several ways. In the first place, a person may develop pathological self-reactions to behavior resulting from his own cerebral incompetence. Thus, during acute delirium the patient's hallucinatory behavior sometimes arouses such exaggerated anxiety reactions in him that schizophrenic disorganization occurs, as we shall see in the section on intoxication. A person with progressive cerebral incompetence, who because of this becomes involved in socially taboo activities, may react to his behavior with self-condemnation and self-reproach that culminate in an agitated depression.

The decrease in the general effectiveness of behavior organization also contributes to the precipitation of behavior disorders in acute and progressive cerebral incompetence. Suppose, for example, that an individual develops cerebral incompetence who for decades has been dealing with serious personal conflicts and ambitendencies — successfully but expensively — through the use of repression. The reduction in cerebral competence, as we pointed out in Chapter 6, is commonly followed by the failure of previously adequate repression. The result is that the patient now suffers what has been called a *return of the repressed,* and he reacts with heightened anxiety. If this anxiety leads to the development of behavior disorder, the particular behavior pathology will naturally correspond to the individual's dominant acquired personality trends.

Behavior disorders arise in some persons, who have grown cerebrally incompetent, because they are unable to recognize and accept the fact of their diminished biosocial adequacy. It is this inability which leads patients to attempt things they are no longer capable of doing and to resist aggressively the restrictive measures that others take against them. One sees examples of such behavior in the irritable, self-assertive excitements of persons with cerebral intoxication or infection. However, the problem is socially far more important and therapeutically more challenging in the maladaptations that occur among the millions of individuals whose cerebral incompetence is slowly progressive. The inability to recognize and accept one's own declining adequacy, when that decline is both inevitable and slow, is a defect which especially in the ageing person often culminates in one of the common preventable behavior disorders.

Finally, we have the important and challenging problem presented by those persons who develop behavior disorders because, even though they recognize and accept the fact of their diminished adequacy, they cannot accept their changed social status. They cannot adapt to their reduced security and prestige, to the neglect and prejudice that others show, or to the restrictions placed upon their range of opportunity and consequently also upon their permitted interests. Of course, the security we speak of is not only a matter of money, food and shelter; and the prestige is not simply that of sitting always in the place of honor and receiving automatic deference.

Persons whose abilities have declined because of cerebral intoxication, injury, infection or deterioration need also the certainty that emotional acceptance and emotional support will be given them whenever they seek it. They need the prestige and the social status that belong to anyone still capable of self-reactions. We are prejudiced against and neglect persons with relative cerebral incompetence because they are inefficient and a social burden, like prisoners and the biosocially ill. By so doing, we give them a standing invitation to develop behavior disorders which further incapacitate them and make them a still greater social burden.

In order to illustrate more specifically the precipitation of behavior disorders in persons who are at the time suffering from relative cerebral incompetence, let us select for special consideration four common and important clinical groups. Acute intoxication will introduce us to behavior disorders in the delirious patient. Head injury is representative of the so-called "traumatic" behavior disorders. We may take general paresis as a cerebral infection whose high incidence and grave consequences make it of first-rate medicosocial importance. Our fourth group, senile and arteriosclerotic cerebral degeneration, is certainly one of the commonest examples to be found of slowly and undramatically progressive cerebral incompetence.

Behavior disorders in acute intoxication

The most interesting direct consequence of acute intoxication, of course, is the syndrome of acute delirium. There is general agreement today that the exact character of the disorientation, the delusions and the hallucinations in acute delirium cannot be predicted solely on the basis of the toxin implicated. Wolff and Curran, for example, made a study of 106 delirious patients whose acute cerebral incompetence was ascribed to twenty-seven different etiological agents.[5] They could find no specific relationship between a particular toxin and the character of the biosocial reactions in the delirium. The behavior of patients having more than one delirious episode was characteristic for a given individual, whether the etiological agent was the same or different on successive occasions. Every patient in this series, regardless of the origin of his intoxication, believed himself at some time in his illness to be the victim of persecution or annoyance.[6] Fear reactions appeared in

---

[5] H. Wolff and D. Curran, "Nature of delirium and allied states," *Arch. Neurol. Psychiat.*, 1935, vol. 33, pp. 1175-1215.

[6] F. Curran reports a similar finding in bromide intoxication. "A study of fifty cases of bromide psychosis," *Jour. Nerv. Ment. Dis.*, 1938, vol. 88, pp. 163-192.

almost all cases — fourteen patients showed great fear, eighty moderate fear, and twelve little or no fear; and neither the presence nor the degree of these reactions was related to the specific agent. Cultural attitudes were reflected in the greater proportion of women than men who believed themselves accused of sex promiscuity.

The relative unimportance of the specific character of the toxin becomes still clearer when we examine the detailed *symptoms* in delirious behavior. It is obvious, for example, that when bromide or alcohol intoxication results in a so-called *occupational delirium,* the occupation attempted will always be one that belongs in the acquired biosocial organization of the individual patient. Neither bromide nor alcohol will make every delirious man a carpenter and every delirious woman a milliner. The *disorientation,* likewise, is on a personal basis just as it is in normal dreaming. The delirious seaman in a shore hospital believes himself on shipboard or at the waterfront; the delirious farmer behaves as though he were in the farmhouse, in the stables or the fields, or at a county fair. Even the most confused and weird disorientative reactions are still products of the patient's individual past — things seen and heard, read about, dreamed and daydreamed — and of his immediately present surroundings.

The *delusional reactions* in acute delirium are also specific for the individual patient and not for the toxic agent. As we have indicated, even the predominance of anxiety in the delusions is in part a reflection of the ease with which almost everyone becomes acutely insecure when the environment fails to support his habitual anticipant behavior. Excepting for the gross disorientation and impaired retentivity, there is nothing about delirious delusions that is essentially different from any other delusions. The particular components of his environmental and fantasy stimulation to which a patient will respond are to a large extent selected on the basis of his acquired reaction-sensitivities, whether his behavior at the moment is well or poorly organized. His habitual reaction-sensitivities will similarly help to determine the characteristics of his delirious response and how he will interpret what he does, sees, hears and imagines. Indeed, as we shall see, patients who develop behavior disorders at one time in a delirious setting, and at another time in a non-delirious setting, are apt to show striking similarities in their delusional reactions under both conditions.

In deliria the *hallucinatory behavior,* like the delusional reaction, is not specifically determined by the properties of the toxic agent. Intoxication may induce the hallucinatory activities; but what the individual hallucinates will depend upon his acquired reaction-sensitivities and his immediate surroundings. In delirium tremens, for example, we know that the auditory hallucinations usually take the form of voices which threaten, rebuke and accuse the alcoholic patient. But threatening, rebuking and accusing voices are common in all deliria, regardless of the agent, and common also in the hallucinatory behavior of non-delirious patients.

These voices, of course, are self-reactions which the patient ascribes to someone else. They are the voices of self-criticism and self-control which, as we pointed out in Chapter 10, are organized into a form of role-taking that the public reifies as *conscience.* Their extreme frequency in delirium tremens calls, therefore, not so much for a study of the interaction of nerve tissue and alcohol, but for a study of the growth and operation of self-reactions in social role-taking, and of the relationship between anxiety and projection.

Hallucinatory behavior in delirium is a popular subject for humorous treatment, with the result that there is a great deal of folklore about it which is not supported by actual observation of the sick person. The visual hallucinations in delirium tremens, for example, are popularly supposed to include pink elephants, rodents, green monkeys and spotted giraffes. A study of 113 delirium tremens patients, however, disclosed only one case reporting a pink elephant and one reporting rodents. The commonest hallucinated animals were dogs, insects and snakes, all three of which are regarded by normal persons as potential threats in ordinary life.[7] The influence of the immediate environment is obvious in the prevalence of hallucinated fish and lobsters in the behavior of delirium tremens patients who are being treated by continuous tub hydrotherapy.[8]

What is true of the symptoms in acute delirium is true also of the *behavior disorders* that sometimes develop during or following

[7] J. Dynes, "Survey of alcoholic patients admitted to the Boston Psychopathic Hospital in 1937," *New Eng. Med. Jour.,* 1939, vol. 220, pp. 195-203.
[8] O. Bumke and F. Kant, "Rausch und Genussgifte: Giftsuchen," in O. Bumke and O. Foerster, *Handbuch der Neurologie* (Berlin: Springer, 1936), vol. 13, p. 828.

a delirious episode. The particular behavior pathology of the disorder will be determined chiefly by the acquired biosocial organization of the patient, not by the specific pharmacological properties of the toxic agent inducing acute cerebral incompetence. The important factors in the situation are the particular adjustive techniques upon which the individual habitually relies, his own selective reaction-sensitivities, his ambitendencies and the nature of his personal conflicts.

It is a well-known fact that schizophrenic disorders may be precipitated in acute deliria resulting from intoxication,[9] infection, high fever and debilitating disease. Levin has recently reported thirteen cases of schizophrenia developing in persons who at the time were taking bromide, and who had not previously shown schizophrenic symptoms. Of these patients, two were severely disoriented on admission, seven were seriously disoriented for time but only occasionally for place and person, while four showed fleeting disorientation for time alone. When the patients were admitted, the serum bromide concentration ranged from 50 to 357 mg per cent. The duration of the schizophrenic disorder after discontinuance of bromide was usually brief. In ten of the cases, it varied from four days to seven and one-half weeks, and in the remaining three cases the duration was five, ten and twelve months.[10]

The most impressive evidence we have of the non-specific effect of toxic agents comes from those cases in which the same behavior disorders occur in both delirious and non-delirious settings. Among Wolff and Curran's patients, for example, two are reported who had developed and recovered from behavior disorders prior to their acute intoxication. In each, the behavior pathology appearing in delirium showed the characteristics of the earlier illnesses which were precipitated by determinants other than acute delirium. Two of our cases illustrate the same point. One developed a manic attack in a bromide delirium and later exhibited the same behavior pathology in a setting of severe marital discord uncomplicated by intoxication. The other suffered a manic attack during litigation that threatened her economic security, and thirty years later, when she

---

[9] For a discussion of alcoholism in relation to schizophrenia, mania and depressions, see K. Bowman and E. Jellinek, "Alcoholic mental disorders," in E. Jellinek (editor), *Alcohol Addiction and Chronic Alcoholism* (New Haven: Yale University Press, 1942), pp. 81-169.

[10] M. Levin, "Transitory schizophrenias produced by bromide intoxication," *Amer. Jour. Psychiat.*, 1946, vol. 103, pp. 229-237.

became disoriented following an operation and the use of sedatives, she again became manic.

The first patient, a married woman of thirty, was admitted to a psychiatric hospital in an acute delirium, grossly disoriented, and with impaired retentivity for remote as well as recent events. She was obviously frightened at the time; and she told retrospectively of delusional fears that she would be poisoned, and of dreamlike visual and auditory hallucinations. Two weeks before her admission she had undergone an operation for uterine suspension at another hospital. She had been apprehensive before the operation, and on the first post-operative day showed such marked anxiety that she was placed on one-sixth grain of morphine six times a day. Instead of quieting her, this procedure alarmed the patient further. She thought she heard the attending surgeon say that she had taken a turn for the worse, and she spoke to her relatives of dying.

On the fourth post-operative day the morphine was discontinued and bromide sedation substituted. The patient, however, remained acutely apprehensive and as time went on grew increasingly irritable, complaining of unkind treatment, odors and the noise of slamming doors. On the fourteenth day she said that she was growing numb and cold, that things seemed mixed up and the nurses were against her. She began refusing food and fluids and she became resistive and combative when they were forced upon her. Unfortunately, there was no psychiatrist on the staff and no place in the hospital where a frightened, confused person could be given the necessary freedom of action without becoming a serious hazard. Consequently, the nurses felt obliged to fasten the patient to her bed with cuffs and tie her legs down. Within a few days she was in full delirium, although she was no longer taking bromide medication. A psychiatric consultation was called for and the patient was admitted to the psychiatric hospital in a severely dehydrated condition and with a bright red rash on her back, thighs and buttocks. Rectal temperature on admission was 102° and the pulse was 120. Serum bromide concentration was only 125 mg per cent, presumably because the patient had taken no medication for several days.

On the psychiatric ward, once hydration had been effected and chloride therapy begun, restraint was of course unnecessary. The patient was free to move about her room as she wished and, after a few days, about the ward also. She remained fearful, confused and easily stirred to resentment, however, for about ten days. While she was still showing considerable fear, her talk began to grow coherent, and then rhyming, punning, swearing and some topical flight became obvious. She appeared distractible, aggressively over-active, overtalkative and erotic. This manic behavior persisted for about three weeks after the delirious symptoms had disappeared and the patient was discharged as recovered a month later. Three years after her discharge, this patient was readmitted in a manic attack which closely resembled the first one, not only in the general behavior, but in most of the specific details. However, this time there were no delirious reactions whatever, and the precipitating situation was one of severe marital discord. Under planned psychiatric therapy she recovered after five months of illness.

Our other patient was a widow of sixty-five. She developed an acute delirium on the ophthalmological service, following an operation for cataract. The delirium began with disorientation which was most obvious at night, and was soon accompanied by visual and auditory hallucinations and poor retentivity. As time went on, she grew progressively noisier, talked loudly, sang and occasionally shouted. Her speech became exceedingly vulgar and profane; she rhymed, punned and showed some topical flight. When sedatives no longer seemed to quiet the patient, a psychiatrist was called in and transfer to the psychiatric service was arranged.

On the psychiatric ward the patient's behavior was typically manic except for the fact that at night she hallucinated, was disoriented and, if she was interfered with or restrained, she developed fearful delusions and misidentifications. The manic excitement subsided with the disappearance of the acute cerebral incompetence, although at a slower rate. There was no clinical evidence to justify a diagnosis of cerebral arteriosclerosis or of senile deterioration. The important point is that thirty years earlier this woman had developed a manic attack with closely similar behavior. The precipitating factor at the time was a lawsuit, following by two years the death of her husband. The aim of this suit was to deprive her of a large inheritance by proving that her husband had been secretly married to another woman before marrying the patient, and that this prior alleged marriage had never been dissolved. The behavior disorder developed out of the patient's reaction to a situation which constituted a serious threat, both to her economic security and her social status. She recovered from both illnesses.

Behavior disorders in head injury

Head injury does not necessarily mean brain injury. But when it does, and the immediately resulting cerebral incompetence is extreme, the patient may go quickly into coma or stupor. If the brain damage is serious, and the injured man survives, he may pass from coma or stupor into a typical acute delirium, and perhaps develop the disoriented amnestic-confabulatory Korsakoff syndrome, before his behavior becomes more nearly adequate.[11] None of these syndromes, of course, is peculiar to head injury; the same phenomena are common in cases of severe cerebral incompetence whose etiology includes acute and chronic intoxication, infection or degeneration. Even the apparent sequence of phases, when it occurs, is no more than a succession of recognizable clinical syndromes which represent different degrees of biosocial adequacy in a recovering organism.

In most cases of head injury resulting in immediate severe cerebral incompetence ("unconsciousness"), the initial improvement is rapid, and neither acute delirium nor the Korsakoff syndrome appears. Instead, there may be only a transient period of confusion, mild ataxia, dulling and amnesia which usually includes events before as well as after the injury. This transient phase is also characteristic of head injury cases with less severe cerebral incompetence, in which stupor and coma do not occur. The course of convalescence after head injury is highly variable, and it can seldom be accurately predicted from a consideration of the apparent brain damage alone.[12] Indeed, there is widespread doubt as to the possibility that progressive deterioration may result from trauma alone in an otherwise healthy brain.[13]

Nothing has brought out more clearly the intricate interweaving of biological and social factors in human behavior than the study of reactions to head injury. For a long time professional interest was directed mainly toward the problem of recognizing and treating the consequences of permanent brain damage — convulsive at-

[11] A. Friedman and C. Brenner, "Amnestic-confabulatory syndrome (Korsakoff psychosis) following head injury," *Amer. Jour. Psychiat.*, 1945, vol. 102, pp. 61-66.

[12] For a detailed discussion of the symptomatology and tissue pathology in head injury, see K. Bowman and A. Blau, "Psychotic states following head and brain injury in adults and children," in S. Brock (editor), *Injuries of the Skull, Brain and Spinal Cord*, 2d edition (Baltimore: Williams and Wilkins, 1943), pp. 294-341.

[13] W. Denny-Brown, "Disability arising from closed head injury," *Jour. Amer. Med. Assn.*, 1945, vol. 127, pp. 429-436; "Intellectual deterioration resulting from head injury," in *Trauma of the Central Nervous System* (Baltimore: Williams and Wilkins, Res. Publ. Assn. Res. Nerv. Ment. Dis., 1945), vol. 24, pp. 467-472.

tacks, deformities, emotional storms and impaired performance of all kinds. When brain injury results in such permanent residuals, of course, a considerable degree of adaptiveness may be demanded of the patient having them. But whether or not these sequelae are present in a given case, there are other aspects of head injury of equal and sometimes greater importance which deserve special consideration.

There are, for example, the reactions to the accident, to the fact of having been injured, helpless, frightened, in pain, comatose, amnestic or confused. In this connection, as Schilder has emphasized, injury to the head in our society is apt to be an object of greater concern to the patient than injury to an arm or leg.[14] We have also to consider the necessity of adjusting to minor residuals, in themselves perhaps unimportant, which frequently become the focus of anxiety, hypochondriacal worry and fatigue complaints or lead to hysterical disorders and chronic invalidism. And finally there are the primary and secondary gains, the effects of which we have already discussed in relation to the various behavior disorders.

Head injury is an exceedingly common incident. Almost every fair-sized community or neighborhood has in it persons who have suffered a permanent reduction in biosocial adequacy as a direct or indirect result of trauma to the head. It is, therefore, encouraging to find a sharp increase within recent years in the number of studies devoted to the post-traumatic signs and symptoms following head injury — that is to say, the so-called "post-concussional" or "post-contusional" syndrome.[15] Many of these studies are chiefly concerned with an enumeration of the symptoms consistently found in persons who fail to recover completely and with attempts to relate the most typical symptoms to known or inferred cerebral damage. But a trend is becoming increasingly evident in the direction of relating chronic residual symptoms, not alone to neurophysiology and neuropathology, but also to the patient's biosocial personality organization — his habitual attitudes, his premorbid need-satisfaction sequences, his preferred adjustive techniques, and the degree of social maturity he had achieved before his accident.

[14] P. Schilder, "Neuroses following head and brain injuries," in S. Brock (editor), *Injuries of the Skull, Brain and Spinal Cord*, 2d edition (Baltimore: Williams and Wilkins, 1943), pp. 263-293.

[15] See, for example, the studies in *Trauma of the Central Nervous System* (Baltimore: Williams and Wilkins, Res. Publ. Assn. Res. Nerv. Ment. Dis., 1945), vol. 24, and S. Brock (editor), *Injuries of the Skull, Brain and Spinal Cord*, 2d edition, Baltimore: Williams and Wilkins, 1945.

One of the most carefully designed clinical investigations of be-havior pathology in the contemporary literature is that of Ruesch, Harris and Bowman.[16] They divided their cases into two main groups. In one group they placed 125 head injury patients with late post-traumatic syndromes. Fifty-eight of these showed signs of brain damage while the remaining sixty-seven showed none. In the other group were 140 control cases. Seventy of these patients were suffering from acute head injuries, thirty from brain disease not related to head injury, and forty from minor behavior disorders (one atopic dermatitis, two mucous colitis, two periodic alcohol ad-diction, and the rest hypochondria, hysteria or reactive depression).

The results of this study may be summarized for our purposes as follows. In the acute head injury cases the complaints were related to the clinical signs and, accordingly, patients with evidence of brain damage had more complaints than those without. However, in the late post-traumatic cases the patients with severe injuries had few complaints, while those with mild injuries had many. More-over, the number of complaints tended to increase, and to grow more diffuse in character, the longer a post-traumatic syndrome lasted; whereas in a majority of control patients recovering post-operatively (brain tumor cases, lobectomies and subdural hema-tomas), the symptoms progressively decreased with time. With the exception of the acute head injury cases, there were no substan-tial differences in number or type of complaints between head injury groups and the control groups. Even headache was not specific for the head injury cases, and was found more frequently in patients without neurological signs than in those with signs. The last-mentioned finding agrees with an observation made by Ander-son,[17] that in his series all patients without the complaint of head-ache showed neurological sequelae of head injury, and with one by Schaller [18] that complaint of headache occurred in ninety-seven out of one hundred neurotic patients, but in only twenty-three out of one hundred "post-concussion" patients.

[16] J. Ruesch, R. Harris and K. Bowman, "Pre- and post-traumatic person-ality in head injuries," in *Trauma of the Central Nervous System* (Baltimore: Williams and Wilkins, Res. Publ. Assn. Res. Nerv. Ment. Dis.), 1945, vol. 24, pp. 507-544; J. Ruesch and K. Bowman, "Prolonged post-traumatic syndromes following head injury," *Amer. Jour. Psychiat.*, 1945, vol. 102, pp. 145-163; J. Ruesch, "Psychophysiological relations in cases with head injuries," *Psychosom. Med.*, 1945, vol. 7, pp. 158-165.

[17] C. Anderson, "Chronic head cases," *Lancet*, 1942, vol. 243, pp. 1-4.

[18] W. Schaller, "After-effects of head injury," *Jour. Amer. Med. Assn.*, 1939, vol. 113, pp. 1779-1784.

Ruesch, Harris and Bowman further substantiated a report by Aubrey Lewis that no essential distinction can be made between the behavior pathology in chronic head injury cases and that in ordinary neuroses.[19] They could find only a few patients in their late post-traumatic group without neurological signs who showed personality changes that could actually be ascribed to the head injury. The majority had had difficulties in interpersonal relationships before their accident.[20] Many seemed to have been chronically dissatisfied and unhappy. Others managed to gain through their symptoms what they had not been able to achieve before; prolongation of the complaints in these patients can best be interpreted as an adjustive technique which reduces the tensions of need or anxiety.

In most of the chronic cases without neurological signs, it was possible to establish a relationship between personal problems and prolonged post-traumatic syndromes. Three varieties of relationship were distinguished. In one group, the patients had evidently lived in fear of losing support and of economic disaster; the trauma was accepted by them as a realization of the long-awaited catastrophe. In another group, the head trauma coincided with biosocial traumata, such as divorce or loss of a loved person; the patient blamed his inability to adapt and the symptoms of his maladaptation upon the head injury. In a third group, smaller than the other two, the patients apparently sought the accident as an escape from intolerable anxiety or guilty conflict. The authors conclude that the factors of injury and brain damage seem of secondary importance. It is primarily the pre-traumatic biosocial organization of the individual patient that determines the post-traumatic adaptation.

Behavior disorders in general paresis

General paresis is a syphilitic meningoencephalitis in which the inflammatory-degenerative process affects with greatest intensity the cerebral cortex of the frontal and parietal regions. The serology during life and the tissue pathology afterwards are pathognomonic. The behavioral changes, however, are not specific, but correspond to those which we have earlier described as *progressive cerebral*

---

[19] A. Lewis, "Discussion and differential diagnosis and treatment of post-contusional states," *Proc. Royal Soc. Med.*, 1942, vol. 35, pp. 607-614.

[20] See also H. Kozol, "Pretraumatic personality and psychiatric sequelae of head injury," *Arch. Neur. Psychiat.*, 1946, vol. 56, pp. 245-275.

incompetence. Certain signs and symptoms, although by no means peculiar to general paresis, occur in it with great frequency. These are the pupillary changes, the tremors, the slow, slurred speech and tremulous or illegible writing, the muscular weakness, the convulsive seizures and the often transient attacks of paralysis. In untreated cases the course is unmistakably downhill and relatively rapid, death coming as a rule in two or three years. Remissions of varying length are not unusual.[21]

In a large percentage of paretic cases the decline in biosocial adequacy is uneventful, following one course or another of progressive cerebral incompetence. Sometimes there is an episode of non-specific excitement, such as one sees in other encephalitides, which may be attributed to an exacerbation of the inflammatory process. During such episodes the paretic can become a dangerous and even homicidal individual.

However, to the behavior pathologist the most impressive thing about general paresis is the high incidence of behavior disorders in it. There is no other encephalitis, with the possible exception of epidemic encephalitis, that is so frequently a determining factor in the development of outspoken hypochondria, fatigue syndromes, anxiety disorders, mania, depression, paranoid disorders and schizophrenia. Indeed, considerable evidence has been accumulating in recent years to indicate that when the paretic patient develops a behavior disorder, his behavior pathology will be determined, as Grinker puts it, "by his premorbid personality structure and its underlying emotional trends and conflicts."[22]

The older classical descriptions of general paresis as typically an elated, expansive excitement have not been substantiated by modern studies. They go back to a period in psychiatry when the serological identification of syphilitic meningoencephalitis had not been perfected. As a matter of fact, when the Wassermann test was introduced, it was found necessary to reclassify a great many patients as manics who had previously been treated as paretics and a great many as paretics who had been treated as manics.[23]

[21] For details of the tissue changes and neurological signs in general paresis, see R. Grinker, *Neurology,* 3d edition (Springfield, Ill.: Thomas, 1943), pp. 904-913; I. Wechsler, *Textbook of Clinical Neurology,* 4th edition (Philadelphia: Saunders, 1939), pp. 463-474.

[22] R. Grinker, *Neurology,* 3d edition (Springfield, Ill.: Thomas, 1943), p. 905.

[23] The incidence of manic syndromes is given by E. Strecker and F. Ebaugh as 10 to 25 per cent of all cases. *Practical Clinical Psychiatry,* 5th edition (Philadelphia: Blakiston, 1940), p. 131.

Unfortunately, this diagnostic reform, while it clarified the noso-logical position of paresis, threw behavior pathologists into greater confusion than ever. For it now became evident that patients with symptoms of behavior disorder might or might not have paresis. Those persons — more numerous and vocable early in the century than today — who believed there could be no behavior disorder without a corresponding neural lesion were greatly strengthened in their faith. The others, thrown more than ever on the defensive, sought to differentiate paretic excitements and depressions from the non-paretic on the basis of differences in behavior pathology as well as in serology.

What both groups missed was the now well-established fact that general paresis, like any other syndrome of cerebral incompetence, may be one of the determinants precipitating a behavior disorder. The behavior disorder developing in the cerebrally incompetent person, as we have already said, differs from that developing in a cerebrally competent person only insofar as the direct effects of cerebral intoxication, injury, infection or deterioration enter into the clinical picture. Schube clearly indicated the modern trend thirteen years ago when, after presenting his clinical evidence, he con-cluded, "The type of psychosis or psychoneurosis exhibited [by the paretic patient] is that which the individual would have developed at that time provided syphilis was absent and any other adequate precipitating factor was present." [24]

As a rule the early development of general paresis is insidious and slowly progressive. The first changes to be noticed, by relatives or by the patient himself, are usually the behavioral indications of reduced cerebral competence or the symptoms of behavior disorder. In a great many of these cases, as Wechsler indicates, the patient's complaints are recognized by the clinician as constituting hypo-chondriacal overconcern, fatigue syndrome or anxiety disorder. [25] Such a diagnosis may be correct, but it is incomplete, like the diag-nosis of compulsive disorder, for example, in a person who is also suffering from myocarditis. With acceleration and ingravescence of the inflammatory-degenerative encephalitis, the patient may react to his increasing inadequacies, or in terms of them, with a rather

24 P. Schube, "Emotional states of general paresis," Amer. Jour. Psychiat., 1934, vol. 91, pp. 625-638.
25 I. Wechsler, Textbook of Clinical Neurology, 4th edition (Philadelphia: Saunders, 1939), p. 470.

typical depressive, manic, schizophrenic or paranoid disorder. Thus, in hospitalized paretic patients under treatment the incidence of neurotic disorders has been estimated at about 6 per cent, of manic and depressive illnesses at 40 to 60 per cent, of schizophrenic disorders at 16 to 19 per cent, and of paranoid disorders at 9 per cent.[26]

Among those patients whose syphilitic meningoencephalitis is arrested or cured may be found some in whom a behavior disorder outlasts the general paresis. This, of course, is exactly what we should expect in view of the findings reported for acute cerebral incompetence, for example in bromide intoxication, and for late post-traumatic syndromes following head injury. Rothschild and Sharp describe cases of manic and of schizophrenic disorders, apparently precipitated under the conditions of cerebral incompetence in paresis, which failed to clear up for years after all the serological, neurological and behavioral evidence of an inflammatory-degenerative cerebral disease had completely disappeared.[27]

In our discussion of acute intoxication we cited cases in which the patient, years after or years before the toxic illness, developed a behavior disorder which closely resembled that which complicated his acute delirium. Again we find a parallel in cerebral infection. Postle has reported four cases of general paresis in patients with a history of previous behavior disorders, three diagnosed manic-depressive and one schizophrenic. In each case the behavior pathology appearing during paretic meningoencephalitis was identical with that of the previous attacks. One patient, after making a complete recovery from both his paresis and his behavior disorder, had two later episodes without paresis in which the behavior pathology was identical with that appearing when he was suffering from paresis; it was identical also with the episode occurring prior to his paretic illness.[28]

[26] P. Schube, "Emotional states of general paresis," Amer. Jour. Psychiat., 1934, vol. 91, pp. 625-638; C. Cheney, "Clinical data on general paresis," Psychiat. Quart., 1935, vol. 9, pp. 467-485.

[27] D. Rothschild, "Dementia paralytica accompanied by manic-depressive and schizophrenic psychoses: the significance of their co-existence," Amer. Jour. Psychiat., 1940, vol. 96, pp. 1043-1061; D. Rothschild and M. Sharp, "Neuropathological features of general paresis in relation to mental disturbance," Dis. Nerv. System, 1942, vol. 3, pp. 310-316.

[28] B. Postle, "Pattern features and constitutional susceptibility as related to organic brain disease with special reference to general paresis," Jour. Nerv. Ment. Dis., 1939, vol. 89, pp. 26-36.

The relationship between the preparetic biosocial organization of a person and the particular behavior disorder he develops is widely recognized by contemporary behavior pathologists. Indeed, Woolley states that, if the preparetic personality of the patient were studied thoroughly before his illness, it would be possible to predict from this the trend of his behavior pathology when he became paretic. He points out that schizoid persons developing paresis react characteristically to the effects of their cerebral damage, and after recovery from the meningoencephalitis may show an "undistorted" schizophrenic reaction.[29] Greenhill and Yorshis have presented important evidence in support of their thesis that the preparetic personality adjustment may determine, not only a patient's specific behavior disorder, but also the course of his paretic illness and even its outcome. The cases in their series were all aggressively treated for their meningoencephalitis.[30]

We may cite two of our own cases that illustrate the influence of preparetic biosocial adjustment upon the character of behavior disorder.

One patient, a married job-carpenter of forty-one, was admitted to a psychiatric hospital because of homicidal threats made by him against his competitors. According to his wife, he had always been a jealous, insecure, suspicious man. Two months before admission he had seemed irritable, moody and fatigued. About three weeks before admission he told his wife that his competitors were stealing his tools and putting inferior ones in their place. When after a search the tools he called stolen were found, the patient insisted that the thieves had surreptitiously returned them to make a fool of him. The wife asserted that this behavior was not in the least out of character for the patient. However, when he made serious threats against the alleged thieves and persecutors, arrangements were made to bring the patient to the hospital for help. There he showed mild defects in recent memory, tremors and sluggish pupils. The cerebrospinal fluid report gave a typical paretic curve. Under malarial therapy his serology cleared and he was able to return to work, still, however, suspicious.

Another patient lived in a small West Virginian city where, because of his minority status, his work was confined to menial serv-

29 L. Woolley, "Personality factors in the psychoses of general paresis," *Urol. Cutan. Rev.*, 1945, vol. 49, pp. 3-6.

30 M. Greenhill and M. Yorshis, "Prognostic criteria in dementia paralytica," *Amer. Jour. Psychiat.*, 1940, vol. 97, pp. 167-188.

ices. Those who knew him well considered him a model citizen —
frugal, honest, hard-working, and, within the social limitations
placed upon him, laudably enterprising and ambitious. The first
change noticed by relatives had its beginnings about two years
before hospitalization. The patient grew increasingly irritable and
intolerant within the family group. As time went on, he developed
angry outbursts which seemed to be provoked more and more easily.

About a month before his admission to the hospital, the patient
showed extreme irritability and the rapid development of obviously
pathological signs. He became seriously forgetful and undependable in his work, surly and resentful when rebuked, and at home
violently angry over the most trivial things. He grew increasingly
restless, talkative and excitable until finally he could no longer be
made to work, eat or sleep as he formerly had. He was full of
grandiose schemes and of boasts about his abilities, achievements
and possessions. When humored, he could be led, but when contradicted or interfered with, he became explosively angry and began
threatening members of his family. These were the conditions that
resulted in his hospitalization.

On examination the patient was found to have slurred speech,
tremors of the fingers, eyelids, facial muscles, lips and tongue. His
pupils were fixed to light, but reacted slightly upon accommodation; cerebrospinal fluid gave a typical paretic curve. Excepting for
impaired recall for recent events and the other signs of relative
cerebral incompetence, the clinical picture was essentially that of a
manic attack developing as a reaction to the effects of meningoencephalitis. The patient was overactive, tense, jovial, aggressive and
expansive. His talk was exceedingly voluble and discursive, and full
of thinly disguised resentment over his lifelong minority status and
of his determination to show that he was as good as anybody else.
The delusions of grandeur he expressed were consonant with manic
excitement in a person of his background. His course was gradually
downgrade and showed progressive cerebral incompetence from
which he did not recover.

Behavior disorders in senile and arteriosclerotic cerebral degeneration

Senile cerebral degeneration is characterized primarily by shrinkage of the brain tissue as a whole, formation of plaques in the in-
tercellular substance, regressive changes in and disappearance of
nerve cells, and compensatory glial proliferation. According to
Rothschild, the anterior frontal regions are as a rule the most
severely affected and the occipital regions the least severely. The
upper layers of the cortex show the greatest damage, particularly

the third lamina, but usually the cortical architecture is relatively well preserved. About one-half the cases of senile cerebral degeneration are complicated by changes based on vascular disease, but, unlike the situation in cerebral arteriosclerosis, these lesions in most instances play a relatively minor part in the total histopathological picture.[31]

Arteriosclerotic cerebral degeneration is characterized primarily by vascular changes and scattered focal lesions consisting of more or less complete destruction of brain tissue, within each circumscribed area of softening, and of acellular "devastated" areas from which the nerve cells have completely disappeared, without dissolution of other brain tissue and without marked glial proliferation. The cerebral structure surrounding the focal lesions is relatively well preserved. Unlike the situation in typical senile cerebral degeneration, the basal nuclei in arteriosclerotic cases are the most severely affected parts of the brain, and the most seriously damaged cortical regions are usually the parieto- and temporo-occipital. About one-half the cases of arteriosclerotic cerebral degeneration are complicated by senile changes; but in most of these the changes constitute a minor characteristic of the total histopathological picture.

The behavioral changes in senile and arteriosclerotic cerebral degeneration are by no means specific; they correspond to the changes that we have already characterized as *progressive cerebral incompetence*. If acute delirium develops, as it does more frequently in arteriosclerotic patients than in senile, the delirious phenomena are not essentially different from those in other cases of *acute cerebral incompetence*. Where it is possible to make a behavioral distinction between the senile and the arteriosclerotic illness, the differences will be found chiefly in the type of onset, the gradual or episodic character of the course, and the relative prominence of environmental stress and of cerebral accident in precipitating behavior disorders.

In the relatively uncomplicated case of senile cerebral degeneration, the onset is often so gradual and insidious that the development of progressive cerebral incompetence is not recognized until

[31] This and succeeding paragraphs on the distinctions between senile and arteriosclerotic cerebral degeneration follow the presentation of D. Rothschild, "Senile psychoses and psychoses with cerebral arteriosclerosis," in O. Kaplan (editor), *Mental Disorders in Later Life* (Stanford University, Calif.: Stanford University Press, 1945), pp. 233-279.

some particularly ineffectual performance in a specific situation calls attention to the change. The patient mentioned earlier in the chapter, who could not find his way back to the unfamiliar hotel, illustrates such an onset. The predominantly arteriosclerotic patient, on the other hand, is more likely to suffer a sudden confusional episode, syncope, an apoplectiform or an epileptiform attack as his first serious sign. We cited such a case in the patient who almost ruined himself financially by an injudicious business deal after his cerebral accident.

The course in both senile and arteriosclerotic cerebral degeneration is downgrade, but the latter much more often than the former includes episodes of unpredictable remission and sudden ingravescence. Confusional, syncopal and convulsive attacks may occur in both forms, but in the senile they are uncommon and when they do occur, it is usually late in the degenerative process. If delirium appears in senile degeneration, it as a rule becomes chronic and is rarely interrupted by the lucid intervals frequently encountered in arteriosclerotic cases.

When *behavior disorders* develop in persons who suffer from senile or arteriosclerotic cerebral degeneration, they exhibit the same diversity as do those developing in persons with undamaged brains. There is one important difference between the problem presented to the patient by senile and by arteriosclerotic degeneration. The typical senile patient is called upon to adapt more or less gradually to a slow, steady decline in biosocial adequacy, whereas the typical arteriosclerotic must adjust to sudden loss and partial recovery, followed by further losses and remissions. Otherwise the situations confronting the two groups are more alike than dissimilar; and, as we have said, about one-half of each group is made up of cases having characteristics of the other group.[32] Therefore, in the interest of simplicity, we shall restrict most of the discussion that follows to behavior disorders complicating senile cerebral degeneration, and we shall regard the arteriosclerotic cases as recognizable variants with special liabilities of their own.

It is no more inevitable, of course, that behavior disorders should arise in these than in any other forms of cerebral degeneration. However, as we said in our discussion of general paresis, behavior disorders are common developments in cases of progressive cerebral

[32] It should be noted that, according to Rothschild, the age of onset is too variable to serve as a distinguishing criterion between the two groups.

incompetence, and this statement applies with special force to senile behavior deterioration. If the environment is favorable, and the ageing individual is especially adaptable, his biosocial behavior organization may deteriorate to an almost vegetative level without the appearance of serious personal maladjustment. But if ageing means a reduction in security and a loss of status, as in our society it nearly always does, the only persons likely to escape behavior disorder are those who have been exceptionally adaptable in earlier maturity, and those whose cerebral incompetence has made them incapable of normal human anxieties or needs.

The average senile or late senescent individual, as his biosocial adequacy declines, does not find that his general conditions of life improve or that they provide new rewards to replace the old rewards denied him. On the contrary, for the vast majority of ageing men and women, increasing years bring only increasing handicaps — biological, personal, social and economic. To these burdens must be added also the consequences of unwise and impulsive reactions, the revival of old conflicts and old ambitendencies, and *the return of the repressed,* which we have already discussed in relation to cerebral incompetence. If we take into consideration the variability of these different factors and the interdependence of their effects, we shall not be surprised to find that neither the severity nor even the fact of behavior disorder in elderly persons need be related to the extent of cerebral damage.[33]

The investigation of behavior disorders occurring in senility has been hampered by the same misunderstandings which, as we have seen, once misled students of general paresis. For it was customary not so long ago to interpret all maladaptive biosocial behavior in old age at once as the inescapable effect of cerebral decay. No distinctions were recognized between the signs of progressive cerebral incompetence and the patient's reactions to his decreasing adequacy, security and prestige. Today, however, we find that even the standard and necessarily conservative textbooks accept such distinctions. Henderson and Gillespie, for example, state that when paranoid or depressive disorders occur in the senile period, they differ from those occurring earlier in life only insofar as the direct

[33] For a discussion of this point, with bibliography, see D. Rothschild, "Senile psychoses and psychoses with cerebral arteriosclerosis," in O. Kaplan (editor), *Mental Disorders in Later Life* (Stanford University, Calif.: Stanford University Press, 1945), pp. 233-279.

effects of cerebral incompetence enter into the clinical picture.[34] Indeed, we might paraphrase Schube's pronouncement on general paresis [35] and say that, if a behavior disorder appears in a setting of senile cerebral incompetence, it is likely to be one that would have developed at that time if cerebral incompetence had been absent and any other adequate precipitating factor present.

It is especially interesting that among senile patients in psychiatric hospitals cases of paranoid disorder and depressions far outnumber those of schizophrenic disorder and mania, and that the incidence of paranoid disorders has been estimated as approximately double the incidence of depressions.[36] The rarity of schizophrenia in senility could be predicted from the relationship between maturity and biosocial behavior organization which we discussed in Chapters 14 and 15. The relatively high incidence of paranoid disorders may in part reflect the greater difficulty that relatives find in tolerating an aggressive, accusing delusional senile than a sad, self-reproachful one. However, it may also reflect a corresponding difference in the senile population as a whole. We know, for example, that at any age the serious impairment of hearing or sight, even more than complete deafness or blindness, frequently gives rise to anxiety and suspicion; and senility is the period of life in which such losses are most frequent. Moreover, in our society it is customary to belittle and restrict the aged, to deny them freedom of action and opportunity whether they need that freedom or not, and to meet their protest and resentment with evasiveness or further aggression. These are, of course, optimal conditions for the development of paranoid reactions.

Meager as our data are for paranoid disorders, mania, depressions and schizophrenia in persons undergoing senile behavior deterioration, the data relating to hypochondria, fatigue syndromes, anxiety disorders, compulsions and hysteria are scantier still. The aged patient is seldom hospitalized for these latter disorders; but when his progressive cerebral incompetence seems to justify or necessitate it, then he is institutionalized. By that time the senile behavior deterioration usually overshadows any symptoms of behavior disorder present, and these are as a rule overlooked or mis-

[34] D. Henderson and R. Gillespie, *Textbook of Psychiatry for Students and Practitioners*, 6th edition (London: Oxford University Press, 1944), p. 491.

[35] P. Schube, "Emotional states of general paresis," *Amer. Jour. Psychiat.*, 1934, vol. 91, pp. 625-638.

[36] E. Strecker and F. Ebaugh, *Practical Clinical Psychiatry*, 5th edition (Philadelphia: Blakiston, 1940), pp. 170-178.

identified as incidental signs of brain degeneration. We are in great need of out-patient department and office consultation studies that make a clear distinction between senile persons who show signs of progressive cerebral incompetence and those who do not. The information available so far makes no such distinction.

What evidence we have seems to indicate a high incidence for hypochondria, fatigue syndromes and anxiety disorders in senility.[37] Frank compulsive disorders appear to be less commonly encountered in this age period, while hysterical inactivation and autonomy are relatively rare.[38] The prevalence of hypochondriacal disorders and fatigue syndromes is not difficult to understand. In the first place, the elderly have neither the strength nor the endurance of the young and their visceral performance is often less effective and more easily disturbed than it was earlier in life. Particularly in the gastrointestinal system, and to a lesser degree in the cardiovascular and genito-urinary systems, disturbances appear which, although not in themselves a threat to continued health and life, are reacted to as if they were. Symptoms of gastrointestinal dysfunction are common secondary results of deficiencies and diseases in other systems, of general malnutrition, or of overexertion and lack of adequate sleep; and all of these conditions appear more frequently in old age than in youth.[39]

Once middle age is reached, the older a person grows the more familiar he becomes with the incursions of illness and death among his associates, and the more likely he is to have been ill himself and to have undergone surgery. The accumulation of such incidents may render an individual reaction-sensitive to signs and symptoms which indicate to him that he is in poor health or beginning to decline. We have discussed in Chapters 7 and 8 the gains to be derived from being treated as a sick or frail person. Since most aged men and women in our culture have reason to consider themselves neglected and in need of more attention, comfort and affection, it should be anticipated that hypochondria and fatigue syndromes as adjustive techniques will develop with great frequency during the

[37] H. Woltmann, "Neuropsychiatric geriatrics," *Arch. Ophthal.*, 1942, vol. 28, pp. 790-801.

[38] K. Bowman, "Types and special factors of mental illness of old age," in *Mental Hygiene in Old Age* (New York: Family Welfare Association of America, 1937), pp. 32-38.

[39] A. Ivy, "Digestive system," in E. Cowdry, *Problems of Ageing*, 2d edition (Baltimore: Williams and Wilkins, 1942), pp. 254-301; E. Bortz, "Geriatrics," *Clinics*, 1942, vol. 1, pp. 386-405.

senile period. The frustrations and unhappiness imposed directly upon the elderly by restrictive social conventions, economic dependence and reduced biosocial adequacy do much to reinforce and perpetuate such developments.[40]

The anxiety disorders that appear in senile persons do not differ fundamentally from those occurring at any other time of life. They are precipitated and perpetuated by the same general factors; only the details are peculiar to old age. The aged have many reasons for being insecure. Most of them become economically dependent upon the good will and sometimes the caprice of others; and many of those who never actually do become dependent live nonetheless in constant dread that some day perhaps they may. The high probability of ultimate infirmity and the certainty of death are also important sources of persistent anxiety; but helplessness is much more dreaded than is death.[41]

Anxiety disorders frequently develop in ageing persons on the basis of guilt reactions. This is sometimes the consequence of progressive cerebral incompetence, as we have indicated earlier. A decline in the adequacy of biosocial behavior organization allows conflicts and ambitendencies to be revived which had earlier been effectively repressed. It allows the patient also to become involved in misconduct because his reactions to an immediate situation no longer include self-control in terms of future consequences. But the senile person may equally well develop ambivalent conflict and anxiety because of hostile and vengeful fantasies, which he has entertained in relation to close relatives who appear to domineer, belittle or obstruct him. Furthermore, in the cerebrally competent senile as well as in the relatively incompetent, sex fantasies and sex conflicts often play an important part in the production and perpetuation of anxiety. Sometimes the lonely, unhappy senile, like the adolescent, finds in the need-satisfaction sequences of sex behavior what he cannot otherwise achieve.

When compulsive behavior appears in senility, with or without progressive cerebral incompetence, it often represents the revival of a technique used earlier in life in dealing with some conflict which has also been revived. But, of course, it may also be a new

[40] For a more detailed discussion of the biosocial background of maladaptive behavior in senescence and senility, see N. Cameron, "Neuroses of later maturity," in O. Kaplan (editor), *Mental Disorders in Later Life* (Stanford University, Calif.: Stanford University Press, 1945), pp. 143-186.

[41] G. Piersol, "The problems of ageing," *Bull. New York Acad. Med.*, 1940, vol. 16, pp. 555-569.

procedure for the ageing individual, developed in the face of newly increased insecurity, conflict and anxiety. In either case there is nothing about these compulsions to distinguish them from those at other ages. Sometimes what looks at first like a compulsive disorder, in senility with progressive cerebral incompetence, is actually much simpler behavior. A person who is attempting to cope with the complexities of a situation, which are beyond his present limits of adaptability, may fall back upon stereotyped, perseverative or ritualistic reactions. This technique, too, is not peculiar to old age or cerebral incompetence. It is found throughout childhood, adolescence and maturity, as we have seen, in games, in stories and in religious practice.

The recent emergence of new attitudes toward maladaptation in cerebral incompetence is in a way representative of the whole evolution of behavior pathology. Originally, the cerebrally incompetent were assigned to psychiatrists, wherever possible, because no one else wanted them. The delirious, the post-traumatic Korsakoff, the paretic, the senile or the cerebral arteriosclerotic patient, in many general hospitals, is still transferred to psychiatry only after he is deemed unmanageable or a chronic nuisance. The psychiatrist for a long time not unnaturally shared the attitudes of his medical colleagues, and ascribed all of the behavior pathology in such patients to their damaged brains. Today we are witnessing the growth of new interpretations in this long-neglected field, a growth to which significant contributions are being made by neuropathologists, behavior pathologists, psychiatrists and psychologists.

The cerebrally competent with behavior disorders that made them unmanageable were also originally assigned to psychiatrists because no one else wanted them; and for centuries their behavior pathology continued to be regarded as the disorderly expression of a diseased brain. Those who were not unmanageable were either treated with nerve tonics for deficiencies they did not have, or else tolerated as weaklings and malingerers without a legitimate claim to the privileges of a sick person. It is chiefly to the credit of Freud and his disciples that behavior disorders, in the easily manageable as well as in the unmanageable patient, have finally achieved the status of equality with other illnesses. It is almost entirely to their credit that therapy in the behavior disorders has grown, from the level of restraint, exhortation, reassurance and cerebral assault, to that of a biosocial interpersonal relationship.

18 Therapy as Biosocial Behavior

MODERN THERAPY in the behavior disorders is based upon two fundamental assumptions, the first of which we shall call the *principle of continuity.* This principle we have already formulated as follows: *All of the attitudes and responses found in behavior pathology are in some way related to and derived from normal biosocial behavior.*[1] In other words, even though a wide chasm may separate the pathological behavior of a patient from the normal behavior of others around him, the chasm is one which the patient himself has spanned by means of a progression of acquired reactions. Furthermore, these reactions, as we have repeatedly seen in our clinical material, include cumulative and self-perpetuating maladaptations which arise from an individual's unskilled or inappropriate use of common, everyday defense and escape techniques.

The other assumption upon which modern therapy is based has been implicit throughout our presentation of the behavior disorders. We may call it the *principle of shared objectification.* According to this principle, *the acquisition of normal biosocial behavior may be greatly facilitated by the organization of a permissive situation, in which the patient has maximal opportunity to work through his attitudes and responses overtly in the presence of a skilled therapist.* In the discussion that follows we shall be concerned chiefly with the permissive therapeutic situation — its aims, its results, the part played in it by the therapist and the part played by the patient.

[1] In Chapter 3, on behavior organization and behavior pathology.

AIMS OF THERAPY IN THE BEHAVIOR DISORDERS

The immediate goal of treatment in the behavior disorders is that of establishing a biosocial interrelationship, the *therapeutic situation*, in which patient and therapist participate. The ultimate goal is that of making this interrelationship unnecessary and terminating it with benefit to the patient. The precise character of a therapeutic situation will depend, of course, upon what the patient needs or prefers, what the therapist is trained and equipped to offer, and the degree to which each is able to share the perspectives of the other. However, the professional attitudes and objectives of the well-prepared therapist are, or should be, fundamentally the same whether his patient requires the protection and support of a hospital environment for twenty-four hours a day, or that of a consultation office for one hour.

Therapists whose training has been restricted to the treatment of hospitalized patients, or to consulting and counseling procedures with office patients, show an understandable tendency to exaggerate the differences between these two groups. Actually, however, the therapist in either situation is faced with essentially the same basic problem. A patient presents himself who is suffering from the effects of inadequate biosocial behavior. The familiar amateur techniques of comforting reassurance, explanation, exhortation, argument, restraint or reprisal have not helped him, and may instead have increased his difficulties. It follows that further attempts, made along the same inexpert lines, hold little promise of remedying the pathological behavior, of shortening its duration or lessening its severity. Whether he comes to an office or a hospital ward, the need that such a person has is the need, usually unformulated, for a situation with interpersonal relationships unlike those in which he originally developed his behavior disorder, and unlike those in which he has so far failed to improve. Let us see what the chief therapeutic aims are that determine the structuring of the situation in office and hospital.

Aims of office treatment

The consultation office provides the setting in which a biosocial interrelationship between patient and therapist may develop and form the basis for treatment. During the therapeutic hour, the patient is protected from the distorting and inhibiting effects of interruption, distraction, approval and disapproval on the part of another person. He is exposed to no evaluative appraisal in terms of social convention other than that of his own socially derived self-reactions, which are themselves exceedingly important objects of investigation. In such a protective, permissive therapeutic situation the patient may react unmolested, in ways that neither he himself nor others could allow in the family setting or in the social environment of the wider community.

This is the primary aim of office treatment, to establish optimal conditions for the patient to work through his attitudes overtly in the presence of a skilled, impartial therapist who reacts with neither praise nor blame. If this aim is realized, the other aims may also be achieved. The patient may be led to verbalize whatever he can in socially communicative terms. For, of course, that which is spoken can to some degree be shared by the therapist, and the sharing in itself changes the private covert reaction into a public statement. And, what is more important, the impartiality of the therapist, his failure to appraise overtly what he hears and sees, provides the patient with genuine sharing, but does not give him the expected evaluative reactions. In other words, here is an interpersonal relationship, unlike any other in adult life, which can provide the shared objectification the patient needs for his own reorientation.

What the patient verbalizes in the presence of the unappraising therapist, he also hears himself, and he hears it with the same ears that receive the words of other persons when they speak. This places what he says, as social stimulation, in the same category as the statements of other persons. Since the therapist does not communicate evaluative attitudes, the patient is left free to develop self-attitudes to his own verbalization, which are not predetermined by the person listening to him, but are evolved out of his biosocial organization in the treatment situation. This is the chief aim of therapeutic verbalization: to make social sharing possible under circumstances which permit the patient to determine his own attitudes and responses, without interference or direction, and to hear his own self-reactions to what he verbalizes.

Of course, a great many of a person's most important determinative attitudes are never adequately verbalized in the presence of others or, for that matter, even in solitude. Some of these belong to the prelanguage period of behavior organization, some have never needed to be formulated and shared, and some have at one time been partially or fully verbalized and then neglected or repressed.[2] The aim of office treatment is to give the patient maximal freedom for developing the verbalization of attitudes and responses which he has seldom or never verbalized before, and for sharing things in words and other overt reactions which he has never shared.

If verbalization were the whole of therapy in the behavior disorders, treatment might well be carried on by telephone. But talking is always biosocial behavior in which the words spoken aloud are only fragmentary responses belonging to more complete reactions. For the most fully shared reactions, these fragments are often quite sufficient to serve as communication, particularly when the topic is a conventional one and the participants share a common attitudinal background. However, as indeed we have already seen, behavior pathology seldom arises in relation to conventional topics that are freely communicated; and patients with behavior disorders have as a rule developed unshared, individualistic attitudes in relation to their difficulties long before they come for expert help. The therapeutic situation, therefore, provides for maximal freedom to act as well as to talk, to render as much as possible of the unverbalized in overt non-verbal behavior. Under these circumstances, both therapist and patient may witness the behavior together, and the patient can have the advantages of working out an unformulated attitude in a shared social situation without being praised or penalized.

It has long been one of the principal aims of therapy in the behavior disorders to increase the accessibility and the communicability of a patient's unformulated, forgotten and repressed reactions. Indeed, the evolution of modern procedures has to a large degree been determined by this aim. Freud began developing his method of motivational analysis by inducing hypnotic relaxation in his patients, as therapists had done for centuries before him. He broke with the tradition of his predecessors, however, and laid the foundations of modern treatment when he substituted for the restrictive techniques and the authoritarian relationship of hypnosis, a freer permissive situation. In this the therapist played a more passive, accepting role and the patient's reactions were determined more by his own behavior than by therapeutic direction.

2 See the discussion of prelanguage behavior organization in Chapters 2 and 3, of language and thought in Chapter 4, and of the unverbalized and the repressed in Chapters 5 and 6.

Freud retained from the classical hypnotic techniques some of the procedures that favored relaxation, progressive training and the development of a special biosocial interrelationship between patient and therapist. He evolved slower but far more effective ways of permitting inaccessible reaction, non-verbal as well as verbal, to become accessible to the patient as well as to the therapist. The emotional crisis, which Charcot had identified as an hysterical curiosity, Freud raised to the status of an essential, expected reaction to rearoused conflict in anyone, whether hysterical or not. He trained his patients, without the use of hypnosis, in the techniques of inhibiting critical self-attitudes and allowing unconventional, anti-social, ambivalent, immature and apparently meaningless responses and attitudes to appear overtly without hindrance or censure. The aim and the achievement of motivational analysis, whether by modifications of Freud's methods or by the use of hypnosis and narcosis, have been directly related to their function in increasing the accessibility and communicability of previously inaccessible and incommunicable reactions.

The acquisition of new perspectives and of skill in shifting them is an aim that is particularly characteristic of the non-directive techniques of motivational analysis which have been derived from Freud. Indeed, the development of increased competence and resourcefulness in social role-taking, in sharing the perspectives of other persons, and in regulating one's behavior in terms of social attitudes, is essential to the achievement of social maturity.[3] And the ultimate goal of biosocial therapy in the behavior disorders, as we have formulated it, includes the maturation of the patient's interpersonal reactions to a point at which the therapeutic relationship becomes unnecessary. This we shall discuss later on in more detail.

It is now evident that the aims of modern treatment are not primarily concerned with getting rid of symptoms, but rather of using them as therapeutic guides and aids. However, when the symptomatology of behavior disorders includes reactions which jeopardize the patient or the community, it becomes necessary to cope first with the symptoms and leave the motivational analysis for later consideration. Therefore, before proceeding to a discussion of the part played by therapist and patient in the therapeutic

[3] See the discussion of role-taking, shifting perspectives and the development of normal social maturity, in Chapters 2 and 4.

situation, we shall take up the indications for hospital treatment and the advantages of hospitalization to the patient.

Aims of hospital treatment

One of the most important responsibilities of the therapist in the behavior disorders is that of determining whether or not the safety of his patient or of the community requires hospitalization as part of the *therapeutic situation*. It is obvious that, if a person is to participate advantageously in therapy, he must not only be kept alive, but also safeguarded against the injurious or neglectful behavior of others and of himself. The patient whose behavior disorder has reduced his biosocial competence to a point where he can no longer provide such safeguards requires the protection of a hospital environment.[4]

The fundamental aim of hospitalization in the behavior disorders is one of providing a patient with special protection and support that will facilitate therapy. This aim, far from being peculiar to behavior disorders, is the chief guiding principle in all hospital care. The cardiac patient, for example, must be protected from the stimulation of a normally active household, from emotional excitement, from the harmful effects of his own behavior and, as much as possible, from spiraling anxiety over the danger to which he believes himself exposed. He must submit, often unwillingly, to restrictive scheduling, to a severe reduction in the permitted scope of his activities, and usually to a restructuring of his biosocial behavior which, in the more favorable cases, ultimately renders the protective and supportive hospital environment unnecessary.

Protection from the ordinary everyday environment is a common need in certain behavior disorders. The manic patient, for example, by his aggressive or excited behavior invites stimulation from other persons, and then characteristically overreacts to the stimulation which he invites. A considerable reduction in the intensity of manic behavior can often be effected, without chemical sedation or forcible restraint, by reducing environmental stimulation in a maximally permissive hospital situation. The case of the married woman living with her in-laws, described in Chapter 16, clearly

[4] We shall limit our consideration to therapeutic hospitalization. Nontherapeutic hospitalization, although it is the prevailing technique in our society for disposing of persons suffering from disabling behavior disorders, is actually a form of protective incarceration and does not belong in a discussion of therapy.

illustrates this point. Forcible restraint, we saw, increased the patient's aggressive resentment while bromides only added delirium to the manic illness. But when transfer was effected to a hospital environment that was primarily concerned with giving the patient maximal freedom and support, even at the expense of the staff's convenience, her downhill course was soon reversed.

Patients reacting with cumulative anxiety also require shielding from the normal reactions of other persons. For example, the individual whose anxiety disorder begins to mount to panic proportions may need immediate seclusion in a supportive, permissive environment if a catastrophe to him or to his associates is to be averted. Depressed, schizophrenic and paranoid patients can frequently be prevented from injuring themselves and others by being removed from their surroundings to a hospital situation, where anxiety-inducing stimulation can be controlled. It is, of course, essential that intensely anxious patients, whatever their diagnosis, be under the immediate care of therapists whose own reactions do not provoke fear and doubt.

If a person succeeds in injuring himself or someone else, or even makes a serious but unsuccessful attempt, his act is almost sure to complicate the therapeutic situation, and usually in a detrimental way. There is always, of course, the likelihood that the community will intervene in cases of assault and self-assault. If such intervention takes the form of a legal procedure, the patient may be subjected to punitive counteraggression which destroys the possibility of constructive therapy. But quite aside from this, the fact and the results of suicidal, homicidal and self-punitive attempts, made under conditions of intense anxiety, may become the most important obstacle to a person's recovery from behavior disorder.

A depressed patient, for example, tried unsuccessfully to kill himself by shooting. Because of this incident he became convinced that he should be incarcerated for life. For in terms of his religious beliefs, the fact that he had actually attempted suicide placed him beyond redemption and made him unfit for decent human company. In terms of his standards of courage and efficiency, the fact that his sinful attempt had failed meant to him that he was not even enough of a man to carry through a despicable crime. These convictions turned out to be by far the most formidable barriers to therapy. Had the attempt been headed off by early hospitalization, the patient's ultimate recovery would undoubtedly have come much sooner than it did.

Hospital treatment protects individuals from still other consequences of their behavior. It prevents the manic, depressed, paranoid or schizophrenic patient from making decisions and entering into commitments, under the influence of delusional reactions, which may seriously compromise him. It segregates the person whose behavior, because of his excitement, aversion or confusion, includes reactions which the social community might regard with contempt, ridicule, disgust or condemnation. The fact that such reactions are witnessed by or reported to a therapist, who understands them, makes it possible to include them in later therapeutic discussions, in case the recovering patient remembers them. Sometimes a reaction which would shock, perplex or surprise the layman can be made the basis for important constructive therapy by the experienced behavior pathologist.

One of the most important gains from hospital treatment, particularly in the case of depressed and schizophrenic patients, is the protection it offers against the consequences of indiscriminate confession. Self-depreciatory, self-accusatory and confused persons often throw a heavy burden upon relatives and friends by a recital of recalled and imagined misdeeds which no one is able afterwards to forget. Moreover, the confessing individual hears what he says, and witnesses its effect upon the others, with the usual result that he finds greater reason than ever to condemn and despise himself, or to grow more perplexed and confused. Under hospital conditions the need to confess diminishes with a reduction in anxiety-provoking stimulation, and what confession does occur is shared with persons who have only a professional interest in what is said.

For many patients, hospitalization means the substitution of a simplified environment for one that has become too complex to handle. It is true that the psychiatric ward reduces drastically the scope of a patient's activities, but within the permitted range it is much less demanding and more accepting than the average home environment. Often the mere absence of relatives and friends, whose expectations a harassed or bewildered patient has been trying to meet, brings a degree of relief from tension that more than compensates for the loss of affectionate companionship. And if the patient is unable to respond with affection to his relatives, because he is depressed or preoccupied, his isolation from them may relieve him of an additional burden of guilt.

In any competently run hospital service the environmental simplification of the ward is accompanied by sufficient routinization and scheduling to support organized behavior in both patients and therapists. The structure of life on the ward is especially important in psychiatry because all the patients are ambulatory. A higher degree of interpersonal cooperation is therefore necessary than on a ward of bed patients. Moreover, in the behavior disorders a high percentage of the patients have serious difficulties with participative activities. Indeed, as we have seen, some of them are reacting primarily in terms rather of an individualistic pseudocommunity, or an autistic community, than of the shared social community.

One of the primary aims of hospital treatment in the case of non-participative, desocialized, preoccupied patients is that of helping them to restructure their behavior in terms of a simplified social community. This aim is frequently all that can be achieved, especially in severe schizophrenic disorders recognized too late. When it becomes obvious that a return to the complex normal environment is out of the question, the next steps must be directed toward adjustment to an intelligently organized institutional life. However, in the vast majority of manic and depressed patients, and in a high percentage of schizophrenic patients, the social community can be progressively complicated as improvement continues.[5] Therapy of a more active, participative character is then gradually introduced until eventually the patient can be treated entirely on the basis of office consultation. The procedure may then be essentially the same as that for the unhospitalized individual.

Hospitalization is frequently advised for patients who need neither protection nor support. In some instances, a twenty-four-hour study of behavior over a period of a few weeks is needed to clear up a therapist's diagnostic and interpretative uncertainties. In others, there is a routine to be established, or to be broken up, as an aid or a provocation to further therapy. The hypochondriacal or the fatigued patient, for example, may benefit from retraining while he is participating in active therapy. Hysterical and compulsive patients sometimes require systematic hospital treatment for the secondary effects of their behavior pathology. Where a clinic is organized into small ward groups, the situation affords opportunities for studying the interpersonal behavior of a given patient under the controlled conditions of a miniature community.

[5] See especially Rennie's data cited in Chapters 15 and 16.

BIOSOCIAL BEHAVIOR IN THE THERAPEUTIC SITUATION

In the behavior disorders the *therapeutic situation* is not a place, of course, but an interpersonal relationship. It is a relationship that is defined by the biosocial interaction of two or more persons, at least one of whom is a patient and one a specially trained therapist. The consultation office or the psychiatric hospital merely provides a setting within which conditions favorable to such interaction may be developed. As we have already indicated, the precise character of the therapeutic situation will depend upon what the therapist is trained and equipped to offer, what the patient requires or prefers, and the degree to which therapist and patient are able to share each other's perspectives.

Of course, there are times, in psychiatry no less than in surgery and internal medicine, when to attempt nothing beyond supportive treatment is to accomplish most. It is often the case that relatives of the patient, and sometimes the patient himself, insist that some aggressive action be taken when the circumstances clearly call for protection and non-intervention. Even the experienced therapist may find such prejudicial pressures difficult to resist. In acute anxiety and panic reactions, in paranoid, manic and schizophrenic excitements, and in severe agitated depressions, for example, the most competently structured therapeutic situation is usually one that does little more than to protect and sustain the patient, until he is able to benefit by a more actively participative relationship.

On the other hand, the deeply preoccupied patient, whether he is silent or talkative, requires as a rule the stimulation of biosocial interaction in shared activities with other persons. In the behavior disorders the silent or mute individual may be one who is living as much as possible in terms of his autistic community where he manages to satisfy his fantasied needs with fantasied rewards. For such a patient the therapeutic situation must include active interpersonal behavior that stimulates him to react in terms of other patients and of therapists in a miniature social community — a small ward or other group. This small group community is sufficiently simplified to make social relearning possible and make it rewarding. It must also be organized in such a way as to minimize the likelihood of delusional misinterpretations that might confront the patient with a threatening pseudocommunity from which his only escape would be to retreat further into his autism.

The preoccupied but not predominantly autistic patient, who is living chiefly in terms of a pseudocommunity, likewise requires participation in the activities of a simplified miniature social community. The small group of patients and therapists provides a treatment situation in which the deleterious effects of critical, evaluative reactions can be minimized and threats of denunciation and retaliation eliminated. The anxious, hostile, suspicious or self-condemnatory person introduced into such a group may thus be protected from some of the reactions of others to his behavior pathology which have been aggravating or perpetuating his disorder. The mildly or moderately excited manic, depressed or schizophrenic individual is similarly protected from the harmful effects of remonstrance, counteraggression, restraint, ridicule or applause. The person who cannot bring himself to talk freely, or to stop talking, finds in group participation the opportunity to do things under conditions which direct the emphasis away from his silence or his loquacity.

When a patient is silent in a shared permissive therapeutic situation, almost anyone is apt to infer that he is preoccupied. It is not so widely recognized, however, that the loquacious patient may be just as seriously preoccupied as the silent patient. There need be no essential difference between them excepting that in one the preoccupation is with covert fantasy while in the other it is with overt talk. The voluble manic, schizophrenic or agitated depressed individual, for example, shows a marked restriction in the range of his topics which is usually not apparent to the casual observer. He may require participation in the activities of a small group no less than the quiet schizophrenic or depressed person. In a group situation the domination of his preoccupations over his biosocial behavior may be replaced, at least for a part of each day, by the greater freedom of activity in concert with other individuals.

What is true of patients operating in terms of a pseudocommunity is sometimes true also of those whose preoccupations are not genuinely delusional in character. If a person builds his whole manner of living around his body overconcern, his fatigue symptoms, his anxiety, guilt, compulsive ritual, hysterical inactivation or hysterical autonomy, he also may require a therapeutic situation like that designed for patients with delusional preoccupations. By methods which we have already described in detail, such an individual has progressively restricted the range of his biosocial inter-

actions with others, until the distorted patterns of his daily life are
the chief perpetuators of his behavior disorder. The ward or other
small group organization provides a setting which aids the patient
materially in restructuring his interpersonal behavior and his routine of living. This procedure seldom disposes of a person's behavior pathology, of course, but it does often supply a behavioral
framework for individual therapy.

It is clear that the therapeutic situations so far discussed have
been those developed on the in-patient service of well-staffed
clinics and hospitals. Within recent years, however, there has been
an important trend in the direction of extending the indubitable
advantages of the small group organization to out-patient services
also, some of them connected with clinics or hospitals and some
not.[6] But whether in-patient or out-patient, and whatever the details of operation, group therapy owes its success to the same general factors. It provides a miniature social community in which
social learning can take place under conditions more favorable for
the maladjusted person than those of the wider community. It
allows role-taking to develop in ways and to degrees that are not
readily permitted in the wider community. It affords unusual practice in shifting and sharing perspectives. In short, it facilitates
communicative behavior under circumstances that promote the
growth of social maturity in the individual who has failed to
achieve it under ordinary conditions.

The objectives and the achievements of group therapy are not
essentially different from the objectives and achievements of individual therapy; only the techniques are somewhat dissimilar. Indeed, as we have seen, the two methods are often carried on advantageously side by side. The biosocial interactions occurring in the
group situation raise personal issues which enter into the productions of the patient during office consultation. Conversely, the
group organization provides the patient with a proving ground for
behavior which he has worked out in the office situation. In the
discussion of individual therapy which follows, we shall find it convenient to distinguish between the behavioral characteristics of the
therapist and those of the patient in their interpersonal relationship.

6 See, for example, S. Slavson, *An Introduction to Group Therapy*. New
York: Commonwealth Fund, 1943. Also the papers in the 1944 round table on
"Levels and applications of group therapy" (Fritz Redl, chairman), *Amer.
Jour. Orthopsychiat.*, 1944, vol. 14, pp. 578-608.

The therapist in the therapeutic situation

The immediate goal of treatment in the behavior disorders, we have said, is that of establishing a participative biosocial interrelationship between patient and therapist; while the ultimate goal is that of rendering such an interrelationship unnecessary and terminating it with benefit to the patient. It is easy to gain the impression from some current discussions of individual treatment and motivational analysis that the ideal therapist in the therapeutic situation does nothing at all. From other discussions it may be inferred that the therapist does nothing until the patient seems ripe for instruction, when slowly increasing doses of indoctrination are introduced until the patient becomes desensitized. But, although much of the training of a therapist is training in silence and in the restructuring of common overt reactions, it is by no means training in suspended animation or training in laying a casuistic ambush.

During the past forty years, under the influence of Freud and his followers, there has been a steady decrease in the use of authoritarian question-answer procedures in office therapy, and a corresponding increase in the practice of giving the patient free rein in verbalization and other communicative behavior. Throughout the greater part of this evolution there has been heated controversy over such questions of technique as, *Shall the patient sit facing the therapist or sit the other way around? Shall the patient sit up or lie down? Shall the therapist say anything at all once the patient's verbalization begins? Shall he sum up at the end of a predetermined period or not?* [7] There were even debates at one time over whether it made any essential difference in the method of free verbalization if the therapist fell asleep, since, after all, this insured non-intervention and non-direction in the procedure.

There are still those, of course, who cling to the authoritarian question-answer relationship and look with derision upon so-called "talking cures"; and there are still defenders of the creed that only a seated or only a recumbent person can be regarded as part of a

---

[7] For discussions of the merits of various techniques see F. Alexander and T. French, *Psychoanalytic Therapy* (New York: Ronald Press, 1946); F. Allen, *Psychotherapy with Children* (New York: Norton, 1942); O. Diethelm, *Treatment in Psychiatry* (New York: Macmillan, 1936); S. Kraines, *Treatment of the Neuroses and Psychoses*, 2d edition (Philadelphia: Lea and Febiger, 1943); S. Lorand, *Technique of Psychoanalytic Therapy* (New York: International University Press, 1946); C. Rogers, *Counseling and Psychotherapy* (Boston: Houghton Mifflin, 1942).

therapeutic situation. But the upshot of the forty-year-old controversy is that today the well-trained therapist may choose, from
among a variety of techniques, the procedure that seems empirically best suited to a particular patient and to himself in a specific
therapeutic situation. The therapist who faces a new developing
therapeutic interrelationship with only one technique in his repertory is like the physician of long ago who relied upon calomel and
the lancet to cure everything. He will find that no matter how
skillfully he performs in the approved way, there will always be a
considerable number of patients who seem unable to respond as
they are supposed to respond, in the therapeutic situation he
initiates.

The initiative in establishing the therapeutic situation belongs
to the therapist. His is the responsibility for providing the setting
in which this unique biosocial interrelationship may develop; and it
is his behavior within the setting that makes the therapeutic interaction unlike anything else with which the patient is familiar. However, even when he is completely silent and overtly unreactive, the
therapist is no more passive than a non-partisan expert spectator at
a football tournament. He is responding actively, intelligently and
impartially to every detail of the patient's behavior, but in ways
that differ in many important respects, both covertly and overtly,
from his reactions to the behavior of others in an ordinary social
situation.

We know that whenever two individuals share the same environment, the behavior of each person becomes an important factor in
structuring the social context for the other person's reactions. This
is no less true of the therapeutic relationship than of other biosocial
interactions. But the characteristically protective, permissive context of this relationship depends at first almost wholly upon the
therapist's behavior — upon what he says and does, and even more
particularly upon what he refrains from saying and doing. As treatment proceeds, if it is successful, the patient learns to extend the
range of his own overt reactions, including his self-responses and
self-attitudes, beyond the limits prescribed by the critical evaluations of others and by his own socially derived critical self-reactions.

The simplest possible formulation of the therapist's function in
office treatment is that he must facilitate whatever behavior is
necessary for the patient to get well. He must lead the patient to

objectify as much as possible in socially communicative responses and attitudes, but without himself predetermining what directions the shared objectification shall or shall not take. We may repeat for emphasis that verbalization is by no means the whole of communication. Indeed, a great deal of that which patient and therapist must share is not and often cannot be adequately verbalized. As Freud long ago insisted, this is particularly true of the emotional components of the patient's behavior in a therapeutic situation, where what a patient says may be far less significant than the fact and the character of emotional participation in his reactions.[8]

The therapist facilitates overt communicative behavior on the patient's part by helping to establish a miniature social community in which the patient's self-reactions are the only possible sources of appraisal. This miniature social community differs from that organized for group therapy in an important respect: the patient, although he is still not alone, must nevertheless supply all of the socially evaluative reactions to his own behavior. He may do this directly by self-responses and self-attitudes, or he may do it indirectly by attributing his self-reactions to the therapist (*assimilative* or *disowning projection*). But in neither case does he receive praise or reproof, corroboration or contradiction, from anyone in the situation but himself.

It is now more than ever clear that special qualifications are demanded of the therapist who must help to structure the therapeutic situation in such a way that the patient may learn to give unique overt reactions to his own behavior. The therapist, as we said earlier, must be able through his professional training to contribute a rigorously detached attitude, highly developed skill in suspending judgment, and an inability to be shocked, surprised or fascinated by the unusual and the taboo in any form. In order to share genuinely the behavior he witnesses, he must be able covertly to take the roles and share the perspectives of his patient, and these are often exceedingly individualistic, ambivalent and mutually contradictory. At the same time, chiefly by means of the unusual social context which his own behavior provides, the therapist makes it possible for the patient to acquire through social learning some of the detachment, impartiality, suspended judgment and tolerance which belong to the professional attitude.

[8] See Chapters 3, 5 and 6 for a more detailed discussion of emotional reactions in the behavior disorders.

The patient in the therapeutic situation

For the patient the therapeutic situation is an active learning situation, whether he shares it with an overtly responsive therapist who sits facing him, or with one who keeps in the background and out of sight. We have said that the therapist must take the initiative in providing a setting and a behavioral context within which the peculiar biosocial interactions that constitute therapy can develop. However, once that initiative has been taken, it is the patient's responsibility to learn the arduous and often painful technique of undirected, uninhibited role-taking which makes up the major part of his contribution to his own treatment.

All office therapy in the behavior disorders involves overt communicative interaction between patient and therapist. But during the last four decades, as we have indicated, the trend has been persistently away from authoritarian question-answer procedures, and toward the practice of extreme self-restraint by the therapist and of non-restraint by the patient. This trend had its origin in Freud's recognition that what the patient needs is not reassurance, information, argument and advice, but an opportunity to talk through and emotionally work through the varieties of his role-taking with all their implications — social, asocial and anti-social.

From this recognition arose also the common practice of having the psychoanalytic trainee record all of his own comments and statements to his patient, and afterwards study their significance and their possible influence with the aid of an experienced therapist — usually his own analyst. In this way trainees learned the importance of self-restraint by observing the distortions, obstructions and directions which their unguarded responses might introduce into the therapeutic situation. They learned to identify the signs of their own special aversions, fascinations and blind-spots in what they had said, and to avoid or at least allow for the effects of such overt behavior in the patient's presence.

Most office treatment is confined to face-to-face discussion in which the therapist's participation is ideally minimal and non-directive, while the patient's is maximal and unhindered.[9] It should be pointed out, however, that this method does provide the patient with a tangible social object toward which he may direct his com-

[9] C. Rogers has given a lucid presentation of this procedure, with recordings of interviews, in his book, *Counseling and Psychotherapy* (Boston: Houghton Mifflin, 1942).

municative behavior. If the patient says or does something which frightens him or of which he is ashamed, he can gain immediate reassurance from the mere fact that the therapist expresses neither alarm nor condemnation. If what he says or does arouses self-reactions of pride, arrogance or elation, the failure of the therapist either to support or oppose the self-reactions is likewise immediately evident to the patient, and may have a directive influence upon his further behavior. In practice, it is virtually impossible for the therapist to avoid making some kind of response now and then, even though it may be little more than an indication of attending. And such a response may give the patient a certain degree of reassurance — the reassurance that at least he is not being frowned upon, ridiculed or rejected.

The *method of recumbent free verbalization* ("free association") was originally developed in the interest of still further minimizing the influence of the therapist's behavior. The therapist seats himself where he cannot be readily seen and speaks only when he deems it absolutely essential. The patient lies on a couch and learns to practice maximal non-restraint within the limits imposed by his recumbency. Under these conditions he must acquire increasing facility in uninterrupted free verbalization, uninhibited role-taking and unimpeded self-reaction. This method, provided it does not include distortion by the interjection of doctrinaire interpretations, is unquestionably the nearest thing we have to a strictly non-directive procedure. Moreover, its products have contributed greatly to our understanding of behavior pathology as well as to the evolution of all modern communicative therapy. We shall therefore interpolate at this point, for future reference, a brief statement of some of the behavioral peculiarities of this method, even though its field of application is more limited than the face-to-face procedure.

In the method of recumbent free verbalization the therapist is known to be present and therefore cannot be completely ignored by the patient. Nevertheless, he remains for the most part invisible and inaudible; and in consequence he is less likely than in the face-to-face relationship to serve as a tangible social object and a sounding-board for communicative behavior. During free verbalization the patient cannot use the therapist's accepting attitude to gain even the most passive reassurance. Perhaps, for all he knows, what he says and does is being greeted by frowns or smiles, by appreciation or depreciation, by affection, indifference, dislike or rejection.

This is obviously a situation in which anxiety may easily mount to acute proportions, and one consequently that demands special skill and experience on the part of the therapist who is responsible for what happens in it and afterwards.

As the recumbent patient continues to elicit no reaction of approval or reproach from his unseen therapist, no sign of satisfaction or annoyance, no reassurance and no guidance, his orientation is likely to undergo a significant change. The therapist, as a particular social person, may become less and less the focus of the patient's reactions, he may even more or less completely lose his identity for the patient. This does not mean, of course, that he necessarily loses his importance. On the contrary, he often gains considerably in significance to the patient as his identity is restructured in the therapeutic situation.

The recumbent, verbalizing patient restructures the identity of his therapist in terms of his own immediate needs. The very fact that the therapist refrains from giving any evaluative reactions during free verbalization makes it possible for the patient to attribute to him whatever attitudes he wishes. And since he is neither criticized nor applauded for his use of assimilative and disowning projection, the patient is at liberty to carry the process as far as he needs to — farther, indeed, than he has ever before been permitted to go in communicative behavior. This aspect of free verbalization plays an important part in the development of so-called positive and negative transference relationships.

It can readily be seen that, with the help of the amorphous presence of an unreactive therapist, the patient may transform the original miniature social community into a miniature pseudocommunity. That is, he may build up a partially fictitious person around the presence of the therapist, and organize his reactions during free verbalization with reference to the attitudes which he attributes to this person. Of course, for the patient one difficulty with such a therapeutic situation is that, no matter how far he goes, he cannot get the reactions to his behavior that he expects, fears or wants. In other words, the pseudocommunity never gives him objective justification for his reactions and, as a result, he must ultimately recognize their origins as being wholly within his own behavior.

This development of a delusional miniature pseudocommunity often plays an essential part in free verbalization therapy. For it provides the patient with a behavioral context of his own making which supports continuous fantasy, in much the same way that the autistic community provides a behavioral context for normal dreaming. But the pseudocommunity in free verbalization has one great advantage over dream autism. Because it arises as a part of overt, communicative behavior, it permits the shared objectification of fantasy, thus enabling the patient to work through overtly in another person's presence his conflicts, his ambivalent, contradictory, repressed and unacknowledged attitudes. In some of these respects the method of free verbalization can achieve what other methods cannot. It is not in itself, however, a complete therapeutic technique. It always requires at some phase in its course to be supplemented by more and more therapist participation, until eventually it approaches the non-directive biosocial interaction of face-to-face procedures.

But whether recumbent free verbalization or the more usual face-to-face procedure is employed, a non-directive therapeutic situation permits the development of role-taking techniques that are unique for the patient. These techniques obviously cannot be acquired in ordinary, everyday social contexts because of the controlling influence of other persons' evaluative reactions. They cannot be acquired by the patient in solitude because of the effects of his own socially derived, critical self-reactions to what he says and does. In the treatment context, of course, the factor of evaluative reactions on the part of other persons is easily controlled, since the therapist himself is the only possible direct source of such behavior. The patient's evaluative self-reactions, on the other hand, are never excluded, since they are among the most important objects of motivational analysis. The patient learns to talk through and emotionally work through the behavioral antecedents and implications of his self-reactions along with those of the rest of his reactions in the therapeutic situation.

In the protective, permissive therapeutic relationship the patient gradually acquires the difficult techniques of uninhibited, unguided communicative role-taking. He learns to react overtly in a shared miniature community as he might react in private fantasy. But he must learn also to allow these overt reactions to proceed unhindered, without introducing the often distorting or amputating criteria of logical consistency, relevance or social acceptability through

his own self-reactions.[10] As the patient finds that he is not expected
to impart information, or to intellectualize, explain and excuse what
he says, his interest is likely to shift from what the therapist may
think to what he thinks himself. And as he discovers that, no matter what he may communicate, he suffers neither reproof nor commendation, neither punishment nor reward, he may eventually
acquire some of the tolerance, impartiality and detachment toward his own behavior that characterizes the therapist's attitudes.

The results of biosocial therapeutic interaction

We have said that shared objectification transforms the private
covert reaction into a public statement. When this occurs in the
therapeutic situation, two persons witness the overt behavior of
the public statement — the tolerant, impartial, detached therapist
and the critical, prejudiced, emotionally involved patient. What is
said and worked through under these conditions, of course, must
approach the status and eventually the organization of genuinely
shared communication. This does not mean that it must be objecti-
fied in terms of rigorous verbal logic, or that it must be formally
correct, any more than overt everyday joy, anger, need, excitement
or anxiety must be logical or conventionally formulated to become
communicative. Moreover, it should be remembered that the skilled
therapist is a person specifically trained in observing and reacting
adequately to fleeting fragments of behavior. And because he is
already practiced in taking the roles of his patients, and hence in
seeing things from their individualistic perspectives, the therapist
is able to share and comprehend attitudes which at first may completely elude the self-reactions of the patient who is showing them.

The patient, by working out his attitudes overtly in such a permissive relationship of biosocial interaction, acquires skill himself in
observing them and in accepting them as his own. After he has
learned not to select and reject his attitudes in terms of what his
two listeners might think — that is, the therapist and himself — he is
free to follow through the responses which these attitudes support
or for which they are a necessary preparation.[11] This procedure of
objectifying and sharing one's attitudes, of learning to accept them

10 For an account of the operation of *self-reactions* in self-control, conscience
and self-criticism, see Chapter 10.

11 A discussion of anticipant and supporting attitudes in behavior organization and behavior pathology will be found in Chapters 3 and 6.

as they appear and to follow through their implications in the form of the responses they facilitate and support, is the procedure by which one increases most effectively the accessibility of behavior that has remained or become inaccessible.

Therapy in the behavior disorders does not have as its goal the complete restructuring of the patient's behavior. It does not aim at rendering everything overt that has been covert, at sharing everything previously unshared, or at formulating and making accessible all behavior that has been unformulated, forgotten or repressed. Its goals are much more finite and realistic than this. The attitudes with their responses that require shared objectification will vary, of course, from patient to patient. They are determined, not by observing a set of *a priori* rules, but by following the lead of the patient, and eventually by having the patient acquire skill in following his own lead regardless of the direction he must take.

The behavior which undergoes shared objectification, in any effective therapeutic relationship, must always include a great deal that has not been previously communicated, and much that the patient has never formulated clearly, analyzed or acknowledged as his own. For we have seen that, in normal as well as in abnormal conduct, the uncommunicated, unformulated, unanalyzed or unacknowledged can be a determining factor in biosocial behavior. It may enter significantly into a person's needs and choices, affect the adequacy of his performance in any sphere of action, give rise to dominant fears and fascinations, and increase or destroy his satisfactions.

We have also seen that the cultural patterns of permission and taboo, in accordance with which a person has been reared, to a considerable degree determine what behavior in his personality organization shall remain at a relatively unshared level.[12] Thus, individuals reared in the same culture or subculture are almost sure to exhibit inadequate sharing, defective role-taking and an inability to shift perspectives in certain identical areas. This means that, although the precise character of the patient's behavior in the therapeutic situation cannot be predicted from a knowledge of his cultural background, the general areas which will demand shared objectification usually can. High on the list of inadequately shared biosocial behavior in our culture, for example, is that concerned

---

[12] See especially Chapters 2 and 5, and the section on the determinants of behavior pathology under each of the behavior disorders.

with sex needs and satisfactions, with attitudes of hostility and aggression toward persons we are expected always to love, and with problems of emotional dependence and emancipation. Hence the therapist is seldom mistaken who anticipates special difficulties when it comes to role-taking, sharing and shifting perspectives in these areas.

But whether behavior is unshared because of cultural taboo, or whether something more personal in origin is responsible, the crucial point is that it tends to remain individualistic and asocial. The unshared, uncommunicated attitude does not undergo the modifications which inevitably result from interpersonal behavior. It cannot form a basis for social role-taking or come under the direct influence of others' perspectives in the social community. If it enters into the organization of one's self-reactions, its effect is more likely to be that of decreasing than of increasing their validity, since its contribution is not a socially matured one.

In human society, the individual becomes socially mature as a result of biosocial interactions with other persons. By this means he acquires socially determined roles, and with the aid of symbolic behavior he develops skill in role-taking and in sharing the perspectives of persons whose roles he learns to take.[13] Whatever is left out of this continuing process of behavioral interchange, of course, does not participate in social maturing. Likewise, reactions that are shared mutually in early childhood, and then abandoned or repressed, are also excluded from participation in social maturing, at least in its later phases. Such non-participative behavior is characteristic of the areas of relative social immaturity to which we have already referred. These areas, although present to some extent in all personality organization, are of special importance in the development and perpetuation of behavior pathology.

The immediate goal of treatment in the behavior disorders — that of establishing a participative biosocial interrelationship between patient and therapist — now gains in significance. It is the patient's task to acquire increased social maturity, particularly in those areas of behavior whose relative immaturity has led to maladaptation. The therapeutic situation provides the unique conditions under which that maturity can be acquired through biosocial interaction in a miniature social community. The patient shares this community with a therapist in whose presence he can learn to work

13 For a discussion of role-taking, see Chapter 4.

through his asocial and anti-social roles with impunity, and from whose participation he can gain new perspectives and new skill in the techniques of social role-taking. By this procedure the ultimate goal of treatment in the behavior disorders may be realized. For with the achievement of increased social maturity the therapeutic behavioral interrelationship finally becomes unnecessary, and it can then be terminated with benefit to the patient.

It is now clear that the same principles can be derived from the development and operation of the therapeutic situation which we earlier derived from the development and operation of normal personality organization and of the behavior disorders. For when we are dealing with the activities of human organisms, we can never afford to slight their social environment, with all its other persons, its cultural objects and cultural products, and the everlasting interplay of interpersonal relationships through which all human behavior is organized and regulated. We can never afford to forget that a person's own self-reactions, whether given overtly or in covert fantasy and whether recognized or unsuspected, can be crucial factors in structuring and maintaining normal personality, in precipitating and perpetuating behavior disorders and in determining the course and outcome of their therapy. The direction of development from infancy to biosocial maturity and from behavior pathology to biosocial health is always one in which individualistic behavior becomes socially organized through shared interpersonal interaction — one in which the human being learns to assimilate his dominant attitudes to those of the culture in which, and by means of which, he lives.

Index

Abnormal, normal and, 7–8, 54, 141, 576, 598
Abnormality, criteria of, 7–9
Abraham, K., 449, 496, 497
Acceptance, behavior disorder and, 62–63, 269–273, 313–314
   neighborhood, 42
   parental, 26–27, 32, 38–39
Accessibility, consciousness and, 127–130, 136–139
   therapy and, 127–130, 576–598
Actual neuroses, fatigue syndromes as, 37
   Freud on, 10
Adience, convergent, 133
   divergent, 133
Adjustive techniques, and behavior disorders, 185–186
   defense, 153–170
   definition, 141
   escape, 170–184
   general, 142–150
   learning and, 185–186
   prelanguage, 151
   special, 151–184
   unformulated, 151–152
   uniformity of, 141–142
Adolescence, 45–52
   body-change and, 47–49, 407–408
   and childhood maladjustment, 49–50
   disorganization in, 441–443, 489–491
   friendships in, 45, 47, 49–51
   negativism in, 172–173
   rebellion in, 18, 47, 50–51
   rumination in, 301
   schizophrenic disorders and, 490–491
   status shifts in, 49–50

Affective flattening, in schizophrenic disorders, 460–462
Age, behavior disorders and, 270–271, 411–412, 441–443, 489–491, 522–523, 568–575
   paranoid disorders and, 441–443, 489–491
   schizophrenic disorders and, 441–443, 489–491
Age of resistance, 17–18, 47
   negativism and, 172
   second, 47
   temper tantrums and, 144
Aggression, as adjustive technique, 142–145
   anxiety disorders as, 273
   behavior disorders and, 39, 143–145
   community, 143
   domination and, 28, 143–145
   fatigue syndrome as, 240–241
   hypochondriacal disorders as, 216–217
   hysterical disorders as, 381
   in manic disorders, 511–513, 519
   paranoid disorders as, 443
   psychopathic, 145
   rejection and, 34
   in schizophrenic disorders, 458, 491
   sibling, 38
Agitation, normal, 524–526
Agrammatism, 465
Aldrich, C., 23
Alexander, F., 299, 588
Allen, F., 588
Allport, G., 16, 102, 127
Alternating personality, 365
Alvarez, W., 200, 234
Ambitendencies, 60–65
   definition, 61–62

606 INDEX

Desocialization, in cerebral incompetence, 550
in schizophrenic disorders, 450–
452, 479, 485–492
Deterioration, of language and
thought, 89, 463–468
Deutsch, A., 4
Diethelm, O., 257, 588
Disarticulation, in cerebral incompetence, 550
language and, 464–467, 551
in schizophrenia, 450–452, 489–
492, 550
Discontinuity, in delirium, 544–545,
547
in progressive cerebral incompetence, 551
Disorders, behavior (see Behavior
disorders)
Disorganization, attitude and, 55
delirious vs. schizophrenic, 545
schizophrenic, 59–60, 450–452,
479, 485–492, 545
Disorientation, in anxiety disorders,
257
delirious, 542–547, 555
Displacement, emotional, 74–77, 246,
251, 297
repression and, 75, 179
Disuse, hysterical inactivation and,
346–347
Doty, E., 535
Double personality, 365
Dreaming, delirium and, 545–546
language and, 89
normal, 545, 547
therapy and, 594
Drewry, P., 446
Dublin, L., 194
Dudycha, C., 21, 138
Dudycha, M., 21, 138
Dynamisms (see Adjustive techniques)
Dynes, J., 556

Eating, acceptance and, 108–111,
324–325
aggression and, 109–110
behavior pathology and, 107–111
and body change, 109, 325
cannibalistic fantasies, 458
magic and, 109–110, 325
personality development and,
15–16, 107–111
pregnancy and, 24, 109

Eating, rejection and, 108–111
and religious ritual, 109, 324–
325
and sex behavior, 109
socialization and, 108–111
Ebaugh, F., 564, 572
Effort syndrome, 226
Elation, in manic disorders, 511–513
Elimination, 23–24, 27
Emancipation, adolescent, 50–52
Emotional decompensation, 75–77,
257
Emotional flattening, 460–462
Emotional incongruity, in schizophrenic disorders, 460–462
Emotional incontinence, 552
Emotional lability, 552
Emotional reactions, 72–80
conflict in, 79–80, 138–139
cumulative, 75–77
decompensation, 75–77, 257
definition, 73–74
discontinuity in, 373
gastric ulcer and, 261–262
hypochondrical disorders and,
206–207
inactivation in, 339–342
and learning, 78–80
nervous system and, 74
overt vs. covert, 78–80
persistence of, 74–77
reaction-insensitivity in, 340–342
regulation of, 78–80
and social communication, 80
social control and, 80
and symbolic behavior, 72–73,
76–80
therapy and, 578–579, 590–591,
595–597
thinking and, 72–73, 76–80, 89
unconscious, 78–80
visceral contributions to, 73–78
English, O., 21
Epilepsy, hysterical autonomy and,
368
Equivalence, learning and, 57
Escape techniques, 170–184
hysterical seizure as, 360
Ethics, ambivalence and, 62–65
cultural transmission of, 25–26,
33
depressive disorders and, 505–
506, 511, 518
eating and, 108–111